Q32

Y0-BVG-610

REFERENCE DATA

for | # RADIO ENGINEERS

third edition

Federal Telephone and Radio Corporation

an associate of

International Telephone and Telegraph Corporation

67 Broad Street • New York 4, N. Y.

Foreword

Reference Data for Radio Engineers in this third edition has grown to twice the size of the preceding edition and is three times as large as the first edition. Wartime restrictions in 1943 on technical data, printing materials, and printing facilities limited sharply the contents of the initial edition. Nor was the second edition, published in 1946, free of these restraints. This third edition is, therefore, the first of these volumes to be prepared in large measure under the freedoms of peace.

Designed to fill a gap in our field of technical books between textbooks and handbooks, Reference Data for Radio Engineers is, as its title indicates, a comprehensive compilation of basic electrical, physical, and mathematical data frequently needed in the solution of engineering problems.

Its usefulness has not been restricted to the practicing radio and electronic engineers for whom it was originally prepared, but it has reached into the realm of the engineer-in-training and has been accepted for student use in many of the leading colleges in the United States. This broadened application has been recognized in the contents of the third edition.

Grateful acknowledgement is made to Professor A. G. Hill and L. D. Smullin of Massachusetts Institute of Technology, Professor J. R. Ragazzini and L. A. Zadeh of Columbia University, and Professor H. R. Mimmo of Harvard University for their many contributions and useful suggestions.

Federal Telephone and Radio Corporation, in the compilation of this reference book, wishes to acknowledge the valuable assistance and advice of the following members of associate companies.

International Telephone and Telegraph Corporation, New York, N. Y.

E. M. Deloraine *Technical Director*
H. P. Westman *Editor, Electrical Communication*
L. C. Edie

Contents

Contents

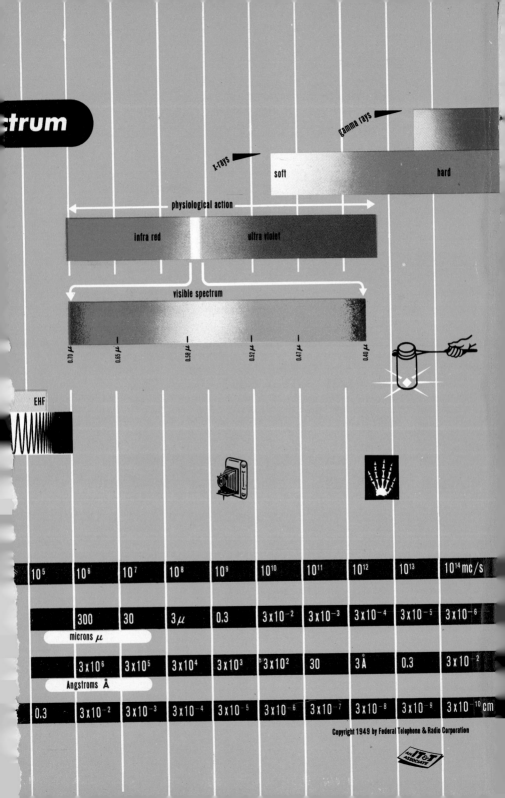

ctrum

gamma rays

x-rays

soft   hard

physiological action

infra red   ultra violet

visible spectrum

0.70 μ   0.65 μ   0.58 μ   0.52 μ   0.47 μ   0.40 μ

EHF

10^5	10^6	10^7	10^8	10^9	10^{10}	10^{11}	10^{12}	10^{13}	10^{14} mc/s
	300	30	3μ	0.3	3×10^{-2}	3×10^{-3}	3×10^{-4}	3×10^{-5}	3×10^{-6}

microns μ

| | 3×10^6 | 3×10^5 | 3×10^4 | 3×10^3 | 3×10^2 | 30 | $3\,\mathring{A}$ | 0.3 | 3×10^{-2} |

Angstroms $\mathring{A}$

| 0.3 | 3×10^{-2} | 3×10^{-3} | 3×10^{-4} | 3×10^{-5} | 3×10^{-6} | 3×10^{-7} | 3×10^{-8} | 3×10^{-9} | 3×10^{-10} cm |

electromagnetic frequency spe

reference data for radio engineers   third edition

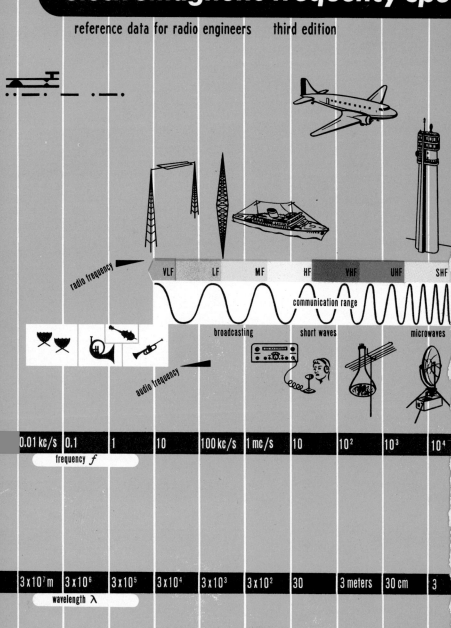

radio frequency

| VLF | LF | MF | HF | VHF | UHF | SHF |

communication range

broadcasting   short waves   microwaves

audio frequency

| 0.01 kc/s | 0.1 | 1 | 10 | 100 kc/s | 1 mc/s | 10 | 10^2 | 10^3 | 10^4 |

frequency *f*

| 3×10^7 m | 3×10^6 | 3×10^5 | 3×10^4 | 3×10^3 | 3×10^2 | 30 | 3 meters | 30 cm | 3 |

wavelength λ

■ Frequency data

Wavelength–frequency conversion

The graph given below permits conversion between frequency and wave-length; by use of multiplying factors such as those at the bottom of the page, this graph will cover any portion of the electromagnetic-wave spectrum.

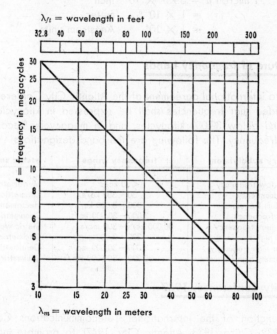

λ_{ft} = wavelength in feet

f = frequency in megacycles

λ_m = wavelength in meters

for frequencies from		multiply f by	multiply λ by
0.03 –	0.3 megacycles	0.01	100
0.3 –	3.0 megacycles	0.1	10
3.0 –	30 megacycles	1.0	1.0
30 –	300 megacycles	10	0.1
300 –	3,000 megacycles	100	0.01
3000 –	30,000 megacycles	1000	0.001

Wavelength–frequency conversion   *continued*

Conversion formulas

Propagation velocity $c \approx 3 \times 10^8$ meters/second

Wavelength in meters $\lambda_m = \dfrac{300,000}{f \text{ in kilocycles}} = \dfrac{300}{f \text{ in megacycles}}$

Wavelength in feet $\lambda_{ft} = \dfrac{300,000 \times 3.28}{f \text{ in kilocycles}} = \dfrac{300 \times 3.28}{f \text{ in megacycles}}$

$$
\begin{aligned}
1 \text{ Angstrom unit } \overset{\circ}{A} &= 3.937 \times 10^{-9} \quad \text{inch} \\
&= 1 \times 10^{-10} \quad \text{meter} \\
&= 1 \times 10^{-4} \quad \text{micron}
\end{aligned}
$$

$$
\begin{aligned}
1 \text{ micron } \mu &= 3.937 \times 10^{-5} \quad \text{inch} \\
&= 1 \times 10^{-6} \quad \text{meter} \\
&= 1 \times 10^{4} \quad \text{Angstrom units}
\end{aligned}
$$

Nomenclature of frequency bands

According to international agreement at the Atlantic City Conference, 1947, it was decided that frequencies shall be expressed in kilocycles/second (kc/s) at and below 30,000 kilocycles, and in megacycles/second (mc/s) above this frequency. The following are the band designations

frequency subdivision		frequency range	metric subdivision
VLF	Very low frequency	<30 kc/s	Myriametric waves
LF	Low frequency	$30 - 300$ kc/s	Kilometric waves
MF	Medium frequency	$300 - 3,000$ kc/s	Hectometric waves
HF	High frequency	$3,000 - 30,000$ kc/s	Decametric waves
VHF	Very high frequency	$30,000$ kc/s $- 300$ mc/s	Metric waves
UHF	Ultra high frequency	$300 - 3,000$ mc/s	Decimetric waves
SHF	Super high frequency	$3,000 - 30,000$ mc/s	Centimetric waves
EHF	Extremely high frequency	$30,000 - 300,000$ mc/s	Millimetric waves

Atlantic City Conference, 1947

It is the function of the International Telecommunications Conferences (Madrid, 1932; Cairo, 1938; Atlantic City, 1947) to promote international cooperation in the development and use of telecommunication services of all sorts. The following material has been extracted from the parts of the Acts of the conference specifically relating to radio. The official publication, "Final Acts of the International Telecommunication and Radio Conference, Atlantic City, 1947," is obtainable at nominal charge from the Secretary, International Telecommunication Union, Berne Bureau, Berne, Switzerland.

Frequency allocations   *Atlantic City, 1947*

The following table of frequency allocations pertains to the western hemisphere (region 2), and covers all frequencies between 10 kilocycles and 10,500 megacycles.

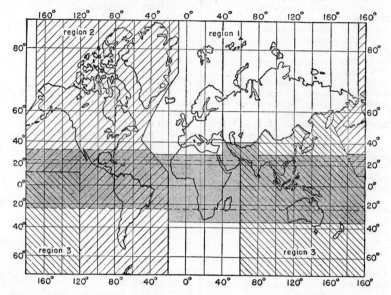

Regions defined in table of frequency allocations. Shaded area is the tropical zone.

Note: An asterisk (*) following a service designation indicates that the allocation has been made on a world-wide basis. All explanatory notes covering region 2 as well as other regions have been omitted. For these explanatory notes the original text of Acts of the Atlantic City Conference should be consulted.

kilocycles	service	kilocycles	service
10– 14	Radio navigation*	325– 405	Aeronautical mobile,* Aeronautical navigation*
14– 70	Fixed,* Maritime mobile*		
70– 90	Fixed, Maritime mobile	405– 415	Aeronautical mobile, Aeronautical navigation, Maritime navigation (radio direction finding)
90– 110	Fixed,* Maritime mobile,* Radio navigation*		
110– 130	Fixed, Maritime mobile		
130– 150	Fixed, Maritime mobile	415– 490	Maritime mobile*
150– 160	Fixed, Maritime mobile	490– 510	Mobile (distress and calling)*
160– 200	Fixed	510– 525	Mobile .
200– 285	Aeronautical mobile, Aeronautical navigation	525– 535	Mobile
		535– 1605	Broadcasting*
285 325	Maritime radio navigation (radio beacons)	1605– 1800	Aeronautical radio navigation, Fixed, Mobile

Frequency allocations *continued*

kilocycles	service	kilocycles	service
1800– 2000	Amateur, Fixed, Mobile except aeronautical mobile, Radio navigation	11275–11400	Aeronautical mobile*
		11400–11700	Fixed*
		11700–11975	Broadcasting*
2000– 2065	Fixed, Mobile	11975–12330	Fixed*
2065– 2105	Maritime mobile	12330–13200	Maritime mobile*
2105– 2300	Fixed, Mobile	13200–13260	Aeronautical mobile*
2300– 2495	Broadcasting, Fixed, Mobile	13260–13360	Aeronautical mobile*
2495– 2505	Standard frequency	13360–14000	Fixed*
2505– 2850	Fixed, Mobile	14000–14350	Amateur*
2850– 3025	Aeronautical mobile*	14350–14990	Fixed*
3025– 3155	Aeronautical mobile*	14990–15010	Standard frequency*
3155– 3200	Fixed,* Mobile except aeronautical mobile*	15010–15100	Aeronautical mobile*
		15100–15450	Broadcasting*
3200– 3230	Broadcasting,* Fixed,* Mobile except aeronautical mobile*	15450–16460	Fixed*
		16460–17360	Maritime mobile*
		17360–17700	Fixed*
3230– 3400	Broadcasting,* Fixed,* Mobile except aeronautical mobile*	17700–17900	Broadcasting*
		17900–17970	Aeronautical mobile*
3400– 3500	Aeronautical mobile*	17970–18030	Aeronautical mobile*
3500– 4000	Amateur, Fixed, Mobile except aeronautical mobile	18030–19990	Fixed*
		19990–20010	Standard frequency*
4000– 4063	Fixed*	20010–21000	Fixed*
4063– 4438	Maritime mobile*	21000–21450	Amateur*
4438– 4650	Fixed, Mobile except aeronautical mobile	21450–21750	Broadcasting*
		21750–21850	Fixed*
4650– 4700	Aeronautical mobile*	21850–22000	Aeronautical fixed, Aeronautical mobile*
4700– 4750	Aeronautical mobile*	22000–22720	Maritime mobile*
4750– 4850	Broadcasting, Fixed	22720–23200	Fixed*
4850– 4995	Broadcasting,* Fixed,* Land mobile*	23200–23350	Aeronautical fixed,* Aeronautical mobile*
4995– 5005	Standard frequency*	23350–24990	Fixed,* Land mobile*
5005– 5060	Broadcasting,* Fixed*	24990–25010	Standard frequency*
5060– 5250	Fixed*	25010–25600	Fixed,* Mobile except aeronautical mobile*
5250– 5450	Fixed, Land mobile	25600–26100	Broadcasting*
5450– 5480	Aeronautical mobile	26100–27500	Fixed,* Mobile except aeronautical mobile*
5480– 5680	Aeronautical mobile*	27500–28000	Fixed, Mobile
5680– 5730	Aeronautical mobile*	28000–29700	Amateur*
5730– 5950	Fixed*		
5950– 6200	Broadcasting*	**megacycles**	**service**
6200– 6525	Maritime mobile*	29.7– 44	Fixed, Mobile
6525– 6685	Aeronautical mobile*	44 – 50	Broadcasting, Fixed, Mobile
6685– 6765	Aeronautical mobile*	50 – 54	Amateur
6765– 7000	Fixed*	54 – 72	Broadcasting, Fixed, Mobile
7000– 7100	Amateur*	72 – 76	Fixed, Mobile
7100– 7300	Amateur	76 – 88	Broadcasting, Fixed, Mobile
7300– 8195	Fixed*		
8195– 8815	Maritime mobile*	88 – 100	Broadcasting*
8815– 8965	Aeronautical mobile*	100 – 108	Broadcasting
8965– 9040	Aeronautical mobile*	108 – 118	Aeronautical radio navigation*
9040– 9500	Fixed*		
9500– 9775	Broadcasting*	118 – 132	Aeronautical mobile*
9775– 9995	Fixed*	132 – 144	Fixed, Mobile
9995–10005	Standard frequency*	144 – 146	Amateur*
10005–10100	Aeronautical mobile*		
10100–11175	Fixed*		
11175–11275	Aeronautical mobile*		

Frequency allocations *continued*

megacycles	service	megacycles	service
146 — 148	Amateur	1660 — 1700	Meteorological aids (radio-sonde)
148 — 174	Fixed, Mobile		
174 — 216	Broadcasting, Fixed, Mobile	1700 — 2300	Fixed,* Mobile*
		2300 — 2450	Amateur*
216 — 220	Fixed, Mobile	2450 — 2700	Fixed,* Mobile*
220 — 225	Amateur	2700 — 2900	Aeronautical radio navigation*
225 — 235	Fixed, Mobile		
235 — 328.6	Fixed,* Mobile*	2900 — 3300	Radio navigation*
328.6— 335.4	Aeronautical radio navigation*	3300 — 3500	Amateur
		3500 — 3900	Fixed, Mobile
335.4— 420	Fixed,* Mobile*	3900 — 4200	Fixed,* Mobile*
420 — 450	Aeronautical radio navigation,* Amateur*	4200 — 4400	Aeronautical radio navigation*
450 — 460	Aeronautical radio navigation, Fixed, Mobile	4400 — 5000	Fixed,* Mobile*
		5000 — 5250	Aeronautical radio navigation*
460 — 470	Fixed,* Mobile*	5250 — 5650	Radio navigation*
470 — 585	Broadcasting*	5650 — 5850	Amateur*
585 — 610	Broadcasting	5850 — 5925	Amateur
610 — 940	Broadcasting*	5925 — 8500	Fixed,* Mobile*
940 — 960	Fixed	8500 — 9800	Radio navigation*
960 — 1215	Aeronautical radio navigation*	9800 —10000	Fixed,* Radio navigation*
1215 — 1300	Amateur*	10000 —10500	Amateur*
1300 — 1660	Aeronautical radio navigation	Above 10500	Not allocated

Frequency tolerances *Atlantic City, 1947*

frequency band	type of service and power	tolerance in percent*	
		column 1	column 2
10–535 kc/s	Fixed stations		
	10–50 kc/s	0.1	0.1
	50 kc/s—end of band	0.1	0.02
	Land stations		
	Coast stations		
	Power > 200 watts	0.1	0.02
	Power < 200 watts	0.1	0.05
	Aeronautical stations	0.1	0.02
	Mobile stations		
	Ship stations	0.3 (6)	0.1 (1)
	Aircraft stations	0.3	0.05
	Emergency (reserve) ship transmitters, and lifeboat, lifecraft, and survival-craft transmitters	0.5	0.5
	Radionavigation stations	0.05	0.02
	Broadcasting stations	20 cycles	20 cycles
535–1605 kc/s	Broadcasting stations	20 cycles	20 cycles

* See notes on page 13

Frequency tolerances *continued*

frequency band	type of service and power	tolerance in percent	
		column 1	column 2
1605–4000 kc/s	Fixed stations		
	Power > 200 watts	0.01 (2)	0.005
	Power < 200 watts	0.02	0.01
	Land stations		
	Coast stations		
	Power > 200 watts	0.02	0.005
	Power < 200 watts	0.02	0.01
	Aeronautical stations		
	Power > 200 watts	0.02	0.005
	Power < 200 watts	0.02	0.01
	Base stations		
	Power > 200 watts	0.02	0.005
	Power < 200 watts	0.02	0.01
	Mobile stations		
	Ship stations	0.05 (6)	0.02 (3)
	Aircraft stations	0.05	0.02 (3)
	Land mobile stations	0.05	0.02
	Radionavigation stations		
	Power > 200 watts	0.02	0.005
	Power < 200 watts	0.02	0.01
	Broadcasting stations	0.005	0.005
4000–30,000 kc/s	Fixed stations		
	Power > 500 watts	0.01	0.003
	Power < 500 watts	0.02	0.01
	Land stations		
	Coast stations	0.02	0.005
	Aeronautical stations		
	Power > 500 watts	0.02	0.005
	Power < 500 watts	0.02	0.01
	Base stations		
	Power > 500 watts	0.02	0.005
	Power < 500 watts	0.02	0.01
	Mobile stations		
	Ship stations	0.05 (6)	0.02 (3)
	Aircraft stations	0.05	0.02 (3)
	Land mobile stations	0.05	0.02
	Transmitters in lifeboats, lifecraft, and survival craft	0.05	0.02
	Broadcasting stations	0.005	0.003
30–100 mc/s	Fixed stations	0.03	0.02
	Land stations	0.03	0.02
	Mobile stations	0.03	0.02
	Radionavigation stations	0.02 (5)	0.02 (5)
	Broadcasting stations	0.01	0.003

Frequency tolerances   *continued*

frequency band	type of service and power	tolerance in percent	
		column 1	column 2
100–500 mc/s	Fixed stations	0.03	0.01
	Land stations	0.03	0.01
	Mobile stations	0.03	0.01 (4)
	Radionavigation stations	0.02 (5)	0.02 (5)
	Broadcasting stations	0.01	0.003
500–10,500 mc/s	———	0.75	0.75 (7)

Notes:

Column 1: Applicable until January 1st, 1953, to transmitters now in use and those to be installed before January 1st, 1950.

Column 2: Applicable to new transmitters installed after January 1st, 1950; and to all transmitters after January 1st, 1953.

For ship stations, in the absence of an assigned frequency to a particular ship or ship transmitter, the substitute for the assigned frequency is that frequency on which an emission begins.

1. It is recognized that certain countries will encounter difficulties in fitting, prior to 1953, all their ships with equipment that will satisfy the indicated tolerance; however, it is requested that these countries complete the necessary conversion as soon as possible.

2. The frequency tolerance of 0.02 percent is maintained temporarily for fixed-station transmitters now in operation using a power between 200 and 500 watts.

3. For this category, the final date of January 1st, 1953, is extended until the date when the Radio Regulations of the next Conference are put into force.

4. In this band and for this category, it is recognized that certain countries are not sure that their equipment can satisfy a stricter frequency tolerance than that fixed for the 30–100-megacycle band; however, these countries will endeavor to satisfy the tolerance for the band 100–500 megacycles.

5. It is recognized that there are in service, in this category, pulse transmitters that cannot meet tolerances closer than 0.5 percent.

6. Frequency deviations are to be measured over a period not exceeding ten minutes from the commencement of an emission. This provision, however, is applicable only to transmitters in service before January 1st, 1950, and until the replacement of these transmitters by modern equipment; and only in exclusive maritime mobile bands, and excepting such parts of these bands as are reserved for ship radiotelephony. Thereafter the frequency tolerance specified shall be adhered to during the whole period of an emission.

7. Until opinion is available from the Comité Consultatif International Radio, no closer tolerances can be specified for this band in this column.

Intensity of harmonics   *Atlantic City, 1947*

In the band 10–30,000 kilocycles, the power of a harmonic or a parasitic emission supplied to the antenna must be at least 40 decibels below the power of the fundamental. In no case shall it exceed 200 milliwatts (mean power).

For mobile stations, endeavor will be made, as far as it is practicable, to reach the above figures.

14

Designation of emissions   *Atlantic City, 1947*

Emissions are designated according to their classification and the width of the frequency band occupied by them. Classification is according to type of modulation, type of transmission, and supplementary characteristics.

Types of modulation   symbol

Amplitude   A

Frequency (or phase)   F

Pulse   P

Types of transmission

Absence of any modulation intended to carry information   0

Telegraphy without the use of modulating audio frequency   1

Telegraphy by keying of a modulating audio frequency or frequencies, or by keying of the modulated emission (Special case: An unkeyed modulated emission.)   2

Telephony   3

Facsimile   4

Television   5

Composite transmission and cases not covered by the above   9

Supplementary characteristics

Double sideband, full carrier   (none)

Single sideband, reduced carrier   a

Two independent sidebands, reduced carrier   b

Other emissions, reduced carrier   c

Pulse, amplitude modulated   d

Pulse, width modulated   e

Pulse, phase (or position) modulated   f

Note: As an exception to the above principles, damped waves are designated by B.

Designation of emissions   *continued*

Examples

The classification of emissions is

type of modulation	type of transmission	supplementary characteristics	symbol
Amplitude modulation	Absence of any modulation	——	A0
	Telegraphy without the use of modulating audio frequency (on-off keying)	——	A1
	Telegraphy by the keying of a modulating audio frequency or audio frequencies, or by the keying of the modulated emission (Special case: An unkeyed modulated emission.)	——	A2
	Telephony	Double sideband, full carrier	A3
		Single sideband, reduced carrier	A3a
		Two independent sidebands, reduced carrier	A3b
	Facsimile	——	A4
	Television	——	A5
	Composite transmissions and cases not covered by the above	——	A9
	Composite transmissions	Reduced carrier	A9c
Frequency (or phase) modulation	Absence of any modulation	——	F0
	Telegraphy without the use of modulating audio frequency (frequency-shift keying)	——	F1
	Telegraphy by the keying of a modulating audio frequency or audio frequencies, or by the keying of the modulated emission (Special case: An unkeyed emission modulated by audio frequency.)	——	F2
	Telephony	——	F3
	Facsimile	——	F4
	Television	——	F5
	Composite transmissions and cases not covered by the above	——	F9

Designation of emissions   *continued*

type of modulation	type of transmission	supplementary characteristics	symbol
Pulse modulation	Absence of any modulation intended to carry information	———	P0
	Telegraphy without the use of modulating audio frequency	———	P1
	Telegraphy by the keying of a modulating audio frequency or audio frequencies, or by the keying of the modulated pulse (Special case: An unkeyed modulated pulse.)	Audio frequency or audio frequencies modulating the pulse in amplitude	P2d
		Audio frequency or audio frequencies modulating the width of the pulse	P2e
		Audio frequency or audio frequencies modulating the phase (or position) of the pulse	P2f
	Telephony	Amplitude modulated	P3d
		Width modulated	P3e
		Phase (or position) modulated	P3f
	Composite transmission and cases not covered by the above	———	P9

Bandwidth   *Atlantic City, 1947*

Wherever the full designation of an emission is necessary, the symbol for that class of emission, as given above, is prefixed by a number indicating the width in kilocycles of the frequency band occupied by it. Bandwidths of 10 kilocycles or less shall be expressed to a maximum of two significant figures after the decimal.

The width of the frequency band that is necessary in the overall system, including both the transmitter and the receiver, for the proper reproduction at the receiver of the desired information, does not necessarily indicate the interfering characteristics of an emission.

Bandwidth   *continued*

The following are examples of the designation of emissions.

description	designation
Telegraphy 25 words/minute, international Morse code, carrier modulated by keying only	0.1A1
Telegraphy, 525-cycle tone, 25 words/minute, international Morse code, carrier and tone keyed or tone keyed only	1.15A2
Amplitude-modulated telephony, 3000-cycle maximum modulation, double sideband, full carrier	6A3
Amplitude-modulated telephony, 3000-cycle maximum modulation, single sideband, reduced carrier	3A3a
Amplitude-modulated telephony, 3000-cycle maximum modulation, two independent sidebands, reduced carrier	6A3b
Vestigial-sideband television (one sideband partially suppressed), full carrier (including a frequency-modulated sound channel)	6000A5, F3
Frequency-modulated telephony, 3000-cycle modulation frequency, 20,000-cycle deviation	46F3
Frequency-modulated telephony, 15,000-cycle modulation frequency, 75,000-cycle deviation	180F3
One-microsecond pulses, unmodulated, assuming a value of $K = 5$	10000P0

Determination of bandwidth

For the determination of this necessary bandwidth, the following table may be considered as a guide. In the formulation of the table, the following working terms have been employed:

B = telegraph speed in bauds (see p. 287)

N/T = maximum possible number of black+white elements to be transmitted per second, in facsimile and television

M = maximum modulation frequency expressed in cycles/second

D = half the difference between the maximum and minimum values of the instantaneous frequencies; D being greater than $2M$, greater than N/T, or greater than B, as the case may be. Instantaneous frequency is the rate of change of phase

t = pulse length expressed in seconds

K = overall numerical factor that differs according to the emission and depends upon the allowable signal distortion and, in television, the time lost from the inclusion of a synchronizing signal

Bandwidth *continued*

amplitude modulation

description and class of emission	necessary bandwidth in cycles/second	examples	
		details	designation of emission
Continuous-wave telegraphy A1	Bandwidth = BK where $K = 5$ for fading circuits $\;\;\;\; = 3$ for nonfading circuits	Morse code at 25 words/minute, $B = 20$; bandwidth = 100 cycles	0.1A1
		Four-channel multiplex, 7-unit code, 60 words/minute/channel, $B = 170$, $K = 5$; bandwidth = 850 cycles	0.85A1
Telegraphy modulated at audio frequency A2	Bandwidth = $BK + 2M$ where $K = 5$ for fading circuits $\;\;\;\; = 3$ for nonfading circuits	Morse code at 25 words/minute, 1000-cycle tone, $B = 20$; bandwidth = 2100 cycles	2.1A2
Commercial telephony A3	Bandwidth = M for single sideband $\;\;\;\;\;\;\;\;\;\;\; = 2M$ for double sideband	For ordinary single-sideband telephony, $M = 3000$	3A3a
		For high-quality single-sideband telephony, $M = 4000$	4A3a
Broadcasting A3	Bandwidth = $2M$	M may vary between 4000 and 10,000 depending upon the quality desired	8A3 to 20A3
Facsimile, carrier modulated by tone and by keying A4	Bandwidth = $\dfrac{KN}{T} + 2M$ where $K = 1.5$	Total number of picture elements (black+white) transmitted per second = circumference of cylinder (height of picture) $\times$ lines/unit length $\times$ speed of cylinder rotation (revolutions/second). If diameter of cylinder = 70 millimeters, lines/millimeter = 3.77, speed of rotation = 1/second, frequency of modulation = 1800 cycles; bandwidth = 3600 + 1242 $\;\;\;\;\;\;\;\;\;\;\;\; = 4842$ cycles	4.84A4
Television A5	Bandwidth = KN/T where $K = 1.5$ (This allows for synchronization and filter shaping.) *Note:* This band can be appropriately reduced when a symmetrical transmission is employed	Total picture elements (black+white) transmitted per second = number lines forming each image $\times$ elements/line $\times$ pictures transmitted/second. If lines = 500, elements/line = 500, pictures/second = 25; bandwidth $\approx$ 9 megacycles	9000A5

Bandwidth *continued*

frequency modulation

description and class of emission	necessary bandwidth in cycles/second	examples	
		details	designation of emission
Frequency-shift telegraphy F1	Bandwidth = $BK + 2D$ where $K = 5$ for fading circuits $ = 3$ for nonfading circuits	Four-channel multiplex with 7-unit code, 60 words/minute/channel. Then, $B = 170$, $K = 5$, $D = 425$; bandwidth = 1700 cycles	1.7F1
Commercial telephony and broadcasting F3	Bandwidth = $2M + 2DK$ For commercial telephony, $K = 1$. For high-fidelity transmission, higher values of K may be necessary	For an average case of commercial telephony, with $D = 15,000$ and $M = 3000$; bandwidth = 36,000 cycles	36F3
Facsimile F4	Bandwidth $$= \frac{KN}{T} + 2M + 2D$$ where $K = 1.5$	(See facsimile, amplitude modulation.) Cylinder diameter = 70 millimeters, lines/millimeter = 3.77, cylinder rotation speed = 1/second, modulation tone = 1800 cycles, $D = 10,000$ cycles; bandwidth ≈ 25,000 cycles	25F4
Unmodulated pulse P0	Bandwidth = $2K/t$ where K varies from 1 to 10 according to the permissible deviation in each particular case from a rectangular pulse shape. In many cases the value of K need not exceed 6	$t = 3 \times 10^{-6}$ and $K = 6$; bandwidth = 4×10^6 cycles	4000P0
Modulated pulse P2 or P3	Bandwidth depends upon the particular types of modulation used, many of these still being in the developmental stage		

Station WWV transmissions*

The Central Radio Propagation Laboratory of the National Bureau of Standards operates radio station WWV, which transmits standard radio and audio frequencies, time announcements, time ticks, and warning notices of radio-propagation disturbances.

* Based on "U.S. Bureau of Standards Letter Circular LC886," Central Radio Propagation Laboratory, National Bureau of Standards, U.S. Department of Commerce, Washington 25, D.C.; January 30, 1948.

Station WWV transmissions   *continued*

There are eight transmitters near Washington, D.C., operating on the frequencies listed below.

carrier frequency in megacycles/second	power in kilowatts	audio modulation in cycles/second
2.5	0.7	440
5	8.0	440
10	9.0	440 and 4000
15	9.0	440 and 4000
20	8.5*	440 and 4000
25	0.1	440 and 4000
30	0.1	440
35	0.1	—

* On first four work days after first Sunday of each month, power is 0.1 kilowatt.

They broadcast continuously, day and night. Vertical nondirectional antennas are used. Time announcements, time ticks, and warning notices are broadcast simultaneously by all transmitters. Some details of the services are noted below.

Standard radio frequency: The carrier frequency of each transmitter is accurate, as transmitted, to better than one part in 50,000,000. Transmission effects in the medium, such as the Doppler effect, result in an instantaneous accuracy of the received signal somewhat poorer than the above figure.

Standard audio frequencies: The carrier is amplitude modulated with audio frequencies as listed in the above table. Accuracy of the audio frequencies, as transmitted, is better than one part in 50,000,000, but is subject to transmission effects as is the carrier frequency.

Standard musical pitch: The 440-cycle/second audio frequency is standard musical pitch, being A above middle C.

Time ticks: On each carrier frequency, at intervals of one second, there is a pulse of 0.005-second duration, which is audible as a faint tick. The pulse is omitted on the 59th second of each minute. A time interval of one second as marked by two successive pulses is accurate, as transmitted, to one microsecond $(1 \times 10^{-6}$ second), while intervals of one minute or longer are accurate to one part in 50,000,000. Longer periods of 1, 4, or 5 minutes, etc., are marked by the beginning and ending of intervals during which no audio modulation is present. These are synchronized with the seconds ticks.

Time announcements: Precisely four minutes past the hour and every five minutes thereafter, the audio modulations are interrupted for exactly one minute. Thus, the last minute of each hour is free of audio modulation, which is resumed again precisely on the hour. The beginnings of the periods when

Station WWV transmissions *continued*

the audio frequencies are resumed are in agreement with the basic time service of the U.S. Naval Observatory. Eastern Standard Time is announced in international Morse code, indicating the end of each period free of audio tones. Thus, 1525 EST (3:25 PM), which is 2025 GMT, is announced by the number 1525 in code.

Station announcements: At the hour and half-hour silent periods, the station announcement is made in voice following the time announcement.

Propagation warning notices: At 19 and 49 minutes past the hour, following the time announcement, a series of W's or a series of N's is sent in telegraphic code. If N's are sent, no warning is in effect. However, W's indicate that there is in progress, or anticipated within 12 hours, a radio-propagation disturbance of the ionospheric-storm type, with its most severe effects on the North-Atlantic transmission path.

Coverage: Reliable reception is generally possible at all times throughout the United States and the North-Atlantic area, and often over the world. Depending on the conditions over the propagation path between Washington, D.C., and the point of reception, choice of the most favorable frequency should be made.

■ Units, constants, and conversion factors

Conversion factors

to convert	into	multiply by	conversely, multiply by
Acres	Square feet	4.356×10^4	2.296×10^{-5}
Acres	Square meters	4047	2.471×10^{-4}
Ampere-hours	Coulomb	3600	2.778×10^{-4}
Amperes per sq cm	Amperes per sq inch	6.452	0.1550
Ampere turns	Gilberts	1.257	0.7958
Ampere turns per cm	Ampere turns per inch	2.540	0.3937
Atmospheres	Mm of mercury @ 0° C	760	1.316×10^{-3}
Atmospheres	Feet of water @ 4° C	33.90	2.950×10^{-2}
Atmospheres	Inches mercury @ 0° C	29.92	3.342×10^{-2}
Atmospheres	Kg per sq meter	1.033×10^4	9.678×10^{-5}
Atmospheres	Pounds per sq inch	14.70	6.804×10^{-2}
Btu	Foot-pounds	778.3	1.285×10^{-3}
Btu	Joules	1054.8	9.480×10^{-4}
Btu	Kilogram-calories	0.2520	3.969
Btu per hour	Horsepower-hours	3.929×10^{-4}	2545
Bushels	Cubic feet	1.2445	0.8036
Centigrade	Fahrenheit	$(C° \times 9/5) + 32$	$(F° - 32) \times 5/9$
Circular mils	Square centimeters	5.067×10^{-6}	1.973×10^5
Circular mils	Square mils	0.7854	1.273
Cubic feet	Cords	7.8125×10^{-3}	128
Cubic feet	Gallons (liq US)	7.481	0.1337
Cubic feet	Liters	28.32	3.531×10^{-2}
Cubic inches	Cubic centimeters	16.39	6.102×10^{-2}
Cubic inches	Cubic feet	5.787×10^{-4}	1728
Cubic inches	Cubic meters	1.639×10^{-5}	6.102×10^4
Cubic inches	Gallons (liq US)	4.329×10^{-3}	231
Cubic meters	Cubic feet	35.31	2.832×10^{-2}
Cubic meters	Cubic yards	1.308	0.7646
Degrees (angle)	Radians	1.745×10^{-2}	57.30
Dynes	Pounds	2.248×10^{-6}	4.448×10^5
Ergs	Foot-pounds	7.367×10^{-8}	1.356×10^7
Fathoms	Feet	6	0.16666
Feet	Centimeters	30.48	3.281×10^{-2}
Feet	Varas	0.3594	2.782
Feet of water @ 4° C	Inches of mercury @ 0° C	0.8326	1.133
Feet of water @ 4° C	Kg per sq meter	304.8	3.281×10^{-3}
Feet of water @ 4° C	Pounds per sq foot	62.43	1.602×10^{-2}
Foot-pounds	Horsepower-hours	5.050×10^{-7}	1.98×10^6
Foot-pounds	Kilogram-meters	0.1383	7.233
Foot-pounds	Kilowatt-hours	3.766×10^{-7}	2.655×10^6
Gallons	Cubic meters	3.785×10^{-3}	264.2
Gallons (liq US)	Gallons (liq Br Imp)	0.8327	1.201
Gauss	Lines per sq inch	6.452	0.1550
Grains (for humidity calculations)	Pounds (avoirdupois)	1.429×10^{-4}	7000
Grams	Dynes	980.7	1.020×10^{-3}
Grams	Grains	15.43	6.481×10^{-2}
Grams	Ounces (avoirdupois)	3.527×10^{-2}	28.35
Grams	Poundals	7.093×10^{-2}	14.10
Grams per cm	Pounds per inch	5.600×10^{-3}	178.6
Grams per cu cm	Pounds per cu inch	3.613×10^{-2}	27.68
Grams per sq cm	Pounds per sq foot	2.0481	0.4883

Conversion factors *continued*

to convert	into	multiply by	conversely, multiply by
Hectares	Acres	2.471	0.4047
Horsepower (boiler)	Btu per hour	3.347×10^{3}	2.986×10^{-5}
Horsepower (metric) (542.5 ft-lb per sec)	Btu per minute	41.83	2.390×10^{-2}
Horsepower (metric) (542.5 ft-lb per sec)	Foot-lb per minute	3.255×10^{4}	3.072×10^{-5}
Horsepower (metric) (542.5 ft-lb per sec)	Kg-calories per minute	10.54	9.485×10^{-2}
Horsepower (550 ft-lb per sec)	Btu per minute	42.41	2.357×10^{-2}
Horsepower (550 ft-lb per sec)	Foot-lb per minute	3.3×10^{4}	3.030×10^{-5}
Horsepower (550 ft-lb per sec)	Kilowatts	0.745	1.342
Horsepower (metric) (542.5 ft-lb per sec)	Horsepower (550 ft-lb per sec)	0.9863	1.014
Horsepower (550 ft-lb per sec)	Kg-calories per minute	10.69	9.355×10^{-2}
Inches	Centimeters	2.540	0.3937
Inches	Feet	8.333×10^{-2}	12
Inches	Miles	1.578×10^{-5}	6.336×10^{4}
Inches	Mils	1000	0.001
Inches	Yards	2.778×10^{-2}	36
Inches of mercury @ 0° C	Lbs per sq inch	0.4912	2.036
Inches of water @ 4° C	Kg per sq meter	25.40	3.937×10^{-2}
Inches of water @ 4° C	Ounces per sq inch	0.5782	1.729
Inches of water @ 4° C	Pounds per sq foot	5.202	0.1922
Inches of water @ 4° C	In of mercury	7.355×10^{-2}	13.60
Joules	Foot-pounds	0.7376	1.356
Joules	Ergs	10^{7}	0^{-7}
Kilogram-calories	Kilogram-meters	426.9	2.343×10^{-3}
Kilogram-calories	Kilojoules	4.186	0.2389
Kilograms	Tons, long (avdp 2240 lb)	9.842×10^{-4}	1016
Kilograms	Tons, short (avdp 2000 lb)	1.102×10^{-3}	907.2
Kilograms	Pounds (avoirdupois)	2.205	0.4536
Kg per sq meter	Pounds per sq foot	0.2048	4.882
Kilometers	Feet	3281	3.048×10^{-4}
Kilowatt-hours	Btu	3413	2.930×10^{-4}
Kilowatt-hours	Foot-pounds	2.655×10^{6}	3.766×10^{-7}
Kilowatt-hours	Joules	3.6×10^{6}	2.778×10^{-7}
Kilowatt-hours	Kilogram-calories	860	1.163×10^{-3}
Kilowatt-hours	Kilogram-meters	3.671×10^{5}	2.724×10^{-6}
Kilowatt-hours	Pounds carbon oxydized	0.235	4.26
Kilowatt-hours	Pounds water evaporated from and at 212° F	3.53	0.283
Kilowatt-hours	Pounds water raised from 62° to 212° F	22.75	4.395×10^{-2}
Leagues	Miles	2.635	0.3795
Liters	Bushels (dry US)	2.838×10^{-2}	35.24
Liters	Cubic centimeters	1000	0.001
Liters	Cubic meters	0.001	1000
Liters	Cubic inches	61.02	1.639×10^{-2}
Liters	Gallons (liq US)	0.2642	3.785
Liters	Pints (liq US)	2.113	0.4732
$\log_e N$ or $\ln N$	$\log_{10} N$	0.4343	2.303

Conversion factors *continued*

to convert	into	multiply by	conversely, multiply by
Lumens per sq foot	Foot-candles	1	1
Lux	Foot-candles	0.0929	10.764
Meters	Yards	1.094	0.9144
Meters	Varas	1.179	0.848
Meters per min	Knots (naut mi per hour)	3.233×10^{-2}	30.88
Meters per min	Feet per minute	3.281	0.3048
Meters per min	Kilometers per hour	0.06	16.67
Microhms per cm cube	Microhms per inch cube	0.3937	2.540
Microhms per cm cube	Ohms per mil foot	6.015	0.1662
Miles (nautical)	Feet	6080.27	1.645×10^{-4}
Miles (nautical)	Kilometers	1.853	0.5396
Miles (statute)	Kilometers	1.609	0.6214
Miles (statute)	Miles (nautical)	0.8684	1.1516
Miles (statute)	Feet	5280	1.894×10^{-4}
Miles per hour	Kilometers per minute	2.682×10^{-2}	37.28
Miles per hour	Feet per minute	88	1.136×10^{-2}
Miles per hour	Knots (naut mi per hour)	0.3634	1.1516
Miles per hour	Kilometers per hour	1.609	0.6214
Nepers	Decibels	8.686	0.1151
Pounds of water (dist)	Cubic feet	1.603×10^{-2}	62.38
Pounds of water (dist)	Gallons	0.1198	8.347
Pounds per cu foot	Kg per cu meter	16.02	6.243×10^{-2}
Pounds per cu inch	Pounds per cu foot	1728	5.787×10^{-4}
Pounds per sq foot	Pounds per sq inch	6.944×10^{-3}	144
Pounds per sq inch	Kg per sq meter	703.1	1.422×10^{-3}
Poundals	Dynes	1.383×10^4	7.233×10^{-5}
Poundals	Pounds (avoirdupois)	3.108×10^{-2}	32.17
Slugs	Pounds	32.174	3.108×10^{-2}
Sq inches	Circular mils	1.273×10^6	7.854×10^{-7}
Sq inches	Sq centimeters	6.452	0.1550
Sq feet	Sq meters	9.290×10^{-2}	10.76
Sq miles	Sq yards	3.098×10^6	3.228×10^{-7}
Sq miles	Acres	640	1.562×10^{-3}
Sq miles	Sq kilometers	2.590	0.3861
Sq millimeters	Circular mils	1973	5.067×10^{-4}
Tons, short (avoir 2000 lb)	Tonnes (1000 kg)	0.9072	1.102
Tons, long (avoir 2240 lb)	Tonnes (1000 kg)	1.016	0.9842
Tons, long (avoir 2240 lb)	Tons, short (avoir 2000 lb)	1.120	0.8929
Tons (US shipping)	Cubic feet	40	0.025
Watts	Btu per minute	5.689×10^{-2}	17.58
Watts	Ergs per second	10^7	10^{-7}
Watts	Foot-lb per minute	44.26	2.260×10^{-2}
Watts	Horsepower (550 ft-lb per sec)	1.341×10^{-3}	745.7
Watts	Horsepower (metric) (542.5 ft-lb per sec)	1.360×10^{-3}	735.5
Watts	Kg-calories per minute	1.433×10^{-2}	69.77

Principal atomic constants*

usual symbol	denomination	value and units
F	Faraday's constant	9649.6 ± 0.7 emu equiv^{-1} (chemical scale) 9652.2 ± 0.7 emu equiv^{-1} (physical scale)
N	Avogadro's number	$(6.0235 \pm 0.0004) \times 10^{23}$ (chemical) $(6.0251 \pm 0.0004) \times 10^{23}$ (physical)
h	Planck's constant	$(6.6234 \pm 0.0011) \times 10^{-27}$ erg sec
m	Electron mass	$(9.1055 \pm 0.0012) \times 10^{-28}$ g
e	Electronic charge	$(4.8024 \pm 0.0005) \times 10^{-10}$ esu $(1.60199 \pm 0.00016) \times 10^{-20}$ emu
e/m	Specific electronic charge	$(1.75936 \pm 0.00018) \times 10^{7}$ emu g^{-1} $(5.2741 \pm 0.0005) \times 10^{17}$ esu g^{-1}
c	Velocity of light in vacuum	$(2.99776 \pm 0.00004) \times 10^{10}$ cm sec^{-1}
h/mc	Compton wavelength	$(2.42650 \pm 0.00025) \times 10^{-10}$ cm
$a_0 = h^2/(4\pi^2 me^2)$	First Bohr electron-orbit radius	$(0.529161 \pm 0.000028) \times 10^{-8}$ cm
σ	Stefan-Boltzmann constant	$(5.6724 \pm 0.0023) \times 10^{-5}$ erg cm^{-2} deg^{-4} sec^{-1}
$\lambda_{max}T$	Wien displacement-law constant	(0.289715 ± 0.000039) cm deg
$\mu_1 = he/4\pi m$	Bohr magneton	$(0.92731 \pm 0.00017) \times 10^{-20}$ erg gauss^{-1}
mN	Atomic weight of the electron	$(5.4847 \pm 0.0006) \times 10^{-4}$ (chemical) $(5.4862 \pm 0.0006) \times 10^{-4}$ (physical)
H^+/mN	Ratio, proton mass to electron mass	1836.57 ± 0.20
$v_0 = [2 \cdot 10^8(e/m)]^{1/2}$	Speed of 1 ev electron	$(5.93188 \pm 0.00030) \times 10^{7}$ cm sec^{-1}
$E_0 = e \cdot 10^8/c$	Energy associated with 1 ev	$(1.60199 \pm 0.00016) \times 10^{-12}$ erg
λ_0	DeBroglie wavelength associated with 1 ev	$(12394.2 \pm 0.9) \times 10^{-8}$ cm
mc^2	Energy equivalent of electron mass	(0.51079 ± 0.00006) Mev
k	Boltzmann's constant	$(1.38032 \pm 0.00011) \times 10^{-16}$ erg deg^{-1}
R_∞	Rydberg constant for "infinite" mass	109737.30 ± 0.05 cm^{-1}
H	Hydrogen atomic mass (physical scale)	1.008131 ± 0.000003
R_0	Gas constant per mol	$(8.31436 \pm 0.00038) \times 10^{7}$ erg mol^{-1} deg^{-1}
V_0	Standard volume of perfect gas	$(22.4146 \pm 0.006) \times 10^{3}$ cm^3 mol^{-1}

* Extracted from: J. W. M. DuMond and E. R. Cohen, "Our Knowledge of the Atomic Constants F, N, m, and h in 1947, and of Other Constants Derivable Therefrom," *Reviews of Modern Physics*, vol. 20, pp. 82–108; January, 1948.

26

Unit conversion table

quantity	symbol	equation in mks(r) units	mks(r) (rationalized) unit	equivalent number of				mks(nr) (nonrationalized) unit
				mks(nr) units	pract units	esu units	emu units	
length	l		meter (m)	1	10^2	10^2	10^2	meter (m)
mass	m		kilogram	1	10^3	10^3	10^3	kilogram
time	t		second	1	1	1	1	second
force	F	$F = ma$	newton	1	10^5	10^5	10^5	newton
work, energy	W	$W = Fl$	joule	1	1	10^7	10^7	joule
power	P	$P = W/t$	watt	1	1	10^7	10^7	watt
electric charge	q		coulomb	1	1	3×10^9	10^{-1}	coulomb
volume charge density	ρ	$\rho = q/v$	coulomb/m³	1	10^{-6}	3×10^3	10^{-7}	coulomb/m³
surface charge density	σ	$\sigma = q/A$	coulomb/m²	1	10^{-4}	3×10^5	10^{-5}	coulomb/m²
electric dipole moment	p	$p = ql$	coulomb-meter	1	10^2	3×10^{11}	10	coulomb-meter
polarization	P	$P = p/v$	coulomb/m²	1	10^{-4}	3×10^5	10^{-5}	coulomb/m²
electric field intensity	E	$E = F/q$	volt/m	1	10^{-2}	$10^{-4}/3$	10^6	volt/m
permittivity	ϵ	$F = q^2/4\pi\epsilon l^2$	farad/m	4π	$4\pi \times 10^{-9}$	$36\pi \times 10^9$	$4\pi \times 10^{-11}$	
displacement	D	$D = \epsilon E$	coulomb/m²	4π	$4\pi \times 10^{-4}$	$12\pi \times 10^5$	$4\pi \times 10^{-5}$	
displacement flux	Ψ	$\Psi = DA$	coulomb	4π	4π	$12\pi \times 10^9$	$4\pi \times 10^{-1}$	
emf, electric potential	V	$V = El$	volt	1	1	$10^{-2}/3$	10^8	volt
current	I	$I = q/t$	ampere	1	1	3×10^9	10^{-1}	ampere
volume current density	J	$J = I/A$	ampere/m²	1	10^{-4}	3×10^5	10^{-5}	ampere/m²
surface current density	K	$K = I/l$	ampere/m	1	10^{-2}	3×10^7	10^{-3}	ampere/m
resistance	R	$R = V/I$	ohm	1	1	$10^{-11}/9$	10^9	ohm
conductance	G	$G = 1/R$	mho	1	1	9×10^{11}	10^{-9}	mho
resistivity	ρ	$\rho = RA/l$	ohm-meter	1	10^2	$10^{-9}/9$	10^{11}	ohm-meter
conductivity	γ	$\gamma = 1/\rho$	mho/meter	1	10^{-2}	9×10^9	10^{-11}	mho/meter
capacitance	C	$C = q/V$	farad	1	1	9×10^{11}	10^{-9}	farad
elastance	S	$S = 1/C$	daraf	1	1	$10^{-11}/9$	10^9	daraf
magnetic charge	m		weber	$1/4\pi$	$10^8/4\pi$	$10^{-2}/12\pi$	$10^8/4\pi$	
magnetic dipole moment	m	$m = ml$	weber-meter	$1/4\pi$	$10^{10}/4\pi$	$1/12\pi$	$10^{10}/4\pi$	
magnetization	M	$M = m/v$	weber/m²	$1/4\pi$	$10^4/4\pi$	$10^{-6}/12\pi$	$10^4/4\pi$	
magnetic field intensity	H	$H = nI/l$	ampere-turn/m	4π	$4\pi \times 10^{-3}$	$12\pi \times 10^7$	$4\pi \times 10^{-3}$	
permeability	μ	$F = m^2/4\pi\mu l^2$	henry/m	$1/4\pi$	$10^7/4\pi$	$10^{-13}/36\pi$	$10^7/4\pi$	
induction	B	$B = \mu H$	weber/m²	1	10^4	$10^{-6}/3$	10^4	weber/m²
induction flux	Φ	$\Phi = BA$	weber	1	10^8	$10^{-2}/3$	10^8	weber
mmf, magnetic potential	M	$M = Hl$	ampere-turn	4π	$4\pi \times 10^{-1}$	$12\pi \times 10^9$	$4\pi \times 10^{-1}$	
reluctance	$\mathcal{R}$	$\mathcal{R} = M/\Phi$	amp-turn/weber	4π	$4\pi \times 10^{-9}$	$36\pi \times 10^{11}$	$4\pi \times 10^{-9}$	
permeance	$\mathcal{P}$	$\mathcal{P} = 1/\mathcal{R}$	weber/amp-turn	$1/4\pi$	$10^9/4\pi$	$10^{-11}/36\pi$	$10^9/4\pi$	
inductance	L	$L = \Phi/I$	henry	1	1	$10^{-11}/9$	10^9	henry

Compiled by J. R. Ragazzini and L. A. Zadeh, Columbia University, New York.

The velocity of light was taken as 3×10^{10} centimeters/second in computing the conversion factors. Equations in the second column are for dimensional purposes only.

equivalent number of			practical (cgs) unit	equivalent number of		esu unit	equivalent number of emu units	emu unit
pract units	esu units	emu units		esu units	emu units			
10^2	10^2	10^2	centimeter (cm)	1	1	centimeter (cm) (G)	1	centimeter (cm)
10^3	10^3	10^3	gram	1	1	gram (G)	1	gram
1	1	1	second	1	1	second (G)	1	second
10^5	10^5	10^5	dyne	1	1	dyne (G)	1	dyne
1	10^7	10^7	joule	10^7	10^7	erg (G)	1	erg
1	10^7	10^7	watt	10^7	10^7	erg/second (G)	1	erg/second
1	3×10^9	10^{-1}	coulomb	3×10^9	10^{-1}	statcoulomb (G)	$10^{-10}/3$	abcoulomb
10^{-6}	3×10^3	10^{-7}	coulomb/cm³	3×10^9	10^{-1}	statcoulomb/cm³ (G)	$10^{-10}/3$	abcoulomb/cm³
10^{-4}	3×10^5	10^{-5}	coulomb/cm²	3×10^9	10^{-1}	statcoulomb/cm² (G)	$10^{-10}/3$	abcoulomb/cm²
10^2	3×10^{11}	10	coulomb-cm	3×10^9	10^{-1}	statcoulomb-cm (G)	$10^{-10}/3$	abcoulomb-cm
10^{-4}	3×10^5	10^{-5}	coulomb/cm²	3×10^9	10^{-1}	statcoulomb/cm² (G)	$10^{-10}/3$	abcoulomb/cm²
10^{-2}	$10^{-4}/3$	10^6	volt/cm	$10^{-2}/3$	10^8	statvolt/cm (G)	3×10^{10}	abvolt/cm
10^{-9}	9×10^9	10^{-11}		9×10^{18}	10^{-2}	(G)	$10^{-20}/9$	
10^{-4}	3×10^5	10^{-5}		3×10^9	10^{-1}	(G)	$10^{-10}/3$	
1	3×10^9	10^{-1}		3×10^9	10^{-1}	(G)	$10^{-10}/3$	
1	$10^{-2}/3$	10^8	volt	$10^{-2}/3$	10^8	statvolt (G)	3×10^{10}	abvolt
1	3×10^9	10^{-1}	ampere	3×10^9	10^{-1}	statampere (G)	$10^{-10}/3$	abampere
10^{-4}	3×10^5	10^{-5}	ampere/cm²	3×10^9	10^{-1}	statampere/cm² (G)	$10^{-10}/3$	abampere/cm²
10^{-2}	3×10^7	10^{-3}	ampere/cm	3×10^9	10^{-1}	statampere/cm (G)	$10^{-10}/3$	abampere/cm
1	$10^{-11}/9$	10^9	ohm	$10^{-11}/9$	10^9	statohm (G)	9×10^{20}	abohm
1	9×10^{11}	10^{-9}	mho	9×10^{11}	10^{-9}	statmho (G)	$10^{-20}/9$	abmho
10^2	$10^{-9}/9$	10^{11}	ohm-cm	$10^{-11}/9$	10^9	statohm-cm (G)	9×10^{20}	abohm-cm
10^{-2}	9×10^9	10^{-11}	mho/cm	9×10^{11}	10^{-9}	statmho/cm (G)	$10^{-20}/9$	abmho/cm
1	9×10^{11}	10^{-9}	farad	9×10^{11}	10^{-9}	statfarad (cm) (G)	$10^{-20}/9$	abfarad
1	$10^{-11}/9$	10^9	daraf	$10^{-11}/9$	10^9	statdaraf (G)	9×10^{20}	abdaraf
10^8	$10^{-2}/3$	10^8		$10^{-10}/3$	1		3×10^{10}	unit pole (G)
10^{10}	$1/3$	10^{10}		$10^{-10}/3$	1		3×10^{10}	pole-cm (G)
10^4	$10^{-6}/3$	10^4		$10^{-10}/3$	1		3×10^{10}	pole/cm² (G)
10^{-3}	3×10^7	10^{-3}	oersted	3×10^{10}	1		$10^{-10}/3$	oersted (G)
10^7	$10^{-13}/9$	10^7	gauss/oersted	$10^{-20}/9$	1		9×10^{20}	gauss/oersted (G)
10^4	$10^{-6}/3$	10^4	gauss	$10^{-10}/3$	1		3×10^{10}	gauss (G)
10^8	$10^{-2}/3$	10^8	maxwell (line)	$10^{-10}/3$	1		3×10^{10}	maxwell (line) (G)
10^{-1}	3×10^9	10^{-1}	gilbert	3×10^{10}	1		$10^{-10}/3$	gilbert (G)
10^{-9}	9×10^{11}	10^{-9}	gilbert/maxwell	9×10^{20}	1		$10^{-20}/9$	gilbert/maxwell (G)
10^9	$10^{-11}/9$	10^9	maxwell/gilbert	$10^{-20}/9$	1		9×10^{20}	maxwell/gilbert (G)
1	$10^{-11}/9$	10^9	henry	$10^{-11}/9$	10^9	stathenry (G)	9×10^{20}	abhenry (cm) (G)

G = Gaussian unit.

Fractions of an inch with metric equivalents

fractions of an inch	decimals of an inch	millimeters	fractions of an inch	decimals of an inch	millimeters
1/64	0.0156	0.397	33/64	0.5156	13.097
1/32	0.0313	0.794	17/32	0.5313	13.494
3/64	0.0469	1.191	35/64	0.5469	13.891
1/16	0.0625	1.588	9/16	0.5625	14.288
5/64	0.0781	1.984	37/64	0.5781	14.684
3/32	0.0938	2.381	19/32	0.5938	15.081
7/64	0.1094	2.778	39/64	0.6094	15.478
1/8	0.1250	3.175	5/8	0.6250	15.875
9/64	0.1406	3.572	41/64	0.6406	16.272
5/32	0.1563	3.969	21/32	0.6563	16.669
11/64	0.1719	4.366	43/64	0.6719	17.066
3/16	0.1875	4.763	11/16	0.6875	17.463
13/64	0.2031	5.159	45/64	0.7031	17.859
7/32	0.2188	5.556	23/32	0.7188	18.256
15/64	0.2344	5.953	47/64	0.7344	18.653
1/4	0.2500	6.350	3/4	0.7500	19.050
17/64	0.2656	6.747	49/64	0.7656	19.447
9/32	0.2313	7.144	25/32	0.7813	19.844
19/64	0.2969	7.541	51/64	0.7969	20.241
5/16	0.3125	7.938	13/16	0.8125	20.638
21/64	0.3281	8.334	53/64	0.8281	21.034
11/32	0.3438	8.731	27/32	0.8438	21.431
23/64	0.3594	9.128	55/64	0.8594	21.828
3/8	0.3750	9.525	7/8	0.8750	22.225
25/64	0.3906	9.922	57/64	0.8906	22.622
13/32	0.4063	10.319	29/32	0.9063	23.019
27/64	0.4219	10.716	59/64	0.9219	23.416
7/16	0.4375	11.113	15/16	0.9375	23.813
29/64	0.4531	11.509	61/64	0.9531	24.209
15/32	0.4688	11.906	31/32	0.9688	24.606
31/64	0.4844	12.303	63/64	0.9844	25.003
1/2	0.5000	12.700	—	1.0000	25.400

Useful numerical data

1 cubic foot of water at 4° C (weight) _____ 62.43 lb

1 foot of water at 4° C (pressure) _____ 0.4335 lb/in²

Velocity of light in vacuum c _____ 186,280 mi/sec = 2.998×10^{10} cm/sec

Velocity of sound in dry air at 20° C, 76 cm Hg _____ 1127 ft/sec

Degree of longitude at equator _____ 69.173 miles

Acceleration due to gravity at sea-level, 40° Latitude, g _____ 32.1578 ft/sec²

$\sqrt{2g}$ _____ 8.020

1 inch of mercury at 4° C _____ 1.132 ft water = 0.4908 lb/in²

Base of natural logs ϵ _____ 2.718

1 radian _____ 180° ÷ π = 57.3°

360 degrees _____ 2 π radians

π _____ 3.1416

Sine 1' _____ 0.00029089

Arc 1° _____ 0.01745 radian

Side of square _____ 0.707 × (diagonal of square)

Greek alphabet

name	capital	small		commonly used to designate
ALPHA	A	α		Angles, coefficients, attenuation constant, absorption factor, area
BETA	B	β		Angles, coefficients, phase constant
GAMMA	Γ	γ		Complex propagation constant (cap), specific gravity, angles, electrical conductivity, propagation constant
DELTA	Δ	δ		Increment or decrement (cap or small), determinant (cap), permittivity (cap), density, angles
EPSILON	E	ϵ		Dielectric constant, permittivity, base of natural logarithms, electric intensity
ZETA	Z	ζ		Coordinates, coefficients
ETA	H	η		Intrinsic impedance, efficiency, surface charge density, hysteresis, coordinates
THETA	Θ	ϑ	θ	Angular phase displacement, time constant, reluctance, angles
IOTA	I	ι		Unit vector
KAPPA	K	κ		Susceptibility, coupling coefficient
LAMBDA	Λ	λ		Permeance (cap), wavelength, attenuation constant
MU	M	μ		Permeability, amplification factor, prefix micro
NU	N	ν		Reluctivity, frequency
XI	Ξ	ξ		Coordinates
OMICRON	O	o		
PI	Π	π		3.1416
RHO	P	ρ		Resistivity, volume charge density, coordinates
SIGMA	Σ	σ	s	Summation (cap), surface charge density, complex propagation constant, electrical conductivity, leakage coefficient
TAU	T	τ		Time constant, volume resistivity, time-phase displacement, transmission factor, density
UPSILON	Υ	υ		
PHI	Φ	ϕ	φ	Scalar potential (cap), magnetic flux, angles
CHI	X	χ		Electric susceptibility, angles
PSI	Ψ	ψ		Dielectric flux, phase difference, coordinates, angles
OMEGA	Ω	ω		Resistance in ohms (cap), solid angle (cap), angular velocity

Small letter is used except where capital is indicated.

Decibels and power, voltage, and current ratios

The decibel, abbreviated db, is a unit used to express the ratio between two amounts of power, P_1 and P_2, existing at two points. By definition,

$$\text{number of db} = 10 \log_{10} \frac{P_1}{P_2}$$

It is also used to express voltage and current ratios;

$$\text{number of db} = 20 \log_{10} \frac{V_1}{V_2} = 20 \log_{10} \frac{I_1}{I_2}$$

Strictly, it can be used to express voltage and current ratios only when the two points at which the voltages or currents in question have identical impedances.

power ratio	voltage and current ratio	decibels	power ratio	voltage and current ratio	decibels
1.0233	1.0116	0.1	19.953	4.4668	13.0
1.0471	1.0233	0.2	25.119	5.0119	14.0
1.0715	1.0351	0.3	31.623	5.6234	15.0
1.0965	1.0471	0.4	39.811	6.3096	16.0
1.1220	1.0593	0.5	50.119	7.0795	17.0
1.1482	1.0715	0.6	63.096	7.9433	18.0
1.1749	1.0839	0.7	79.433	8.9125	19.0
1.2023	1.0965	0.8	100.00	10.0000	20.0
1.2303	1.1092	0.9	158.49	12.589	22.0
1.2589	1.1220	1.0	251.19	15.849	24.0
1.3183	1.1482	1.2	398.11	19.953	26.0
1.3804	1.1749	1.4	630.96	25.119	28.0
1.4454	1.2023	1.6	1000.0	31.623	30.0
1.5136	1.2303	1.8	1584.9	39.811	32.0
1.5849	1.2589	2.0	2511.9	50.119	34.0
1.6595	1.2882	2.2	3981.1	63.096	36.0
1.7378	1.3183	2.4	6309.6	79.433	38.0
1.8197	1.3490	2.6	10^4	100.000	40.0
1.9055	1.3804	2.8	$10^4 \times 1.5849$	125.89	42.0
1.9953	1.4125	3.0	$10^4 \times 2.5119$	158.49	44.0
2.2387	1.4962	3.5	$10^4 \times 3.9811$	199.53	46.0
2.5119	1.5849	4.0	$10^4 \times 6.3096$	251.19	48.0
2.8184	1.6788	4.5	10^5	316.23	50.0
3.1623	1.7783	5.0	$10^5 \times 1.5849$	398.11	52.0
3.5481	1.8836	5.5	$10^5 \times 2.5119$	501.19	54.0
3.9811	1.9953	6.0	$10^5 \times 3.9811$	630.96	56.0
5.0119	2.2387	7.0	$10^5 \times 6.3096$	794.33	58.0
6.3096	2.5119	8.0	10^6	1,000.00	60.0
7.9433	2.8184	9.0	10^7	3,162.3	70.0
10.0000	3.1623	10.0	10^8	10,000.0	80.0
12.589	3.5481	11.0	10^9	31,623	90.0
15.849	3.9811	12.0	10^{10}	100,000	100.0

To convert
    Decibels to nepers multiply by 0.1151
    Nepers to decibels multiply by 8.686

Where the power ratio is less than unity, it is usual to invert the fraction and express the answer as a decibel loss.

■ Properties of materials

Atomic weights

element	symbol	atomic number	atomic weight	element	symbol	atomic number	atomic weight
Aluminum	Al	13	26.97	Molybdenum	Mo	42	95.95
Antimony	Sb	51	121.76	Neodymium	Nd	60	144.27
Argon	A	18	39.944	Neon	Ne	10	20.183
Arsenic	As	33	74.91	Nickel	Ni	28	58.69
Barium	Ba	56	137.36	Nitrogen	N	7	14.008
Beryllium	Be	4	9.02	Osmium	Os	76	190.2
Bismuth	Bi	83	209.00	Oxygen	O	8	16.0000
Boron	B	5	10.82	Palladium	Pd	46	106.7
Bromine	Br	35	79.916	Phosphorus	P	15	30.98
Cadmium	Cd	48	112.41	Platinum	Pt	78	195.23
Calcium	Ca	20	40.08	Potassium	K	19	39.096
Carbon	C	6	12.010	Praseodymium	Pr	59	140.92
Cerium	Ce	58	140.13	Protactinium	Pa	91	231
Cesium	Cs	55	132.91	Radium	Ra	88	226.05
Chlorine	Cl	17	35.457	Radon	Rn	86	222
Chromium	Cr	24	52.01	Rhenium	Re	75	186.31
Cobalt	Co	27	58.94	Rhodium	Rh	45	102.91
Columbium	Cb	41	92.91	Rubidium	Rb	37	85.48
Copper	Cu	29	63.57	Ruthenium	Ru	44	101.7
Dysprosium	Dy	66	162.46	Samarium	Sm	62	150.43
Erbium	Er	68	167.2	Scandium	Sc	21	45.10
Europium	Eu	63	152.0	Selenium	Se	34	78.96
Fluorine	F	9	19.00	Silicon	Si	14	28.06
Gadolinium	Gd	64	156.9	Silver	Ag	47	107.880
Gallium	Ga	31	69.72	Sodium	Na	11	22.997
Germanium	Ge	32	72.60	Strontium	Sr	38	87.63
Gold	Au	79	197.2	Sulfur	S	16	32.06
Hafnium	Hf	72	178.6	Tantalum	Ta	73	180.88
Helium	He	2	4.003	Tellurium	Te	52	127.61
Holmium	Ho	67	164.94	Terbium	Tb	65	159.2
Hydrogen	H	1	1.0080	Thallium	Tl	81	204.39
Indium	In	49	114.76	Thorium	Th	90	232.12
Iodine	I	53	126.92	Thulium	Tm	69	169.4
Iridium	Ir	77	193.1	Tin	Sn	50	118.70
Iron	Fe	26	55.85	Titanium	Ti	22	47.90
Krypton	Kr	36	83.7	Tungsten	W	74	183.92
Lanthanum	La	57	133.92	Uranium	U	92	238.07
Lead	Pb	82	207.21	Vanadium	V	23	50.95
Lithium	Li	3	6.940	Xenon	Xe	54	131.3
Lutecium	Lu	71	174.99	Ytterbium	Yb	70	173.04
Magnesium	Mg	12	24.32	Yttrium	Y	39	88.92
Manganese	Mn	25	54.93	Zinc	Zn	30	65.38
Mercury	Hg	80	200.61	Zirconium	Zr	40	91.22

From *Journal of American Chemical Society*, v. 70, n. 11, p. 3532; December 8, 1948.

Electromotive force

Series of the elements

element	volts	ion		element	volts	ion
Lithium	2.9595			Tin	0.136	
Rubidium	2.9259			Lead	0.122	Pb^{++}
Potassium	2.9241			Iron	0.045	Fe^{+++}
Strontium	2.92			Hydrogen	0.000	
Barium	2.90			Antimony	−0.10	
Calcium	2.87			Bismuth	−0.226	
Sodium	2.7146			Arsenic	−0.30	
Magnesium	2.40			Copper	−0.344	Cu^{++}
Aluminum	1.70			Oxygen	−0.397	
Beryllium	1.69			Polonium	−0.40	
Uranium	1.40			Copper	−0.470	Cu^+
Manganese	1.10			Iodine	−0.5345	
Tellurium	0.827			Tellurium	−0.558	Te^{++++}
Zinc	0.7618			Silver	−0.7978	
Chromium	0.557			Mercury	−0.7986	
Sulphur	0.51			Lead	−0.80	Pb^{++++}
Gallium	0.50			Palladium	−0.820	
Iron	0.441	Fe^{++}		Platinum	−0.863	
Cadmium	0.401			Bromine	−1.0648	
Indium	0.336			Chlorine	−1.3583	
Thallium	0.330			Gold	−1.360	Au^{++++}
Cobalt	0.278			Gold	−1.50	Au^+
Nickel	0.231			Fluorine	−1.90	

Position of metals in the galvanic series

Corroded end (anodic, or least noble)

Magnesium
Magnesium alloys
Zinc
Aluminum 2S
Cadmium
Aluminum 17ST
Steel or Iron
Cast Iron
Chromium-iron (active)
Ni-Resist
18–8 Stainless (active)
18–8–3 Stainless (active)
Lead-tin solders
Lead
Tin

Nickel (active)
Inconel (active)
Brasses
Copper
Bronzes
Copper-nickel alloys
Monel
Silver solder
Nickel (passive)
Inconel (passive)
Chromium-iron (passive)
18–8 Stainless (passive)
18–8–3 Stainless (passive)
Silver
Graphite
Gold
Platinum
Protected end (cathodic, or most noble)

Note: Groups of metals indicate they are closely similar in properties.

continued **Electromotive force**

Thermocouples and their characteristics

type	copper/constantan	iron/constantan	chromel/constantan	chromel/alumel	platinum/platinum rhodium (10)	platinum/platinum rhodium (13)	carbon/silicon carbide
Composition, percent	100Cu 99.9Cu / 54Cu 46Ni 55Cu 45Ni 60Cu 40Ni	100Fe / 55Cu 44Ni 0.5Mn+Fe, Si	90Ni 10Cr / 55Cu 45Ni	90Ni 10Cr 89.6Ni 8.9Cr 89Ni 10Cr 89Ni 9.8Cr / 95Ni 2Al 2Mn 1Si 97Ni 3Al+Si 94Ni 2Al 1Si 2.5Mn 0.5Fe 1Fe 0.2Mn	90Pt 10Rh Pt	87Pt 13Rh Pt	C SiC
Range of application, °C	−250 to +600	−200 to +1050	0 to 1100	0 to 1100	0 to 1550		1 to 2000
Resistivity, micro-ohm-cm	1.75 / 49	10 / 49	70 / 49	70 / 29.4	10 / 21		
Temperature coefficient of resistivity, °C	0.0039 / 0.00001	0.005 / 0.00001	0.00035 / 0.0002	0.00035 / 0.000125	0.0030 / 0.0018		
Melting temperature, °C	1085 / 1190	1535 / 1190	1400 / 1190	1400 / 1430	1755 / 1700		3000 / 2700
emf in millivolts; reference junction at 0° C	100°C 4.24mv 200 9.06 300 14.42	100°C 5.28mv 200 10.78 400 21.82 600 33.16 800 45.48 1000 58.16	100°C 6.3mv 200 13.3 400 28.5 600 44.3	100°C 4.1 mv 200 8.13 400 16.39 600 24.90 800 33.31 1000 41.31 1200 48.85 1400 55.81	100°C 0.643mv 200 1.436 400 3.251 600 5.222 800 7.330 1000 9.569 1200 11.924 1400 14.312 1600 16.674	100°C 0.646mv 200 1.464 400 3.398 600 5.561 800 7.927 1000 10.470 1200 13.181 1400 15.940 1600 18.680	1210°C 353.6mv 1300 385.2 1360 403.2 1450 424.9
Influence of temperature and gas atmosphere	Subject to oxidation and alteration above 400°C due Cu, above 600° due constantan. Ni-plating of Cu tube gives protection, in acid-containing gas. Contamination of Cu affecting calibration greatly, good. Resistance to oxid. atm. good. Resistance to reducing atm. good. Requires protection from acid fumes.	Oxidizing and reducing atmosphere have little effect on accuracy. Best used in dry atmosphere. Resistance to oxidation good to 400°C. Resistance to reducing atmosphere good to 400°C. Protect from oxygen, moisture, sulphur.	Chromel attacked by sulphurous atmosphere. Resistance to oxidation good. Resistance to reducing atmosphere poor.	Resistance to oxidizing atmosphere very good. Resistance to reducing atmosphere poor. Affected by sulphur, reducing atmosphere or sulphurous gas, SO₂ and H₂S.	Resistance to oxidizing atmosphere very good. Resistance to reducing atmosphere poor. Susceptible to chemical alteration by As, Si, P vapor in reducing gas (CO₂, H₂, H₂S, SO₂). Pt corrodes easily above 1000°. Used in gas-tight protecting tube.		Used as tube element. Carbon sheath chemically inert.
Particular applications	Low temperature, industrial. Internal combustion engine.	Low temperature, industrial. Steel annealing. Used nealing, boiler flues, as a tube element for tube stills. Used in measurements in reducing or neutral steam line.		Used in oxidizing atmosphere. Industrial. Ceramic kilns, stills, electric furnaces.	International Standard 630 to 1065° C.	Similar to Pt/PtRh(10) but has higher emf.	Steel furnace and ladle temperatures. Laboratory measurements.

Electromotive force   continued

Temperature–emf characteristics of thermocouples

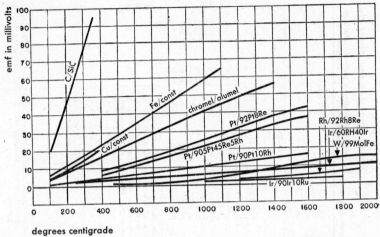

degrees centigrade

Compiled from R. L. Weber, "Temperature Measurement and Control," Blakiston Co., Philadelphia, Pennsylvania; 1941: see pp. 68–71.

deg C

Physical constants of various metals and alloys

Definitions of physical constants in table

Relative resistance: The table of relative resistances gives the ratio of the resistance of any material to the resistance of a piece of annealed copper of identical physical dimensions and temperature. The resistance of any substance of uniform cross-section is proportional to the length and inversely proportional to the cross-sectional area.

$$R = \frac{\rho L}{A}$$

where

ρ = resistivity, the proportionality constant
L = length
A = cross-sectional area
R = resistance in ohms

Physical constants of various metals and alloys *continued*

material	relative resistance*	temp coefficient of resistivity at 20°C	specific gravity	coefficient of thermal cond K watts/cm°C	melting point °C
Advance (55 Cu, 45 Ni)	see	Constantan			
Aluminum	1.64	0.004	2.7	2.03	660
Antimony	24.21	0.0036	6.6	0.187	630
Arsenic	19.33	0.0042	5.73	—	sublimes
Bismuth	69.8	0.004	9.8	0.0755	270
Brass (66 Cu, 34 Zn)	3.9	0.002	8.47	1.2	920
Cadmium	4.4	0.0038	8.64	0.92	321
Chromax (15 Cr, 35 Ni, balance Fe)	58.0	0.00031	7.95	0.130	1380
Cobalt	5.6	0.0033	8.71	—	1480
Constantan (55Cu,45Ni)	28.45	±0.0002	8.9	0.218	1210
Copper—annealed	1.00	0.00393	8.89	3.88	1083
hard drawn	1.03	0.00382	8.89	—	1083
Eureka (55 Cu, 45 Ni)	see	Constantan			
Gas carbon	2900	−0.0005	—	—	3500
Gold	1.416	0.0034	19.32	0.296	1063
German silver	16.9	0.00027	8.7	0.32	1110
Ideal (55 Cu, 45 Ni)	see	Constantan			
Iron, pure	5.6	0.0052–0.0062	7.8	0.67	1535
Kovar A (29 Ni, 17 Co, 0.3 Mn, balance Fe)	28.4	—	8.2	0.193	1450
Lead	12.78	0.0042	11.35	0.344	327
Magnesium	2.67	0.004	1.74	1.58	651
Manganin (84 Cu, 12 Mn, 4 Ni)	26	±0.00002	8.5	0.63	910
Mercury	55.6	0.00089	13.55	0.063	−38.87
Molybdenum, drawn	3.3	0.0045	10.2	1.46	2630
Monel metal (67 Ni, 30 Cu, 1.4 Fe, 1 Mn)	27.8	0.002	8.8	0.25	1300–1350
Nichrome I (65 Ni, 12 Cr, 23 Fe)	65.0	0.00017	8.25	0.132	1350
Nickel	5.05	0.0047	8.85	0.6	1452
Nickel silver (64 Cu, 18 Zn, 18 Ni)	16.0	0.00026	8.72	0.33	1110
Palladium	6.2	0.0038	12.16	0.7	1557
Phosphor-bronze (4 Sn, 0.5 P, balance Cu)	5.45	0.003	8.9	0.82	1050
Platinum	6.16	0.0038	21.4	0.695	1771
Silver	0.95	0.004	10.5	4.19	960.5
Steel, manganese (13 Mn, 1 C, 86 Fe)	41.1	—	7.81	0.113	1510
Steel, SAE 1045 (0.4–0.5 C, balance Fe)	7.6–12.7	—	7.8	0.59	1480
Steel, 18–8 stainless (0.1 C, 18 Cr, 8 Ni, balance Fe)	52.8	—	7.9	0.163	1410
Tantalum	9.0	0.0033	16.6	0.545	2850
Tin	6.7	0.0042	7.3	0.64	231.9
Tophet A (80 Ni, 20 Cr)	62.5	0.02–0.07	8.4	0.136	1400
Tungsten	3.25	0.0045	19.2	1.6	3370
Zinc	3.4	0.0037	7.14	1.12	419
Zirconium	2.38	0.0044	6.4	—	1860

* Resistivity of copper = 1.7241×10^{-6} ohm-centimeters.

Physical constants of various metals and alloys   *continued*

If L and A are measured in centimeters, ρ is in ohm-centimeters. If L is measured in feet, and A in circular mils, ρ is in ohm-circular-mils/foot.

Relative resistance = ρ divided by the resistivity of copper (1.7241×10^{-6} ohm-centimeters)

Temperature coefficient: Of resistivity gives the ratio of the change in resistivity due to a change in temperature of 1 degree centigrade relative to the resistivity at 20 degrees centigrade. The dimensions of this quantity are ohms/degree centigrade/ohm, or 1/degree centigrade.

The resistance at any temperature is

$$R = R_0 \, (1 + \alpha T)$$

where

R_0 = resistance at $0°$ in ohms
T = temperature in degrees centigrade
α = temperature coefficient of resistivity/degree centigrade

Specific gravity: Of a substance is defined as the ratio of the weight of a given volume of the substance to the weight of an equal volume of water. In the cgs system, the specific gravity of a substance is exactly equal to the weight in grams of one cubic centimeter of the substance.

Coefficient of thermal conductivity: Is defined as the time rate of heat transfer through unit thickness, across unit area, for a unit difference in temperature. Expressing rate of heat transfer in watts, the coefficient of thermal conductivity

$$K = \frac{WL}{A\Delta T}$$

where

W = watts
L = thickness in centimeters
A = area in centimeters^2
ΔT = temperature difference in degrees centigrade

Specific heat: Is defined as the number of calories required to heat one gram of a substance one degree centigrade. If H is the number of calories,

Physical constants of various metals and alloys   *continued*

$H = ms \, \Delta T$ or change in heat

where

ΔT = temperature change in degrees centigrade
m = mass in grams
s = specific heat in calories/gram/degree centigrade

Temperature charts of metals

On the following two pages are given centigrade and Fahrenheit temperatures relating to the processing of metals and alloys.

Soldering, brazing, and welding: This chart has been prepared to provide, in a convenient form, the melting points and components of various common soldering and brazing alloys. The temperature limits of various joining processes are indicated with the type and composition of the flux best suited for the process. Two pairs of identical Fahrenheit and centigrade temperature scales are shown with the low values at the bottom of the chart. The chart is a compilation of present good practice and does not indicate that the processes and materials cannot be used in other ways under special conditions.

Melting points: The melting-point chart is a thermometer-type graph upon which are placed the melting points of metals, alloys, and ceramics most commonly used in electron tubes and other components in the radio industry. Centigrade and the equivalent Fahrenheit scales are given; above 2000 degrees centigrade the scale is condensed. Pure metals are shown opposite their respective melting points on the right side of the thermometer. Ceramic materials and metal alloys are similarly shown on the left. The melting temperature shown for ceramic bodies is that temperature above which no crystalline phase normally exists. No attempt has been made to indicate their progressive softening characteristic.

When a specific material is being considered for use because of desirable electrical, chemical, or other properties, the melting point is easily obtained. Conversely, where the temperature range within which materials must work is known, suitable ones can be quickly selected.

Fabrication techniques may employ soldering, brazing, or welding, and the most suitable method for a particular material may be determined from the two charts. Similarly, where sequential heating operations are planned, they are useful.

Temperature charts of metals   *continued*

Soldering, brazing, and welding processes*

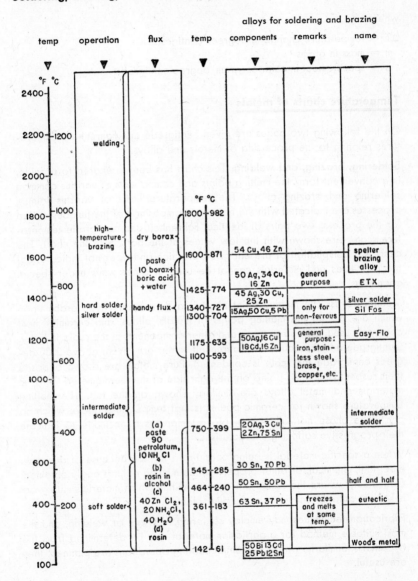

alloys for soldering and brazing

temp	operation	flux	temp	components	remarks	name

°F °C

2400—

2200— 1200   welding

2000—

1800— 1000   high-temperature brazing   dry borax   °F °C
1800— 982

1600—   paste 10 borax + boric acid + water   1600— 871   54 Cu, 46 Zn   spelter brazing alloy

— 800   1425— 774   50 Ag, 34 Cu, 16 Zn   general purpose   ETX

1400—   hard solder silver solder   handy flux   1340— 727   45 Ag, 30 Cu, 25 Zn   silver solder
1300— 704   15 Ag, 50 Cu, 5 Pb   only for non-ferrous   Sil Fos

1200—   1175— 635   50 Ag, 16 Cu   general purpose: iron, stainless steel, brass, copper, etc.   Easy-Flo
1100— 593   18 Cd, 16 Zn

— 600

1000—

800—   intermediate solder   (a) paste 90 petrolatum, 10 NH₃Cl   750— 399   20 Ag, 3 Cu 2 Zn, 75 Sn   intermediate solder
— 400

600—   (b) rosin in alcohol   545— 285   30 Sn, 70 Pb
(c)   464— 240   50 Sn, 50 Pb   half and half

400— 200   soft solder   40 Zn Cl₂, 20 NH₄Cl, 40 H₂O   361— 183   63 Sn, 37 Pb   freezes and melts at same temp.   eutectic
(d) rosin

200—   142— 61   50 Bi 13 Cd 25 Pb 12 Sn   Wood's metal

100—

* By R. C. Hitchcock, Research Laboratories, Westinghouse Electric Corp., East Pittsburgh, Pa. Reprinted by permission from *Product Engineering*, vol. 18, p. 171; October, 1947.

Temperature charts of metals   *continued*

Melting points of metals, alloys, and ceramics*

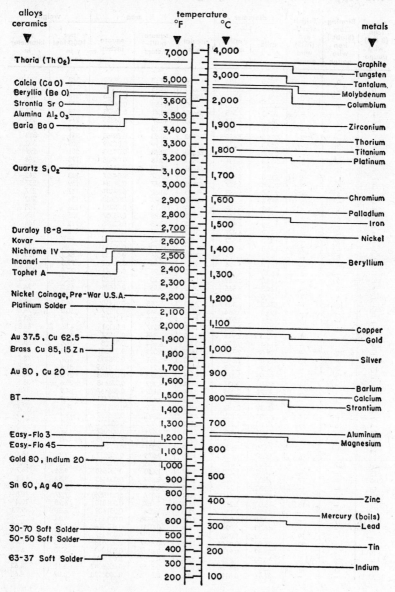

* By K. H. McPhee. Reprinted by permission from *Electronics*, vol. 21, p. 118; December, 1948.

40

Wire tables*

Solid copper—comparison of gauges

American (B & S) wire gauge	Birmingham (Stubs') iron wire gauge	British standard (NBS) wire gauge	diameter			area		weight	
			mils	milli-meters	circular mils	square milli-meters	square inches	per 1000 feet in pounds	per kilometer in kilograms
–	0	–	340.0	8.636	115600	58.58	0.09079	350	521
0	–	–	324.9	8.251	105500	53.48	0.08289	319	475
–	–	0	324.0	8.230	105000	53.19	0.08245	318	472
–	1	1	300.0	7.620	90000	45.60	0.07069	273	405
1	–	–	289.3	7.348	83690	42.41	0.06573	253	377
–	2	–	284.0	7.214	80660	40.87	0.06335	244	363
–	–	–	283.0	7.188	80090	40.58	0.06290	242	361
–	–	2	276.0	7.010	76180	38.60	0.05963	231	343
–	3	–	259.0	6.579	67080	33.99	0.05269	203	302
2	–	–	257.6	6.544	66370	33.63	0.05213	201	299
–	–	3	252.0	6.401	63500	32.18	0.04988	193	286
–	4	–	233.0	6.045	56640	28.70	0.04449	173	255
–	–	4	232.0	5.893	53820	27.27	0.04227	163	242
3	–	–	229.4	5.827	52630	26.67	0.04134	159	237
–	5	–	220.0	5.588	48400	24.52	0.03801	147	217
–	–	5	212.0	5.385	44940	22.77	0.03530	136	202
4	–	–	204.3	5.189	41740	21.18	0.03278	126	188
–	6	–	203.0	5.156	41210	20.88	0.03237	125	186
–	–	6	192.0	4.877	36860	18.68	0.02895	112	166
5	–	–	181.9	4.621	33100	16.77	0.02600	100	149
–	7	–	180.0	4.572	32400	16.42	0.02545	98.0	146
–	–	7	176.0	4.470	30980	15.70	0.02433	93.6	139
–	8	–	165.0	4.191	27220	13.86	0.02138	86.2	123
6	–	–	162.0	4.116	26250	13.30	0.02062	79.5	118
–	–	8	160.0	4.064	25600	12.97	0.02011	77.5	115
–	9	–	148.0	3.759	21900	11.10	0.01720	66.3	98.6
7	–	–	144.3	3.665	20820	10.55	0.01635	63.0	93.7
–	–	9	144.0	3.658	20740	10.51	0.01629	62.8	93.4
–	10	–	134.0	3.404	17960	9.098	0.01410	54.3	80.8
8	–	–	128.8	3.264	16510	8.366	0.01297	50.0	74.4
–	–	10	128.0	3.251	16380	8.302	0.01267	49.6	73.8
–	11	–	120.0	3.048	14400	7.297	0.01131	43.6	64.8
–	–	11	116.0	2.946	13460	6.818	0.01057	40.8	60.5
9	–	–	114.4	2.906	13090	6.634	0.01028	39.6	58.9
–	12	–	109.0	2.769	11880	6.020	0.009331	35.9	53.5
–	–	12	104.0	2.642	10820	5.481	0.008495	32.7	48.7
10	–	–	101.9	2.588	10380	5.261	0.008155	31.4	46.8
–	13	–	95.00	2.413	9025	4.573	0.007088	27.3	40.6
–	–	13	92.00	2.337	8464	4.289	0.006648	25.6	38.1
11	–	–	90.74	2.305	8234	4.172	0.006467	24.9	37.1
–	14	–	83.00	2.108	6889	3.491	0.005411	20.8	31.0
12	–	–	80.81	2.053	6530	3.309	0.005129	19.8	29.4
–	–	14	80.00	2.032	6400	3.243	0.005027	19.4	28.8
–	15	15	72.00	1.829	5184	2.627	0.004072	16.1	23.4
13	–	–	71.96	1.828	5178	2.624	0.004067	15.7	23.3
–	16	–	65.00	1.651	4225	2.141	0.003318	12.8	19.0
14	–	–	64.08	1.628	4107	2.081	0.003225	12.4	18.5
–	–	16	64.00	1.626	4096	2.075	0.003217	12.3	18.4
–	17	–	58.00	1.473	3364	1.705	0.002642	10.2	15.1
15	–	–	57.07	1.450	3257	1.650	0.002558	9.86	14.7
–	–	17	56.00	1.422	3136	1.589	0.002463	9.52	14.1
16	–	–	50.82	1.291	2583	1.309	0.002028	7.82	11.6
–	18	–	49.00	1.245	2401	1.217	0.001886	7.27	10.8
–	–	18	48.00	1.219	2304	1.167	0.001810	6.98	10.4
17	–	–	45.26	1.150	2048	1.038	0.001609	6.20	9.23
–	19	–	42.00	1.067	1764	0.8938	0.001385	5.34	7.94
18	–	–	40.30	1.024	1624	0.8231	0.001276	4.92	7.32
–	–	19	40.00	1.016	1600	0.8107	0.001257	4.84	7.21
–	–	20	36.00	0.9144	1296	0.6567	0.001018	3.93	5.84
19	–	–	35.89	0.9116	1288	0.6527	0.001012	3.90	5.80
–	20	–	35.00	0.8890	1225	0.6207	0.0009621	3.71	5.52
–	21	21	32.00	0.8128	1024	0.5189	0.0008042	3.11	4.62
20	–	–	31.96	0.8118	1022	0.5176	0.0008023	3.09	4.60

* For information on insulated wire for inductor windings, see pp. 74 and 190.

Wire tables *continued*

Standard annealed copper (B & S)

AWG B & S gauge	diameter in mils	cross section		ohms per 1000 ft at 20° C (68° F)	lbs per 1000 ft	ft per lb	ft per ohm at 20° C (68° F)	ohms per lb at 20° C (68° F)
		circular mils	square inches					
0000	460.0	211,600	0.1662	0.04901	640.5	1.561	20,400	0.00007652
000	409.6	167,800	0.1318	0.06180	507.9	1.968	16,180	0.0001217
00	364.8	133,100	0.1045	0.07793	402.8	2.482	12,830	0.0001935
0	324.9	105,500	0.08289	0.09827	319.5	3.130	10,180	0.0003076
1	289.3	83,690	0.06573	0.1239	253.3	3.947	8,070	0.0004891
2	257.6	66,370	0.05213	0.1563	200.9	4.977	6,400	0.0007778
3	229.4	52,640	0.04134	0.1970	159.3	6.276	5,075	0.001237
4	204.3	41,740	0.03278	0.2485	126.4	7.914	4,025	0.001966
5	181.9	33,100	0.02600	0.3133	100.2	9.980	3,192	0.003127
6	162.0	26,250	0.02062	0.3951	79.46	12.58	2,531	0.004972
7	144.3	20,820	0.01635	0.4982	63.02	15.87	2,007	0.007905
8	128.5	16,510	0.01297	0.6282	49.98	20.01	1,592	0.01257
9	114.4	13,090	0.01028	0.7921	39.63	25.23	1,262	0.01999
10	101.9	10,380	0.008155	0.9989	31.43	31.82	1,001	0.03178
11	90.74	8,234	0.006467	1.260	24.92	40.12	794	0.05053
12	80.81	6,530	0.005129	1.588	19.77	50.59	629.	0.08035
13	71.96	5,178	0.004067	2.003	15.68	63.80	499.3	0.1278
14	64.08	4,107	0.003225	2.525	12.43	80.44	396.0	0.2032
15	57.07	3,257	0.002558	3.184	9.858	101.4	314.0	0.3230
16	50.82	2,583	0.002028	4.016	7.818	127.9	249.0	0.5136
17	45.26	2,048	0.001609	5.064	6.200	161.3	197.5	0.8167
18	40.30	1,624	0.001276	6.385	4.917	203.4	156.6	1.299
19	35.89	1,288	0.001012	8.051	3.899	256.5	124.2	2.065
20	31.96	1,022	0.0008023	10.15	3.092	323.4	98.50	3.283
21	28.46	810.1	0.0006363	12.80	2.452	407.8	78.11	5.221
22	25.35	642.4	0.0005046	16.14	1.945	514.2	61.95	8.301
23	22.57	509.5	0.0004002	20.36	1.542	648.4	49.13	13.20
24	20.10	404.0	0.0003173	25.67	1.223	817.7	38.96	20.99
25	17.90	320.4	0.0002517	32.37	0.9699	1,031.0	30.90	33.37
26	15.94	254.1	0.0001996	40.81	0.7692	1,300	24.50	53.06
27	14.20	201.5	0.0001583	51.47	0.6100	1,639	19.43	84.37
28	12.64	159.8	0.0001255	64.90	0.4837	2,067	15.41	134.2
29	11.26	126.7	0.00009953	81.83	0.3836	2,607	12.22	213.3
30	10.03	100.5	0.00007894	103.2	0.3042	3,287	9.691	339.2
31	8.928	79.70	0.00006260	130.1	0.2413	4,145	7.685	539.3
32	7.950	63.21	0.00004964	164.1	0.1913	5,227	6.095	857.6
33	7.080	50.13	0.00003937	206.9	0.1517	6,591	4.833	1,364
34	6.305	39.75	0.00003122	260.9	0.1203	8,310	3.833	2,168
35	5.615	31.52	0.00002476	329.0	0.09542	10,480	3.040	3,448
36	5.000	25.00	0.00001964	414.8	0.07568	13,210	2.411	5,482
37	4.453	19.83	0.00001557	523.1	0.06001	16,660	1.912	8,717
38	3.965	15.72	0.00001235	659.6	0.04759	21,010	1.516	13,860
39	3.531	12.47	0.000009793	831.8	0.03774	26,500	1.202	22,040
40	3.145	9.888	0.000007766	1049.0	0.02993	33,410	0.9534	35,040

Temperature coefficient of resistance: The resistance of a conductor at temperature t in degrees centigrade is given by

$$R_t = R_{20} \left[1 + a_{20}(t - 20) \right]$$

where R_{20} is the resistance at 20 degrees centigrade and a_{20} is the temperature coefficient of resistance at 20 degrees centigrade. For copper, $a_{20} = 0.00393$. That is, the resistance of a copper conductor increases approximately 4/10 of 1 percent per degree centigrade rise in temperature.

Wire tables *continued*

Bare solid copper—hard-drawn (B & S)*

AWG B & S gauge	wire diameter in inches	breaking load in pounds	tensile strength in lbs/in²	weight		maximum resistance (ohms per 1000 feet at 68° F)	cross-sectional area	
				pounds per 1000 feet	pounds per mile		circular mils	square inches
4/0	0.4600	8143	49,000	640.5	3382	0.05045	211,600	0.1662
3/0	0.4096	6722	51,000	507.9	2682	0.06361	167,800	0.1318
2/0	0.3648	5519	52,800	402.8	2127	0.08021	133,100	0.1045
1/0	0.3249	4517	54,500	319.5	1687	0.1011	105,500	0.08289
1	0.2893	3688	56,100	253.3	1338	0.1287	83,690	0.06573
2	0.2576	3003	57,600	200.9	1061	0.1625	66,370	0.05213
3	0.2294	2439	59,000	159.3	841.2	0.2049	52,630	0.04134
4	0.2043	1970	60,100	126.4	667.1	0.2584	41,740	0.03278
5	0.1819	1591	61,200	100.2	529.1	0.3258	33,100	0.02600
−	0.1650	1326	62,000	82.41	435.1	0.3961	27,225	0.02138
6	0.1620	1280	62,100	79.46	419.6	0.4108	26,250	0.02062
7	0.1443	1030	63,000	63.02	332.7	0.5181	20,820	0.01635
−	0.1340	894.0	63,400	54.35	287.0	0.6006	17,956	0.01410
8	0.1285	826.0	63,700	49.97	263.9	0.6533	16,510	0.01297
9	0.1144	661.2	64,300	39.63	209.3	0.8238	13,090	0.01028
−	0.1040	550.4	64,800	32.74	172.9	0.9971	10,816	0.008495
10	0.1019	529.2	64,900	31.43	165.9	1.039	10,380	0.008155
11	0.09074	422.9	65,400	24.92	131.6	1.310	8,234	0.006467
12	0.08081	337.0	65,700	19.77	104.4	1.652	6,530	0.005129
13	0.07196	268.0	65,900	15.68	82.77	2.083	5,178	0.004067
14	0.06408	213.5	66,200	12.43	65.64	2.626	4,107	0.003225
15	0.05707	169.8	66,400	9.858	52.05	3.312	3,257	0.002558
16	0.05082	135.1	66,600	7.818	41.28	4.176	2,533	0.002028
17	0.04526	107.5	66,800	6.200	32.74	5.256	2,048	0.001609
18	0.04030	85.47	67,000	4.917	25.96	6.640	1,624	0.001276

*Courtesy of Copperweld Steel Co., Glassport, Pa. Based on ASA Specification H–4.2 and ASTM Specification B–1.

Modulus of elasticity is 17,000,000 lbs/inch². Coefficient of linear expansion is 0.0000094/degree Fahrenheit. Weights are based on a density of 8.89 grams/cm³ at 20 degrees centigrade (equivalent to 0.00302699 lbs/circular mil/1000 feet).
The resistances are maximum values for hard-drawn copper and are based on a resistivity of 10.674 ohms/circular-mil foot at 20 degrees centigrade (97.16 percent conductivity) for sizes 0.325 inch and larger, and 10.785 ohms/circular-mil foot at 20 degrees centigrade (96.16 percent conductivity) for sizes 0.324 inch and smaller.

Tensile strength of copper wire (B & S)*

AWG B & S gauge	wire diameter in inches	hard drawn		medium-hard drawn		soft or annealed	
		minimum tensile strength lbs/in²	breaking load in pounds	minimum tensile strength lbs/in²	breaking load in pounds	maximum tensile strength lbs/in²	breaking load in pounds
1	0.2893	56,100	3688	46,000	3024	37,000	2432
2	0.2576	57,600	3003	47,000	2450	37,000	1929
3	0.2294	59,000	2439	48,000	1984	37,000	1530
4	0.2043	60,100	1970	48,330	1584	37,000	1213
5	0.1819	61,200	1591	48,660	1265	37,000	961.9
−	0.1650	62,000	1326	—	—	—	—
6	0.1620	62,100	1280	49,000	1010	37,000	762.9
7	0.1443	63,000	1030	49,330	806.6	37,000	605.0
−	0.1340	63,400	894.0	—	—	—	—
8	0.1285	63,700	826.0	49,660	643.9	37,000	479.8
9	0.1144	64,300	661.2	50,000	514.2	37,000	380.5
−	0.1040	64,800	550.4	—	—	—	—
10	0.1019	64,900	529.2	50,330	410.4	38,500	314.0
11	0.09074	65,400	422.9	50,660	327.6	38,500	249.0
12	0.08081	65,700	337.0	51,000	261.6	38,500	197.5

*Courtesy of Copperweld Steel Co., Glassport, Pa.

continued Wire tables

Solid copperweld (B & S)

AWG B & S gauge	diam inch	cross-sectional area		weight		feet per pound	resistance ohms/1000 ft at 68° F		breaking load, pounds		attenuation in decibels/mile*				characteristic impedance*	
		circular mils	square inch	pounds per 1000 feet	pounds per mile		40% conduct	30% conduct	40% conduct	30% conduct	40% cond dry	40% cond wet	30% cond dry	30% cond wet	40% cond	30% cond
4	.2043	41,740	.03278	115.8	611.6	8.63	0.6337	0.8447	3,541	3,934	—	—	—	—	—	—
5	.1819	33,100	.02600	91.86	485.0	10.89	0.7990	1.065	2,938	3,250	—	—	—	—	—	—
6	.1620	26,250	.02062	72.85	384.6	13.73	1.008	1.343	2,433	2,680	.078	.086	.103	.109	650	686
7	.1443	20,820	.01635	57.77	305.0	17.31	1.270	1.694	2,011	2,207	.093	.100	.122	.127	685	732
8	.1285	16,510	.01297	45.81	241.9	21.83	1.602	2.136	1,660	1,815	.111	.118	.144	.149	727	787
9	.1144	13,090	.01028	36.33	191.8	27.52	2.020	2.693	1,368	1,491	.132	.138	.169	.174	776	852
10	.1019	10,380	.008155	28.81	152.1	34.70	2.547	3.396	1,130	1,231	.156	.161	.196	.200	834	920
11	.0907	8,234	.006467	22.85	120.6	43.76	3.212	4.28	896	975	.183	.188	.228	.233	910	1,013
12	.0808	6,530	.005129	18.12	95.68	55.19	4.05	5.40	711	770	.216	.220	.262	.266	1,000	1,120
13	.0720	5,178	.004067	14.37	75.88	69.59	5.11	6.81	490	530						
14	.0641	4,107	.003225	11.40	60.17	87.75	6.44	8.59	400	440						
15	.0571	3,257	.002558	9.038	47.72	110.6	8.12	10.83	300	330						
16	.0508	2,583	.002028	7.167	37.84	139.5	10.24	13.65	250	270						
17	.0453	2,048	.001609	5.684	30.01	175.9	12.91	17.22	185	205						
18	.0403	1,624	.001276	4.507	23.80	221.9	16.28	21.71	153	170						
19	.0359	1,288	.001012	3.575	18.87	279.8	20.53	27.37	122	135						
20	.0320	1,022	.0008023	2.835	14.97	352.8	25.89	34.52	100	110						
21	.0285	810.1	.0006363	2.248	11.87	444.8	32.65	43.52	73.2	81.1						
22	.0253	642.5	.0005046	1.783	9.413	560.9	41.17	54.88	58.0	64.3						
23	.0226	509.5	.0004002	1.414	7.465	707.3	51.92	69.21	46.0	51.0						
24	.0201	404.0	.0003173	1.121	5.920	891.9	65.46	87.27	36.5	40.4						
25	.0179	320.4	.0002517	0.889	4.695	1,125	82.55	110.0	28.9	32.1						
26	.0159	254.1	.0001996	0.705	3.723	1,418	104.1	138.8	23.0	25.4						
27	.0142	201.5	.0001583	0.559	2.953	1,788	131.3	175.0	18.2	20.1						
28	.0126	159.8	.0001255	0.443	2.342	2,255	165.5	220.6	14.4	15.9						
29	.0113	126.7	.0000995	0.352	1.857	2,843	208.7	278.2	11.4	12.6						
30	.0100	100.5	.0000789	0.279	1.473	3,586	263.2	350.8	9.08	10.0						
31	.0089	79.70	.0000626	0.221	1.168	4,521	331.9	442.4	7.20	7.95						
32	.0080	63.21	.0000496	0.175	0.926	5,701	418.5	557.8	5.71	6.30						
33	.0071	50.13	.0000394	0.139	0.734	7,189	527.7	703.4	4.53	5.00						
34	.0063	39.75	.0000312	0.110	0.582	9,065	665.4	887.0	3.59	3.97						
35	.0056	31.52	.0000248	0.087	0.462	11,430	839.0	1,119	2.85	3.14						
36	.0050	25.00	.0000196	0.069	0.366	14,410	1,058	1,410	2.26	2.49						
37	.0045	19.83	.0000156	0.055	0.290	18,180	1,334	1,778	1.79	1.98						
38	.0040	15.72	.0000123	0.044	0.230	22,920	1,682	2,243	1.42	1.57						
39	.0035	12.47	.00000979	0.035	0.183	28,900	2,121	2,828	1.13	1.24						
40	.0031	9.89	.00000777	0.027	0.145	36,440	2,675	3,566	0.893	0.986						

* DP insulators, 12-inch wire spacing at 1000 cycles/second.

Wire tables *continued*

Physical properties of various wires*

property	copper		aluminum 99 percent pure
	annealed	hard–drawn	
Conductivity, Matthiessen's standard in percent	99 to 102	96 to 99	61 to 63
Ohms/mil-foot at 68°F = 20°C	10.36	10.57	16.7
Circular-mil-ohms/mile at 68°F = 20°C	54,600	55,700	88,200
Pounds/mile-ohm at 68°F = 20°C	875	896	424
Mean temp coefficient of resistivity/°F	0.00233	0.00233	0.0022
Mean temp coefficient of resistivity/°C	0.0042	0.0042	0.0040
Mean specific gravity	8.89	8.94	2.68
Pounds/1000 feet/circular mil	0.003027	0.003049	0.000909
Weight in pounds/inch³	0.320	0.322	0.0967
Mean specific heat	0.093	0.093	0.214
Mean melting point in °F	2,012	2,012	1,157
Mean melting point in °C	1,100	1,100	625
Mean coefficient of linear expansion/°F	0.00000950	0.00000950	0.00001285
Mean coefficient of linear expansion/°C	0.0000171	0.0000171	0.0000231

Solid wire (Values in pounds/in²)	Ultimate tensile strength	30,000 to 42,000	45,000 to 68,000	20,000 to 35,000
	Average tensile strength	32,000	60,000	24,000
	Elastic limit	6,000 to 16,000	25,000 to 45,000	14,000
	Average elastic limit	15,000	30,000	14,000
	Modulus of elasticity	7,000,000 to 17,000,000	13,000,000 to 18,000,000	8,500,000 to 11,500,000
	Average modulus of elasticity	12,000,000	16,000,000	9,000,000
Concentric strand (Values in pounds/in²)	Tensile strength	29,000 to 37,000	43,000 to 65,000	25,800
	Average tensile strength	35,000	54,000	—
	Elastic limit	5,800 to 14,800	23,000 to 42,000	13,800
	Average elastic limit	—	27,000	—
	Modulus of elasticity	5,000,000 to 12,000,000	12,000,000	Approx 10,000,000

* Reprinted by permission from "Transmission Towers," American Bridge Company, Pittsburgh, Pa.; 1925: p. 169.

Stranded copper conductors (B & S)*

circular mils	AWG B & S gauge	number of wires	individual wire diam in inches	cable diam inches	area square inches	weight lbs per 1000 ft	weight lbs per mile	*maximum resistance ohms/1000 ft at 20° C
211,600	4/0	19	0.1055	0.528	0.1662	653.3	3,450	0.05093
167,800	3/0	19	0.0940	0.470	0.1318	518.1	2,736	0.06422
133,100	2/0	19	0.0837	0.419	0.1045	410.9	2,170	0.08097
105,500	1/0	19	0.0745	0.373	0.08286	325.7	1,720	0.1022
83,690	1	19	0.0664	0.332	0.06573	258.4	1,364	0.1288
66,370	2	7	0.0974	0.292	0.05213	204.9	1,082	0.1624
52,640	3	7	0.0867	0.260	0.04134	162.5	858.0	0.2048
41,740	4	7	0.0772	0.232	0.03278	128.9	680.5	0.2582
33,100	5	7	0.0688	0.206	0.02600	102.2	539.6	0.3256
26,250	6	7	0.0612	0.184	0.02062	81.05	427.9	0.4105
20,820	7	7	0.0545	0.164	0.01635	64.28	339.4	0.5176
16,510	8	7	0.0486	0.146	0.01297	50.98	269.1	0.6528
13,090	9	7	0.0432	0.130	0.01028	40.42	213.4	0.8233
10,380	10	7	0.0385	0.116	0.008152	32.05	169.2	1.038
6,530	12	7	0.0305	0.0915	0.005129	20.16	106.5	1.650
4,107	14	7	0.0242	0.0726	0.003226	12.68	66.95	2.624
2,583	16	7	0.0192	0.0576	0.002029	7.975	42.11	4.172
1,624	18	7	0.0152	0.0456	0.001275	5.014	26.47	6.636
1,022	20	7	0.0121	0.0363	0.008027	3.155	16.66	10.54

* The resistance values in this table are trade maxima for soft or annealed copper wire and are higher than the average values for commercial cable. The following values for the conductivity and resistivity of copper at 20 degrees centigrade were used:
Conductivity in terms of International Annealed Copper Standard: 98.16 percent
Resistivity in pounds per mile-ohm: 891.58
The resistance of hard-drawn copper is slightly greater than the values given, being about 2 percent to 3 percent greater for sizes from 4/0 to 20 AWG.

iron (Ex BB)	steel (Siemens-Martin)	crucible steel, high strength	plow steel, extra-high strength	copper-clad	
				30% cond	40% cond
16.8	8.7	—	—	29.4	39.0
62.9	119.7	122.5	125.0	35.5	26.6
332,000	632,000	647.000	660,000	187,000	140,000
4,700	8,900	9,100	9,300	2.775	2.075
0.0028	0.00278	0.00278	0.00278	0.0024	—
0.0050	0.00501	0.00501	0.00501	0.0044	0.0041
7.77	7.85	7.85	7.85	8.17	8.25
0.002652	0.002671			0.00281	0.00281
0.282	0.283	0.283	0.283	0.298	0.298
0.113	0.117	—	—	—	—
2,975	2,480	—	—	—	—
1,635	1,360	—	—	—	—
0.00000673	0.00000662	—	—	0.0000072	0.0000072
0.0000120	0.0000118	—	—	0.0000129	0.0000129
50,000 to 55,000	70,000 to 80,000	—	—	—	—
55,000	75,000	125,000	187,000	60,000	100,000
25,000 to 30,000	35,000 to 50,000	—	—	—	—
30,000	38,000	69,000	130,000	30,000	50,000
22,000,000 to 27,000,000	22,000,000 to 29,000,000	—	—	—	—
26,000,000	29,000,000	30,000,000	30,000,000	19,000,000	21,000,000
—	74,000 to 98,000	85,000 to 165,000	140,000 to 245,000	70,000 to 97,000	—
—	80,000	125,000	180,000	80,000	—
—	37,000 to 49,000	—	—	—	—
—	40,000	70,000	110,000	—	—
—	12,000,000	15,000,000	15,000,000	—	—

Machine screws

Head styles—method of length measurement

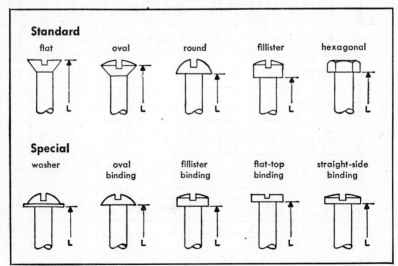

continued **Machine screws**

Dimensions and other data

screw no	screw dia	threads per inch coarse	threads per inch fine	clearance drill* no	clearance drill* dia	tap drill† no	tap drill† inches	tap drill† mm	head round max OD	head round max height	head flat max OD	head fillister max OD	head fillister max height	hex nut across flat	hex nut across corner	hex nut thickness	washer OD	washer ID	washer thickness
0	0.060	—	80	52	0.064	56	0.047	1.2	0.113	0.053	0.119	0.096	0.059	0.156	0.171	0.046	—	—	—
1	0.073	64	72	47	0.079	53	0.060	1.5	0.138	0.061	0.146	0.118	0.070	0.156	0.171	0.046	—	—	—
2	0.086	56	64	42	0.094	50	0.070	1.8	0.162	0.070	0.172	0.140	0.083	0.187	0.205	0.062	1/4	0.093	0.032
3	0.099	48	56	37	0.104	47	0.079	2.0	0.187	0.078	0.199	0.161	0.095	0.187	0.205	0.062	1/4	0.105	0.020
						45	0.082	2.1											
4	0.112	40	48	31	0.120	43	0.089	2.3	0.211	0.086	0.225	0.183	0.107	0.250	0.275	0.093	5/16	0.125	0.032
						42	0.094	2.4											
5	0.125	40	44	29	0.136	38	0.102	2.6	0.236	0.095	0.252	0.205	0.120	0.312	0.344	0.109	3/8	0.140	0.032
						37	0.104	2.6											
6	0.138	32	40	27	0.144	36	0.107	2.7	0.260	0.103	0.279	0.226	0.132	0.312	0.344	0.109	5/16	0.156	0.026
						33	0.113	2.9									3/8		0.046
8	0.164	32	36	18	0.170	29	0.136	3.5	0.309	0.119	0.332	0.270	0.156	0.344	0.373	0.125	3/8	0.186	0.032
						29	0.136	3.5									7/16		0.046
10	0.190	24	32	9	0.196	25	0.150	3.8	0.359	0.136	0.385	0.313	0.180	0.375	0.413	0.125	7/16	0.218	0.036
						21	0.159	4.0									1/2		0.063
12	0.216	24	28	2	0.221	16	0.177	4.5	0.408	0.152	0.438	0.357	0.205	0.437	0.488	0.156	1/2	0.250	0.063
						14	0.182	4.6									9/16		0.063
1/4	0.250	20	28	—	17/64	7	0.201	5.1	0.472	0.174	0.507	0.414	0.237	0.437	0.488	0.203	9/16	0.281	0.040
						3	0.213	5.5						0.500	0.577	0.250	5/8		0.063

All dimensions in inches except where noted.

* Clearance-drill sizes are practical values for use of the engineer or technician doing his own shop work.

† Tap-drill sizes are for use in hand tapping material such as brass or soft steel. For copper, aluminum, Norway iron, cast iron, bakelite, or for very thin material, the drill should be a size or two larger diameter than shown.

Commercial insulating materials*

The tables on the following pages give a few of the important electrical and physical properties of insulating or dielectric materials. The dielectric constant and dissipation factor of most materials depend on the frequency and temperature of measurement. For this reason, these properties are given at a number of frequencies, but because of limited space, only the values at room temperature are given. The dissipation factor is defined as the ratio of the energy dissipated to the energy stored in the dielectric per cycle, or as the tangent of the loss angle. For dissipation factors less than 0.1, the dissipation factor may be considered equal to the power factor of the dielectric, which is the cosine of the phase angle by which the current leads the voltage.

Many of the materials listed are characterized by a peak dissipation factor occurring somewhere in the frequency range, this peak being accompanied by a rapid change in the dielectric constant. These effects are the result of a resonance phenomenon occurring in polar materials. The position of the dissipation-factor peak in the frequency spectrum is very sensitive to temperature. An increase in the temperature increases the frequency at which the peak occurs, as illustrated qualitatively in the sketch at the right. Nonpolar materials have very low losses without a noticeable peak, and the dielectric constant remains essentially unchanged over the frequency range.

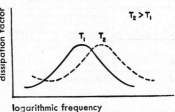

Another effect that contributes to dielectric losses is that of ionic or electronic conduction. This loss, if present, is important usually at the lower end of the frequency range only, and is distinguished by the fact that the dissipation factor varies inversely with frequency. An increase in temperature increases the loss due to ionic conduction because of the increased mobility of the ions.

The data given on dielectric strength are accompanied by the thickness of the specimen tested because the dielectric strength, expressed in volts/mil, varies inversely with the square root of thickness, approximately.

The direct-current volume resistivity of many materials is influenced by changes in temperature or humidity. The values given in the table may be reduced several decades by raising the temperature toward the higher end of the working range of the material, or by raising the relative humidity of the air surrounding the material to above 90 percent.

* The data listed in these tables have been taken from various sources including "Tables of Dielectric Materials," vols. I–III, prepared by the Laboratory for Insulation Research of the Massachusetts Institute of Technology, Cambridge, Massachusetts; June, 1948.

Commercial insulating materials *continued*

material	composition	T °C	\(60\)	\(10^3\)	\(10^6\)	\(10^8\)	\(3 \times 10^9\)	\(2.5 \times 10^{10}\)	\(60\)
ceramics									
AlSiMag A–35	Magnesium silicate	23	6.14	5.96	5.84	5.75	5.60	5.36	0.017
AlSiMag A–196	Magnesium silicate	25	5.90	5.88	5.70	5.60	5.42	5.18	0.0022
AlSiMag 211	Magnesium silicate	25	6.00	5.98	5.97	5.96	5.80	—	0.012
AlSiMag 228	Magnesium silicate	25	6.41	6.40	6.36	6.20	5.97	5.83	0.0013
AlSiMag 243	Magnesium silicate	22	6.32	6.30	6.22	6.10	5.78	5.75	0.0015
Porcelain	Dry process	25	5.5	5.36	5.08	5.04	—	—	0.03
Porcelain	Wet process	25	6.5	6.24	5.87	5.80	—	—	0.03
Steatite 410	—	25	5.77	5.77	5.77	5.77	5.7	—	—
TamTicon B	Barium titanate*	26	1250	1200	1143	—	600	100	0.0056
TamTicon BS	Barium-strontium titanate*	27	7600	7500	—	—	—	—	0.0141
TamTicon C	Calcium titanate	26	168	167.5	167.5	167.5	—	—	0.006
TamTicon MB	Magnesium titanate	28	13.4	13.4	13.4	13.3	—	—	0.0016
TamTicon S	Strontium titanate	25	215	209	206.5	205	—	—	0.035
TI Pure 0–600	Titanium dioxide—rutile	23	99	99	99	99	—	—	0.0006
glasses									
Corning 001	Soda-potash-lead silicate	24	6.70	6.63	6.43	6.33	6.10	5.87	0.0084
Corning 012	Soda-potash-lead silicate	23	6.76	6.70	6.65	6.65	6.61	6.51	0.0050
Corning 199–1	Soda-potash-lead silicate	24	8.10	8.10	8.08	8.00	7.92	—	0.0027
Corning 704	Soda-potash-borosilicate	25	4.85	4.82	4.73	4.68	4.67	4.52	0.0055
Corning 705	Soda-potash-borosilicate	25	4.90	4.84	4.78	4.75	4.74	4.64	0.0093
Corning 707	Low-alkali, potash-lithioborosilicate	23	4.00	4.00	4.00	4.00	4.00	3.9	0.0006
Corning 772	Soda-lead borosilicate	24	4.75	4.70	4.62	4.50	4.40	—	0.0093
Corning 790	96% SiO₂	20	3.85	3.85	3.85	3.85	3.84	3.82	0.0006
Corning 1990	Iron-sealing glass	24	8.41	8.38	8.30	8.20	7.99	7.84	—
Quartz (fused)	100% SiO₂	25	3.78	3.78	3.78	3.78	3.78	3.78	0.0009
plastics									
Bakelite BM120	Phenol-formaldehyde	25	4.90	4.74	4.36	3.95	3.70	3.55	0.08
Bakelite BM262	Phenol-aniline-formaldehyde, 62% mica	25	4.87	4.80	4.67	4.65	—	4.5	0.010
Bakelite B T–48–306	100% phenol-formaldehyde	24	8.6	7.15	5.4	4.4	3.64	—	0.15
Beetle resin	Urea-formaldehyde, cellulose	27	6.6	6.2	5.65	5.1	4.57	—	0.032
Catalin 200 base	Phenol-formaldehyde	22	8.8	8.2	7.0	—	4.89	—	0.05
Cibanate	100% aniline-formaldehyde	25	3.60	3.58	3.42	3.40	3.40	—	0.0036
DC 2101	Cross-linked organo-siloxane polymer	25	2.9	2.9	2.9	2.9	—	—	0.0074
Dilectene-100	100% aniline-formaldehyde	25	3.70	3.68	3.52	3.50	3.44	3.42	0.0033
Durez 1601 natural	Phenol-formaldehyde, 67% mica	26	5.1	4.94	4.60	4.51	4.48	—	0.03
Durez 11863	Phenol-aniline-formaldehyde, 43% mica, 5% misc	25	4.80	4.70	4.55	4.48	4.45	—	0.011
Durite 550	Phenol-formaldehyde, 65% mica, 4% lubricants	24	5.1	5.03	4.78	4.72	4.71	—	0.015
Ethocel Q–180	Ethylcellulose, plasticized	26	2.90	2.83	2.75	2.75	2.72	—	0.0155
Formica FF–41	Melamine-formaldehyde, 55% filler	26	—	6.00	5.75	5.5	—	—	—
Formica XX	Phenol-formaldehyde, 50% paper laminate	26	5.25	5.15	4.60	4.04	3.57	—	0.025
Formvar E	Polyvinylformal	26	3.20	3.12	2.92	2.80	2.76	2.7	0.003
Geon 2046	59% polyvinyl-chloride, 30% dioctyl phthalate, 6% stabilizer, 5% filler	23	7.5	6.10	3.55	3.00	2.89	—	0.08
Kel-F	Polychlorotrifluoroethylene	25	2.72	2.63	2.42	2.32	2.29	2.28	0.015
Koroseal 5CS–243	63.7% polyvinyl-chloride, 33.1% di-2-ethylhexyl-phthalate, lead silicate	27	6.2	5.65	3.60	2.9	2.73	—	0.07
Kriston	Chlorine-containing allyl resin	25	3.05	3.00	2.88	2.79	2.77	—	0.011
Lucite HM–119	Polymethylmethacrylate	23	3.30	2.84	2.63	2.58	2.58	2.57	0.066
Lumarith 22361	Ethylcellulose, 13% plasticizer	24	3.12	3.06	2.92	2.80	2.74	2.65	—

* Dielectric constant and dissipation factor are dependent on electrical field strength.

dissipation factor at (frequency in cycles/second)					dielectric strength in volts/mil at 25° C	d-c volume resistivity in ohm-cm at 25° C	thermal expansion (linear) in parts/°C	softening point in ° C	moisture absorption in percent
10^3	10^6	10^8	3×10^9	2.5×10^{10}					
0.0100	0.0038	0.0037	0.0041	0.0058	225 ($\frac{1}{2}''$)	$>10^{14}$	8.7×10^{-6}	1450	<0.1
0.0059	0.0031	0.0016	0.0018	0.0038	240 ($\frac{1}{2}''$)	$>10^{14}$	8.9×10^{-5}	1450	<0.1
0.0034	0.0005	0.0004	0.0012	—	—	$>10^{14}$	9.2×10^{-6}	1300	0.1–1
0.0020	0.0012	0.0010	0.0013	0.0042		—	6–8×10^{-6}	1450	<0.05
0.00045	0.00037	0.0003	0.0006	0.0012	200 ($\frac{1}{4}''$)	$>10^{14}$	10.5×10^{-6}	1450	<0.1
0.0140	0.0075	0.0078	—	—					
0.0180	0.0090	0.0135	—	—	—	—	—	—	—
0.0030	0.0007	0.0006	0.00089	—	—	—	—	—	—
0.0130	0.0105	—	0.30	0.50	75	10^{12}–10^{13}	—	1400–1430	0.1
0.0168	—	—	—	—	75	10^{12}–10^{13}	—	1430	<0.1
0.00045	0.00032	0.008	—	—	109	10^{12}–10^{14}	—	1510	<0.1
0.00108	0.0007	0.0004	—	—	100	10^{13}–10^{14}	—	1430	<0.1
0.0070	0.0006	0.0020	—	—	100	10^{12}–10^{14}	—	1510	0.1
0.0002	0.0001	0.0007	—	—	—	—	—	—	—
0.00535	0.00165	0.0023	0.0060	0.0110	—.	10^9 at 250°	90×10^{-7}	626	—
0.0030	0.0012	0.0018	0.0041	0.0127	—	10^{10} at 250°	87×10^{-7}	630	—
0.0009	0.0005	0.0012	0.0038	—	—	4×10^9 at 250°	128×10^{-7}	527	—
0.0034	0.0019	0.0027	0.0044	0.0073	—	5×10^9 at 250°	49×10^{-7}	697	—
0.0056	0.0027	0.0035	0.0052	0.0083	—	10^8 at 250°	46×10^{-7}	703	—
0.0005	0.0006	0.0012	0.0012	0.0031	—	10^{11} at 250°	31×10^{-7}	746	—
0.0042	0.0020	0.0032	0.0051	—	—	6×10^8 at 250°	36×10^{-7}	756	—
0.0006	0.0006	0.0006	0.0068	0.0013	—	5×10^9 at 250°	8×10^{-7}	1450	—
0.0004	0.0005	0.0009	0.00199	0.0112	—	10^{10} at 250°	132×10^{-7}	484	Poor
0.00075	0.0002	0.0002	0.00006	0.00025	15,000 ($\frac{1}{8}''$)	$>10^{19}$	5.7×10^{-7}	1667	—
0.0220	0.0280	0.0380	0.0438	0.0390	300 ($\frac{1}{8}''$)	10^{11}	30–40×10^{-6}	<135 (distortion)	<0.6
0.0082	0.0055	0.0057	—	0.0089	325–375 ($\frac{1}{8}''$)	2×10^{14}	10–20×10^{-6}	100–115 (distortion)	0.3
0.082	0.060	0.077	0.052	—	277 ($\frac{1}{8}''$)	—	8.3–13×10^{-5}	50 (distortion)	0.42
0.024	0.027	0.050	0.0555	—	375 ($0.085''$)	—	2.6×10^{-5}	152 (distortion)	2
0.0290	0.050	—	0.108	—	200 ($\frac{1}{8}''$)	—	7.5–15×10^{-5}	40–60 (distortion)	—
0.0041	0.0078	0.0034	0.0029	—	600 ($\frac{1}{8}''$)	—	6.49×10^{-5}	126	0.05–0.08
0.0056	0.0045	0.0045	—	—	—	—	—	>250	Nil
0.0032	0.0061	0.0033	0.0026	0.005	810 ($0.068''$)	$>10^{16}$	5.4×10^{-5}	125	0.06–0.08
0.021	0.0080	0.0064	0.0062	—	—	—	—	—	—
0.010	0.0052	0.0052	0.0069	—	450 ($\frac{1}{8}''$)	4×10^{12}	1.9×10^{-5}	110 (distortion)	0.03
0.0104	0.0082	0.0115	0.0126	—	—	—	—	71 (distortion)	—
0.0109	0.0109	0.014	0.0169	—	—	—	—	—	1.4
0.0119	0.0115	0.020	—	—	—	—	1.7×10^{-5}	—	0.6
0.0165	0.034	0.057	0.060	—	—	—	—	—	—
0.0100	0.019	0.013	0.0113	0.0115	860 ($0.034''$)	$>5 \times 10^{16}$	7.7×10^{-5}	190	1.3
0.110	0.089	0.030	0.0116	—	400 ($0.075''$)	8×10^{14}	—	60 (stable)	0.5
0.0270	0.0082	—	0.028	0.0053	—	10^{13}	—	—	—
0.100	0.093	0.030	0.0112	—	—	—	—	—	—
0.0110	0.0086	0.0043	0.0023	0.0032	990 ($0.030''$)	$>5 \times 10^{16}$	11–14×10^{-5}	72 (distortion)	0.4
0.044	0.0145	0.0067	0.0051	0.030	522 ($\frac{1}{8}''$)	5×10^{16}	—	51 (distortion)	1.50
0.0048	0.0115	0.0180	0.0196						

Commercial insulating materials *continued*

material	composition	T °C	dielectric constant at (frequency in cycles/second) 60	10^3	10^6	10^8	3×10^9	2.5×10^{10}	60
Melmac resin 592	Melamine-formaldehyde, mineral filler	27	8.0	6.25	5.20	4.70	4.67	—	0.08
Micarta 254	Cresylic acid—formaldehyde, 50% α-cellulose	25	5.45	4.95	4.51	3.85	3.43	3.21	0.098
Nylon 610	Polyhexamethylene-adipamide	25	3.7	3.50	3.14	3.0	2.84	2.73	0.018
Piccolastic D–125	Methylstryrene–styrene copolymer	25	2.58	2.58	2.58	2.58	2.55	—	0.0002
Plexiglass	Polymethylmethacrylate	27	3.45	3.12	2.76	2.70	2.60	—	0.064
Polyethylene DE–3401	1% antioxidant	25	2.26	2.26	2.26	2.26	2.26	2.26	<0.0002
Polyisobutylene	—	25	2.23	2.23	2.23	2.23	2.23	—	0.0004
Polystyrene	—	25	2.56	2.56	2.56	2.55	2.55	2.54	<0.00005
—	58.1% poly-2,5 dichlorostyrene, 41.9% TiO₂	23	5.30	5.30	5.30	5.30	5.30	5.30	0.0032
—	34.7% poly-2,5 dichlorostyrene, 65.3% TiO₂	24	10.2	10.2	10.2	10.2	10.2	10.2	0.0018
—	18.6% poly-2,5 dichlorostyrene, 81.4% TiO₂	23	23.7	23.4	23.0	23.0	23.0	23.0	0.006
Pyralin	Cellulose-nitrate, 25% camphor	27	11.4	8.4	6.6	5.2	3.74	—	2.0
Resinox L8241	Phenol-formaldehyde, 71% mica	24	4.66	4.64	4.64	4.62	4.60	—	0.006
Resinox 7013	Phenol-aniline-formaldehyde, 58% mica, 2% misc	25	4.72	4.55	4.37	4.30	4.27	—	0.017
RH–35 resin	Dihydronaphthalene tetramer	24	2.7	2.7	2.7	2.7	2.63	—	0.0009
Saran B–115	Vinylidene-vinyl chloride copolymer	23	5.0	4.65	3.18	2.82	2.71	—	0.042
Styrofoam 103.7	Foamed polystyrene, 0.25% filler	25	1.03	1.03	1.03	—	1.03	1.03	<0.0002
Teflon	Polytetrafluoroethylene	22	2.1	2.1	2.1	2.1	2.1	2.08	<0.0005
Tenite I (008A, H₄)	Cellulose acetate, plasticized	26	4.59	4.48	3.90	3.40	3.25	3.11	0.0075
Tenite II (205A, H₄)	Cellulose acetobutyrate, plasticized	26	3.60	3.48	3.30	3.08	2.91	—	0.0045
Textolite 1422	Cross-linked polystyrene	25	—	—	—	—	2.53	—	—
Vibron 140	Cross-linked polystyrene	25	2.59	2.59	2.58	2.58	2.58	—	0.0004
Vinylite QYNA	100% polyvinyl-chloride	20	3.20	3.10	2.88	2.85	2.84	—	0.0115
Vinylite VG5901	62.5% polyvinyl-chloride-acetate, 29% plasticizer, 8.5% misc	25	—	5.5	3.4	3.0	2.88	—	—
Vinylite VG5904	54% polyvinyl-chloride-acetate, 41% plasticizer, 5% misc	25	—	7.5	4.3	3.3	2.94	—	—
Vinylite VYNW	Polymer of 95% vinyl-chloride, 5% vinyl-acetate	20	—	3.15	2.90	2.8	2.74	—	—
organic liquids									
Aroclor 1254	Chlorinated diphenyls	25	5.05	5.05	4.30	2.75	2.70	—	0.0002
Bayol–D	77.6% paraffins, 22.4% naphthenes	24	2.06	2.06	2.06	2.06	2.06	—	0.0001
Benzene	Chemically pure, dried	25	2.28	2.28	2.28	2.28	2.28	2.28	<0.0001
Cable oil 5314	Aliphatic, aromatic hydrocarbons	25	2.25	2.25	2.25	2.25	2.22	—	0.0006
Carbon tetracnloride		25	2.17	2.17	2.17	2.17	2.17	—	0.007
Ethyl alcohol	Absolute	25	—	—	24.5	23.7	6.5	—	—
Fluorolube	Polychlortrifluorethylene (low mol. wt.)	25	2.84	2.84	2.84	2.57	2.16	—	0.0002
Fractol A	57.4% paraffins, 31.1% naphthenes	26	2.17	2.17	2.17	2.17	2.17	2.12	<0.0001
Halowax oil 1000	60% mon-, 40% di-, trichloronaphthalenes	25	4.80	4.77	4.77	—	3.44	—	0.30
Ignition-sealing compound 4	Organo-siloxane polymer	25	2.75	2.75	2.75	2.74	2.65	—	0.002
IN–420	Chlorinated Indan	24	5.77	5.71	—	—	—	—	0.00004
Marcol	72.4% paraffins, 27.6% naphthenes	24	2.14	2.14	2.14	2.14	2.14	—	<0.002
Methyl alcohol	Absolute analytical grade	25	—	—	31.	31.0	23.9	—	—
Primol–D	49.4% paraffins, 27.6% naphthenes	24	2.17	2.17	2.17	2.17	2.17	—	<0.002
Pyranol 1467	Chlorinated benzenes, diphenyls	25	4.40	4.40	4.40	4.04	2.84	—	—
Pyranol 1476	Isomeric pentachlorodiphenyls	26	5.04	5.04	3.85	—	2.70	—	—
Pyranol 1478	Isomeric trichlorobenzenes	26	4.55	4.53	4.53	4.5	3.80	—	0.02
Silicone fluid 200	Methyl or ethyl siloxane polymer (1000 cs)	22	2.78	2.78	2.78	—	2.74	—	0.0001

dissipation factor at (frequency in cycles/second)					dielectric strength in volts/mil at 25° C	d–c volume resistivity in ohm–cm at 25° C	thermal expansion (linear) in parts/°C	softening point in ° C	moisture absorption in percent
10^3	10^6	10^8	3×10^9	2.5×10^{10}					
0.0470	0.0347	0.0360	0.0410	—	450 ($\frac{1}{2}''$)	3×10^{13}	3.5×10^{-5}	125 (distortion)	0.1
0.033	0.036	0.055	0.051	0.038	1020 (0.033″)	3×10^{13}	3×10^{-5}	>125	1.2
0.0186	0.0218	0.0200	0.0117	0.0105	400 ($\frac{1}{8}''$)	8×10^{14}	10.3×10^{-5}	65 (distortion)	1.5
0.00015	0.0001	0.0003	0.0005	—	—	—	$8-9 \times 10^{-5}$	70-75 (distortion)	—
0.0465	0.0140	0.007	0.0057	—	990 (0.030″)	$>5 \times 10^{16}$	19×10^{-5}	95-105 (distortion)	0.3-0.6
<0.0002	<0.0002	0.0002	0.00031	0.0006	1200 (0.033″)	10^{17}	(varys)		0.03
0.0001	0.0001	0.0003	0.00047	—	600 (0.010″)	—	—	25 (distortion)	Low
<0.00005	0.00007	<0.0001	0.00033	0.0012	500-700 ($\frac{1}{8}''$)	10^{18}	$6-8 \times 10^{-5}$	82 (distortion)	0.05
0.0021	0.0003	0.0003	0.0006	0.0015	—	—	5.6×10^{-5}	—	—
0.0008	0.0003	0.0003	0.00075	0.002	—	—	3.3×10^{-5}	—	—
0.0041	0.0012	0.0098	0.0012	0.002	—	—	1.4×10^{-5}	—	—
0.100	0.064	0.103	0.165	—	—	—	9.8×10^{-5}	—	2.0
0.0040	0.0019	—	0.0042	—	400 ($\frac{1}{8}''$)	—	—	135 (distortion)	0.03
0.0137	0.0062	0.0077	0.0123	—	400 ($\frac{1}{8}''$)	—	—	>100 (distortion)	0.07-0.10
<0.0003	<0.0002	<0.0003	0.0004	0.0006	—	—	—	100	—
0.063	0.057	0.0180	0.0072	—	300 ($\frac{1}{8}''$)	$10^{14}-10^{16}$	15.8×10^{-5}	150	<0.1
<0.0001	<0.0002	—	0.0001	—	—	—	—	85	Low
<0.0003	<0.0002	<0.0002	0.00015	0.0006	1000-2000 (0.005″-0.012″)	10^{17}	9.0×10^{-5}	66 (distortion, stable to 300)	0.00
0.0175	0.039	0.038	0.031	0.030	290-600 ($\frac{1}{8}''$)	—	$8-16 \times 10^{-5}$	60-121	2.9
0.0097	0.018	0.017	0.028	—	250-400 ($\frac{1}{8}''$)	—	$11-17 \times 10^{-5}$	60-121	2.3
			0.0005	—	—	—	—	—	—
0.0005	0.0016	0.0020	0.0019	—	—	—	—	—	—
0.0185	0.0160	0.0081	0.0055	—	400 ($\frac{1}{8}''$)	10^{14}	6.9×10^{-5}	54 (distortion)	0.05-0.15
0.118	0.074	0.020	0.0106	—	—	—	—	—	—
0.071	0.140	0.067	0.034	—	—	—	—	—	—
0.0165	0.0150	0.0080	0.0059	—	—	—	—	—	—
0.00035	0.20	0.0170	0.0032	—	—	—	1×10^{-3}	−26 (pour point)	Slight
<0.0001	<0.0003	0.0005	0.00133	—	300 (0.100″)	—	—	—	—
<0.0001	<0.0001	<0.0001	<0.0001	<0.0001	—	—	—	—	—
<0.00004	0.0008	—	0.0018	—	300 (0.100″)	—	—	−40 (pour point)	—
0.0008	<0.00004	<0.0002	0.0004	—	—	—	—	—	—
—	0.090		0.062	0.250	—	—	—	—	—
<0.0001	0.0092	0.060	0.031	—	300 (0.100″)	—	—	—	Slight
<0.0001	<0.0003	0.0004	0.00072	0.0019	—	—	7.06×10^{-4}	<−15 (pour point)	—
0.0050	<0.0002	—	0.25	—	—	—	2.1×10^{-4}	−38 (melts)	—
0.0006	0.0004	0.0015	0.0092	—	500 (0.010″)	1×10^{13}	63×10^{-5}	—	—
0.0010	—	—	—	—	—	10^{14}	—	10 (pour point)	—
<0.0001	<0.0002	—	0.00097	—	300 (0.100″)	—	7.5×10^{-4}	−12 (pour point)	Slight
—	0.20	0.038	0.64	—	—	—	—	—	—
<0.0001	<0.0002	—	0.00077	—	—	—	6.91×10^{-4}	<−15 (pour point)	Slight
0.0003	0.0190	0.13	0.0116	—	309 (0.100″)	—	—	—	—
0.0006	0.25	—	0.0042	—	—	—	—	10 (pour point)	—
0.0014	0.0003	0.014	0.23	—	—	—	—	—	—
0.00008	0.0003	—	0.0096	—	—	—	—	—	—

Commercial insulating materials *continued*

material	composition	T °C	dielectric constant at (frequency in cycles/second)						60
			60	10³	10⁶	10⁸	3 ×10⁹	2.5 ×10¹⁰	
Silicone fluid 500	Methyl or ethyl siloxane polymer (0.65 cs)	22	2.20	2.20	2.20	2.20	2.20	2.13	<0.001
Styrene dimer	—	25	—	—	2.7	2.7	2.5	—	—
Styrene N–100	Monomeric styrene	22	2.40	2.40	2.40	2.40	2.40	—	0.01
Transil oil 10C	Aliphatic, aromatic hydrocarbons	26	2.22	2.22	2.22	2.20	2.18	—	0.001
Vaseline	—	25	2.16	2.16	2.16	2.16	2.16	—	0.0004
waxes									
Acrowax C	Cetylacetamide	24	2.60	2.58	2.54	2.52	2.48	2.44	0.025
Beeswax, yellow	—	23	2.76	2.73	2.53	2.45	2.39	—	—
Ceresin, white	Vegetable and mineral waxes	25	2.3	2.3	2.3	2.3	2.25	—	0.0009
Halowax 11–314	Dichloronaphthalenes	23	3.14	3.04	2.98	2.93	2.89	—	0.10
Halowax 1001, cold-molded	Tri- and tetrachloronaphthalenes	26	5.45	5.45	5.40	4.2	2.92	2.84	0.002
Opalwax	Mainly 12-hydroxystearin	24	14.2	10.3	3.2	2.7	2.55	2.5	0.12
Paraffin wax, 132° ASTM	Mainly C_{22} to C_{29} aliphatic, saturated hydrocarbons	25	2.25	2.25	2.25	2.25	2.25	—	<0.0002
Vistawax	Polybutene	25	2.34	2.34	2.34	2.30	2.27	—	0.0002
rubbers									
GR-I (butyl rubber)	Copolymer of 98–99% isobutylene, 1–2% isoprene	25	2.39	2.38	2.35	2.35	2.35	—	0.0034
GR-I compound	100 pts polymer, 5 pts zinc oxide, 1 pt tuads, 1.5 pts sulfur	25	2.43	2.42	2.40	2.39	2.38	—	0.005
GR-S (Buna S) cured	Styrene-butadiene copolymer, fillers, lubricants, etc.	25	2.96	2.96	2.90	2.82	2.75	—	0.0008
GR-S (Buna S), uncured	Copolymer of 75% butadiene, 25% styrene	26	2.5	2.5	2.50	2.45	2.45	—	0.0005
Gutta-percha	—	25	2.61	2.60	2.53	2.47	2.40	—	0.0005
Hevea rubber	Pale crepe	25	2.4	2.4	2.4	2.4	2.15	—	0.0030
Hevea rubber, vulcanized	100 pts pale crepe, 6 pts sulfur	27	2.94	2.94	2.74	2.42	2.36	—	0.005
Marbon B	Cyclized pale crepe	27	2.48	2.48	2.46	2.44	2.37	—	0.0021
Neoprene compound	38% GR-M	24	6.7	6.60	6.26	4.5	4.00	4.0	0.018
Silastic 120	50% siloxane elastomer, 50% TiO_2	25	5.78	5.76	5.75	5.75	5.73	—	0.056
Styraloy 22	Copolymer of butadiene, styrene	23	2.4	2.4	2.4	2.4	2.4	2.35	0.001
woods*									
Balsawood	—	26	1.4	1.4	1.37	1.30	1.22	—	0.058
Douglas Fir	—	25	2.05	2.00	1.93	1.88	1.82	1.78	0.004
Douglas Fir, plywood	—	25	2.1	2.1	1.90	—	—	1.6	0.012
Mahogany	—	25	2.42	2.40	2.25	2.07	1.88	1.6	0.008
Yellow Birch	—	25	2.9	2.88	2.70	2.47	2.13	1.87	0.007
Yellow Poplar	—	25	1.85	1.79	1.75	—	1.50	1.4	0.004
miscellaneous									
Amber	Fossil resin	25	2.7	2.7	2.65	—	2.6	—	0.0010
Cenco Sealstix	DeKhotinsky cement	23	3.95	3.75	3.23	—	2.96	—	0.049
Plicene cement	—	25	2.48	2.48	2.48	2.47	2.40	—	0.005
Gilsonite	99.9% natural bitumen	26	2.69	2.66	2.58	2.56	2.56	—	0.006
Shellac (natural XL)	Contains ~ 3.5% wax	28	3.87	3.81	3.47	3.10	2.86	—	0.006
Mycalex 2821	Glass-bonded mica	25	7.50	7.50	7.50	7.45	—	—	—
Ruby mica	Muscovite	26	5.4	5.4	5.4	5.4	5.4	—	0.005
Paper, Royalgrey	—	25	3.30	3.29	2.99	2.77	2.70	—	0.010
Sodium chloride	Fresh crystals	25	—	5.90	5.90	—	—	—	—
Ice	From pure distilled water	−12	—	—	4.15	3.45	3.20	—	—
Snow	Hard-packed snow followed by light rain	−6	—	—	1.55	—	1.5	—	—
Water	Distilled	25	—	—	78.2	78	76.7	—	—

*Field perpendicular to grain.

dissipation factor at (frequency in cycles/second)					dielectric strength in volts/mil at 25° C	d-c volume resistivity in ohm-cm at 25° C	thermal expansion (linear) in parts/°C	softening point in ° C	moisture absorption in percent
10^3	10^6	10^8	3×10^9	2.5×10^{10}					
<0.00004	<0.0003	0.00014	0.00145	0.0060	250–300 (0.100″)	—	1.598×10^{-3}	−68 (melts)	Nil
—	0.0003	0.0018	0.011	—	—	—	—	—	—
0.005	0.0003	—	0.0020	—	300 (0.100″)	3×10^{12}	—	—	0.06
<0.0001	<0.0005	0.0048	0.0028	—	300 (0.100″)	—	—	−40 (pour point)	—
0.0002	<0.0001	<0.0004	0.00066	—	—	—	—	—	—
0.0068	0.0020	0.0012	0.0015	0.0021	—	—	—	137–139 (melts)	—
0.0140	0.0092	0.0090	0.0075	—	—	—	—	45–64 (melts)	—
0.0006	0.0004	0.0004	0.00046	—	—	—	—	57	—
0.0110	0.0003	0.0017	0.0037	0.020	—	—	—	35–63 (melts)	Nil
0.0017	0.0045	0.27	0.058	—	—	—	—	91–94	Low
0.21	0.145	0.027	0.0167	0.0160	—	—	—	86–88 (melts)	—
<0.0002	<0.0002	<0.0002	0.0002	—	1060 (0.027″)	>5×10^{16}	13.0×10^{-5}	36	Very low
0.0003	0.00133	0.00133	0.0009	—	—	—	—	—	—
0.0035	0.0010	0.0010	0.0009	—	—	—	—	—	—
0.0060	0.0022	0.0010	0.00093	—	—	—	—	—	—
0.0024	0.0120	0.0080	0.0057	—	870 (0.040″)	2×10^{15}	—	—	—
0.0009	0.0038	0.0071	0.0044	—	—	—	—	—	—
0.0004	0.0042	0.0120	0.0060	—	—	10^{15}	—	—	—
0.0018	0.0018	0.0050	0.0030	—	—	—	—	—	—
0.0024	0.0446	0.0180	0.0047	—	620 ($\frac{1}{8}$″)	5×10^{16}	—	40–90	<0.1
0.0014	0.0009	0.0014	0.0029	—	300 ($\frac{1}{8}$″)	8×10^{12}	—	—	Nil
0.011	0.038	0.090	0.034	0.025	—	—	—	—	—
0.0030	0.0008	0.0027	0.0254	—	1070 (0.030″)	6×10^{14}	5.9×10^{-5}	125	—
0.00055	0.0012	0.0052	0.0032	0.0018	—	—	—	—	0.2–0.4
0.0040	0.0120	0.0135	0.100	0.032	—	—	—	—	—
0.0080	0.026	0.033	0.027	—	—	—	—	—	—
0.0105	0.0230	—	—	0.0220	—	—	—	—	—
0.0120	0.025	0.032	0.025	0.020	—	—	—	—	—
0.0090	0.029	0.040	0.033	0.026	—	—	—	—	—
0.0054	0.019	—	0.015	0.017	—	—	—	—	—
0.0018	0.0056	—	0.0090	—	2300 ($\frac{1}{8}$″)	Very high	—	200	—
0.0335	0.024	—	0.021	—	—	—	9.8×10^{-5}	80–85	—
0.00355	0.00255	0.0015	0.00078	—	—	—	—	60–65	—
0.0035	0.0016	0.0011	0.0010	—	—	—	—	155 (melts)	—
0.0074	0.031	0.030	0.0254	—	—	10^{16}	—	80	Low after baking
0.0028	0.0010	0.0009	—	—	—	—	—	—	—
0.0006	0.0003	0.0002	0.0003	—	118–276 (0.040″)	5×10^{13}	—	—	—
0.0077	0.038	0.066	0.056	—	202 ($\frac{1}{8}$″)	—	—	—	—
<0.0001	<0.0002	—	—	—	—	—	—	—	—
—	0.12	0.035	0.0009	—	—	—	—	—	—
—	0.29	—	0.0009	—	—	—	—	—	—
—	0.040	0.050	0.157	—	—	10^6	—	—	—

■ Components

Standards in general

Standardization in the field of components for radio equipment is organized and governed mainly by three cooperating agencies, the *Armed Services Electro Standards Agency* (ASESA), which issues Joint Army-Navy (JAN) specifications; the *American Standards Association* (ASA); and the *Radio Manufacturers Association* (RMA). Part of the function of these bodies is to set the standards for radio components (and equipments, in many cases) with the purpose of providing for interchangeability among different manufacturers' products as to size, performance, and identification; minimum number of sizes and designs; uniform testing of products for acceptance; and minimum manufacturing costs. In this chapter is presented a brief outline of the requirements, characteristics, and designations for the major types of radio components.

Color coding

The color code of Fig. 1 is used as a basis for marking radio components.

Fig. 1—Standard radio-industry color code.

color	significant figure	decimal multiplier	tolerance in percent*	voltage rating	character-istic
Black	0	1	±20 (M)	—	A
Brown	1	10	——	100	B
Red	2	100	±2 (G)	200	C
Orange	3	1,000	——	300	D
Yellow	4	10,000	——	400	E
Green	5	100,000	——	500	F
Blue	6	1,000,000	——	600	G
Violet	7	10,000,000	——	700	–
Grey	8	100,000,000	——	800	I
White	9	1,000,000,000	——	900	J
Gold	–	0.1	±5 (J)	1000	–
Silver	–	0.01	±10 (K)	2000	–
No color	–	——	±20	500	–

* Letter symbol is used at end of type designations in RMA standards and JAN specifications to indicate tolerance

Tolerance

The maximum deviation allowed from the specified nominal value is known as the tolerance. It is usually given as a percentage of the nominal value, though for very small capacitors, the tolerance may be specified in micro-microfarads ($\mu\mu f$). For critical applications it is important to specify the permissible tolerance; where no tolerance is specified, components are likely to vary by ±20 percent from the nominal value.

Standards in general   *continued*

Preferred values

To maintain an orderly progression of sizes, preferred numbers are frequently used for the nominal values. A further advantage is that all components manufactured are salable as one or another of the preferred values. Each preferred value differs from its predecessor by a constant multiplier, and the final result is conveniently rounded to two significant figures.

The ASA has adopted as an "American Standard" a series of preferred numbers based on $\sqrt[5]{10}$ and $\sqrt[10]{10}$ as listed in Fig. 2. This series has been widely used for fixed wirewound power-type resistors and for time-delay fuses.

Because of the established practice of ±20-, ±10-, and ±5-percent tolerances in the radio-component industry, a series of values based on $\sqrt[6]{10}$, $\sqrt[12]{10}$, and $\sqrt[24]{10}$ has been adopted by the RMA and is widely used for small radio components, as fixed composition resistors and fixed ceramic, mica, and molded paper capacitors. These values are listed in Fig. 2.

Voltage rating

Distinction must be made between the breakdown-voltage rating (test volts) and the working-voltage rating. The maximum voltage that may be applied (usually continuously) over a long period of time without causing failure of the component determines the working-voltage rating. Application of the test voltage for more than a very few minutes, or even repeated applications of short duration, may result in permanent damage or failure of the component.

Characteristic

This term is frequently used to include various qualities of a component such as temperature coefficient of capacitance or resistance, Q value, maximum permissible operating termperature, stability when subjected to repeated cycles of high and low temperature, and deterioration experienced when the component is subjected to moisture either as humidity or water immersion. One or two letters are assigned in RMA or JAN type designations, and the characteristic may be indicated by color coding on the component. An explanation of the characteristics applicable to a component will be found in the following sections covering that component.

Standards in general   *continued*

Fig. 2—ASA and RMA preferred values. RMA series is standard in the radio industry.

Name of series	ASA standard		RMA standard*		
	"5"	"10"	±20%	±10%	±5%
Percent step size	60	25	≈40	20	10
Step multiplier	$\sqrt[5]{10} = 1.58$	$\sqrt[10]{10} = 1.26$	$\sqrt[6]{10} = 1.46$	$\sqrt[12]{10} = 1.21$	$\sqrt[24]{10} = 1.10$
Values in the series	10	10	**10**	**10**	**10**
	–	12.5 ⎱	–	–	11
	–	(12) ⎰	–	**12**	12
	–	–	–	–	13
	–	–	**15**	**15**	15
	16	16	–	–	16
	–	–	–	**18**	18
	–	20	–	–	20
	–	–	**22**	**22**	22
	–	–	–	–	24
	25	25	–	–	–
	–	–	–	**27**	27
	–	31.5 ⎱	–	–	30
	–	(32) ⎰	–	–	–
	–	–	**33**	**33**	33
	–	–	–	–	36
	–	–	–	**39**	39
	40	40	–	–	–
	–	–	–	–	43
	–	–	**47**	**47**	47
	–	50	–	–	–
	–	–	–	–	51
	–	–	–	**56**	56
	–	–	–	–	62
	63	63	–	–	–
	–	–	**68**	**68**	68
	–	–	–	–	75
	–	80	–	–	–
	–	–	–	**82**	82
	–	–	–	–	91
	100	100	**100**	**100**	**100**

* Use decimal multipliers for smaller and larger values. Associate the tolerance ±20%, ±10%, or ±5% only with the values listed in the corresponding column: Thus, 1200 ohms may be either ±10 or ±5, but not ±20 percent; 750 ohms may be ±5, but neither ±20 nor ±10 percent.

Resistors—fixed composition

Color code

RMA-standard and JAN-specification requirements for color coding of fixed composition resistors are identical (Fig. 3). The exterior body color of insulated axial-lead composition resistors is usually tan, but other colors, except black, are permitted. Noninsulated, axial-lead composition resistors

Resistors—fixed composition   *continued*

have a black body color. Radial-lead composition resistors may have a body color representing the first significant figure of the resistance value.

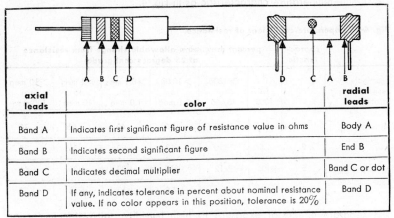

axial leads	color	radial leads
Band A	Indicates first significant figure of resistance value in ohms	Body A
Band B	Indicates second significant figure	End B
Band C	Indicates decimal multiplier	Band C or dot
Band D	If any, indicates tolerance in percent about nominal resistance value. If no color appears in this position, tolerance is 20%	Band D

Fig. 3—Resistor color coding. Colors of Fig. 1 determine values.

Examples: Code of Fig. 1 determines resistor values. Examples are

resistance in ohms and tolerance	band designation			
	A	B	C	D
3300 ± 20%	Orange	Orange	Red	Black or no band
510 ± 5%	Green	Brown	Brown	Gold
1.8 megohms ± 10%	Brown	Gray	Green	Silver

Tolerance

Standard resistors are furnished in ±20-, ±10-, and ±5-percent tolerances, and in the preferred-value series previously tabulated. "Even" values, such as 50,000 ohms, may be found in old equipment, but they are seldom used in new designs.

Temperature and voltage coefficients

Resistors are rated for maximum wattage for an ambient temperature of 40 degrees centigrade;* above this figure it is necessary to operate at reduced wattage ratings. Resistance values are found to be a function of voltage as well as temperature; current JAN specifications allow a maximum

---

* Recently revised standards provide an additional characteristic (G) with 70-degree-centigrade ambient allowed at 100-percent rating.

Resistors—fixed composition   *continued*

voltage coefficient of 0.035 percent/volt for $\frac{1}{4}$- and $\frac{1}{2}$-watt ratings, and 0.02 percent/volt for larger ratings. Specification JAN–R–11 permits a resistance–temperature characteristic as in Fig. 4.

Fig. 4—Temperature coefficient of resistance.

Nominal resistance in ohms	charac- teristic	percent maximum allowable change from resistance at 25 degrees centigrade					
		0 to 1000	>1000 to 10,000	>10,000 to 0.1 meg	>0.1 meg to 1.0 meg	>1 meg to 10 meg	>10 meg to 100 meg
At —55 deg cent ambient	E	13	20	25	40	52	70
	F	6.5	10	13	20	26	35
At +105 deg cent ambient	E	±10	±12	±15	±20	±36	±44
	F	±5	±6	±7.5	±10	±18	±22

The separate effects of exposure to high humidity, salt-water immersion (applied to immersion-proof resistors only), and a 1000-hour rated-load life test should not exceed a 10-percent change in the resistance value. Soldering the resistor in place may cause a maximum resistance change of ±3 percent. Simple temperature cycling between —55 and +85 degrees centigrade for 5 cycles should not change the resistance value as measured at 25 degrees centigrade by more than 2 percent. The above summary of composition-resistor performance indicates that tolerances closer than ±5 percent may not be satisfactorily maintained in service; for a critical application, other types of small resistors should be employed.

Resistors—fixed-wirewound low-power types

Color coding

Small wirewound resistors in $\frac{1}{2}$-, 1-, or 2-watt ratings may be color coded as described in Fig. 3 for insulated composition resistors, but band *A* will be twice the width of the other bands.

Maximum resistance

For reliable continuous operation, it is recommended that the resistance wire used in the manufacture of these resistors be not less than 0.0015 inch in diameter. This limits the maximum resistance available in a given physical size or wattage rating as follows:

$\frac{1}{2}$-watt: 470 ohms   1-watt: 2200 ohms   2-watt: 3300 ohms

Resistors—fixed-wirewound low-power types   *continued*

Wattage

Wattage ratings are determined for a temperature rise of 70 degrees in free air at a 40-degree-centigrade ambient. If the resistor is mounted in a confined area, or may be required to operate in higher ambient temperatures, the allowable dissipation must be reduced.

Temperature coefficient

The temperature coefficient of resistance over the range -55 to $+110$ degrees, referred to 25 degrees centigrade, may have maximums as follows:

Above 10 ohms: ± 0.025 percent/degree centigrade

10 ohms or less: 0.050 percent/degree centigrade

Stability of these resistors is somewhat better than that of composition resistors, and they may be preferred except where a noninductive resistor is required.

Capacitors—fixed ceramic

Ceramic-dielectric capacitors of one grade are used for temperature compensation of tuned circuits and have many other applications. In certain styles, if the temperature coefficient is unimportant (i.e., general-purpose applications), they are competitive with mica capacitors. Another grade of ceramic capacitors offers the advantage of very high capacitance in a small physical volume; unfortunately this grade has other properties that limit its use to noncritical applications such as bypassing.

Color code

If the capacitance tolerance and temperature coefficient are not printed on the capacitor body (Fig. 5), the color code of Fig. 6 may be used.

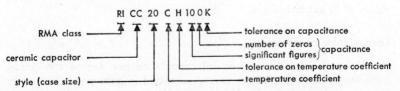

Fig. 5—Type designation for ceramic capacitors. RMA class is omitted on JAN-specification capacitors.

Capacitors—fixed ceramic   *continued*

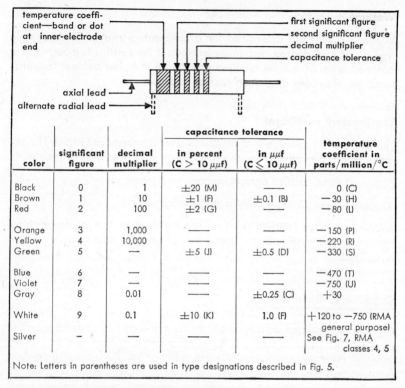

Fig. 6—Color code for fixed ceramic capacitors.

color	significant figure	decimal multiplier	capacitance tolerance		temperature coefficient in parts/million/°C
			in percent (C > 10 μμf)	in μμf (C ≤ 10 μμf)	
Black	0	1	±20 (M)	——	0 (C)
Brown	1	10	±1 (F)	±0.1 (B)	—30 (H)
Red	2	100	±2 (G)	——	—80 (L)
Orange	3	1,000	——	——	—150 (P)
Yellow	4	10,000	——	——	—220 (R)
Green	5	—	±5 (J)	±0.5 (D)	—330 (S)
Blue	6	—	——	——	—470 (T)
Violet	7	—	——	——	—750 (U)
Gray	8	0.01	——	±0.25 (C)	+30
White	9	0.1	±10 (K)	1.0 (F)	+120 to —750 (RMA general purpose)
Silver	–	——	——	——	See Fig. 7, RMA classes 4, 5

Note: Letters in parentheses are used in type designations described in Fig. 5.

Capacitance and capacitance tolerance

Preferred-number values on RMA and JAN specifications are standard for capacitors above 10 micromicrofarads (μμf). The physical size of a capacitor is determined by its capacitance, its temperature coefficient, and its class. Note that the capacitance tolerance is expressed in μμf for nominal capacitance values below 10μμf and in percent for nominal capacitance values of 10 μμf and larger.

Temperature coefficient

The change in capacitance per unit capacitance per degree centigrade is the temperature coefficient, usually expressed in parts per million parts per degree centigrade (ppm/°C). Preferred temperature coefficients are those listed in Fig. 6.

Capacitors—fixed ceramic *continued*

Temperature-coefficient tolerance: Because of the nonlinear nature of the temperature coefficient, specification of the tolerance requires a statement of the temperature range over which it is to be measured (usually —55 to +85 degrees centigrade, or +25 to +85 degrees centigrade), and a

Fig. 7—Quality of fixed ceramic capacitors. Summary of test requirements.

	specification JAN–C–20	RMA class				
		1	2	3	4	5
Minimum initial insulation resistance in megohms	>7500	7500	7500	7500	1000	1000
Minimum Q for $C > 30\,\mu\mu f$ (See Fig. 8 for smaller C)	>1000	1000	650	335	100	40
Maximum allowable capacitance drift with temperature cycling (percent or $\mu\mu f$, whichever is greater)	0.2% or 0.25 $\mu\mu f$	0.3% or 0.25 $\mu\mu f$	0.3% or 0.25 $\mu\mu f$	0.3% or 0.25 $\mu\mu f$	—	—
Maximum capacitance change in percent over range —55 to to +85 C	—	—	—	—	±25	—50 +25
Working voltage = sum of dc and peak ac	—	500	500	5C0	350	350
Humidity test	100 hours exposure at 40°C, 95% relative humidity					
Life test at 85°C	1000 hours, 750 vdc plus 250 vac at 100 cycles or less	1000 hours, 1000 volts			1000 hours, 750 volts	
After humidity test or life test — Minimum Q (C > 30 $\mu\mu f$)	>½ initial limits	350	350	170	50	20
After humidity test or life test — Minimum insulation resistance in megohms	>1000	1000	1000	1000	100	100
After life test — Maximum capacitance change	1%	1% or 0.5 $\mu\mu f$	1% or 0.5 $\mu\mu f$	5% or 0.5 $\mu\mu f$	10%	Not yet determined
Application	Temperature compensation; stable, general-purpose uses		Intermediate quality		High-capacitance general-purpose, noncritical uses only	
Volume efficiency ($\mu\mu f/inch^3$)	Low		Low		High	

Capacitors—fixed ceramic   *continued*

statement of the measuring procedure to be employed. Standard tolerances based on +25 to +85 degrees centigrade are symmetrical:

tolerance in ppm/°C	±15	±30	±60	±120	±250	±500
code	(F)	(G)	(H)	(J)	(K)	(L)

The smaller tolerances can be supplied only for capacitors of 10 $\mu\mu f$ or larger, and only for the smaller temperature coefficients.

Quality

Insulation resistance, internal loss (conveniently expressed in terms of Q), capacitance drift with temperature cycling, together with the permissible effects of humidity and accelerated life tests, are summarized in Fig. 7. This data will be a guide to the probable performance under favorable or moderately severe ambient conditions.

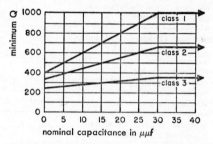

Fig. 8—Minimum Q requirements for ceramic capacitors where capacitance <30 $\mu\mu f$.

Capacitors—molded mica-dielectric

Type designation

Small fixed mica capacitors in molded plastic cases are manufactured to performance standards established by the RMA or in accordance with a JAN specification. A comprehensive numbering system, the *type designation*, is used to identify the component. The mica-capacitor type designations are of the form

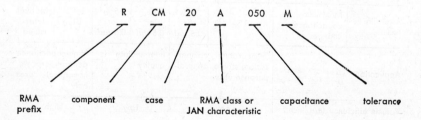

Capacitors—molded mica-dielectric *continued*

Component designation: Fixed mica-dielectric capacitors are identified by the symbol *CM* for JAN specification, or *RCM* for RMA standard.

Case designation: The case designation is a two-digit symbol that identifies a particular case size and shape.

Characteristic: The JAN characteristic or RMA class is indicated by a single letter in accordance with Fig. 9.

Fig. 9—Fixed-mica-capacitor requirements by JAN characteristic and RMA class.

JAN char or RMA class	JAN-specification requirements				RMA-standard requirements			
	maximum capacitance drift in percent	maximum range of temperature coefficient (ppm/°C)	minimum Q		maximum capacitance drift	maximum range of temperature coefficient (ppm/°C)	minimum insulation resistance in megohms	minimum Q
A	—	—	33% of JAN value in Fig. 10.		±(5% + 1 μμf)	±1000	3000	30% of RMA value in Fig. 10.
B	—	—			±(3% + 1 μμf)	±500	6000	
C	0.5	±200			±(0.5% + 0.5 μμf)	±200	6000	
I	—	—	See Fig. 10, JAN values, for all capacitors not assigned specific current ratings		±(0.3% + 0.2 μμf)	−50 to +150	6000	See Fig. 10, RMA values, applicable only up to 1000 μμf
D	0.2	±100			±(0.3% ± 0.1 μμf)	±100	6000	
J	—	—			±(0.2% + 0.2 μμf)	−50 to +100	6000	
E	0.05	0 to +100			±(0.1% + 0.1 μμf)	−20 to +100	6000	
F	0.025	0 to +50			—	—	—	—
G	0.025	0 to −50			—	—	—	—

Insulation resistance of all JAN capacitors *must* exceed 7500 megohms.
ppm/°C = parts/million/degree centigrade.
Where no data are given, such characteristics are not included in that particular standard.

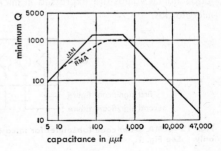

Fig. 10—Minimum Q versus capacitance for JAN mica capacitors (Q measured at 1.0 megacycle), and for RMA mica capacitors (Q measured at 0.5 to 1.5 megacycles).

Capacitors—molded mica-dielectric   *continued*

Capacitance value: The nominal capacitance value in micromicrofarads is indicated by a 3-digit number. The first two digits are the first two digits of the capacitance value in micromicrofarads. The final digit specifies the number of zeros that follow the first two digits. If more than two significant figures are required, additional digits may be used, the last digit always indicating the number of zeros.

Capacitance tolerance: The symmetrical capacitance tolerance in percent is designated by a letter as shown in Fig. 1.

Color coding

The significance of the various colored dots is explained by Figs. 11–13. The meaning of each color may be interpreted from Fig. 1.

JAN specifications and 1948 RMA standard: Are shown in Fig. 11.

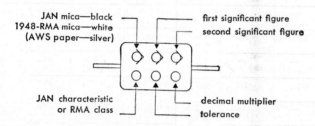

Fig. 11—New standard code for fixed mica capacitors. See color code, Fig. 1.

Older RMA standards—not in current use: The 1938 RMA standard covered a simple 3-dot color code (Fig. 12) showing directly only the capacitance, and a more comprehensive 6-dot color code (Fig. 13) showing 3 significant figures and tolerance of the capacitance value, and a voltage rating. Capacitance values are expressed in micromicrofarads up to 10,000 micromicrofarads.

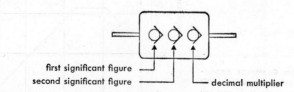

Fig. 12—RMA 3-dot code (obsolete) for mica capacitors; 500-volt, ±20% tolerance only. See Fig. 1.

Capacitors—molded mica-dielectric *continued*

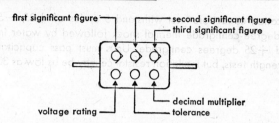

Fig. 13—RMA 6-dot color code (obsolete) for mica capacitors. See Fig. 1.

Examples

type	top row left	top row center	top row right	bottom row left	bottom row tolerance center	bottom row multiplier right	description
RMA (3 dot)	red	green	brown	none	none	none	250 μμf ± 20%, 500 volts
RMA	brown	black	black	blue	green	brown	1000 μμf ± 5%, 600 volts
RMA	brown	red	green	gold	red	brown	1250 μμf ± 2%, 1000 volts
CM30B681J	black	blue	gray	brown	gold	brown	680 μμf ± 5%, characteristic B
CM35E332G	black	orange	orange	yellow	red	red	3300 μμf ± 2%, characteristic E
RCM20A221M	white	red	red	black	black	brown	220 μμf ± 20%, RMA class A

Capacitance

Measured at 500 kilocycles for capacitors of 1000 μμf or smaller; larger capacitors are measured at 1 kilocycle.

Temperature coefficient

Measurements to determine the temperature coefficient of capacitance and the capacitance drift are based on one cycle over the following temperature values (all in degrees centigrade).

JAN: +25, −40, −10, +25, +35, +45, +55, +65, +85, +25

RMA: +25, −20, +25, +85, +25

Dielectric strength

Molded-mica capacitors are subjected to a test potential of twice their direct-current voltage rating.

Humidity and thermal-shock resistance

RMA-standard capacitors must withstand a 120-hour humidity test: Five cycles of 16 hours at 40 degrees centigrade, 90-percent relative humidity, and 8 hours at standard ambient. Units must pass capacitance and dielectric-strength tests, but insulation resistance may be as low as 1000 megohms for class-A, and 2000 megohms for other classes.

Capacitors—molded mica-dielectric   *continued*

JAN-specification capacitors must withstand 5 cycles of +25, −55, +25, +85, +25 degree-centigrade thermal shock followed by water immersion at +65 and +25 degrees centigrade. Units must pass capacitance and dielectric-strength tests, but insulation resistance may be as low as 3000 megohms.

Life

Capacitors are given accelerated life tests at 85 degrees centigrade with 150 percent of rated voltage applied. No failures are permitted before: 1000 hours for JAN specification; or 500 hours for RMA standard.

Capacitors—button-style fixed mica-dielectric

Color code

"Button" mica capacitors are color coded in several different ways, of which the two most widely used methods are shown in Fig. 14.

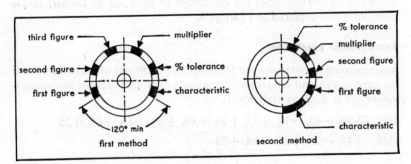

Fig. 14—Color coding of button-mica capacitors. See Fig. 1 for color code.

Characteristic

characteristic	max range of temp coeff (ppm/°C)	maximum capacitance drift
C	±200	±0.5%
D	±100	±0.3%
E	−20 to +100	±(0.1% + 0.1 μμf)

Capacitors—button-style fixed mica-dielectric *continued*

Initial Q values shall exceed 500 for capacitors 5 to 50 $\mu\mu f$; 700 for capacitors 51 to 100 $\mu\mu f$; and 1000 for capacitors 101 to 5000 $\mu\mu f$. Initial insulation resistance should exceed 10,000 megohms. Dielectric-strength tests should be made at twice rated voltage.

Thermal-shock and humidity tests

These are commercial requirements. After 5 cycles of $+25$, -55, $+85$, $+25$ degrees centigrade, followed by 96 hours at 40 degrees centigrade and 95-percent relative humidity, capacitors should have an insulation resistance of at least 500 megohms; a Q of at least 70 percent of initial minimum requirements; a capacitance change of not more than 2 percent of initial value; and should pass the dielectric-strength test.

Capacitors—paper-dielectric

The proper application of paper capacitors is a complex problem requiring consideration of the equipment duty cycle, desired capacitor life, ambient temperature, applied voltage and waveform, and the capacitor-impregnant characteristics. From the data below, a suitable capacitor rating may be determined for a specified life under normal use.

Life—voltage and ambient temperature

Normal paper-dielectric-capacitor voltage ratings are for an ambient temperature of 40 degrees centigrade, and provide a life expectancy of approximately 1 year continuous service. For ambient temperatures outside the range 0 to $+40$ degrees centigrade, the applied voltage must be reduced in accordance with Fig. 15.

The energy content of a capacitor may be found from

$W = CE^2/2$ watt-seconds

where

C = capacitance in microfarads (μf)

E = applied voltage in kilovolts

In multiple-section capacitors, the sum of the watt-second ratings should be used to determine the proper derating of the unit.

Longer life in continuous service may be secured by operating at voltages lower than those determined from Fig. 15. Experiment has shown that

68

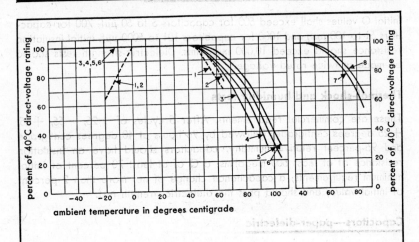

JAN specification				RMA standard		
JAN char	watt-second rating	voltage rating	curve	watt-second rating	voltage rating	curve
H	0.5–5	All, plus those excluded from group of curve 2	1	>50	1500 and over	7
	0–0.5	1500 v and below—small cased tubular styles; 1000 v and below—other styles	2	5–50	2000 and below	
					2500 and above	8
				0–5	All	
D E F	>50	All	3			
	5–50	All	4			
	0.5–5	All, plus those excluded from group of curve 6	5			
	0–0.5	1500 v and below—small cased tubular styles; 1000 v and below—other styles	6			

Fig. 15—Life-expectancy rating for paper capacitors as a function of ambient temperature.

Capacitors—paper-dielectric *continued*

capacitor life is approximately inversely proportional to the 5th power of the applied voltage:

desired life in years (at ambient ≈ 45°C)	1	2	5	10	20
applied voltage in percent of rated voltage	100	85	70	60	53

The above life derating is to be applied together with the ambient-temperature derating to determine the adjusted-voltage rating of the paper capacitor for a specific application.

Waveform

Normal filter capacitors are rated for use with direct current. Where alternating voltages are present, the adjusted-voltage rating of the capacitor should be calculated as the sum of the direct voltage and the peak value of the alternating voltage. The alternating component must not exceed 20 percent of the rating at 60 cycles, 15 percent at 120 cycles, 6 percent at 1000 cycles, or 1 percent at 10,000 cycles.

Where alternating-current rather than direct-current conditions govern, this fact must be included in the capacitor specification, and capacitors specially designed for alternating-current service should be procured.

Where heavy transient or pulse currents are present, standard capacitors may not give satisfactory service unless an allowance is made for the unusual conditions.

Capacitor impregnants

Fig. 16 lists the various impregnating materials in common use together with their distinguishing properties. At the bottom will be found recommendations for application of capacitors according to their impregnating material.

Insulation resistance

For ordinary electronic circuits, the exact value of capacitor insulation resistance is unimportant. In many circuits little difference in performance is observed when the capacitor is shunted by a resistance as low as 5 megohms. In the very few applications where insulation resistance is important (e.g., some RC-coupled amplifiers), the capacitor value is usually small and megohm×microfarad products of 10 to 20 are adequate.

The insulation resistance of a capacitor is a function of the impregnant; its departure from maximum value is an indication of the care taken in

Capacitors — paper-dielectric *continued*

Fig. 16—Characteristics of impregnants for paper capacitors.

property			castor oil		mineral oil		askarels* (chlorinated synthetic)		Halowax (chlorinated naphthalene synthetic)	mineral wax
Characteristic		From Specification JAN–C–5	D	—	E†	→	F†	—	H	—
		From RMA standard	—	C	—	A	—	B	—	—
Measurements at 25°C ambient	Megohms × microfarads‡	Nominal	1500		7000		6000		3000	15,000
		Specification minimum	**500**	**500**	**2000**	**3000**	**1500**	**1000**	**2000**	—
	Minimum insulation resistance in megohms		**1500**	**1500**	**6000**	**6000**	**4500**	**1500**	**6000**	—
	Power factor in percent	60 c/s	< 0.2		0.3		< 0.3		0.5 to 3	0.5 to 1.5
		1000 c/s	—		≈ 1		—		≈ 2	—
Measurements at high-ambient temperature	High-ambient test temperature in degrees centigrade		**85**	**85**	**85**	**85**	**85**	**85**	**55**	85
	Megohms × microfarads‡	Nominal	10		40		30		100	50
		Specification minimum	**5**	**5**	**20**	**30**	**15**	**10**	**100**	—
	Minimum insulation resistance in megohms		**150**	**150**	**600**	**600**	**450**	**150**	**1000**	—
	Power factor in percent		2 to 6		0.3 to 1.6		1 to 5		1 to 3	0.2 to 1.5
	Percent capacitance change from value at 25 degrees centigrade		−4 to +1		−1 to +1.5		−6 to −2		−4.5 to 0	−10 to −6
Measurements at low-ambient temperature	Low-ambient test temperature in degrees centigrade		**−55**	**−40**	**−55**	**−40**	**−55**	**−40**	**−20**	−55
	Power factor in percent		1.5 to 4		0.5 to 3		0.8 to 3		0.5 to 4	3 to 4
	Percent capacitance change from value at 25 degrees centigrade	Nominal	−20 to +4		−10 to +2		−30 to −20		−10 to −5	−6 to −2
		Specification maximum	**−30**	+5 to −30	**−15**	±5	**−30**	+5 to −30	**−10**	—
Application data	Recommended ambient temperature range in degrees centigrade		−55 to +85		−55 to +85		−55 to +85		−20 to +55	to +85
	Relative capacitor volume (for units of equal capacitance)		100		135		100		100	135
	Recommended uses		General-purpose dc. Also ac if temperature range is limited		General-purpose dc and ac; high-temp applications. High-stability requirements		General-purpose dc and ac. Non-inflammable		General-purpose dc over limited temperature range	General-purpose dc over wider temp range than Halowax units allow

Notes:

Bold figures in tabulation are Specification JAN–C–25 or RMA-standard limits for that property.

* Trade names Aroclor, Pyranol, Dykanol A, Inerteen, etc.

† JAN–C–25 characteristics A and B (not tabulated above) are essentially long-life versions of JAN characteristics E and F, respectively.

‡ At 25 degrees centigrade, applies to capacitors of approximately $\frac{1}{3}$ microfarad or larger. At any test temperature, capacitors are not expected to show megohm × microfarad products in excess of the insulation-resistance requirements.

Capacitors—paper-dielectric *continued*

manufacture to avoid undesirable contamination of the impregnant. For example, if an askarel-impregnated capacitor has the same insulation resistance as a good castor-oil-impregnated capacitor of equal rating, the askarel impregnant is strongly contaminated, and the capacitor life will be considerably reduced.

Measurements are made with potentials between 100 and 500 volts, and a maximum charging time of 2 minutes.

Power factor

This is a function of the capacitor impregnant. In most filter applications where a specified maximum capacitor impedance at a known frequency may not be exceeded, the determining factor is the capacitor reactance and not the power factor. A power factor of 14 percent will increase the impedance only 1 percent, a negligible amount.

For alternating-current applications, however, the power factor determines the capacitor internal heating. Consideration must be given to the alternating voltage and the operating temperature. Power factor is a function of the voltage applied to the capacitor; any specification should include actual capacitor operating conditions, rather than arbitrary bridge-measurement conditions.

For manufacturing purposes, power factor is measured at room temperature (≈ 25 degrees centigrade), with 1000 cycles applied to capacitors of 1 μf or less, rated 3000 volts or less; and with 60 cycles applied to capacitors larger than 1 μf, or rated higher than 3000 volts. Under these conditions the power factor should not exceed 1 percent.

Temperature coefficient of capacitance

Depending upon the impregnant characteristics, low temperature may cause an appreciable drop in capacitance. Due allowance for this must be made if low-temperature operation of the equipment is to be satisfactory. This temperature effect is nonlinear.

Life tests

Accelerated life tests run on paper capacitors are based on 250-hour operation at the high-ambient-temperature limit shown in Fig. 16 with an applied direct voltage determined by the watt-second and 40-degree-centigrade voltage ratings.

I–F transformer frequencies

Recognized standard frequencies for receiver intermediate-frequency transformers are

Standard broadcast (540 to 1600 kilocycles) _____ **455,** 175 kilocycles
Very-high-frequency broadcast _____ 10.7 megacycles
Very-, ultra-, and super-high-frequency equipment ___ **30,** 60, 100 megacycles

Color codes for transformer leads

Radio power transformers[1]

Primary	Black		Amplifier	
If tapped:			Filament No. 1	Green
Common	Black		Center tap	Green-Yellow
Tap	Black-Yellow		Filament No. 2	Brown
Finish	Black-Red		Center tap	Brown-Yellow
			Filament No. 3	Slate
			Center tap	Slate-Yellow
Rectifier				
Plate	Red			
Center tap	Red-Yellow			
Filament	Yellow			
Center tap	Yellow-Blue			

Audio-frequency transformers[2]

Primary	single	push-pull	Secondary	single	push-pull
Plate	Blue	Blue	Grid (or high side		
B+	Red	Red	of moving coil)	Green	Green
Plate	—	Blue or	Return (or low side		
		Brown[3]	of moving coil)	Black	Black
			Grid	—	Green or
					Yellow[3]

Intermediate-frequency transformers[4]

Primary		For full-wave transformer:	
Plate	Blue	Second diode	Violet
B+	Red	Old standard[5] is same as above, except:	
Secondary		Grid return	Black
Grid or diode	Green	Second diode	Green-Black
Grid return	White		

[1] Radio Manufacturer's Association Standard M4–505.
[2] Radio Manufacturer's Association Standard M4–507.
[3] The brown and yellow colors are used to indicate the starts of the windings, but only when polarity must be indicated. In an output transformer, the black lead is the start of the secondary.
[4] Radio Manufacturer's Association Standard REC–114.
[5] Radio Manufacturer's Association Standard M4–506.

◼ Fundamentals of networks

Inductance of single-layer solenoids

The approximate value of the *low-frequency* inductance of a single-layer solenoid is*

$L = Fn^2d$ microhenries

where F = form factor, a function of the ratio d/l. (Value of F may be read from the accompanying chart, Fig. 1. Also, n = number of turns, d = diameter of coil (inches), between centers of conductors, l = length of coil (inches) = n times the distance between centers of adjacent turns.

The formula is based on the assumption of a uniform current sheet, but the correction due to the use of spaced round wires is usually negligible for practical purposes. For higher frequencies, skin effect alters the inductance slightly. This effect is not readily calculated, but is often negligibly small. However, it must be borne in mind that the formula gives approximately the *true* value of inductance. In contrast, the *apparent* value is affected by the shunting effect of the distributed capacitance of the coil.

Example: Required a coil of 100 microhenries inductance, wound on a form 2 inches diameter by 2 inches winding length. Then $d/l = 1.00$, and $F = 0.0173$ on Fig. 1.

$$n = \sqrt{\frac{L}{Fd}} = \sqrt{\frac{100}{0.0173 \times 2}} = 54 \text{ turns}$$

Reference to Magnet-wire data, page 74, will assist in choosing a desirable size of wire, allowing for a suitable spacing between turns according to the application of the coil. A slight correction may then be made for the increased diameter (diameter of form plus two times radius of wire), if this small correction seems justified.

Approximate formula

For single-layer solenoids of the proportions normally used in radio work, the inductance is given to an accuracy of about 1 percent by

$$L = n^2 \frac{r^2}{9r + 10l} \text{ microhenries}$$

where $r = d/2$.

General remarks

In the use of various charts, tables, and calculators for designing inductors, the following relationships are useful in extending the range of the devices.

* Formulas and chart (Fig. 1) derived from equations and tables in Bureau of Standards Circular No. C74.

Inductance of single-layer solenoids   *continued*

They apply to coils of any type or design.

a. If all dimensions are held constant, inductance is proportional to n^2.

b. If the proportions of the coil remain unchanged, then for a given number of turns the inductance is proportional to the dimensions of the coil. A coil with all dimensions m times those of a given coil (having the same number of turns) has m times the inductance of the given coil. That is, inductance has the dimensions of *length*.

Magnet-wire data

AWG B&S gauge	bare nom diam in inches	enam nom diam in inches	SCC* diam in inches	DCC* diam in inches	SCE* diam in inches	SSC* diam in inches	DSC* diam in inches	SSE* diam in inches	bare		enameled	
									min diam inches	max diam inches	min diam inches	diam* in inches
10	.1019	.1039	.1079	.1129	.1104	—	—	—	.1009	.1029	.1024	.1044
11	.0907	.0927	.0957	.1002	.0982	—	—	—	.0898	.0917	.0913	.0932
12	.0808	.0827	.0858	.0903	.0882	—	—	—	.0800	.0816	.0814	.0832
13	.0720	.0738	.0770	.0815	.0793	—	—	—	.0712	.0727	.0726	.0743
14	.0641	.0659	.0691	.0736	.0714	—	—	—	.0634	.0647	.0648	.0664
15	.0571	.0588	.0621	.0666	.0643	.0591	.0611	.0613	.0565	.0576	.0578	.0593
16	.0508	.0524	.0558	.0603	.0579	.0528	.0548	.0549	.0503	.0513	.0515	.0529
17	.0453	.0469	.0503	.0548	.0523	.0473	.0493	.0493	.0448	.0457	.0460	.0473
18	.0403	.0418	.0453	.0498	.0472	.0423	.0443	.0442	.0399	.0407	.0410	.0422
19	.0359	.0374	.0409	.0454	.0428	.0379	.0399	.0398	.0355	.0363	.0366	.0378
20	.0320	.0334	.0370	.0415	.0388	.0340	.0360	.0358	.0316	.0323	.0326	.0338
21	.0285	.0299	.0335	.0380	.0353	.0305	.0325	.0323	.0282	.0287	.0292	.0303
22	.0253	.0266	.0303	.0343	.0320	.0273	.0293	.0290	.0251	.0256	.0261	.0270
23	.0226	.0238	.0276	.0316	.0292	.0246	.0266	.0262	.0223	.0228	.0232	.0242
24	.0201	.0213	.0251	.0291	.0266	.0221	.0241	.0236	.0199	.0203	.0208	.0216
25	.0179	.0190	.0224	.0264	.0238	.0199	.0219	.0213	.0177	.0181	.0186	.0193
26	.0159	.0169	.0204	.0244	.0217	.0179	.0199	.0192	.0158	.0161	.0166	.0172
27	.0142	.0152	.0187	.0227	.0200	.0162	.0182	.0175	.0141	.0144	.0149	.0155
28	.0126	.0135	.0171	.0211	.0183	.0146	.0166	.0158	.0125	.0128	.0132	.0138
29	.0113	.0122	.0158	.0198	.0170	.0133	.0153	.0145	.0112	.0114	.0119	.0125
30	.0100	.0108	.0145	.0185	.0156	.0120	.0140	.0131	.0099	.0101	.0105	.0111
31	.0089	.0097	.0134	.0174	.0144	.0109	.0129	.0119	.0088	.0090	.0094	.0099
32	.0080	.0088	.0125	.0165	.0135	.0100	.0120	.0110	.0079	.0081	.0085	.0090
33	.0071	.0078	.0116	.0156	.0125	.0091	.0111	.0100	.0070	.0072	.0075	.0080
34	.0063	.0069	.0108	.0148	.0116	.0083	.0103	.0091	.0062	.0064	.0067	.0071
35	.0056	.0061	.0101	.0141	.0108	.0076	.0096	.0083	.0055	.0057	.0059	.0063
36	.0050	.0055	.0090	.0130	.0097	.0070	.0090	.0077	.0049	.0051	.0053	.0057
37	.0045	.0049	.0085	.0125	.0091	.0065	.0085	.0071	.0044	.0046	.0047	.0051
38	.0040	.0044	.0080	.0120	.0086	.0060	.0080	.0066	.0039	.0041	.0042	.0046
39	.0035	.0038	.0075	.0115	.0080	.0055	.0075	.0060	.0034	.0036	.0036	.0040
40	.0031	.0034	.0071	.0111	.0076	.0051	.0071	.0056	.0030	.0032	.0032	.0036
41	.0028	.0031	—	—	—	—	—	—	.0027	.0029	.0029	.0022
42	.0025	.0028	—	—	—	—	—	—	.0024	.0026	.0026	.0029
43	.0022	.0025	—	—	—	—	—	—	.0021	.0023	.0023	.0026
44	.0020	.0023	—	—	—	—	—	—	.0019	.0021	.0021	.0024

* Nominal bare diameter plus maximum additions.
For additional data on copper wire, see pp. 40–45 and p. 190.

Inductance of single-layer solenoids *continued*

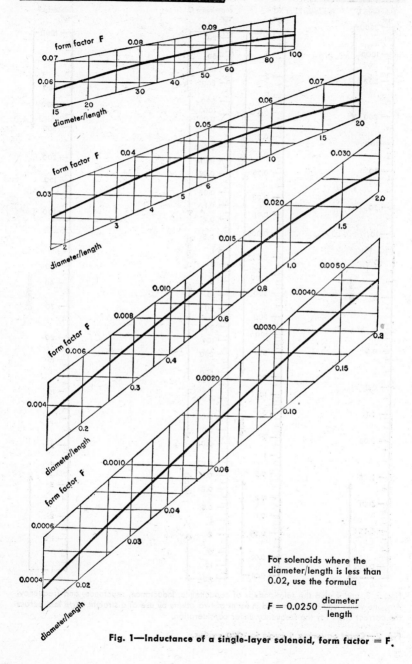

For solenoids where the diameter/length is less than 0.02, use the formula

$$F = 0.0250 \frac{\text{diameter}}{\text{length}}$$

Fig. 1—Inductance of a single-layer solenoid, form factor = F.

Reactance charts

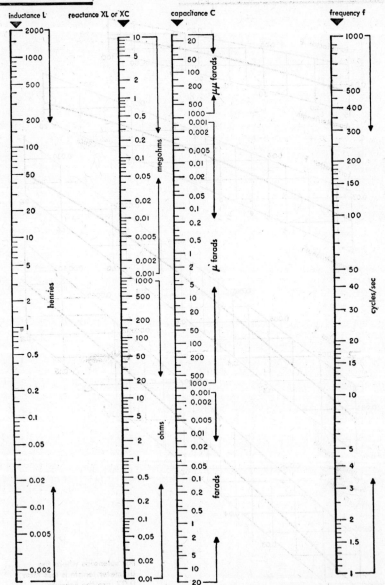

Figs. 2, 3, and 4 give the relationships of capacitance, inductance, reactance, and frequency. Any one value may be determined in terms of two others by use of a straight edge laid across the correct chart for the frequency under consideration.

Fig. 2—Chart covering 1 cycle to 1000 cycles.

Reactance charts *continued*

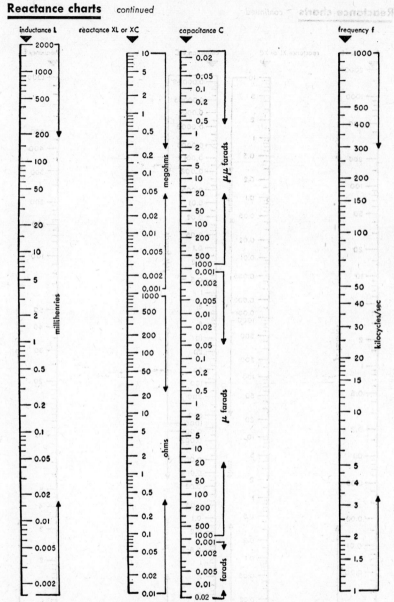

inductance L reactance XL or XC capacitance C frequency f

Example: Given a capacitance of 0.001 μf, find the reactance at 50 kilocycles and inductance required to resonate. Place a straight edge through these values and read the intersections on the other scales, giving 3,180 ohms and 10.1 millihenries.

Fig. 3—Chart covering 1 kilocycle to 1000 kilocycles.

Reactance charts   *continued*

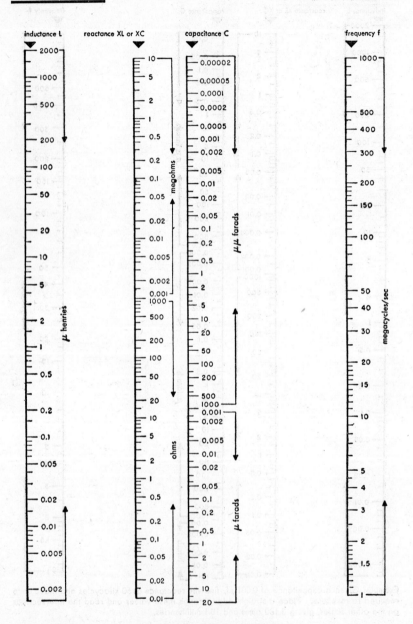

Fig. 4—Chart covering 1 megacycle to 1000 megacycles.

Impedance formulas

Parallel and series circuits and their equivalent relationships

Conductance $G = \dfrac{1}{R_p}$ $\qquad \omega = 2\pi f$

Susceptance $B = -\dfrac{1}{X_p} = \omega C_p - \dfrac{1}{\omega L_p}$

Reactance $X_p = \dfrac{\omega L_p}{1 - \omega^2 L_p C_p}$

Admittance $Y = \dfrac{I}{E} = \dfrac{1}{Z} = G + jB$

$\qquad\qquad = \sqrt{G^2 + B^2}\ \angle -\phi = |Y|\ \angle -\phi$

Impedance $Z = \dfrac{E}{I} = \dfrac{1}{Y} = \dfrac{R_p X_p}{R_p{}^2 + X_p{}^2}\ (X_p + jR_p)$

$\qquad\qquad = \dfrac{R_p X_p}{\sqrt{R_p{}^2 + X_p{}^2}}\ \angle\phi = |Z|\ \angle\phi$

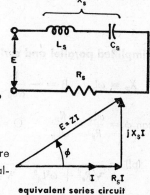

parallel circuit

Phase angle $-\phi = \tan^{-1}\dfrac{B}{G} = \cos^{-1}\dfrac{G}{|Y|} = -\tan^{-1}\dfrac{R_p}{X_p}$

Resistance $= R_s$

Reactance $X_s = \omega L_s - \dfrac{1}{\omega C_s}$

Impedance $Z = \dfrac{E}{I} = R_s + jX_s$

$\qquad\qquad = \sqrt{R_s{}^2 + X_s{}^2}\ \angle\phi = |Z|\ \angle\phi$

Phase angle $\phi = \tan^{-1}\dfrac{X_s}{R_s} = \cos^{-1}\dfrac{R_s}{|Z|}$

Vectors E and I, phase angle ϕ, and Z, Y are identical for the parallel circuit and its equivalent series circuit

equivalent series circuit

$Q = |\tan\phi| = \dfrac{|X_s|}{R_s} = \dfrac{R_p}{|X_p|} = \dfrac{|B|}{G}$

$\text{(pf)} = \cos\phi = \dfrac{R_s}{|Z|} = \dfrac{|Z|}{R_p} = \dfrac{G}{|Y|} = \sqrt{\dfrac{R_s}{R_p}} = \dfrac{1}{\sqrt{Q^2 + 1}} = \dfrac{\text{(kw)}}{\text{(kva)}}$

$Z^2 = R_s{}^2 + X_s{}^2 = \dfrac{R_p{}^2 X_p{}^2}{R_p{}^2 + X_p{}^2} = R_s R_p = X_s X_p$

Impedance formulas   *continued*

$$Y^2 = G^2 + B^2 = \frac{1}{R_p{}^2} + \frac{1}{X_p{}^2} = \frac{G}{R_s}$$

$$R_s = \frac{Z^2}{R_p} = \frac{G}{Y^2} = R_p \frac{X_p{}^2}{R_p{}^2 + X_p{}^2} = R_p \frac{1}{Q^2 + 1}$$

$$X_s = \frac{Z^2}{X_p} = -\frac{B}{Y^2} = X_p \frac{R_p{}^2}{R_p{}^2 + X_p{}^2} = X_p \frac{1}{1 + 1/Q^2}$$

$$R_p = \frac{1}{G} = \frac{Z^2}{R_s} = \frac{R_s{}^2 + X_s{}^2}{R_s} = R_s\,(Q^2 + 1)$$

$$X_p = -\frac{1}{B} = \frac{Z^2}{X_s} = \frac{R_s{}^2 + X_s{}^2}{X_s} = X_s\left(1 + \frac{1}{Q^2}\right) = \frac{R_s R_p}{X_s} = \pm\, R_p \sqrt{\frac{R_s}{R_p - R_s}}$$

Approximate formulas

Reactor $R_s = \dfrac{X^2}{R_p}$ and $X = X_s = X_p$ (See Note 1, p. 81)

Resistor $R = R_s = R_p$ and $X_s = \dfrac{R^2}{X_p}$ (See Note 2, p. 81)

Simplified parallel and series circuits

$$X_p = \omega L_p \qquad B = -\frac{1}{\omega L_p} \qquad X_s = \omega L_s$$

$$\tan\phi = \frac{\omega L_s}{R_s} = \frac{R_p}{\omega L_p} \qquad Q = \frac{\omega L_s}{R_s} = \frac{R_p}{\omega L_p}$$

$$\text{(pf)} = \frac{R_s}{\sqrt{R_s{}^2 + \omega^2 L_s{}^2}} = \frac{\omega L_p}{\sqrt{R_p{}^2 + \omega^2 L_p{}^2}}$$

$$\text{(pf)} = \frac{1}{Q} \text{ approx}\quad \text{(See Note 3, p. 81)}$$

$$R_s = R_p \frac{1}{Q^2 + 1} \qquad R_p = R_s\,(Q^2 + 1) \qquad Z = R_p \frac{1 + jQ}{1 + Q^2}$$

$$L_s = L_p \frac{1}{1 + 1/Q^2} \qquad L_p = L_s\left(1 + \frac{1}{Q^2}\right) \qquad Y = \frac{1}{R_s} \frac{1 - jQ}{1 + Q^2}$$

Impedance formulas *continued*

$$X_p = \frac{-1}{\omega C_p} \qquad B = \omega C_p \qquad X_s = \frac{-1}{\omega C_s}$$

$$\tan \phi = \frac{-1}{\omega C_s R_s} = -\omega C_p R_p$$

$$Q = \frac{1}{\omega C_s R_s} = \omega C_p R_p$$

$$(pf) = \frac{\omega C_s R_s}{\sqrt{1 + \omega^2 C_s^2 R_s^2}} = \frac{1}{\sqrt{1 + \omega^2 C_p^2 R_p^2}}$$

$$(pf) \approx \frac{1}{Q} \qquad \text{(See Note 3)}$$

$$R_s = R_p \frac{1}{Q^2 + 1} \qquad R_p = R_s (Q^2 + 1)$$

$$C_s = C_p \left(1 + \frac{1}{Q^2} \right) \qquad C_p = C_s \frac{1}{1 + 1/Q^2}$$

$$Z = R_p \frac{1 - jQ}{1 + Q^2} \qquad Y = \frac{1}{R_s} \frac{1 + jQ}{1 + Q^2}$$

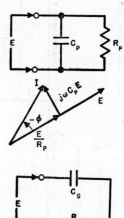

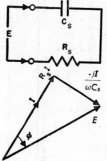

Approximate formulas

Inductor $R_s = \omega^2 L^2 / R_p$ and $L = L_p = L_s$ (See Note 1)

Resistor $R = R_s = R_p$ and $L_p = R^2 / \omega^2 L_s$ (See Note 2)

Capacitor $R_s = 1/\omega^2 C^2 R_p$ and $C = C_p = C_s$ (See Note 1)

Resistor $R = R_s = R_p$ and $C_s = 1/\omega^2 C_p R^2$ (See Note 2)

Note 1: (Small resistive component) Error in percent $= - 100/Q^2$
(for $Q = 10$, error $= 1$ percent low)

Note 2: (Small reactive component) Error in percent $= - 100 Q^2$
(for $Q = 0.1$, error $= 1$ percent low)

Note 3: Error in percent $= + 50/Q^2$ approximately
(for $Q = 7$, error $= 1$ percent high)

impedance $Z = R + jX$ ohms

magnitude $|Z| = [R^2 + X^2]^{\frac{1}{2}}$ ohms

phase angle $\phi = \tan^{-1} \dfrac{X}{R}$

admittance $Y = \dfrac{1}{Z}$ mhos

diagram	impedance Z	magnitude |Z|	phase angle ϕ	admittance Y
R	R	R	0	$\dfrac{1}{R}$
L	$j\omega L$	ωL	$+\dfrac{\pi}{2}$	$-j\dfrac{1}{\omega L}$
C	$-j\dfrac{1}{\omega C}$	$\dfrac{1}{\omega C}$	$-\dfrac{\pi}{2}$	$j\omega C$
L_1 M L_2	$j\omega(L_1 + L_2 \pm 2M)$	$\omega(L_1 + L_2 \pm 2M)$	$+\dfrac{\pi}{2}$	$-j\dfrac{1}{\omega(L_1 + L_2 \pm 2M)}$
C_1 C_2	$-j\dfrac{1}{\omega}\left(\dfrac{1}{C_1} + \dfrac{1}{C_2}\right)$	$\dfrac{1}{\omega}\left(\dfrac{1}{C_1} + \dfrac{1}{C_2}\right)$	$-\dfrac{\pi}{2}$	$j\omega\dfrac{C_1 C_2}{C_1 + C_2}$
R L	$R + j\omega L$	$[R^2 + \omega^2 L^2]^{\frac{1}{2}}$	$\tan^{-1}\dfrac{\omega L}{R}$	$\dfrac{R - j\omega L}{R^2 + \omega^2 L^2}$
R C	$R - j\dfrac{1}{\omega C}$	$\dfrac{1}{\omega C}[1 + \omega^2 C^2 R^2]^{\frac{1}{2}}$	$-\tan^{-1}\dfrac{1}{\omega CR}$	$\dfrac{R + j\dfrac{1}{\omega C}}{R^2 + \dfrac{1}{\omega^2 C^2}}$
L C	$j\left(\omega L - \dfrac{1}{\omega C}\right)$	$\left(\omega L - \dfrac{1}{\omega C}\right)$	$\dfrac{\pi}{2}$	$j\dfrac{\omega C}{1 - \omega^2 LC}$
R L C	$R + j\left(\omega L - \dfrac{1}{\omega C}\right)$	$\left[R^2 + \left(\omega L - \dfrac{1}{\omega C}\right)^2\right]^{\frac{1}{2}}$	$\tan^{-1}\dfrac{\left(\omega L - \dfrac{1}{\omega C}\right)}{R}$	$\dfrac{R - j\left(\omega L - \dfrac{1}{\omega C}\right)}{R^2 + \left(\omega L - \dfrac{1}{\omega C}\right)^2}$

Circuit				
R_1, R_2 (parallel)	$\dfrac{R_1 R_2}{R_1+R_2}$	$\dfrac{R_1 R_2}{R_1+R_2}$	0	$\left(\dfrac{1}{R_1}+\dfrac{1}{R_2}\right)$
L_1, M, L_2	$j\omega\left[\dfrac{L_1 L_2 - M^2}{L_1+L_2 \mp 2M}\right]$	$\omega\left[\dfrac{L_1 L_2 - M^2}{L_1+L_2 \mp 2M}\right]$	$+\dfrac{\pi}{2}$	$-j\dfrac{1}{\omega}\left[\dfrac{L_1+L_2 \mp 2M}{L_1 L_2 - M^2}\right]$
C_1, C_2	$-j\dfrac{1}{\omega(C_1+C_2)}$	$\dfrac{1}{\omega(C_1+C_2)}$	$-\dfrac{\pi}{2}$	$j\omega(C_1+C_2)$
R, L	$\omega L R\left[\dfrac{\omega L + jR}{R^2+\omega^2 L^2}\right]$	$\dfrac{\omega L R}{[R^2+\omega^2 L^2]^{\frac12}}$	$\tan^{-1}\dfrac{R}{\omega L}$	$\dfrac{1}{R}-j\dfrac{1}{\omega L}$
R, C	$\dfrac{R(1-j\omega CR)}{1+\omega^2 C^2 R^2}$	$\dfrac{R}{[1+\omega^2 C^2 R^2]^{\frac12}}$	$-\tan^{-1}\omega CR$	$\dfrac{1}{R}+j\omega C$
L, C	$j\dfrac{\omega L}{1-\omega^2 LC}$	$\dfrac{\omega L}{1-\omega^2 LC}$	$\pm\dfrac{\pi}{2}$	$j\left(\omega C - \dfrac{1}{\omega L}\right)$
R, L, C	$\dfrac{\dfrac{1}{R}-j\left(\omega C - \dfrac{1}{\omega L}\right)}{\left(\dfrac{1}{R}\right)^2 + \left(\omega C - \dfrac{1}{\omega L}\right)^2}$	$\dfrac{1}{\left[\left(\dfrac{1}{R}\right)^2 + \left(\omega C - \dfrac{1}{\omega L}\right)^2\right]^{\frac12}}$	$\tan^{-1}R\left(\dfrac{1}{\omega L}-\omega C\right)$	$\dfrac{1}{R}+j\left(\omega C - \dfrac{1}{\omega L}\right)$
R_1, L, R_3	$R_2\left[\dfrac{R_1(R_1+R_2)+\omega^2 L^2 R_2 + j\omega L R_2}{(R_1+R_2)^2 + \omega^2 L^2}\right]$	$R_2\left[\dfrac{R_1^2+\omega^2 L^2}{(R_1+R_2)^2 + \omega^2 L^2}\right]^{\frac12}$	$\tan^{-1}\dfrac{\omega L R_2}{R_1(R_1+R_2)+\omega^2 L^2}$	$\dfrac{R_1(R_1+R_2)+\omega^2 L^2 R_2 - j\omega L R_2}{R_2(R_1^2+\omega^2 L^2)}$

continued Impedance formulas

impedance $Z = R + jX$ ohms

magnitude $|Z| = [R^2 + X^2]^{\frac{1}{2}}$ ohms

phase angle $\phi = \tan^{-1} \dfrac{X}{R}$

admittance $Y = \dfrac{1}{Z}$ mhos

impedance Z	$\dfrac{R + j\omega[L(1 - \omega^2 LC) - CR^2]}{(1 - \omega^2 LC)^2 + \omega^2 C^2 R^2}$
magnitude $|Z|$	$\left[\dfrac{R^2 + \omega^2 L^2}{(1 - \omega^2 LC)^2 + \omega^2 C^2 R^2}\right]^{\frac{1}{2}}$
phase angle ϕ	$\tan^{-1} \dfrac{\omega[L(1 - \omega^2 LC) - CR^2]}{R}$
admittance Y	$\dfrac{R - j\omega[L(1 - \omega^2 LC) - CR^2]}{R^2 + \omega^2 L^2}$
impedance Z	$X_1 \dfrac{X_1 R_2 + j[R_2^2 + X_2(X_1 + X_2)]}{R_2^2 + (X_1 + X_2)^2}$
magnitude $|Z|$	$X_1 \left[\dfrac{R_2^2 + X_2^2}{R_2^2 + (X_1 + X_2)^2}\right]^{\frac{1}{2}}$
phase angle ϕ	$\tan^{-1} \dfrac{R_2^2 + X_2(X_1 + X_2)}{X_1 R_2}$
admittance Y	$\dfrac{R_2 X_1 - j(R_2^2 + X_2^2 + X_1 X_2)}{X_1(R_2^2 + X_2^2)}$

impedance Z	$$\frac{R_1(R_1+R_2)+\omega^2L^2R_2+\dfrac{R_1}{\omega^2C^2}+\left(\omega L-\dfrac{1}{\omega C}\right)^2}{(R_1+R_2)^2+\left(\omega L-\dfrac{1}{\omega C}\right)^2}+j\frac{\omega LR_2^2-\dfrac{R_1^2}{\omega C}-\dfrac{L}{C}\left(\omega L-\dfrac{1}{\omega C}\right)}{(R_1+R_2)^2+\left(\omega L-\dfrac{1}{\omega C}\right)^2}$$
magnitude |Z|	$$\left[\frac{(R_1^2+\omega^2L^2)\left(R_2^2+\dfrac{1}{\omega^2C^2}\right)}{(R_1+R_2)^2+\left(\omega L-\dfrac{1}{\omega C}\right)^2}\right]^{\frac{1}{2}}$$
phase angle φ	$$\tan^{-1}\left[\frac{\omega LR_2^2-\dfrac{R_1^2}{\omega C}-\dfrac{L}{C}\left(\omega L-\dfrac{1}{\omega C}\right)}{R_1R_2(R_1+R_2)+\omega^2L^2R_2+\dfrac{R_1}{\omega^2C^2}}\right]$$
admittance Y	$$\frac{R_1+\omega^2C^2R_1R_2(R_1+R_2)+\omega^4L^2C^2R_2}{(R_1^2+\omega^2L^2)(1+\omega^2C^2R_2^2)}+j\omega\frac{[CR_1^2-L+\omega^2LC(L-CR_2^2)]}{(R_1^2+\omega^2L^2)(1+\omega^2C^2R_2^2)}$$
impedance Z	$$\frac{(R_1R_2-X_1X_2)+j(R_1X_2+R_2X_1)}{(R_1+R_2)+j(X_1+X_2)}$$
magnitude |Z|	$$\left[\frac{(R_1^2+X_1^2)(R_2^2+X_2^2)}{(R_1+R_2)^2+(X_1+X_2)^2}\right]^{\frac{1}{2}}$$
phase angle φ	$$\tan^{-1}\frac{X_1}{R_1}+\tan^{-1}\frac{X_2}{R_2}-\tan^{-1}\frac{X_1+X_2}{R_1+R_2}$$
admittance Y	$$\frac{1}{R_1+jX_1}+\frac{1}{R_2+jX_2}$$

Note: When $R_1=R_2=\sqrt{L/C}$, then $Z=R_1=R_2$, a pure resistance at any frequency. Compare Case 3a, p. 106.

Skin effect

A = correction coefficient

D = diameter of conductor in inches

f = frequency in cycles/second

R_{ac} = resistance at frequency f

R_{dc} = direct-current resistance

T = thickness of tubular conductor in inches

T_1 = depth of penetration of current

μ = permeability of conductor material ($\mu = 1$ for copper and other nonmagnetic materials)

ρ = resistivity of conductor material at any temperature

ρ_c = resistivity of copper at 20 degrees centigrade
 = 1.724 microhm-centimeter

Fig. 5 shows the relationship of R_{ac}/R_{dc} versus $D\sqrt{f}$ for copper, or versus $D\sqrt{f} \sqrt{\mu\rho_c/\rho}$ for any conductor material, for an isolated straight solid conductor of circular cross section. Negligible error in the formulas for R_{ac} results when the conductor is spaced at least $10D$ from adjacent conductors. When the spacing between axes of parallel conductors carrying the same current is $4D$, the resistance R_{ac} is increased about 3 percent, when the depth of penetration is small. The formulas are accurate for concentric lines due to their circular symmetry.

For values of $D\sqrt{f} \sqrt{\mu\rho_c/\rho}$ greater than 40,

$$\frac{R_{ac}}{R_{dc}} = 0.0960 \, D\sqrt{f} \, \sqrt{\mu\rho_c/\rho} + 0.26 \qquad (1)$$

The high-frequency resistance of an isolated straight conductor: either solid; or tubular for $T < D/8$ or $T_1 < D/8$; is given in equation (2). If the current flow is along the inside surface of a tubular conductor, D is the inside diameter.

$$R_{ac} = A\frac{\sqrt{f}}{D} \sqrt{\mu\frac{\rho}{\rho_c}} \times 10^{-6} \text{ ohms/foot} \qquad (2)$$

The values of the correction coefficient A for solid conductors and for tubular conductors are shown in Fig. 6.

The value of $T\sqrt{f}\sqrt{\mu\rho_c/\rho}$ that just makes $A = 1$ indicates the penetration of

Skin effect *continued*

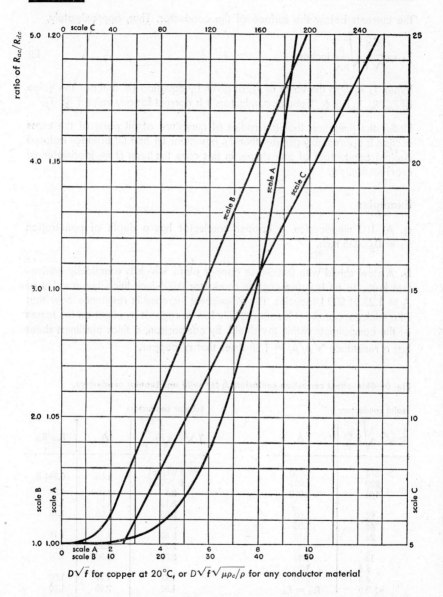

$D\sqrt{f}$ for copper at 20°C, or $D\sqrt{f}\sqrt{\mu\rho_c/\rho}$ for any conductor material

Fig. 5—Resistance ratio for isolated straight solid conductors of circular cross section.

Skin effect   *continued*

the currents below the surface of the conductor. Thus, approximately,

$$T_1 = \frac{3.5}{\sqrt{f}} \sqrt{\frac{\rho}{\mu \rho_c}} \text{ inches.} \tag{3}$$

When $T_1 < D/8$ the value of R_{ac} as given by equation (2) (but not the value of R_{ac}/R_{dc} in Fig. 6, "Tubular conductors") is correct for any value $T \geqslant T_1$.

Under the limitation that the radius of curvature of all parts of the cross section is appreciably greater than T_1, equations (2) and (3) hold for isolated straight conductors of any shape. In this case the term $D = $ (perimeter of cross section)$/\pi$.

Examples

a. At 100 megacycles, a copper conductor has a depth of penetration $T_1 = 0.00035$ inch.

b. A steel shield with 0.005-inch copper plate, which is practically equivalent in R_{ac} to an isolated copper conductor 0.005-inch thick, has a value of $A = 1.23$ at 200 kilocycles. This 23-percent increase in resistance over that of a thick copper sheet is satisfactorily low as regards its effect on the losses of the components within the shield. By comparison, a thick aluminum sheet has a resistance $\sqrt{\rho/\rho_c} = 1.28$ times that of copper.

Fig. 6—Skin-effect correction coefficient A for solid and tubular conductors.

solid conductors		tubular conductors		
$D \sqrt{f} \sqrt{\mu \dfrac{\rho_c}{\rho}}$	A	$T \sqrt{f} \sqrt{\mu \dfrac{\rho_c}{\rho}}$	A	R_{ac}/R_{dc}
> 370	1.000	$= B$ where$\Big\}$ $B > 3.5$	1.00	0.384 B
220	1.005		1.00	1.35
160	1.010	3.5	1.00	1.35
		3.15	1.01	1.23
98	1.02	2.85	1.05	1.15
48	1.05			
26	1.10	2.60	1.10	1.10
		2.29	1.20	1.06
13	1.20	2.08	1.30	1.04
9.6	1.30			
5.3	2.00	1.77	1.50	1.02
< 3.0	$R_{ac} \approx R_{dc}$	1.31	2.00	1.00
$R_{dc} = \dfrac{10.37}{D^2} \dfrac{\rho}{\rho_c} \times 10^{-6}$ ohms/foot		$= B$ where$\Big\}$ $B < 1.3$	$\dfrac{2.60}{B}$	1.00

Network theorems

Reciprocity theorem

If an emf of any character whatsoever located at one point in a linear network produces a current at any other point in the network, the same emf acting at the second point will produce the same current at the first point.

Corollary: If a given current flowing at one point of a linear network produces a certain open-circuit voltage at a second point of the network, the same current flowing at the second point will produce a like open-circuit voltage at the first point.

Thévenin's theorem

If an impedance Z is connected between two points of a linear network, the resulting steady-state current I through this impedance is the ratio of the potential difference V between the two points prior to the connection of Z, and the sum of the values of (1) the connected impedance Z, and (2) the impedance Z_1 of the network measured between the two points, when all generators in the network are replaced by their internal impedances:

$$I = \frac{V}{Z + Z_1}$$

Corollary: When the admittance of a linear network is Y_{12} measured between two points with all generators in the network replaced by their internal impedances, and the current which would flow between the points if they were short-circuited is I_{sc}, the voltage between the points is $V_{12} = I_{sc}/Y_{12}$.

Principle of superposition

The current that flows at any point in a network composed of constant resistances, inductances, and capacitances, or the potential difference which exists between any two points in such a network, due to the simultaneous action of a number of emf's distributed in any manner throughout the network, is the sum of the component currents at the first point, or the potential differences between the two points, that would be caused by the individual emf's acting alone. (Applicable to emf's of any character.)

In the application of this theorem, it is to be noted that for any impedance element Z through which flows a current I, there may be substituted a virtual source of voltage of value $-ZI$.

Formulas for simple R, L, and C networks*

1. Self-inductance of circular ring of round wire at radio frequencies, for nonmagnetic materials

$$L = \frac{a}{100} \left[7.353 \log_{10} \frac{16a}{d} - 6.386 \right] \text{ microhenries}$$

a = mean radius of ring in inches
d = diameter of wire in inches

$$\frac{a}{d} > 2.5$$

2. Capacitance of a parallel-plate capacitor

$$C = 0.0885 \, K \, \frac{(N-1) \, A}{t} \text{ micromicrofarads}$$

A = area of one side of one plate in square centimeters
N = number of plates
t = thickness of dielectric in centimeters
K = dielectric constant

This formula neglects "fringing" at the edges of the plates.

3. Reactance of an inductor

$X = 2\pi f L$ ohms

f = frequency in cycles per second
L = inductance in henries

or f in kilocycles and L in millihenries; or f in megacycles and L in microhenries.

4. Reactance of a capacitor

$$X = \frac{-1}{2\pi f C} \text{ ohms}$$

f = frequency in cycles/second
C = capacitance in farads

This may be written $\quad X = \frac{-159.2}{fC}$ ohms

f = frequency in kilocycles/second
C = capacitance in microfarads
or f in megacycles and C in millimicrofarads $(0.001 \mu f)$.

---

* Many formulas for computing capacitance, inductance, and mutual inductance will be found in Bureau of Standards Circular No. C74.

Formulas for simple R, L, and C networks   *continued*

5. Resonant frequency of a series-tuned circuit

$$f = \frac{1}{2\pi\sqrt{LC}} \text{ cycles/second}$$

L = inductance in henries
C = capacitance in farads

This may be written $LC = \dfrac{25{,}330}{f^2}$

f = frequency in kilocycles
L = inductance in millihenries
C = capacitance in millimicrofarads $(0.001\,\mu f)$
or f in megacycles, L in microhenries, and C in micromicrofarads.

6. Dynamic resistance of a parallel-tuned circuit at resonance

$$r = \frac{X^2}{R} = \frac{L}{CR} \text{ ohms}$$

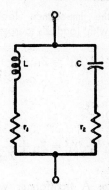

$X = \omega L = 1/\omega C$
$R = r_1 + r_2$
L = inductance in henries
C = capacitance in farads
R = resistance in ohms

The formula is accurate for engineering purposes provided $X/R > 10$.

7. Parallel impedances

If Z_1 and Z_2 are the two impedances that are connected in parallel, then the resultant impedance is

$$Z = \frac{Z_1 Z_2}{Z_1 + Z_2}$$

Refer also to page 85.

Given one impedance Z_1 and the desired resultant impedance Z, the other impedance is

$$Z_2 = \frac{Z Z_1}{Z_1 - Z}$$

Formulas for simple R, L, and C networks *continued*

8. Input impedance of a 4-terminal network*

$$Z_{11} = R_{11} + jX_{11}$$

is the impedance of the first circuit, measured at terminals $1 - 1$ with terminals $2 - 2$ open-circuited.

$$Z_{22} = R_{22} + jX_{22}$$

is the impedance of the second circuit, measured at terminals $2 - 2$ with load Z_2 removed and terminals $1 - 1$ open-circuited.

$$Z_{12} = R_{12} + jX_{12}$$

is the transfer impedance between the two pairs of terminals, i.e., the open-circuit voltage appearing at either pair when unit current flows at the other pair.

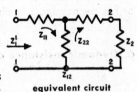

Then the impedance looking into terminals $1 - 1$ with load Z_2 across terminals $2 - 2$ is

equivalent circuit

$$Z_1' = R_1' + jX_1' = Z_{11} - \frac{Z^2_{12}}{Z_{22} + Z_2} = R_{11} + jX_{11} - \frac{R^2_{12} - X^2_{12} + 2jR_{12}X_{12}}{R_{22} + R_2 + j(X_{22} + X_2)}$$

When

$$R_{12} = 0$$

$$Z_1' = R_1' + jX_1' = Z_{11} + \frac{X^2_{12}}{Z_{22} + Z_2}$$

Example: A transformer with tuned secondary and negligible primary resistance.

$$Z_{11} = j\omega L_1$$

$$Z_{22} + Z_2 = R_2 \qquad \text{since } X_{22} + X_2 = 0$$

$$Z_{12} = j\omega M$$

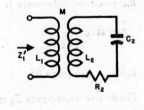

Then $Z_1' = j\omega L_1 + \dfrac{\omega^2 M^2}{R_2}$

---

* **Scope and limitations:** The formulas for 4-terminal networks, given in paragraphs 8 to 12 inclusive, are applicable to any such network composed of linear passive elements. The elements may be either lumped or distributed, or a combination of both kinds.

Formulas for simple R, L, and C networks *continued*

9. Input admittance of a 4-terminal network*

Y_{11} = admittance measured at terminals 1 — 1 with terminals 2 — 2 short-circuited.

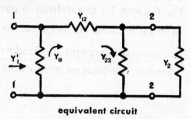

equivalent circuit

Y_{22} = admittance measured at terminals 2 — 2 with load Y_2 disconnected, and terminals 1 — 1 short-circuited.

Y_{12} = transfer admittance, i.e., the short-circuit current that would flow at one pair of terminals when unit voltage is impressed across the other pair.

Then the admittance looking into terminals 1 — 1 with load Y_2 connected across 2 — 2 is

$$Y_1' = G_1' + jB_1' = Y_{11} - \frac{Y^2_{12}}{Y_{22} + Y_2}$$

10. 4-terminal network with loads equal to image impedances*

When Z_1 and Z_2 are such that $Z' = Z_1$ and $Z'' = Z_2$ they are called the *image impedances*. Let the input impedance measured at terminals 1 — 1 with terminals 2 — 2 open-circuited be Z'_{oc} and with 2 — 2 short-circuited be Z'_{sc}. Similarly Z''_{oc} and Z''_{sc} measured at terminals 2 — 2. Then

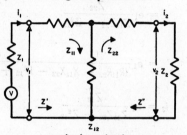

equivalent circuit

$$Z' = [Z'_{oc}Z'_{sc}]^{\frac{1}{2}} = \left[Z_{11}\left(Z_{11} - \frac{Z^2_{12}}{Z_{22}}\right)\right]^{\frac{1}{2}} = \left[Y_{11}\left(Y_{11} - \frac{Y^2_{12}}{Y_{22}}\right)\right]^{-\frac{1}{2}}$$

$$Z'' = [Z''_{oc}Z''_{sc}]^{\frac{1}{2}} = \left[Z_{22}\left(Z_{22} - \frac{Z^2_{12}}{Z_{11}}\right)\right]^{\frac{1}{2}} = \left[Y_{22}\left(Y_{22} - \frac{Y^2_{12}}{Y_{11}}\right)\right]^{-\frac{1}{2}}$$

$$\tanh(\alpha + j\beta) = \pm\left[\frac{Z'_{sc}}{Z'_{oc}}\right]^{\frac{1}{2}} = \pm\left[\frac{Z''_{sc}}{Z''_{oc}}\right]^{\frac{1}{2}} = \pm\left[1 - \frac{Z^2_{12}}{Z_{11}Z_{22}}\right]^{\frac{1}{2}}$$

$$= \pm\left[1 - \frac{Y^2_{12}}{Y_{11}Y_{22}}\right]^{\frac{1}{2}}$$

* See footnote on p. 92.

Formulas for simple R, L, and C networks   *continued*

The quantities Z_{11}, Z_{22}, and Z_{12} are defined in paragraph 8, above, while Y_{11}, Y_{22}, and Y_{12} are defined in paragraph 9.

$(\alpha + j\beta)$ is called the *image transfer constant*, defined by

$$\left(\frac{\text{complex volt-amperes into load from 2-2}}{\text{complex volt-amperes into network at 1-1}}\right) = \frac{v_2 i_2}{v_1 i_1} = \frac{v_2^2 Z_1}{v_1^2 Z_2} = \frac{i_2^2 Z_2}{i_1^2 Z_1}$$

$$= \epsilon^{-2(\alpha + j\beta)} = \epsilon^{-2\alpha} \underline{/-2\beta}$$

when the load is equal to the image impedance. The quantities α and β are the same irrespective of the direction in which the network is working.

When Z_1 and Z_2 have the same phase angle, α is the attenuation in nepers and β is the angle of lag of i_2 behind i_1.

11. Currents in a 4-terminal network*

$$i_1 = \frac{e_1}{Z_1'}$$

$$= e_1 \frac{Z_{22}}{Z_{11}Z_{22} - Z_{12}^2}$$

$$= e_1 \frac{R_{22} + jX_{22}}{(R_{11}R_{22} - X_{11}X_{22} - R_{12}^2 + X_{12}^2) + j(R_{11}X_{22} + R_{22}X_{11} - 2R_{12}X_{12})}$$

$$i_2 = e_1 \frac{Z_{12}}{Z_{11}Z_{22} - Z_{12}^2}$$

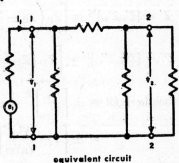

equivalent circuit

12. Voltages in a 4-terminal network*

Let

i_{1sc} = current that would flow between terminals 1–1 when they are short-circuited.

Y_{11} = admittance measured across terminals 1 – 1 with generator replaced by its internal impedance, and with terminals 2 – 2 short-circuited.

equivalent circuit

* See footnote on p. 92.

Formulas for simple R, L, and C networks *continued*

Y_{22} = admittance measured across terminals 2 — 2 with load connected and terminals 1 — 1 short-circuited.

Y_{12} = transfer admittance between terminals 1 — 1 and 2 — 2 (defined in paragraph 9 above).

Then the voltage across terminals 1 — 1, which are on the end of the network nearest the generator, is

$$v_1 = \frac{i_{1sc}Y_{22}}{Y_{11}Y_{22} - Y^2_{12}}$$

The voltage across terminals 2 — 2, which are on the load end of the network is

$$v_2 = \frac{i_{1sc}Y_{12}}{Y_{11}Y_{22} - Y^2_{12}}$$

13. Power transfer between two impedances connected directly

Let $Z_1 = R_1 + jX_1$ be the impedance of the source, and $Z_2 = R_2 + jX_2$ be the impedance of the load.

The maximum power transfer occurs when

$R_2 = R_1$ and $X_2 = -X_1$

$$\frac{P}{P_m} = \frac{4R_1R_2}{(R_1 + R_2)^2 + (X_1 + X_2)^2}$$

P = power delivered to the load when the impedances are connected directly.

P_m = power that would be delivered to the load were the two impedances connected through a perfect impedance-matching network.

14. Power transfer between two meshes coupled reactively

In the general case, X_{11} and X_{22} are not equal to zero and X_{12} may be any reactive coupling. When only one of the quantities X_{11}, X_{22}, and X_{12} can be varied, the best power transfer under the circumstances is given by:

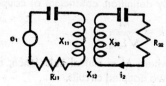

Formulas for simple R, L, and C networks   *continued*

For X_{22} variable

$$X_{22} = \frac{X^2{}_{12}X_{11}}{R^2{}_{11} + X^2{}_{11}} \text{ (zero reactance looking into load circuit)}$$

For X_{11} variable

$$X_{11} = \frac{X^2{}_{12}X_{22}}{R^2{}_{22} + X^2{}_{22}} \text{ (zero reactance looking into source circuit)}$$

For X_{12} variable

$$X^2{}_{12} = \sqrt{(R^2{}_{11} + X^2{}_{11})\ (R^2{}_{22} + X^2{}_{22})}$$

When two of the three quantities can be varied, a perfect impedance match is attained and maximum power is transferred when

$$X^2{}_{12} = \sqrt{(R^2{}_{11} + X^2{}_{11})\ (R^2{}_{22} + X^2{}_{22})}$$

and

$$\frac{X_{11}}{R_{11}} = \frac{X_{22}}{R_{22}} \text{ (both circuits of same Q or phase angle)}$$

For perfect impedance match the current is

$$i_2 = \frac{e_1}{2\sqrt{R_{11}R_{22}}} \angle \tan^{-1} \frac{R_{11}}{X_{11}}$$

In the most common case, the circuits are tuned to resonance $X_{11} = 0$ and $X_{22} = 0$. Then $X^2{}_{12} = R_{11}R_{22}$ for perfect impedance match.

15. Optimum coupling between two circuits tuned to the same frequency

From the last result in paragraph 14, maximum power transfer (or an impedance match) is obtained for $\omega^2 M^2 = R_1 R_2$ where M is the mutual inductance between the circuits, and R_1 and R_2 are the resistances of the two circuits.

16. Coefficient of coupling—geometrical consideration

By definition, coefficient of coupling k is

$$k = \frac{M}{\sqrt{L_1 L_2}}$$

where M = mutual inductance, and L_1 and L_2 are the inductances of the two coupled circuits.

Formulas for simple R, L, and C networks   *continued*

Coefficient of coupling of two coils is a geometrical property, being a function of the proportions of the configuration of coils, including their relationship to any nearby objects that affect the field of the system. As long as these proportions remain unchanged, the coefficient of coupling is independent of the physical size of the system, and of the number of turns of either coil.

17. T—π or Y—Δ transformation

The two networks are equivalent, as far as conditions at the terminals are concerned, provided the following equations are satisfied. Either the impedance equations or the admittance equations may be used:

$$Y_1 = 1/Z_1, \ Y_{12} = 1/Z_{12}, \text{ etc.}$$

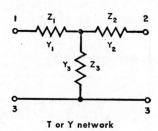

T or Y network

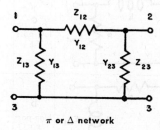

π or Δ network

Impedance equations

$$Z_{12} = \frac{Z_1 Z_2 + Z_1 Z_3 + Z_2 Z_3}{Z_3}$$

$$Z_{13} = \frac{Z_1 Z_2 + Z_1 Z_3 + Z_2 Z_3}{Z_2}$$

$$Z_{23} = \frac{Z_1 Z_2 + Z_1 Z_3 + Z_2 Z_3}{Z_1}$$

$$Z_1 = \frac{Z_{12} Z_{13}}{Z_{12} + Z_{13} + Z_{23}}$$

$$Z_2 = \frac{Z_{12} Z_{23}}{Z_{12} + Z_{13} + Z_{23}}$$

$$Z_3 = \frac{Z_{13} Z_{23}}{Z_{12} + Z_{13} + Z_{23}}$$

Admittance equations

$$Y_{12} = \frac{Y_1 Y_2}{Y_1 + Y_2 + Y_3}$$

$$Y_{13} = \frac{Y_1 Y_3}{Y_1 + Y_2 + Y_3}$$

$$Y_{23} = \frac{Y_2 Y_3}{Y_1 + Y_2 + Y_3}$$

$$Y_1 = \frac{Y_{12} Y_{13} + Y_{12} Y_{23} + Y_{13} Y_{23}}{Y_{23}}$$

$$Y_2 = \frac{Y_{12} Y_{13} + Y_{12} Y_{23} + Y_{13} Y_{23}}{Y_{13}}$$

$$Y_3 = \frac{Y_{12} Y_{13} + Y_{12} Y_{23} + Y_{13} Y_{23}}{Y_{12}}$$

Formulas for simple R, L, and C networks *continued*

Fig. 7—Simple filter sections containing R, L, and C. See also Fig. 8.

diagram	type	time constant or resonant freq	formula and approximation
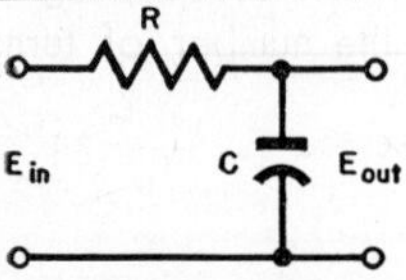 R, E_{in}, C, E_{out}	**A** low-pass R-C	$T = RC$	$\dfrac{E_{out}}{E_{in}} = \dfrac{1}{\sqrt{1 + \omega^2 T^2}} \approx \dfrac{1}{\omega T}$ $\phi_A = -\tan^{-1}(R\omega C)$
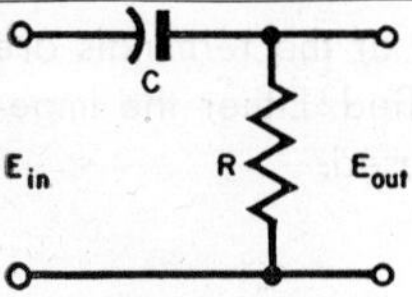 C, E_{in}, R, E_{out}	**B** high-pass R-C	$T = RC$	$\dfrac{E_{out}}{E_{in}} = \dfrac{1}{\sqrt{1 + \dfrac{1}{\omega^2 T^2}}} \approx \omega T$ $\phi_B = \tan^{-1}(1/R\omega C)$
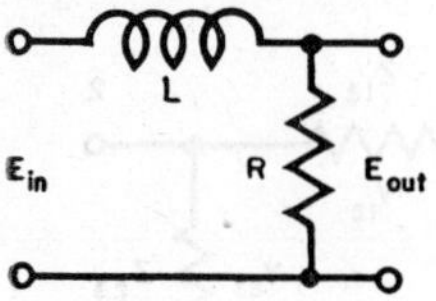 L, E_{in}, R, E_{out}	**C** low-pass R-L	$T = \dfrac{L}{R}$	$\dfrac{E_{out}}{E_{in}} = \dfrac{1}{\sqrt{1 + \omega^2 T^2}} \approx \dfrac{1}{\omega T}$ $\phi_C = -\tan^{-1}(\omega L/R)$
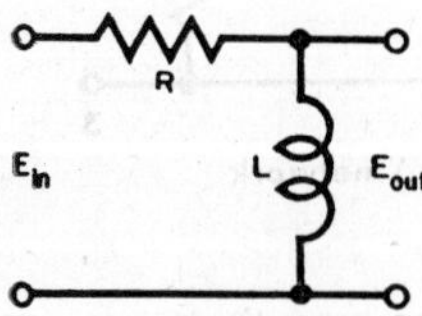 R, E_{in}, L, E_{out}	**D** high-pass R-L	$T = \dfrac{L}{R}$	$\dfrac{E_{out}}{E_{in}} = \dfrac{1}{\sqrt{1 + \dfrac{1}{\omega^2 T^2}}} \approx \omega T$ $\phi_D = \tan^{-1}(R/\omega L)$
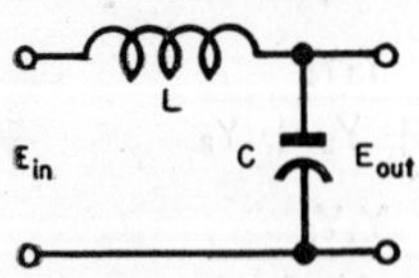 L, E_{in}, C, E_{out}	**E** low-pass L-C	$f_0 = \dfrac{0.1592}{\sqrt{LC}}$	$\dfrac{E_{out}}{E_{in}} = \dfrac{1}{1 - \omega^2 LC} = \dfrac{1}{1 - f^2/f_0^2}$ $\approx -\dfrac{1}{\omega^2 LC} = -\dfrac{f_0^2}{f^2}$ $\phi = 0$ for $f < f_0$; $\phi = \pi$ for $f > f_0$
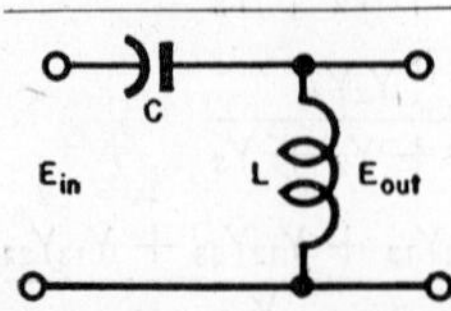 C, E_{in}, L, E_{out}	**F** high-pass L-C	$f_0 = \dfrac{0.1592}{\sqrt{LC}}$	$\dfrac{E_{out}}{E_{in}} = \dfrac{1}{1 - 1/\omega^2 LC} = \dfrac{1}{1 - f_0^2/f^2}$ $\approx -\omega^2 LC = -\dfrac{f^2}{f_0^2}$ $\phi = 0$ for $f > f_0$; $\phi = \pi$ for $f < f_0$

R in ohms; L in henries; C in farads ($1\mu f = 10^{-6}$ farad).

T = time constant (seconds), f_0 = resonant frequency (cps), $\omega = 2\pi f$,

$2\pi = 6.28$, $1/2\pi = 0.1592$, $4\pi^2 = 39.5$, $1/4\pi^2 = 0.0253$.

The relationships for low-pass filters are plotted in Figs. 9 and 10.

Formulas for simple R, L, and C networks   *continued*

18. Elementary R-C, R-L, and L-C filters and equalizers

Simple attenuating sections of broad frequency discriminating characteristics, as used in power supplies, grid-bias feed, etc. are shown in Figs. 7 and 8. The output load impedance is assumed to be high compared to the impedance of the shunt element of the filter. The phase angle ϕ is that of E_{out} with respect to E_{in}.

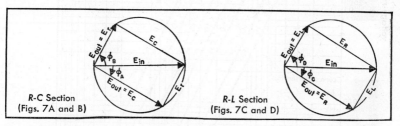

R-C Section
(Figs. 7A and B)

R-L Section
(Figs. 7C and D)

Fig. 8—Circle diagrams for R-L and R-C filter sections.

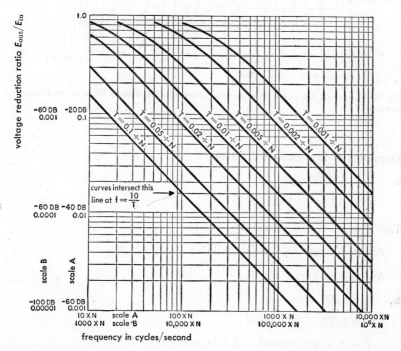

voltage reduction ratio E_{out}/E_{in}

curves intersect this line at $f = \dfrac{10}{T}$

frequency in cycles/second

Fig. 9—Low-pass R-C and R-L filters. N is any convenient factor, usually taken as an integral power of 10.

100

Formulas for simple R, L, and C networks   *continued*

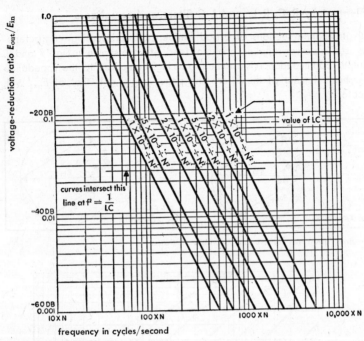

Fig. 10—Low-pass *L-C* filters. *N* is any convenient factor, usually taken as an integral power of 10.

Examples of low-pass R-C filters

a. $R = 100,000$ ohms

$C = 0.1 \times 10^{-6}$ (0.1 μf)

Then $T = RC = 0.01$ second

At $f = 100$ cps: $E_{out}/E_{in} = 0.16-$

At $f = 30,000$ cps: $E_{out}/E_{in} = 0.00053$

b. $R = 1,000$ ohms

$C = 0.001 \times 10^{-6}$ farad

$T = 1 \times 10^{-6}$ second $= 0.1/N$, where $N = 10^5$

At $f = 10$ megacycles $= 100 \times N$: $E_{out}/E_{in} = 0.016-$

Formulas for simple R, L, and C networks   *continued*

Example of low-pass L-C filter

At $f = 120$ cps, required $E_{out}/E_{in} = 0.03$

Then from curves: $LC = 6 \times 10^{-5}$ approximately.

Whence, for $C = 4$ μf, we require $L = 15$ henries.

Effective and average values of alternating current

(Similar equations apply to a-c voltages)

$i = I \sin \omega t$

Average value $I_{av} = \dfrac{2}{\pi} I$

which is the direct current that would be obtained were the original current fully rectified, or approximately proportional to the reading of a rectifier-type meter.

Effective or root-mean-square (rms) value $I_{eff} = \dfrac{I}{\sqrt{2}}$

which represents the heating or power effectiveness of the current, and is proportional to the reading of a dynamometer or thermal-type meter.

When

$$i = I_0 + I_1 \sin \omega_1 t + I_2 \sin \omega_2 t + \ldots$$

$$I_{eff} = \sqrt{I_0{}^2 + \tfrac{1}{2}(I_1{}^2 + I_2{}^2 + \ldots)}$$

Note: The *average* value of a complex current is *not* equal to the sum of the average values of the components.

Transients—elementary cases

The complete transient in a linear network is, by the principle of superposition, the sum of the individual transients due to the store of energy in each inductor and capacitor and to each external source of energy connected to the network. To this is added the steady-state condition due to each external source of energy. The transient may be computed as starting from any arbitrary time $t = 0$ when the initial conditions of the energy of the network are known.

Transients—elementary cases   *continued*

Time constant (designated T): Of the discharge of a capacitor through a resistor is the time $t_2 - t_1$ required for the voltage or current to decay to $1/\epsilon$ of its value at time t_1. For the charge of a capacitor the same definition applies, the voltage "decaying" toward its steady-state value. The time constant of discharge or charge of the current in an inductor through a resistor follows an analogous definition.

Energy stored in a capacitor $= \frac{1}{2} CE^2$ joules (watt-seconds)
Energy stored in an inductor $= \frac{1}{2} LI^2$ joules (watt-seconds)
$\epsilon = 2.718$ $1/\epsilon = 0.3679$ $\log_{10}\epsilon = 0.4343$ T and t in seconds
R in ohms L in henries C in farads E in volts I in amperes

Capacitor charge and discharge

Closing of switch occurs at time $t = 0$
Initial conditions (at $t = 0$): Battery $= E_b$; $e_c = E_o$.
Steady state (at $t = \infty$): $i = 0$; $e_c = E_b$.

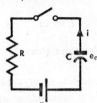

Transient:

$$i = \frac{E_b - E_0}{R} \epsilon^{-t/RC} = I_0\, \epsilon^{-t/RC} \qquad \log_{10}\left(\frac{i}{I_0}\right) = -\frac{0.4343}{RC}\, t$$

$$e_c = E_0 + \frac{1}{C} \int_0^t i\,dt = E_0\, \epsilon^{-t/RC} + E_b\,(1 - \epsilon^{-t/RC})$$

Time constant: $T = RC$

Fig. 11 shows current: $i/I_0 = \epsilon^{-t/T}$

Fig. 11 shows discharge (for $E_b = 0$): $e_c/E_0 = \epsilon^{-t/T}$

Fig. 12 shows charge (for $E_0 = 0$): $e_c/E_b = 1 - \epsilon^{-t/T}$

These curves are plotted on a larger scale in Fig. 13.

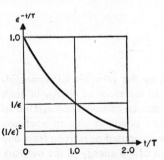

Fig. 11—Capacitor discharge.

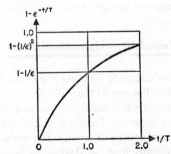

Fig. 12—Capacitor charge.

Transients—elementary cases *continued*

Two capacitors

Closing of switch occurs at time $t = 0$
Initial conditions (at $t = 0$):
$e_1 = E_1$; $e_2 = E_2$.
Steady state (at $t = \infty$):
$e_1 = E_f$; $e_2 = -E_f$; $i = 0$.

$$E_f = \frac{E_1 C_1 - E_2 C_2}{C_1 + C_2} \qquad C' = \frac{C_1 C_2}{C_1 + C_2}$$

Transient:

$$i = \frac{E_1 + E_2}{R} \epsilon^{-t/RC'}$$

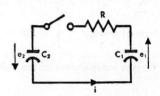

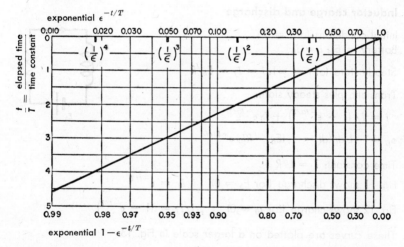

exponential $\epsilon^{-t/T}$

exponential $1 - \epsilon^{-t/T}$

Use exponential $\epsilon^{-t/T}$ for charge or discharge of capacitor or discharge of inductor:	Use exponential $1 - \epsilon^{-t/T}$ for charge of capacitor:
$$\frac{\text{(current at time } t)}{\text{(initial current)}}$$	$$\frac{\text{(voltage at time } t)}{\text{(battery or final voltage)}}$$
Discharge of capacitor:	Charge of inductor:
$$\frac{\text{(voltage at time } t)}{\text{(initial voltage)}}$$	$$\frac{\text{(current at time } t)}{\text{(final current)}}$$

Fig. 13—Exponential functions $\epsilon^{-t/T}$ **and** $1 - \epsilon^{-t/T}$ **applied to transients in R-C and L-R circuits.**

104

Transients—elementary cases   *continued*

$$e_1 = E_f + (E_1 - E_f)\, \epsilon^{-t/RC'} = E_1 - (E_1 + E_2)\, \frac{C'}{C_1}\, (1 - \epsilon^{-t/RC'})$$

$$e_2 = -E_f + (E_2 + E_f)\, \epsilon^{-t/RC'} = E_2 - (E_1 + E_2)\, \frac{C'}{C_2}\, (1 - \epsilon^{-t/RC'})$$

Original energy $= \frac{1}{2}\, (C_1 E_1{}^2 + C_2 E_2{}^2)$ joules

Final energy $= \frac{1}{2}\, (C_1 + C_2)\, E_f{}^2$ joules

Loss of energy $= \displaystyle\int_0^\infty i^2\, R dt = \frac{1}{2}\, C'\, (E_1 + E_2)^2$ joules

(Loss is independent of the value of R.)

Inductor charge and discharge

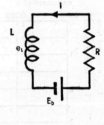

Initial conditions (at $t = 0$):
Battery $= E_b$; $i = I_0$

Steady state (at $t = \infty$): $i = I_f = E_b/R$

Transient, plus steady state:

$$i = I_f\, (1 - \epsilon^{-Rt/L}) + I_0\, \epsilon^{-Rt/L}$$
$$e_L = -L\, di/dt = -(E_b - RI_0)\, \epsilon^{-Rt/L}$$

Time constant: $T = L/R$

Fig. 11 shows discharge (for $E_b = 0$) $i/I_0 = \epsilon^{-t/T}$

Fig. 12 shows charge (for $I_0 = 0$) $i/I_f = (1 - \epsilon^{-t/T})$

These curves are plotted on a larger scale in Fig. 13.

Series R-L-C circuit charge and discharge

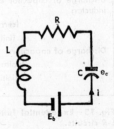

Initial conditions (at $t = 0$):
Battery $= E_b$; $e_c = E_0$; $i = I_0$
Steady state (at $t = \infty$): $i = 0$; $e_c = E_b$

Differential equation:

$$E_b - E_0 - \frac{1}{C}\int_0^t i dt - Ri - L\frac{di}{dt} = 0$$

Transients—elementary cases   *continued*

when $L \dfrac{d^2 i}{dt^2} + R \dfrac{di}{dt} + \dfrac{i}{C} = 0$

Solution of equation:

$$i = \epsilon^{-Rt/2L} \left[\frac{2(E_b - E_0) - RI_0}{R\sqrt{D}} \sinh \frac{Rt}{2L}\sqrt{D} + I_0 \cosh \frac{Rt}{2L}\sqrt{D} \right]$$

where $D = 1 - \dfrac{4L}{R^2 C}$

Case 1: When $\dfrac{L}{R^2 C}$ is small

$$i = \frac{1}{(1 - 2A - 2A^2)} \left\{ \left[\frac{E_b - E_0}{R} - I_0\,(A + A^2) \right] \epsilon^{-\frac{t}{RC}(1 + A + 2A^2)} \right.$$
$$\left. + \left[I_0(1 - A - A^2) - \frac{E_b - E_0}{R} \right] \epsilon^{-\frac{Rt}{L}(1 - A - A^2)} \right\}$$

where $A = \dfrac{L}{R^2 C}$

For practical purposes, the terms A^2 can be neglected when $A < 0.1$. The terms A may be neglected when $A < 0.01$.

Case 2: When $\dfrac{4L}{R^2 C} < 1$ for which $\sqrt{D}$ is real

$$i = \frac{\epsilon^{-Rt/2L}}{\sqrt{D}} \left\{ \left[\frac{E_b - E_0}{R} - \frac{I_0}{2}\left(1 - \sqrt{D}\right) \right] \epsilon^{\frac{Rt}{2L}\sqrt{D}} \right.$$
$$\left. + \left[\frac{I_0}{2}\left(1 + \sqrt{D}\right) - \frac{E_b - E_0}{R} \right] \epsilon^{-\frac{Rt}{2L}\sqrt{D}} \right\}$$

Case 3: When D is a small positive or negative quantity

$$i = \epsilon^{-Rt/2L} \left\{ \frac{2(E_b - E_0)}{R} \left[\frac{Rt}{2L} + \frac{1}{6}\left(\frac{Rt}{2L}\right)^3 D \right] \right.$$
$$\left. + I_0 \left[1 - \frac{Rt}{2L} + \frac{1}{2}\left(\frac{Rt}{2L}\right)^2 D - \frac{1}{6}\left(\frac{Rt}{2L}\right)^3 D \right] \right\}$$

This formula may be used for values of D up to ± 0.25, at which values the error in the computed current i is approximately 1 percent of I_0 or of

$\dfrac{E_b - E_0}{R}$

Transients—elementary cases *continued*

Case 3a: When $4L/R^2C = 1$ for which $D = 0$, the formula reduces to

$$i = \epsilon^{-Rt/2L}\left[\frac{E_b - E_0}{R}\frac{Rt}{L} + I_0\left(1 - \frac{Rt}{2L}\right)\right]$$

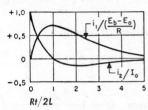

or $i = i_1 + i_2$, plotted in Fig. 14. For practical purposes, this formula may be used when $4L/R^2C = 1 \pm 0.05$ with errors of 1 percent or less.

Fig. 14—Transients for $4L/R^2C = 1$.

Case 4: When $\dfrac{4L}{R^2C} > 1$ for which $\sqrt{D}$ is imaginary

$$i = \epsilon^{-Rt/L2}\left\{\left[\frac{E_b - E_0}{\omega_0 L} - \frac{RI_0}{2\omega_0 L}\right]\sin \omega_0 t + I_0 \cos \omega_0 t\right\}$$

$$= I_m \epsilon^{-Rt/2L}\sin(\omega_0 t + \psi)$$

where $\omega_0 = \sqrt{\dfrac{1}{LC} - \dfrac{R^2}{4L^2}}$

$$I_m = \frac{1}{\omega_0 L}\sqrt{\left(E_b - E_0 - \frac{RI_0}{2}\right)^2 + \omega_0^2 L^2 I_0^2} \qquad \psi = \tan^{-1}\frac{\omega_0 L\, I_0}{E_b - E_0 - \dfrac{RI_0}{2}}$$

The envelope of the voltage wave across the inductor is:

$$\pm\,\epsilon^{-Rt/2L}\frac{1}{\omega_0\sqrt{LC}}\sqrt{\left(E_b - E_0 - \frac{RI_0}{2}\right)^2 + \omega_0^2 L^2 I_0^2}$$

Example: Relay with transient-suppressing capacitor.

Switch closed till time $t = 0$, then opened.

Let $L = 0.10$ henries, $R_1 = 100$ ohms,

$\quad E = 10$ volts

Suppose we choose

$C = 10^{-6}$ farads

$R_2 = 100$ ohms

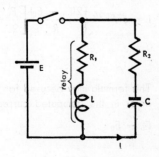

Transients—elementary cases   *continued*

Then

$R = 200$ ohms
$I_0 = 0.10$ amperes
$E_0 = 10$ volts
$\omega_0 = 3 \times 10^3$
$f_0 = 480$ cps

Maximum peak voltage across L (envelope at $t = 0$) is approximately 30 volts. Time constant of decay of envelope is 0.001 second.

It is preferable that the circuit be just nonoscillating (Case 3a) and that it present a pure resistance at the switch terminals for any frequency (see note on p. 85).

$R_2 = R_1 = R/2 = 100$ ohms

$4L/R^2C = 1$

$C = 10^{-5}$ farad $= 10$ microfarads

At the instant of opening the switch, the voltage across the parallel circuit is $E_0 - R_2I_0 = 0$.

Series R-L-C circuit with sinusoidal applied voltage

By the principle of superposition, the transient and steady-state conditions are the same for the actual circuit and the equivalent circuit shown in the accompanying illustrations, the closing of the switch occurring at time $t = 0$. In the equivalent circuit, the steady state is due to the source e acting continuously from time $t = -\infty$, while the transient is due to short-circuiting the source $-e$ at time $t = 0$.

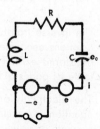

actual circuit

equivalent circuit

Source: $e = E \sin (\omega t + \alpha)$

Steady state: $i = \dfrac{e}{Z} \angle -\phi = \dfrac{E}{Z} \sin (\omega t + \alpha - \phi)$

where

$$Z = \sqrt{R^2 + \left(\omega L - \frac{1}{\omega C} \right)^2}$$

$$\tan \phi = \frac{\omega^2 LC - 1}{\omega CR}$$

The transient is found by determining current $i = I_0$

and capacitor voltage $e_c = E_0$ at time $t = 0$, due to the source $-e$. These values of I_0 and E_0 are then substituted in the equations of Case 1, 2, 3, or 4, above, according to the values of R, L, and C.

At time $t = 0$, *due to the source* $-e$:

$$i = I_0 = -\frac{E}{Z} \sin (\alpha - \phi)$$

$$e_c = E_0 = \frac{E}{\omega C Z} \cos (\alpha - \phi)$$

This form of analysis may be used for any periodic applied voltage e. The steady-state current and the capacitor voltage for an applied voltage $-e$ are determined, the periodic voltage being resolved into its harmonic components for this purpose, if necessary. Then the instantaneous values $i = I_0$ and $e_c = E_0$ at the time of closing the switch are easily found, from which the transient is determined. It is evident, from this method of analysis, that the waveform of the transient need bear no relationship to that of the applied voltage, depending only on the constants of the circuit and the hypothetical initial conditions I_0 and E_0.

Transients—operational calculus and Laplace transforms

Among the various methods of operational calculus used to solve transient problems, one of the most efficient makes use of the Laplace transform.

If we have a function $v = f(t)$, then by *definition* the Laplace transform is $T(v) = F(p)$, where

$$F(p) = \int_0^\infty \epsilon^{-pt} f(t) \, dt \qquad (4)$$

The inverse transform of $F(p)$ or $T(v)$ is $v = f(t)$. Most of the mathematical functions encountered in practical work fall in the class for which Laplace transforms exist. The transforms of a number of functions are given in the table of pages 611 to 613.

The electrical (or other) system for which a solution of the differential equation is required, is considered only in the time domain $t \geqslant 0$. Any currents or voltages existing at $t = 0$, before the driving force is applied, constitute the initial conditions. The driving force is assumed to be zero when $t < 0$.

Transients—operational calculus and Laplace transforms *continued*

Example

Take the circuit of Fig. 15, in which the switch is closed at time $t = 0$. Prior to the closing of the switch, suppose the capacitor is charged; then at $t = 0$, we have $v = V_0$. It is required to find the voltage v across capacitor C as a function of time.

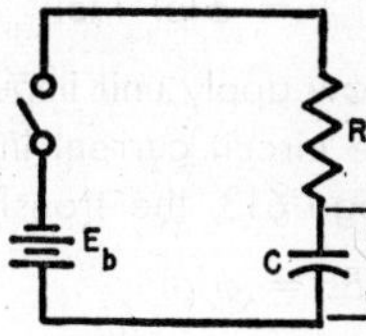

Writing the differential equation of the circuit in terms of voltage, and since $i = dq/dt = C(dv/dt)$, the equation is

$$e(t) = v + Ri = v + RC(dv/dt) \qquad (5)$$

where $e(t) = E_b$

Fig. 15.

Referring to the table of transforms, the applied voltage is E_b multiplied by unit step, or $E_b S_{-1}(t)$; the transform for this is E_b/p. The transform of v is $T(v)$. That of $RC(dv/dt)$ is $RC[pT(v) - v(0)]$, where $v(0) = V_0 =$ value of v at $t = 0$. Then the transform of (5) is

$$\frac{E_b}{p} = T(v) + RC[pT(v) - V_0]$$

Rearranging, and resolving into partial fractions,

$$T(v) = \frac{E_b}{p(1 + RCp)} + \frac{RCV_0}{1 + RCp} = E_b\left(\frac{1}{p} - \frac{1}{p + 1/RC}\right) + \frac{V_0}{p + 1/RC} \qquad (6)$$

Now we must determine the equation that would transform into (6). The inverse transform of $T(v)$ is v, and those of the terms on the right-hand side are found in the table of transforms. Then, in the time domain $t \geqslant 0$,

$$v = E_b(1 - \epsilon^{-t/RC}) + V_0\,\epsilon^{-t/RC} \qquad (7)$$

This solution is also well known by classical methods. However, the advantages of the Laplace-transform method become more and more apparent in reducing the labor of solution as the equations become more involved.

Circuit response related to unit impulse

Unit impulse is defined on page 611. It has the dimensions of time^{-1}. For example, suppose a capacitor of one microfarad is suddenly connected to a battery of 100 volts, with the circuit inductance and resistance negligibly small. Then the current flow is 10^{-4} coulombs multiplied by unit impulse.

The general transformed equation of a circuit or system may be written

$$T(i) = \phi(p)\,T(e) + \psi(p) \qquad (8)$$

Here $T(i)$ is the transform of the required current (or other quantity), $T(e)$ is

Transients—operational calculus and Laplace transforms   *continued*

the transform of the applied voltage or driving force $e(t)$. The transform of the initial conditions, at $t = 0$, is included in $\psi(p)$.

First considering the case when the system is initially at rest, $\psi(p) = 0$. Writing i_a for the current in this case,

$$T(i_a) = \phi(p)\, T(e) \tag{9}$$

Now apply unit impulse $S_0(t)$ (multiplied by one volt-second), and designate the circuit current in this case by $B(t)$ and its transform by $T(B)$. By pair 13, page 613, the transform of $S_0(t)$ is 1, so

$$T(B) = \phi(p) \tag{10}$$

Equation (9) becomes, for any driving force

$$T(i_a) = T(B)\, T(e) \tag{11}$$

Applying pair 4, page 612,

$$i_a = \int_0^t B(t - \lambda)\, e(\lambda)\, d\lambda = \int_0^t B(\lambda)\, e(t - \lambda)\, d\lambda \tag{12}$$

To this there must be added the current i_0 due to any initial conditions that exist. From (8),

$$T(i_0) = \psi(p) \tag{13}$$

Then i_0 is the inverse transform of $\psi(p)$.

Circuit response related to unit step

Unit step is defined and designated $S_{-1}(t) = 0$ for $t < 0$ and equals unity for $t > 0$. It has no dimensions. Its transform is $1/p$ as given in pair 12, page 613. Let the circuit current be designated $A(t)$ when the applied voltage is $e = S_{-1}(t) \times (1\text{ volt})$. Then, the current i_a for the case when the system is initially at rest, and for any applied voltage $e(t)$, is given by any of the following formulas:

$$
\left.
\begin{aligned}
i_a &= A(t)\, e(0) + \int_0^t A(t - \lambda)\, e'(\lambda)\, d\lambda \\[4pt]
&= A(t)\, e(0) + \int_0^t A(\lambda)\, e'(t - \lambda)\, d\lambda \\[4pt]
&= A(0)\, e(t) + \int_0^t A'(t - \lambda)\, e(\lambda)\, d\lambda \\[4pt]
&= A(0)\, e(t) + \int_0^t A'(\lambda)\, e(t - \lambda)\, d\lambda
\end{aligned}
\right\} \tag{14}
$$

where A' is the first derivative of A and similarly for e' of e.

Transients—operational calculus and Laplace transforms   *continued*

As an example, consider the problem of Fig. 15 and (5) to (7) above. Suppose $V_0 = 0$, and that the battery is replaced by a linear source

$$e(t) = Et/T_1$$

where T_1 is the duration of the voltage rise in seconds. By (7), setting $E_b = 1$,

$$A(t) = 1 - \epsilon^{-t/RC}$$

Then using the first equation in (14) and noting that $e(0) = 0$, and $e'(t) = E/T_1$ when $0 \leqslant t \leqslant T_1$, the solution is

$$v = \frac{Et}{T_1} - \frac{ERC}{T_1} (1 - \epsilon^{-t/RC})$$

This result can, of course, be found readily by direct application of the Laplace transform to (5) with $e(t) = Et/T_1$.

Heaviside expansion theorem

When the system is initially at rest, the transformed equation is given by (9) and may be written

$$T(i_a) = \frac{M(p)}{G(p)} T(e) \tag{15}$$

$M(p)$ and $G(p)$ are rational functions of p. In the following, $M(p)$ must be of lower degree than $G(p)$, as is usually the case. The roots of $G(p) = 0$ are p_r, where $r = 1, 2, \ldots n$, and there must be no repeated roots. The response may be found by application of the *Heaviside expansion theorem*.

For a force $e = E_{\max} \epsilon^{j\omega t}$ applied at time $t = 0$,

$$\frac{i_a(t)}{E_{\max}} = \frac{M(j\omega)}{G(j\omega)} \epsilon^{j\omega t} + \sum_{r=1}^{n} \frac{M(p_r) \epsilon^{p_r t}}{(p_r - j\omega) G'(p_r)} \tag{16a}$$

$$= \frac{\epsilon^{j\omega t}}{Z(j\omega)} + \sum_{r=1}^{n} \frac{\epsilon^{p_r t}}{(p_r - j\omega) Z'(p_r)} \tag{16b}$$

The first term on the right-hand side of either form of (16) gives the steady-state response, and the second term gives the transient. When $e = E_{\max} \cos \omega t$, take the real part of (16), and similarly for $\sin \omega t$ and the imaginary part. $Z(p)$ is defined in (19) below. If the applied force is the unit step, set $\omega = 0$ in (16).

Application to linear networks

The equation for a single mesh is of the form

$$A_n \frac{d^n i}{dt^n} + \ldots + A_1 \frac{di}{dt} + A_0 i + B \int idt = e(t) \tag{17}$$

Transients—operational calculus and Laplace transforms *continued*

System initially at rest: Then, (17) transforms into

$$(A_n p^n + \ldots + A_1 p + A_0 + B p^{-1}) \, T(i) = T(e) \tag{18}$$

where the expression in parenthesis is the operational impedance, equal to the alternating-current impedance when we set $p = j\omega$.

If there are m meshes in the system, we get m simultaneous equations like (17) with m unknowns $i_1, i_2, \ldots, i_m$. The m algebraic equations like (18) are solved for $T(i_1)$, etc., by means of determinants, yielding an equation of the form of (15) for each unknown, with a term on the right-hand side for each mesh in which there is a driving force. Each such driving force may of course be treated separately and the responses added.

Designating any two meshes by the letters h and k, the driving force $e(t)$ being in either mesh and the mesh current $i(t)$ in the other, then the fraction $M(p)/G(p)$ in (15) becomes

$$\frac{M_{hk}(p)}{G(p)} = \frac{1}{Z_{hk}(p)} = Y_{hk}(p) \tag{19}$$

where $Y_{hk}(p)$ is the operational transfer admittance between the two meshes. The determinant of the system is $G(p)$, and $M_{hk}(p)$ is the cofactor of the row and column that represent $e(t)$ and $i(t)$.

System not initially at rest: The transient due to the initial conditions is solved separately and added to the above solution. The driving force is set equal to zero in (17), $e(t) = 0$, and each term is transformed according to

$$T\left(\frac{d^n i}{dt^n}\right) = p^n T(i) - \sum_{r=1}^{n} p^{n-r} \left[\frac{d^{r-1} i}{dt^{r-1}}\right]_{t=0} \tag{20a}$$

$$T\left[\int_0^t i \, dt\right] = \frac{1}{p} T(i) + \frac{1}{p}\left[\int i \, dt\right]_{t=0} \tag{20b}$$

where the last term in each equation represents the initial conditions. For example, in (20b) the last term would represent, in an electrical circuit, the quantity of electricity existing on a capacitor at time $t = 0$, the instant when the driving force $e(t)$ commences to act.

Resolution into partial fractions: The solution of the operational form of the equations of a system involves rational fractions that must be simplified before finding the inverse transform. Let the fraction be $h(p)/g(p)$ where $h(p)$ is of lower degree than $g(p)$, for example $(3p + 2)/(p^2 + 5p + 8)$. If $h(p)$ is of equal or higher degree than $g(p)$, it can be reduced by division.

The reduced fraction can be expanded into partial fractions. Let the factors of the denominator be $(p - p_r)$ for the n nonrepeated roots p_r of the equation $g(p) = 0$, and $(p - p_a)$ for a root p_a repeated m times.

Transients—operational calculus and Laplace transforms   *continued*

$$\frac{h(p)}{g(p)} = \sum_{r=1}^{n} \frac{A_r}{p - p_r} + \sum_{r=1}^{m} \frac{B_r}{(p - p_a)^{m-r+1}} \tag{21a}$$

There is a summation term for each root that is repeated. The constant coefficients A_r and B_r can be evaluated by re-forming the fraction with a common denominator. Then the coefficients of each power of p in $h(p)$ and the re-formed numerator are equated and the resulting equations solved for the constants. More formally, they may be evaluated by

$$A_r = \frac{h(p_r)}{g'(p_r)} = \left[\frac{h(p)}{g(p)/(p - p_r)}\right]_{p = p_r} \tag{21b}$$

$$B_r = \frac{1}{(r - 1)!} f^{(r-1)}(p_a) \tag{21c}$$

where

$$f(p) = (p - p_a)^m \frac{h(p)}{g(p)}$$

and $f^{(r-1)}(p_a)$ indicates that the $(r - 1)$th derivative of $f(p)$ is to be found, after which we set $p = p_a$.

Fractions of the form $\dfrac{A_1 p + A_2}{p^2 + \omega^2}$ or, more generally,

$$\frac{A_1 p + A_2}{p^2 + 2ap + b} = \frac{A(p + a) + B\omega}{(p + a)^2 + \omega^2} \tag{22a}$$

where $b > a^2$ and $\omega^2 = b - a^2$, need not be reduced further. By pairs 8, 23, and 24 of the table on pages 612 and 613, the inverse transform of (22a) is

$$\epsilon^{-at}(A \cos \omega t + B \sin \omega t) \tag{22b}$$

where

$$A = \frac{h(-a + j\omega)}{g'(-a + j\omega)} + \frac{h(-a - j\omega)}{g'(-a - j\omega)} \tag{22c}$$

$$B = j\left[\frac{h(-a + j\omega)}{g'(-a + j\omega)} - \frac{h(-a - j\omega)}{g'(-a - j\omega)}\right] \tag{22d}$$

Similarly, the inverse transform of the fraction $\dfrac{A(p + a) + B\alpha}{(p + a)^2 - \alpha^2}$

is $\epsilon^{-at}(A \cosh \alpha t + B \sinh \alpha t)$, where A and B are found by (22c) and (22d), except that $j\omega$ is replaced by α and the coefficient j is omitted in the expression for B.

■ Selective circuits

Coefficient of coupling*

Several types of coupled circuits are shown in Figs. 1B to F, together with formulas for the coefficient of coupling in each case. Also shown is the dependence of bandwidth on resonance frequency. This dependence is only a rough approximation to show the trend, and may be altered radically if L_m, M, or C_m are adjusted as the circuits are tuned to various frequencies.

$$k = X_{120}/\sqrt{X_{10}X_{20}} = \text{coefficient of coupling}$$

X_{120} = coupling reactance at resonance frequency f_0

X_{10} = reactance of inductor (or capacitor) of first circuit at f_0

X_{20} = reactance of similar element of second circuit at f_0

$(bw)_C$ = bandwidth with capacitive tuning

$(bw)_L$ = bandwidth with inductive tuning

Gain at resonance

Single circuit

In Fig. 1A,

$$\frac{E_0}{E_g} = -g_m |X_{10}| Q$$

where

E_0 = output volts at resonance frequency f_0

E_g = input volts to grid of driving tube

g_m = transconductance of driving tube

Pair of coupled circuits   (Figs. 2 and 3)

In any figure—Figs. 1B to F,

$$\frac{E_0}{E_g} = jg_m\sqrt{X_{10}X_{20}}\, Q\, \frac{kQ}{1 + k^2Q^2}$$

This is maximum at critical coupling, where $kQ = 1$.

$Q = \sqrt{Q_1 Q_2}$ = geometric-mean Q for the two circuits, as loaded with the tube grid and plate impedances

* See also "Coefficient of coupling—geometrical consideration," p. 96.

Fig. 1—Several types of coupled circuits, showing coefficient of coupling and selectivity formulas in each case.

diagram	coefficient of coupling	approximate bandwidth variation with frequency	selectivity far from resonance — formula*	curve in Fig. 4
A (vacuum tube circuit with L, C, E_{out}, E_g; terminals P, G, F, B, P', B')			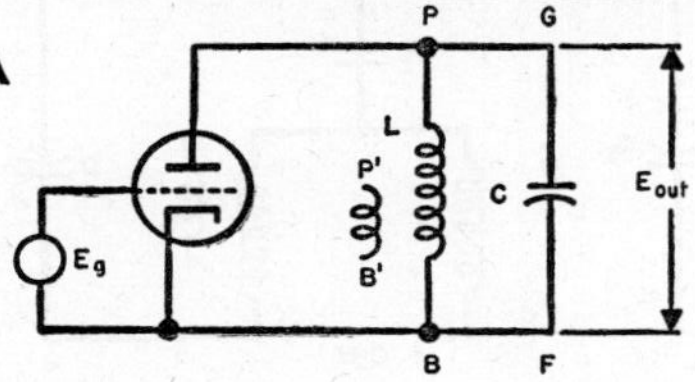 Input to PB or to P'B': $\dfrac{E_0}{E} = jQ\left(\dfrac{f}{f_0} - \dfrac{f_0}{f}\right)$	A
B (M·0 circuit with C_1, C_2, L_1, L_2, L_m; terminals P, G, F, B, P', B')	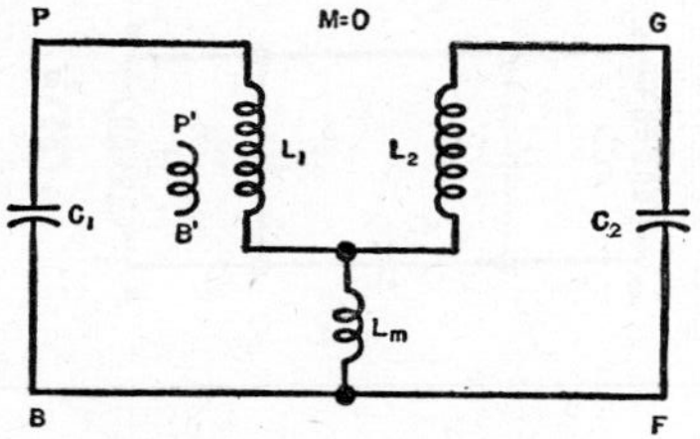 $k = L_m/\sqrt{(L_1 + L_m)(L_2 + L_m)}$ $= \omega_0^2 L_m \sqrt{C_1 C_2}$ $\approx L_m/\sqrt{L_1 L_2}$	$(\mathrm{bw})_C \propto f_0$ $(\mathrm{bw})_L \propto f_0^3$	Input to PB: $\dfrac{E_0}{E} = -A\dfrac{f}{f_0}$	C
			Input to P'B': $\dfrac{E_0}{E} = -A\dfrac{f_0}{f}$	D
C (circuit with C_1, C_2, L_1, L_2, M; terminals P, G, F, B, P', B')	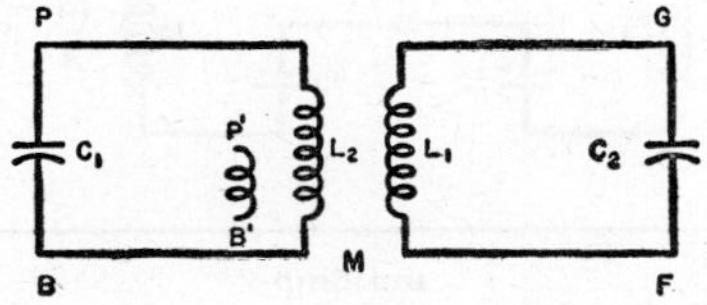 $k = M/\sqrt{L_1 L_2}$ $= \omega_0^2 M \sqrt{C_1 C_2}$ M may be positive or negative	$(\mathrm{bw})_C \propto f_0$ $(\mathrm{bw})_L \propto f_0^3$	Input to PB: $\dfrac{E_0}{E} = -A\dfrac{f}{f_0}$	C
			Input to P'B': $\dfrac{E_0}{E} = -A\dfrac{f_0}{f}$	D

*Where $A = \dfrac{Q^2}{1 + k^2 Q^2}\left(\dfrac{f}{f_0} - \dfrac{f_0}{f}\right)$

Fig. 1—continued

	diagram	coefficient of coupling	approximate bandwidth variation with frequency	selectivity far from resonance — formula*	selectivity far from resonance — curve in Fig. 4
D	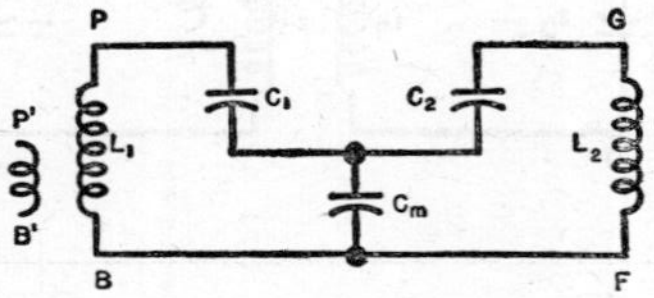	$k = -\left[\dfrac{C_1 C_2}{(C_1 + C_m)(C_2 + C_m)}\right]^{\frac{1}{2}}$ $= -1/\omega_0^2 C_m \sqrt{L_1 L_2}$ $\approx -\sqrt{C_1 C_2}/C_m$	$(\text{bw})_C \propto 1/f_0$ $(\text{bw})_L \propto f_0$	Input to PB or to $P'B'$: $\dfrac{E_0}{E} = -A\,\dfrac{f_0}{f}$	D
E	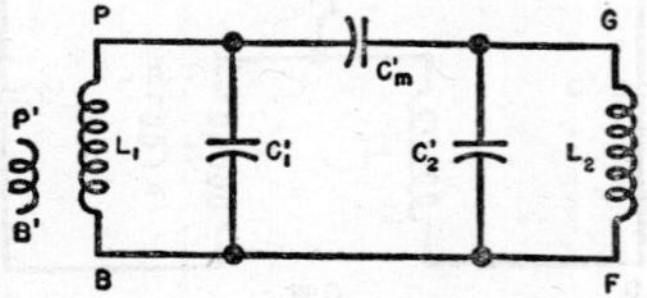	$k = \dfrac{-C_m'}{\sqrt{(C_1' + C_m')(C_2' + C_m')}}$ $= -\omega_0^2 C_m' \sqrt{L_1 L_2}$ $\approx -C_m'/\sqrt{C_1' C_2'}$	$(\text{bw})_C \propto f^3$ $(\text{bw})_L \propto f$	Input to PB or to $P'B'$: $\dfrac{E_0}{E} = -A\,\dfrac{f_0}{f}$	D
F		$k = -\left[\dfrac{C_1 C_2}{(C_1 + C_m)(C_2 + C_m)}\right]^{\frac{1}{2}}$ $= -1/\omega_0^2 C_m \sqrt{L_1 L_2}$ $\approx -\sqrt{C_1 C_2}/C_m$	$(\text{bw})_C \propto 1/f_0$ $(\text{bw})_L \propto f_0$	Input to PB: $\dfrac{E_0}{E} = -A\left(\dfrac{f}{f_0}\right)^3$ Input to $P'B'$: $\dfrac{E_0}{E} = -A\,\dfrac{f}{f_0}$	B C

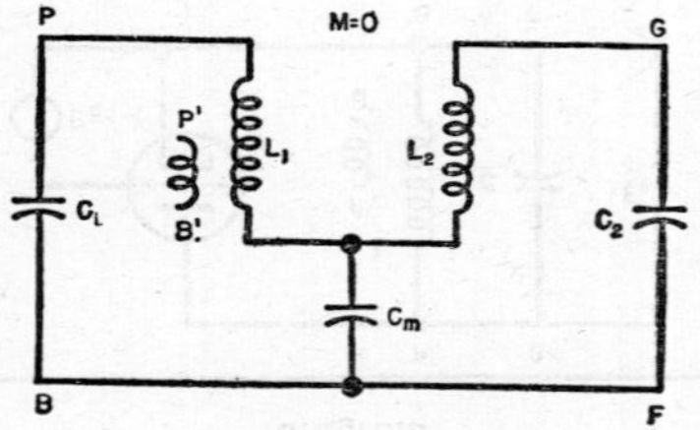

*Where $A = \dfrac{Q^2}{1 + k^2 Q^2}\left(\dfrac{f}{f_0} - \dfrac{f_0}{f}\right)^2$

Gain at resonance   *continued*

For circuits with critical coupling and over coupling, the approximate gain is

$$\left|\frac{E_0}{E_g}\right| \approx \frac{0.1\, g_m}{\sqrt{C_1 C_2}\ (\text{bw})}$$

where (bw) is the useful pass band in megacycles, g_m is in micromhos, and C is in micromicrofarads.

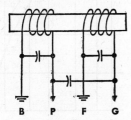

Fig. 2—Connection wherein k_m opposes k_c. (k_c may be due to stray capacitance.) Peak of attenuation is at $f = f_0 \sqrt{-k_m/k_c}$. Reversing connections or winding direction of one coil causes k_m to aid k_c.

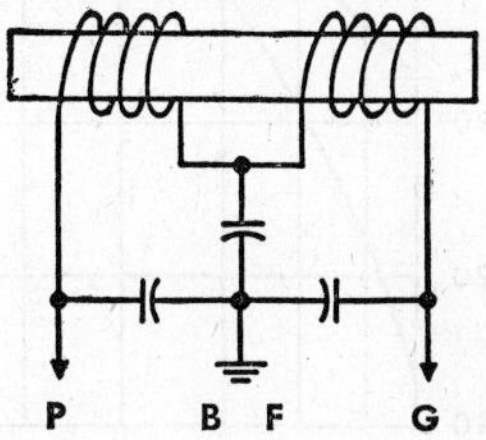

Fig. 3—Connection wherein k_m aids k_c. If mutual-inductance coupling is reversed, k_m will oppose k_c and there will be a transfer minimum at $f = f_0 \sqrt{-k_m/k_c}$.

Selectivity far from resonance

The selectivity curves of Fig. 4 are based on the presence of only a single type of coupling between the circuits. The curves are useful beyond the peak region treated on pp. 119-124.

In the equations for selectivity in Fig. 1

$E =$ output volts at signal frequency f for same value of E_g as that producing E_0

For inductive coupling

$$A = \frac{Q^2}{1 + k^2 Q^2}\left[\left(\frac{f}{f_0} - \frac{f_0}{f}\right)^2 - k^2\left(\frac{f}{f_0}\right)^2\right] \approx \frac{Q^2}{1 + k^2 Q^2}\left(\frac{f}{f_0} - \frac{f_0}{f}\right)^2$$

For capacitive coupling

A is defined by a similar equation, except that the neglected term is $-k^2(f_0/f)^2$. The 180-degree phase shift far from resonance is indicated by the minus sign in the expression for E_0/E.

118

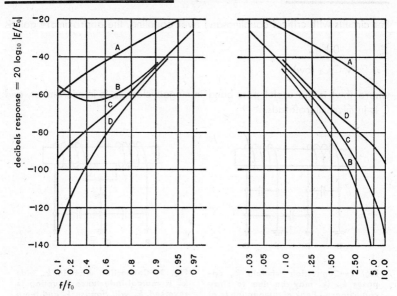

Fig. 4—Selectivity for frequencies far from resonance.   Q = 100 and |k| Q = 1.0.

Example: The use of the curves, Figs. 4, 5, and 6, is indicated by the following example. Given the circuit of Fig. 1C with input to PB, across capacitor C_1. Let $Q = 50$, $kQ = 1.50$ and $f_0 = 16.0$ megacycles. Required is the response at $f = 8.0$ megacycles.

Here $f/f_0 = 0.50$ and curve C, Fig. 4, gives −75 decibels. Then applying the corrections from Figs. 5 and 6 for Q and kQ, we find

Response $= -75 + 12 + 4 = -59$ decibels

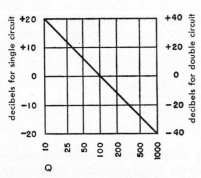

Fig. 5—Correction for Q ≠ 100.

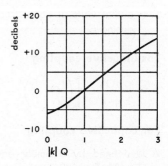

Fig. 6—Correction for |k|Q ≠ 1.0.

Selectivity of single- and double-tuned circuits near resonance

Formulas and curves are presented for the selectivity and phase shift:

Of n single-tuned circuits
Of m pairs of coupled tuned circuits

The conditions assumed are

a. All circuits are tuned to the same frequency f_0.

b. All circuits have the same Q, or each pair of circuits includes one circuit having Q_1, and the other having Q_2.

c. Otherwise the circuits need not be identical.

d. Each successive circuit or pair of circuits is isolated from the preceding and following ones by tubes, with no regeneration around the system.

Certain approximations have been made in order to simplify the formulas. In most actual applications of the types of circuits treated, the error involved is negligible from a practical standpoint. Over the narrow frequency band in question, it is assumed that

a. The reactance around each circuit is equal to $2X_0 \, \Delta f / f_0$.

b. The resistance of each circuit is constant and equal to X_0/Q.

c. The coupling between two circuits of a pair is reactive and constant. (When an untuned link is used to couple the two circuits, this condition frequently is far from satisfied, resulting in a lopsided selectivity curve.)

d. The equivalent input voltage, taken as being in series with the tuned circuit (or the first of a pair), is assumed to bear a constant proportionality to the grid voltage of the input tube or other driving source, at all frequencies in the band.

e. Likewise, the output voltage across the circuit (or the final circuit of a pair) is assumed to be proportional only to the current in the circuit.

The following symbols are used in the formulas in addition to those defined on pages 114 and 117.

$$\frac{\Delta f}{f_0} = \frac{f - f_0}{f_0} = \frac{\text{(deviation from resonance frequency)}}{\text{(resonance frequency)}}$$

(bw) $=$ bandwidth $= 2\Delta f$
X_0 $=$ reactance at f_0 of inductor in tuned circuit
n $=$ number of single-tuned circuits
m $=$ number of pairs of coupled circuits
ϕ $=$ phase shift of signal at f relative to shift at f_0, as signal passes through cascade of circuits

Selectivity of single- and double-tuned circuits

$p = k^2Q^2$ or $p = k^2Q_1Q_2$, a parameter determining the form of the selectivity curve of coupled circuits

$$B = p - \frac{1}{2}\left(\frac{Q_1}{Q_2} + \frac{Q_2}{Q_1}\right)$$

Selectivity and phase shift of single-tuned circuits

$$\frac{E}{E_0} = \left[\frac{1}{\sqrt{1 + \left(2Q\frac{\Delta f}{f_0}\right)^2}}\right]^n$$

$$\frac{\Delta f}{f_0} = \pm\frac{1}{2Q}\sqrt{\left(\frac{E_0}{E}\right)^{\frac{2}{n}} - 1}$$

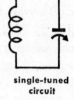

single-tuned circuit

Decibel response $= 20 \log_{10}\left(\frac{E}{E_0}\right)$

(db response of n circuits) $= n \times$ (db response of single circuit)

$$\phi = n \tan^{-1}\left(-2Q\frac{\Delta f}{f_0}\right)$$

These equations are plotted in Figs. 7 and 8, following.

Q determination by 3-decibel points

For a single-tuned circuit, when

$E/E_0 = 0.707$ (3 decibels down)

$$Q = \frac{f_0}{2\Delta f} = \frac{\text{(resonance frequency)}}{\text{(bandwidth)}_{3db}}$$

Selectivity and phase shift of pairs of coupled tuned circuits

Case 1: When $Q_1 = Q_2 = Q$

These formulas can be used with reasonable accuracy when Q_1 and Q_2 differ by ratios up to 1.5 or even 2 to 1. In such cases use the value $Q = \sqrt{Q_1Q_2}$.

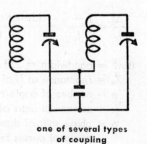

$$\frac{E}{E_0} = \left[\frac{p + 1}{\sqrt{\left[\left(2Q\frac{\Delta f}{f_0}\right)^2 - (p - 1)\right]^2 + 4p}}\right]^m$$

one of several types of coupling

Selectivity of single- and double-tuned circuits

near resonance *continued*

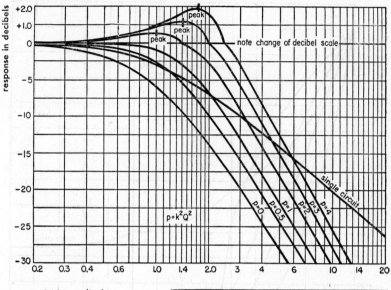

$$Q\frac{2\Delta f}{f_0} = Q\frac{(bw)}{f_0}$$

Fig. 7 — Selectivity curves showing response of a single circuit $n = 1$, and a pair of coupled circuits $m = 1$.

The selectivity curves are symmetrical about the axis $Q\dfrac{\Delta f}{f_0} = 0$ for practical purposes.

Extrapolation beyond lower limits of chart:

Δ response for doubling Δf	circuit	at $\dfrac{(bw)}{f_0}$	useful limit error becomes
− 6 db	← single →	± 0.6	1 to 2 db
− 12 db	← pair →	± 0.4	3 to 4 db

Example: Of the use of Figs. 7 and 8. Suppose there are three single-tuned circuits ($n = 3$). Each circuit has a $Q = 200$ and is tuned to 1000 kilocycles. The results are shown in the following table:

abscissa $Q\dfrac{(bw)}{f_0}$	bandwidth kilocycles	ordinate db response for $n = 1$	decibels response for $n = 3$	ϕ^* for $n = 1$	ϕ^* for $n = 3$
1.0	5.0	−3.0	−9	∓45°	∓135°
3.0	15	−10.0	−30	∓71½°	∓215°
10.0	50	−20.2	−61	∓84°	∓252°

* ϕ is negative for $f > f_0$, and vice versa.

Selectivity of single- and double-tuned circuits

near resonance _continued_

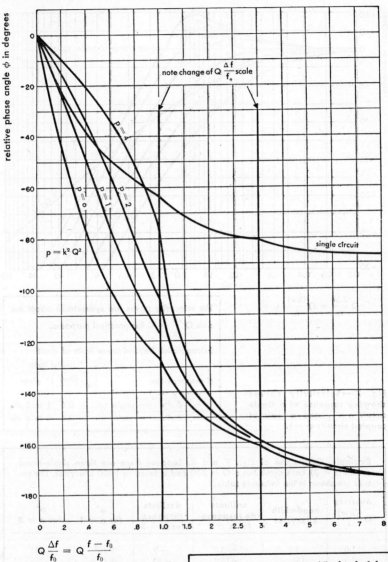

$$Q \frac{\Delta f}{f_0} = Q \frac{f - f_0}{f_0}$$

Fig. 8—Phase-shift curves for a single circuit $n = 1$ and a pair of coupled circuits $m = 1$.

For $f > f_0$, ϕ is negative, while for $f < f_0$, ϕ is positive. The numerical value is identical in either case for the same $|f - f_0|$.

Selectivity of single- and double-tuned circuits

near resonance *continued*

$$\frac{\Delta f}{f_0} = \pm \frac{1}{2Q} \sqrt{(p-1) \pm \sqrt{(p+1)^2 \left(\frac{E_0}{E}\right)^{\frac{2}{m}} - 4p}}$$

For very small values of E/E_0 the formulas reduce to

$$\frac{E}{E_0} = \left[\frac{p+1}{\left(2Q\frac{\Delta f}{f_0}\right)^2}\right]^m$$

Decibel response $= 20 \log_{10} (E/E_0)$

(db response of m pairs of circuits) $= m \times$ (db response of one pair)

$$\phi = m \tan^{-1}\left[\frac{-4Q\frac{\Delta f}{f_0}}{(p+1) - \left(2Q\frac{\Delta f}{f_0}\right)^2}\right]$$

As p approaches zero, the selectivity and phase shift approach the values for n single circuits, where $n = 2m$ (gain also approaches zero).

The above equations are plotted in Figs. 7 and 8.

For overcoupled circuits ($p > 1$)

Location of peaks: $\dfrac{f_{\text{peak}} - f_0}{f_0} = \pm \dfrac{1}{2Q}\sqrt{p-1}$

Amplitude of peaks: $\dfrac{E_{\text{peak}}}{E_0} = \left(\dfrac{p+1}{2\sqrt{p}}\right)^m$

Phase shift at peaks: $\phi_{\text{peak}} = m \tan^{-1}(\mp\sqrt{p-1})$

Approximate pass band (where $E/E_0 = 1$) is

$$\frac{f_{\text{unity}} - f_0}{f_0} = \sqrt{2}\,\frac{f_{\text{peak}} - f_0}{f_0} = \pm\frac{1}{Q}\sqrt{\frac{p-1}{2}}$$

Case 2: General formula for any Q_1 and Q_2

$$\frac{E}{E_0} = \left[\frac{p+1}{\sqrt{\left[\left(2Q\frac{\Delta f}{f_0}\right)^2 - B\right]^2 + (p+1)^2 - B^2}}\right]^m \qquad \text{(For B see top of p. 120.)}$$

Selectivity of single- and double-tuned circuits

near resonance   *continued*

$$\frac{\Delta f}{f_0} = \pm \frac{1}{2Q} \sqrt{B \pm \left[(p+1)^2 \left(\frac{E_0}{E}\right)^{\frac{2}{m}} - (p+1)^2 + B^2 \right]^{\frac{1}{2}}}$$

$$\phi = m \tan^{-1} \left[-\frac{2Q\frac{\Delta f}{f_0}\left(\sqrt{\frac{Q_1}{Q_2}} + \sqrt{\frac{Q_2}{Q_1}}\right)}{(p+1) - \left(2Q\frac{\Delta f}{f_0}\right)^2} \right]$$

For overcoupled circuits

Location of peaks: $\dfrac{f_{peak} - f_0}{f_0} = \pm \dfrac{\sqrt{B}}{2Q} = \pm \dfrac{1}{2}\sqrt{k^2 - \dfrac{1}{2}\left(\dfrac{1}{Q_1^2} + \dfrac{1}{Q_2^2}\right)}$

Amplitude of peaks: $\dfrac{E_{peak}}{E_0} = \left[\dfrac{p+1}{\sqrt{(p+1)^2 - B^2}} \right]^m$

Case 3: Peaks just converged to a single peak

Here $B = 0$ or $k^2 = \dfrac{1}{2}\left(\dfrac{1}{Q_1^2} + \dfrac{1}{Q_2^2}\right)$

$$\frac{E}{E_0} = \left[\frac{2}{\sqrt{\left(2Q'\frac{\Delta f}{f_0}\right)^4 + 4}} \right]^m$$

where $Q' = \dfrac{2Q_1Q_2}{Q_1 + Q_2}$

$$\frac{\Delta f}{f_0} = \pm \frac{\sqrt{2}}{4}\left(\frac{1}{Q_1} + \frac{1}{Q_2}\right) \sqrt[4]{\left(\frac{E_0}{E}\right)^{\frac{2}{m}} - 1}$$

$$\phi = m \tan^{-1} \left[-\frac{4Q'\frac{\Delta f}{f_0}}{2 - \left(2Q'\frac{\Delta f}{f_0}\right)^2} \right]$$

The curves of Figs. 7 and 8 may be applied to this case, using the value $p = 1$, and substituting Q' for Q.

Triple-tuned circuits

Exact design formulas for n identical cascaded triple-tuned stages used to produce the "maximally-flat" amplitude-response shape are given. Typical circuit is shown in Fig. 9, together with the response.

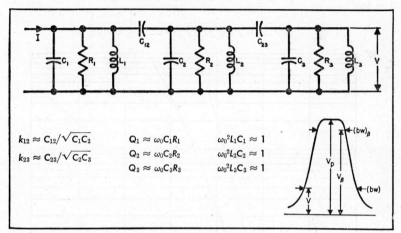

$$k_{12} \approx C_{12}/\sqrt{C_1 C_2}$$
$$k_{23} \approx C_{23}/\sqrt{C_2 C_3}$$

$$Q_1 \approx \omega_0 C_1 R_1$$
$$Q_2 \approx \omega_0 C_2 R_2$$
$$Q_3 \approx \omega_0 C_3 R_3$$

$$\omega_0^2 L_1 C_1 \approx 1$$
$$\omega_0^2 L_2 C_2 \approx 1$$
$$\omega_0^2 L_3 C_3 \approx 1$$

Fig. 9—Typical triple-tuned circuit and response curve.

To obtain the required Q's,

$$\frac{Q_1}{f_0/(bw)_\beta} = 0.737 \sqrt[6]{(V_p/V_\beta)^{2/n} - 1}$$

$$Q_2 = Q_3 = 4.24 Q_1$$

in the above formulas, Q_3 and Q_1 may be interchanged.

To obtain the required coefficient of coupling,

$$k_{12} = k_{23} = \frac{0.527}{Q_1}$$

To obtain the gain per stage,

$$\frac{(\text{stage gain})}{g_m/4\pi(bw)_\beta \sqrt{C_1 C_3}} = \sqrt[6]{(V_p/V_\beta)^{2/n} - 1}$$

The exact amplitude response is given by

$$\frac{V_p}{V} = \left\{ 1 + [(V_p/V_\beta)^{2/n} - 1] \left[\frac{(bw)}{(bw)_\beta} \right]^6 \right\}^{\frac{n}{2}} \quad \text{or} \quad \frac{(bw)}{(bw)_\beta} = \frac{\sqrt[6]{(V_p/V)^{2/n} - 1}}{\sqrt[6]{(V_p/V_\beta)^{2/n} - 1}}$$

This equation is plotted in Fig. 10.

Triple-tuned circuits   *continued*

The exact phase response for one stage is given by

$$\theta = \tan^{-1} \frac{\left(\dfrac{2}{\sqrt[3]{(V_p/V_\beta)^{2/n} - 1}}\right)\left[\dfrac{(bw)}{(bw)_\beta}\right] - \left[\dfrac{(bw)}{(bw)_\beta}\right]^3}{\dfrac{1}{\sqrt{(V_p/V_\beta)^{2/n} - 1}} - \dfrac{2}{\sqrt[6]{(V_p/V_\beta)^{2/n} - 1}}\left[\dfrac{(bw)}{(bw)_\beta}\right]^2}$$

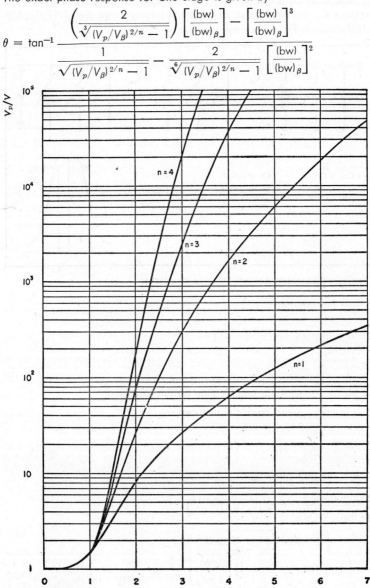

Fig. 10—Selectivity of *n* cascaded maximally flat triple-tuned circuits.

Stagger tuning of single-tuned interstages

Response shape B (Butterworth) (Fig. 11)

The required Q's are given by

$$\frac{1}{Q_m} = \frac{(bw)_\beta/f_0}{\sqrt[2n]{(V_p/V_\beta)^2 - 1}} \sin\left(\frac{2m-1}{n} 90°\right)$$

The required stagger tuning is given by

$$(f_a - f_b)_m = \frac{(bw)_\beta}{\sqrt[2n]{(V_p/V_\beta)^2 - 1}} \cos\left(\frac{2m-1}{n} 90°\right)$$

$$(f_a + f_b)_m = 2f_0$$

The amplitude response is given by

$$V_p/V = \left\{1 + \left[(V_p/V_\beta)^2 - 1\right]\left[(bw)/(bw)_\beta\right]^{2n}\right\}^{\frac{1}{2}}$$

$$\frac{(bw)}{(bw)_\beta} = \left[\frac{(V_p/V)^2 - 1}{(V_p/V_\beta)^2 - 1}\right]^{1/2n}$$

$$n = \frac{\log\left[\dfrac{(V_p/V)^2 - 1}{(V_p/V_\beta)^2 - 1}\right]}{2\log\left[(bw)/(bw)_\beta\right]}$$

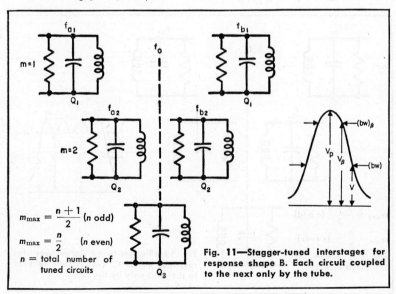

$$m_{max} = \frac{n+1}{2} \text{ (n odd)}$$

$$m_{max} = \frac{n}{2} \text{ (n even)}$$

n = total number of tuned circuits

Fig. 11—Stagger-tuned interstages for response shape B. Each circuit coupled to the next only by the tube.

Stagger tuning of single-tuned interstages *continued*

$$\text{Stage gain} = \frac{g_m}{2\pi (bw)_\beta C} \sqrt[2n]{(V_p/V_\beta)^2 - 1}$$

or

$$n = \frac{\log\left[\dfrac{(total\ gain)}{\sqrt{(V_p/V_\beta)^2 - 1}}\right]}{\log\left(\dfrac{g_m}{2\pi (bw)_\beta C}\right)}$$

where

g_m = geometric-mean transconductance of n tubes
C = geometric-mean capacitance

Response shape C (Chebishev) *(Fig. 12)*

The required Q's are given by

$$\frac{1}{Q_m} = \frac{(bw)_\beta}{f_0} S_n \sin\left[\frac{2m-1}{n} 90°\right]$$

$$S_n = \sinh\left[\frac{1}{n} \sinh^{-1} \frac{1}{\sqrt{(V_p/V_\beta)^2 - 1}}\right]$$

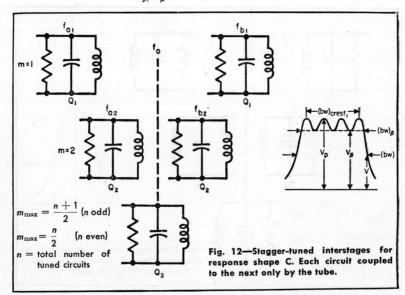

$m_{max} = \dfrac{n+1}{2}$ (n odd)

$m_{max} = \dfrac{n}{2}$ (n even)

n = total number of tuned circuits

Fig. 12—Stagger-tuned interstages for response shape C. Each circuit coupled to the next only by the tube.

Stagger tuning of single-tuned interstages *continued*

The required stagger tuning is given by

$$(f_a - f_b)_m = (bw)_\beta C_n \cos\left(\frac{2m-1}{n}90°\right)$$

$$(f_a + f_b)_m = 2f_0$$

$$C_n = \cosh\left[\frac{1}{n}\sinh^{-1}\frac{1}{\sqrt{(V_p/V_\beta)^2 - 1}}\right]$$

Shape outside pass band is

$$\frac{V_p}{V} = \sqrt{1 + \left[\left(\frac{V_p}{V_\beta}\right)^2 - 1\right]\left\{\cosh^2\left[n\cosh^{-1}\frac{(bw)}{(bw)_\beta}\right]\right\}}$$

$$\frac{(bw)}{(bw)_\beta} = \cosh\left\{\frac{1}{n}\cosh^{-1}\left[\frac{(V_p/V)^2 - 1}{(V_p/V_\beta)^2 - 1}\right]^{\frac{1}{2}}\right\}$$

$$n = \frac{\cosh^{-1}\left[\dfrac{(V_p/V)^2 - 1}{(V_p/V_\beta)^2 - 1}\right]^{\frac{1}{2}}}{\cosh^{-1}\left[(bw)/(bw)_\beta\right]}$$

Shape inside pass band is

$$\frac{V_p}{V} = \sqrt{1 + \left[\left(\frac{V_p}{V_\beta}\right)^2 - 1\right]\left\{\cos^2\left[n\cos^{-1}\frac{(bw)}{(bw)_\beta}\right]\right\}}$$

$$\frac{(bw)_{\text{crest}}}{(bw)_\beta} = \cos\left(\frac{2m-1}{n}90°\right)$$

$$\frac{(bw)_{\text{trough}}}{(bw)_\beta} = \cos\left(\frac{2m}{n}90°\right)$$

$$\text{Stage gain} = \frac{g_m}{2^{1/n}\pi(bw)_\beta C}\sqrt[2n]{(V_p/V_\beta)^2 - 1}$$

$$n = \frac{\log\left[\dfrac{(\text{total gain})}{\frac{1}{2}\sqrt{(V_p/V_\beta)^2 - 1}}\right]}{\log\left[\dfrac{g_m}{\pi(bw)_\beta C}\right]}$$

where

g_m = geometric-mean transconductance of n tubes

C = geometric-mean capacitance

General

The basic filter half section and the full sections derived from it are shown in Fig. 1. The fundamental filter equations follow, with filter characteristics and design formulas next. Also given is the method of building up a composite filter and the effect of the design parameter m on the image-impedance characteristic. An example of the design of a low-pass filter completes the chapter. It is to be noted that while the impedance characteristics and design formulas are given for the half sections as shown, the attenuation and phase characteristics are for full sections, either T or π.

Fig. 1—Basic filter sections.

description	diagram
A Half section	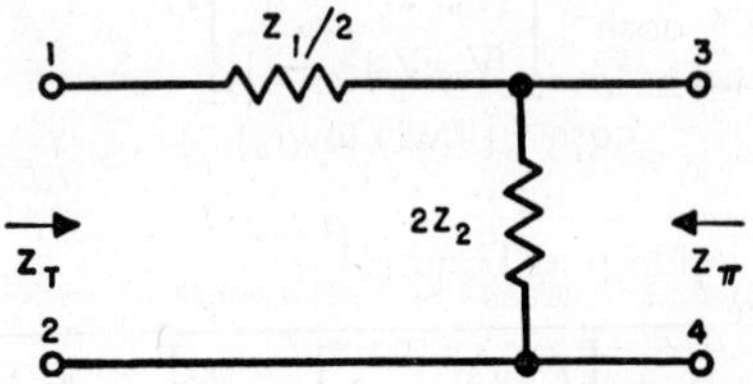
B Full T-section	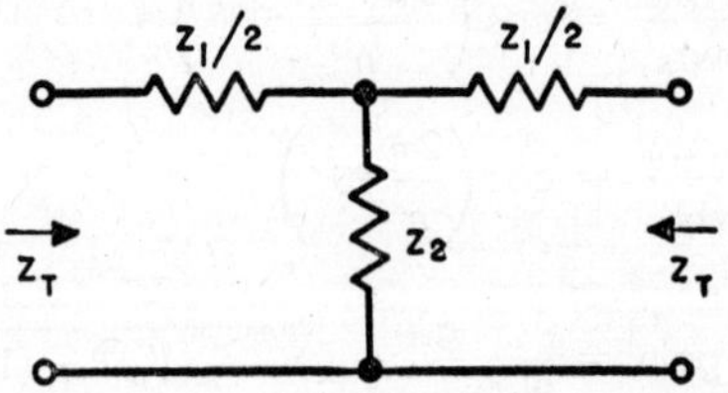
C Full π-section	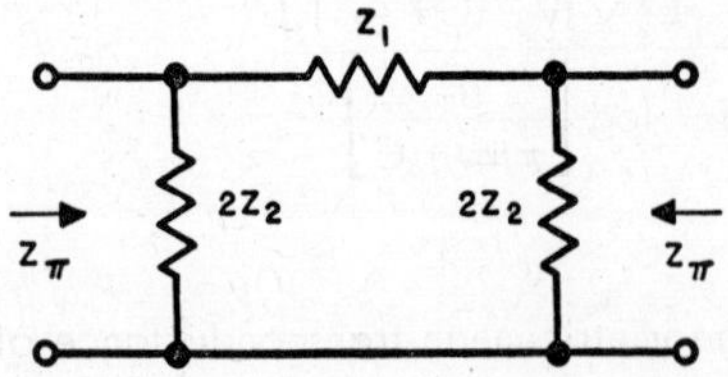

Fundamental filter equations

Image impedances Z_T and Z_π

Z_T = mid-series image impedance = impedance looking into 1–2 (Fig. 1A) with Z_π connected across 3–4.

Z_π = mid-shunt image impedance = impedance looking into 3–4 (Fig. 1A) with Z_T connected across 1–2.

Formulas for the above are

$$Z_T = \sqrt{Z_1 Z_2 + Z_1^2/4} = \sqrt{Z_1 Z_2}\,\sqrt{1 + Z_1/4Z_2}\ \text{ohms}$$

$$Z_\pi = \frac{Z_1 Z_2}{\sqrt{Z_1 Z_2 + Z_1^2/4}} = \frac{\sqrt{Z_1 Z_2}}{\sqrt{1 + Z_1/4Z_2}}\ \text{ohms}$$

$$Z_T Z_\pi = Z_1 Z_2$$

Image transfer constant θ

The transfer constant $\theta = \alpha + j\beta$ of a network is defined as one-half the natural logarithm of the complex ratio of the steady-state volt-amperes entering and leaving the network when the latter is terminated in its image impedance. The real part α of the transfer constant is called the image attenuation constant, and the imaginary part β is called the image phase constant.

Formulas in terms of full sections are

$$\cosh \theta = 1 + Z_1/2Z_2$$

Pass band

$\alpha = 0$, for frequencies making $-1 \leqslant Z_1/4Z_2 \leqslant 0$

$$\beta = \cos^{-1}(1 + Z_1/2Z_2) = \pm 2\sin^{-1}\sqrt{-Z_1/4Z_2}\ \text{radians}$$

Image impedance = pure resistance

Stop band

$$\begin{cases} \alpha = \cosh^{-1}|1 + Z_1/2Z_2| = 2\sinh^{-1}\sqrt{Z_1/4Z_2}\ \text{nepers} \quad \text{for } Z_1/4Z_2 > 0 \\ \beta = 0\ \text{radians} \end{cases}$$

$$\begin{cases} \alpha = \cosh^{-1}|1 + Z_1/2Z_2| = 2\cosh^{-1}\sqrt{-Z_1/4Z_2}\ \text{nepers for } Z_1/4Z_2 < -1 \\ \beta = \pm\pi\ \text{radians} \end{cases}$$

Image impedance = pure reactance

The above formulas are based on the assumption that the impedance arms are pure reactances with zero loss.

132

Low-pass filter design

type and half section	impedance characteristics

Constant-k

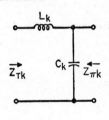

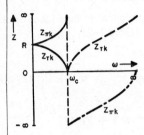

$$Z_{Tk} = R\sqrt{1 - \omega^2/\omega_c^2}$$

$$Z_{\pi k} = \frac{R}{\sqrt{1 - \omega^2/\omega_c^2}}$$

Series m-derived

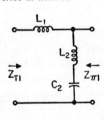

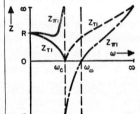

$$Z_{T1} = Z_{Tk}$$

$$Z_{\pi 1} = \frac{R(1 - \omega^2/\omega_\infty^2)}{\sqrt{1 - \omega^2/\omega_c^2}}$$

$$= \frac{R\left[1 - \frac{\omega^2}{\omega_c^2}(1 - m^2)\right]}{\sqrt{1 - \omega^2/\omega_c^2}}$$

Shunt m-derived

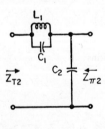

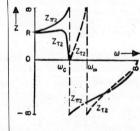

$$Z_{T2} = \frac{R\sqrt{1 - \omega^2/\omega_c^2}}{1 - \omega^2/\omega_\infty^2}$$

$$= \frac{R\sqrt{1 - \omega^2/\omega_c^2}}{1 - \frac{\omega^2}{\omega_c^2}(1 - m^2)}$$

$$= R^2/Z_{\pi 1}$$

$$Z_{\pi 2} = Z_{\pi k}$$

Notations:

Z in ohms, α in nepers, and β in radians

$\omega_c = 2\pi f_c$ = angular cutoff frequency
$= 1/\sqrt{L_k C_k}$

$\omega_\infty = 2\pi f_\infty$ = angular frequency of peak attenuation

$m = \sqrt{1 - \omega_c^2/\omega_\infty^2}$

R = nominal terminating resistance
$= \sqrt{L_k/C_k}$
$= \sqrt{Z_{Tk} Z_{\pi k}}$

	design formulas	
full-section attenuation α and phase β characteristics	series arm	shunt arm

When $0 \leqslant \omega \leqslant \omega_c$
$\alpha = 0$

$\beta = 2 \sin^{-1} \dfrac{\omega}{\omega_c}$

When $\omega_c < \omega < \infty$
$\beta = \pi$

$\alpha = 2 \cosh^{-1} \dfrac{\omega}{\omega_c}$

$L_k = \dfrac{R}{\omega_c}$

$C_k = \dfrac{1}{\omega_c R}$

$L_i = mL_k$

$L_2 = \dfrac{1-m^2}{m} L_k$

$C_2 = mC_k$

When $\omega_c < \omega < \omega_\infty$, $\beta = \pi$ and

$\alpha = \cosh^{-1}\left[2\dfrac{1/\omega_\infty{}^2 - 1/\omega_c{}^2}{1/\omega_\infty{}^2 - 1/\omega^2} - 1 \right]$

$= \cosh^{-1}\left[2\dfrac{m^2}{\omega_c{}^2/\omega^2 - (1-m^2)} - 1 \right]$

When $0 \leqslant \omega \leqslant \omega_c$, $\alpha = 0$ and

$\beta = \cos^{-1}\left[1 - 2\dfrac{1/\omega_\infty{}^2 - 1/\omega_c{}^2}{1/\omega_\infty{}^2 - 1/\omega^2} \right]$

$= \cos^{-1}\left[1 - 2\dfrac{m^2}{\omega_c{}^2/\omega^2 - (1-m^2)} \right]$

When $\omega_\infty < \omega < \infty$, $\beta = 0$ and

$\alpha = \cosh^{-1}\left[1 - 2\dfrac{1/\omega_\infty{}^2 - 1/\omega_c{}^2}{1/\omega_\infty{}^2 - 1/\omega^2} \right]$

$= \cosh^{-1}\left[1 - 2\dfrac{m^2}{\omega_c{}^2/\omega^2 - (1-m^2)} \right]$

$L_1 = mL_k$

$C_1 = \dfrac{1-m^2}{m} C_k$

$C_2 = mC_k$

For constant-k type
$R^2 = Z_{1k} Z_{2k} = k^2$

For m-derived type
Curves drawn for $m \approx 0.6$
$R^2 = Z_{T2} Z_{\pi 1}$
$\quad = Z_{1(\text{series-}m)} Z_{2(\text{shunt-}m)}$
$\quad = Z_{1(\text{shunt-}m)} Z_{2(\text{series-}m)}$

High-pass filter design

type and half section	impedance characteristics

Constant-k

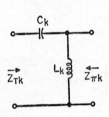 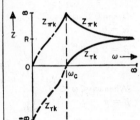

$$Z_{Tk} = R \sqrt{1 - \frac{\omega_c^2}{\omega^2}}$$

$$Z_{\pi k} = \frac{R}{\sqrt{1 - \frac{\omega_c^2}{\omega^2}}}$$

Series m-derived

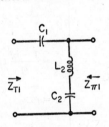 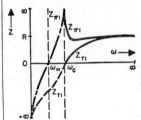

$$Z_{T1} = Z_{Tk}$$

$$Z_{\pi 1} = \frac{R \left(1 - \frac{\omega_\infty^2}{\omega^2}\right)}{\sqrt{1 - \omega_c^2/\omega^2}}$$

$$= \frac{R \left[1 - \frac{\omega_c^2}{\omega^2}(1 - m^2)\right]}{\sqrt{1 - \omega_c^2/\omega^2}}$$

Shunt m-derived

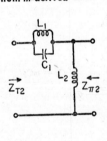 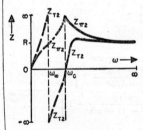

$$Z_{T2} = \frac{R\sqrt{1 - \omega_c^2/\omega^2}}{1 - \omega_\infty^2/\omega^2}$$

$$= \frac{R\sqrt{1 - \omega_c^2/\omega^2}}{1 - \frac{\omega_c^2}{\omega^2}(1 - m^2)}$$

$$= R^2/Z_{\pi 1}$$

$$Z_{\pi 2} = Z_{\pi k}$$

Notations:

Z in ohms, α in nepers, and β in radians

$\omega_c = 2\pi f_c$ = angular cutoff frequency

$\qquad = 1/\sqrt{L_k C_k}$

$\omega_\infty = 2\pi f_\infty$ = angular frequency of peak attenuation

$m = \sqrt{1 - \omega_\infty^2/\omega_c^2}$

R = nominal terminating resistance

$\qquad = \sqrt{L_k/C_k}$

$\qquad = \sqrt{Z_{Tk} Z_{\pi k}}$

	design formulas	
full-section **attenuation α and phase β characteristics**	series arm	shunt arm

When $0 < \omega < \omega_c$

$\alpha = 2 \cosh^{-1} \dfrac{\omega_c}{\omega}$

$\beta = -\pi$

When $\omega_c < \omega < \infty$

$\alpha = 0$

$\beta = -2 \sin^{-1} \dfrac{\omega_c}{\omega}$

$C_k = \dfrac{1}{\omega_c R}$ (series arm)

$L_k = \dfrac{R}{\omega_c}$ (shunt arm)

$C_1 = \dfrac{C_k}{m}$ (series arm)

$L_2 = \dfrac{L_k}{m}$ (shunt arm)

$C_2 = \dfrac{m}{1 - m^2} C_k$

When

$\omega_\infty < \omega < \omega_c$
$\beta = -\pi$ and $\alpha = \cosh^{-1}\left[2\,\dfrac{\omega_c^2 - \omega_\infty^2}{\omega^2 - \omega_\infty^2} - 1 \right]$

$= \cosh^{-1}\left[2\,\dfrac{m^2}{\dfrac{\omega^2}{\omega_c^2} - (1 - m^2)} - 1 \right]$

When

$0 < \omega < \omega_\infty$
$\beta = 0$ and $\alpha = \cosh^{-1}\left[1 - 2\,\dfrac{\omega_\infty^2 - \omega_c^2}{\omega_\infty^2 - \omega^2} \right]$

$= \cosh^{-1}\left[1 + 2\,\dfrac{m^2}{(1 - m^2) - \dfrac{\omega^2}{\omega_c^2}} \right]$

When

$\omega_c < \omega < \infty$
$\alpha = 0$ and $\beta = \cos^{-1}\left[1 - 2\,\dfrac{\omega_\infty^2 - \omega_c^2}{\omega_\infty^2 - \omega^2} \right]$

$= \cos^{-1}\left[1 + 2\,\dfrac{m^2}{(1 - m^2) - \dfrac{\omega^2}{\omega_c^2}} \right]$

$L_1 = \dfrac{m}{1 - m^2} L_k$ (series arm)

$C_1 = \dfrac{C_k}{m}$

$L_2 = \dfrac{L_k}{m}$ (shunt arm)

For constant-k type

$R^2 = Z_{1k} Z_{2k} = k^2$

For m-derived type

Curves drawn for $m \approx 0.6$

$R^2 = Z_{T2} Z_{\pi 1}$

$= Z_{1(\text{series-}m)}\, Z_{2(\text{shunt-}m)}$

$= Z_{1(\text{shunt-}m)}\, Z_{2(\text{series-}m)}$

Band-pass filter design

Notations:

The following notations apply to the charts on band-pass filter design that appear on pp. 136–145

Z in ohms, α in nepers, and β in radians

$\omega_1 = 2\pi f_1 =$ lower cutoff angular frequency

$\omega_2 = 2\pi f_2 =$ upper cutoff angular frequency

$\omega_0 = \sqrt{\omega_1 \omega_2} =$ midband angular frequency

$\omega_2 - \omega_1 =$ width of pass band

$R =$ nominal terminating resistance

$\omega_{1\infty} = 2\pi f_{1\infty} =$ lower angular frequency of peak attenuation

$\omega_{2\infty} = 2\pi f_{2\infty} =$ upper angular frequency of peak attenuation

$$m_1 = \frac{\dfrac{\omega_1 \omega_2}{\omega_{2\infty}^2} g + h}{1 - \dfrac{\omega_{1\infty}^2}{\omega_{2\infty}^2}}$$

$$m_2 = \frac{g + h \dfrac{\omega_{1\infty}^2}{\omega_1 \omega_2}}{1 - \dfrac{\omega_{1\infty}^2}{\omega_{2\infty}^2}}$$

type and half section	impedance characteristics

Constant-k

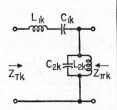

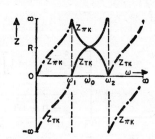

$$Z_{Tk} = \frac{R\sqrt{(\omega_2^2 - \omega^2)(\omega^2 - \omega_1^2)}}{\omega(\omega_2 - \omega_1)}$$

$$Z_{\pi k} = \frac{R\,\omega(\omega_2 - \omega_1)}{\sqrt{(\omega_2^2 - \omega^2)(\omega^2 - \omega_1^2)}}$$

$$g = \sqrt{\left(1 - \frac{\omega_{1\infty}^2}{\omega_1^2}\right)\left(1 - \frac{\omega_{1\infty}^2}{\omega_2^2}\right)}$$

$$h = \sqrt{\left(1 - \frac{\omega_1^2}{\omega_{2\infty}^2}\right)\left(1 - \frac{\omega_2^2}{\omega_{2\infty}^2}\right)}$$

$$L_{1k}C_{1k} = L_{2k}C_{2k} = \frac{1}{\omega_1\omega_2} = \frac{1}{\omega_0^2}$$

$$R^2 = \frac{L_{1k}}{C_{2k}} = \frac{L_{2k}}{C_{1k}}$$

$$= Z_{1k}\,Z_{2k} = k^2$$

$$= Z_{Tk}\,Z_{\pi k}$$

$$\left.\begin{aligned} &= Z_{1(\text{series-}m)}\,Z_{2(\text{shunt-}m)}\\ &= Z_{2(\text{series-}m)}\,Z_{1(\text{shunt-}m)}\\ &= Z_{T(\text{shunt-}m)}\,Z_{\pi(\text{series-}m)} \end{aligned}\right\} \text{ for any one pair of } m\text{-derived half-sections}$$

$$\left.\begin{aligned} Z_{T(\text{series-}m)} &= Z_{Tk}\\ Z_{\pi(\text{shunt-}m)} &= Z_{\pi k} \end{aligned}\right\}$$

full-section attenuation α and phase β characteristics	frequen- cies of peak α	design formulas	
		series arm	shunt arm
  When $\omega_2 < \omega < \infty$, $\beta = \pi$ and $\alpha = 2\cosh^{-1}\left[\dfrac{\omega^2 - \omega_0^2}{\omega(\omega_2 - \omega_1)}\right]$ When $0 < \omega < \omega_1$, $\beta = -\pi$ and $\alpha = 2\cosh^{-1}\left[\dfrac{\omega_0^2 - \omega^2}{\omega(\omega_2 - \omega_1)}\right]$ When $\omega_1 < \omega < \omega_2$, $\alpha = 0$ and $\beta = 2\sin^{-1}\left[\dfrac{\omega^2 - \omega_0^2}{\omega(\omega_2 - \omega_1)}\right]$	$\omega_{1\infty} = 0$ $\omega_{2\infty} = \infty$	$L_{1k} = \dfrac{R}{\omega_2 - \omega_1}$ $C_{1k} = \dfrac{\omega_2 - \omega_1}{R\omega_0^2}$	$L_{2k} = \dfrac{R(\omega_2 - \omega_1)}{\omega_0^2}$ $C_{2k} = \dfrac{1}{R(\omega_2 - \omega_1)}$

Band-pass filter design* *continued*

type and half section	impedance characteristics

3-element series I

$$Z_{T1} = Z_{Tk}$$

$$Z_{\pi 1} = \frac{R(\omega_2 + \omega_1)}{\omega}\sqrt{\frac{\omega^2 - \omega_1{}^2}{\omega_2{}^2 - \omega^2}}$$

3-element shunt I

$$Z_{T2} = \frac{R\omega}{(\omega_2 + \omega_1)}\sqrt{\frac{\omega_2{}^2 - \omega^2}{\omega^2 - \omega_1{}^2}}$$

$$= R^2/Z_{\pi 1}$$

$$Z_{\pi 2} = Z_{\pi k}$$

3-element series II

$$Z_{T3} = Z_{Tk}$$

$$Z_{\pi 3} = \frac{R\omega(\omega_2 + \omega_1)}{\omega_2{}^2}\sqrt{\frac{\omega_2{}^2 - \omega^2}{\omega^2 - \omega_1{}^2}}$$

3-element shunt II

$$Z_{T4} = \frac{R\omega_2{}^2}{\omega(\omega_2 + \omega_1)}\sqrt{\frac{\omega^2 - \omega_1{}^2}{\omega_2{}^2 - \omega^2}}$$

$$= R^2/Z_{\pi 3}$$

$$Z_{\pi 4} = Z_{\pi k}$$

* See notations on pp. 136–137.

full-section attenuation α and phase β characteristics	condi-tions	frequen-cies of peak α	design formulas	
			series arm	shunt arm

When $0 < \omega < \omega_1$, $\beta = 0$ and
$$\alpha = \cosh^{-1}\left[\, 1 - 2\frac{\omega^2 - \omega_1^2}{\omega_2^2 - \omega_1^2}\,\right]$$

When $\omega_1 < \omega < \omega_2$, $\alpha = 0$ and
$$\beta = \cos^{-1}\left[\, 1 - 2\frac{\omega^2 - \omega_1^2}{\omega_2^2 - \omega_1^2}\,\right]$$

When $\omega_2 < \omega < \infty$, $\beta = \pi$ and
$$\alpha = \cosh^{-1}\left[\, 2\frac{\omega^2 - \omega_1^2}{\omega_2^2 - \omega_1^2} - 1\,\right]$$

conditions:
$$m_1 = 1$$
$$m_2 = \frac{\omega_1}{\omega_2}$$

frequencies of peak α:
$$\omega_{2\infty} = \infty$$

series arm (upper):
$$L_1 = L_{1k}$$
$$C_1 = \frac{C_{1k}}{m_2}$$

shunt arm (upper):
$$C_2 = \frac{1 - m_2}{1 + m_2}\,C_{2k}$$

series arm (lower):
$$L_1 = \frac{1 - m_2}{1 + m_2}\,L_{1k}$$

shunt arm (lower):
$$L_2 = \frac{L_{2k}}{m_2}$$
$$C_2 = C_{2k}$$

When $0 < \omega < \omega_1$, $\beta = -\pi$ and
$$\alpha = \cosh^{-1}\left[\, 2\frac{\omega_1^2(\omega_2^2 - \omega^2)}{\omega^2(\omega_2^2 - \omega_1^2)} - 1\,\right]$$

When $\omega_1 < \omega < \omega_2$, $\alpha = 0$ and
$$\beta = \cos^{-1}\left[\, 1 - 2\frac{\omega_1^2(\omega_2^2 - \omega^2)}{\omega^2(\omega_2^2 - \omega_1^2)}\,\right]$$

When $\omega_2 < \omega < \infty$, $\beta = 0$ and
$$\alpha = \cosh^{-1}\left[\, 1 - 2\frac{\omega_1^2(\omega_2^2 - \omega^2)}{\omega^2(\omega_2^2 - \omega_1^2)}\,\right]$$

conditions:
$$m_1 = \frac{\omega_1}{\omega_2}$$
$$m_2 = 1$$

frequencies of peak α:
$$\omega_{1\infty} = 0$$

series arm (upper):
$$L_1 = m_1 L_{1k}$$
$$C_1 = C_{1k}$$

shunt arm (upper):
$$L_2 = \frac{1 + m_1}{1 - m_1}\,L_{2k}$$

series arm (lower):
$$C_1 = \frac{1 + m_1}{1 - m_1}\,C_{1k}$$

shunt arm (lower):
$$L_2 = L_{2k}$$
$$C_2 = m_1 C_{2k}$$

Band-pass filter design* *continued*

type and half section	impedance characteristics

4-element series I

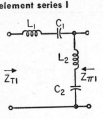

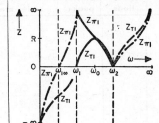

$$Z_{T1} = Z_{Tk}$$

$$Z_{\pi1} = \frac{R}{\omega(\omega_2 - \omega_1)} \sqrt{\frac{\omega_2^2 - \omega^2}{\omega^2 - \omega_1^2}}$$

$$\times \left[(\omega^2 - \omega_1^2) + m_1^2(\omega_2^2 - \omega^2) \right]$$

4-element shunt I

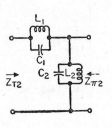

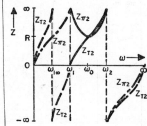

$$Z_{T2} = \frac{R\omega(\omega_2 - \omega_1)}{(\omega^2 - \omega_1^2) + m_1^2(\omega_2^2 - \omega^2)}$$

$$\times \sqrt{\frac{\omega^2 - \omega_1^2}{\omega_2^2 - \omega^2}}$$

$$= R^2/Z_{\pi1}$$

$$Z_{\pi2} = Z_{\pi k}$$

4-element series II

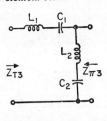

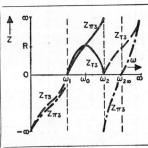

$$Z_{T3} = Z_{Tk}$$

$$Z_{\pi3} = \frac{R}{\omega(\omega_2 - \omega_1)} \sqrt{\frac{\omega^2 - \omega_1^2}{\omega_2^2 - \omega^2}}$$

$$\times \left[(\omega_2^2 - \omega^2) + m_1^2(\omega^2 - \omega_1^2) \right]$$

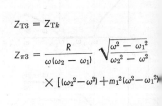

4-element shunt II

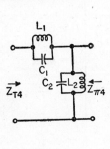

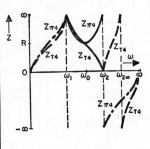

$$Z_{T4} = \frac{R\omega(\omega_2 - \omega_1)}{(\omega_2^2 - \omega^2) + m_1^2(\omega^2 - \omega_1^2)}$$

$$\times \sqrt{\frac{\omega_2^2 - \omega^2}{\omega^2 - \omega_1^2}}$$

$$= R^2/Z_{\pi3}$$

$$Z_{\pi4} = Z_{\pi k}$$

* See notations on pp 136–137.

full-section attenuation α and phase β characteristics	conditions	frequency of peak α	design formulas series arm	design formulas shunt arm

First section

Graph of α vs ω with axis markings: ∞, 0, $\omega_{1\infty}$, ω_1, ω_0, ω_2, ∞, ω.

Graph of β vs ω with axis markings: π, 0, $-\pi$, $\omega_{1\infty}$, ω_1, ω_0, ω_2, ∞, ω.

Conditions:
$$\frac{\omega_1}{\omega_2} = \frac{m_1}{m_2}$$

$$m_2 = \left|\frac{1 - \dfrac{\omega_1^2}{\omega_\infty^2}}{1 - \dfrac{\omega_0^2}{\omega_\infty^2}}\ \cdot\ 1 - \dfrac{\omega_0^2}{\omega_2^2}\right|$$

$$A = 1 - \frac{2}{1 + \dfrac{(\omega^2 - \omega_1^2)(\omega_2^2 - \omega^2)}{m_1^2(\omega_2^2 - \omega^2)}}$$

Frequency of peak α:
$$\omega_{1\infty} = \sqrt{\frac{\omega_1^2 - \omega_0^2 m_1^2}{1 - m_1^2}}$$

Design formulas (upper):

series arm:
$$L_1 = m_1 L_{1k} \qquad C_1 = \frac{C_{1k}}{m_2}$$

shunt arm:
$$L_2 = \frac{1 - m_1^2}{m_1} L_{1k} \qquad C_2 = \frac{m_2}{1 - m_2^2} C_{1k}$$

Design formulas (lower):

series arm:
$$L_1 = \frac{m_2}{1 - m_2^2} L_{2k} \qquad C_1 = \frac{1 - m_1^2}{m_1} C_{2k}$$

shunt arm:
$$L_2 = \frac{L_{2k}}{m_2} \qquad C_2 = m_1 C_{2k}$$

When $\omega_1 < \omega < \omega_2$, $\alpha = 0$ and $\beta = \cos^{-1} A$

When $0 < \omega < \omega_{1\infty}$, $\beta = 0$ and $\alpha = \cosh^{-1} A$

When $\omega_{1\infty} < \omega < \omega_1$, $\beta = -\pi$ and $\alpha = \cosh^{-1}(-A)$

When $\omega_2 < \omega < \infty$, $\beta = 0$ and $\alpha = \cosh^{-1} A$

Second section

Graph of α vs ω with axis markings: ∞, 0, ω_1, ω_0, ω_2, $\omega_{2\infty}$, ∞, ω.

Graph of β vs ω with axis markings: π, 0, $-\pi$, ω_1, ω_0, ω_2, $\omega_{2\infty}$, ∞, ω.

Conditions:
$$\frac{\omega_2}{\omega_1} = \frac{m_1}{m_2}$$

$$m_1 = \left|\frac{1 - \dfrac{\omega_2^2}{\omega_\infty^2}}{1 - \dfrac{\omega_0^2}{\omega_\infty^2}}\ \cdot\ 1 - \dfrac{\omega_1^2}{\omega_\infty^2}\right|$$

$$B = 1 - \frac{2}{1 + \dfrac{(\omega^2 - \omega_1^2)(\omega^2 - \omega_2^2)}{m_1^2(\omega^2 - \omega_1^2)}}$$

Frequency of peak α:
$$\omega_{2\infty} = \sqrt{\frac{m_1^2 \omega_1^2 - \omega_2^2}{m_1^2 - 1}}$$

Design formulas (upper):

series arm:
$$L_1 = m_1 L_{1k} \qquad C_1 = \frac{C_{1k}}{m_2}$$

shunt arm:
$$L_2 = \frac{1 - m_1^2}{m_1} L_{1k} \qquad C_2 = \frac{m_2}{1 - m_2^2} C_{1k}$$

Design formulas (lower):

series arm:
$$L_1 = \frac{m_2}{1 - m_2^2} L_{2k} \qquad C_1 = \frac{1 - m_1^2}{m_1} C_{2k}$$

shunt arm:
$$L_2 = \frac{L_{2k}}{m_2} \qquad C_2 = m_1 C_{2k}$$

When $\omega_2 < \omega < \omega_{2\infty}$, $\beta = \pi$ and $\alpha = \cosh^{-1}(-B)$

When $0 < \omega < \omega_1$, $\beta = 0$ and $\alpha = \cosh^{-1} B$

When $\omega_1 < \omega < \omega_2$, $\alpha = 0$ and $\beta = \cos^{-1} B$

When $\omega_{2\infty} < \omega < \infty$, $\beta = 0$ and $\alpha = \cosh^{-1} B$

Band-pass filter design* continued

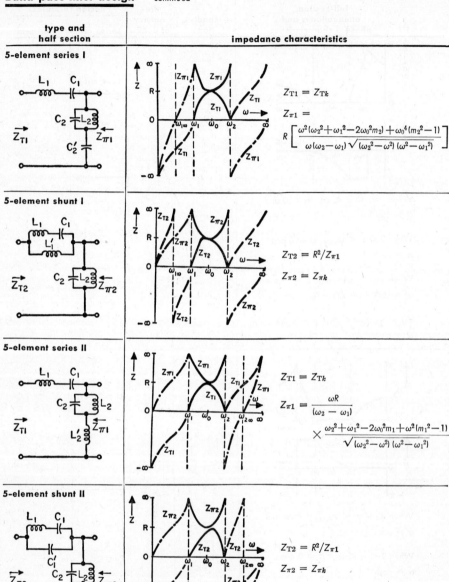

type and half section	impedance characteristics

5-element series I

$$Z_{T1} = Z_{Tk}$$

$$Z_{\pi 1} =$$

$$R\left[\frac{\omega^2(\omega_2{}^2+\omega_1{}^2-2\omega_0{}^2m_2)+\omega_0{}^4(m_2{}^2-1)}{\omega(\omega_2-\omega_1)\sqrt{(\omega_2{}^2-\omega^2)(\omega^2-\omega_1{}^2)}}\right]$$

5-element shunt I

$$Z_{T2} = R^2/Z_{\pi 1}$$

$$Z_{\pi 2} = Z_{\pi k}$$

5-element series II

$$Z_{T1} = Z_{Tk}$$

$$Z_{\pi 1} = \frac{\omega R}{(\omega_2-\omega_1)}$$

$$\times \frac{\omega_2{}^2+\omega_1{}^2-2\omega_0{}^2m_1+\omega^2(m_1{}^2-1)}{\sqrt{(\omega_2{}^2-\omega^2)(\omega^2-\omega_1{}^2)}}$$

5-element shunt II

$$Z_{T2} = R^2/Z_{\pi 1}$$

$$Z_{\pi 2} = Z_{\pi k}$$

* See notations on pp. 136–137.

full-section attenuation α and phase β characteristics	conditions	frequency of peak α	design formulas — series arm	design formulas — shunt arm

When $\omega_1 < \omega < \omega_2$
$\alpha = 0$ and

$$\beta = \cos^{-1}\left[1 - \frac{2(\omega^2 - \omega_0^2 m_2)^2}{\omega^2(\omega_2^2 + \omega_1^2 - 2\omega_0^2 m_2) + \omega_0^4(m_2^2 - 1)}\right]$$

When $0 < \omega < \omega_{1\infty}$, $\beta = 0$ and

$$\alpha = \cosh^{-1}\left[1 - \frac{2(\omega^2 - \omega_0^2 m_2)^2}{\omega^2(\omega_2^2 + \omega_1^2 - 2\omega_0^2 m_2) + \omega_0^4(m_2^2 - 1)}\right]$$

When $\omega_{1\infty} < \omega < \omega_1$, $\beta = -\pi$ and

$$\alpha = \cosh^{-1}\left[\frac{2(\omega^2 - \omega_0^2 m_2)^2}{\omega^2(\omega_2^2 + \omega_1^2 - 2\omega_0^2 m_2) + \omega_0^4(m_2^2 - 1)} - 1\right]$$

When $\omega_2 < \omega < \infty$, $\beta = \pi$ and
$\alpha =$ same formula as for $0 < \omega < \omega_{1\infty}$

When $\omega_2 < \omega < \omega_{2\infty}$
$\beta = \pi$ and

$$\alpha = \cosh^{-1}\left\{1 - \frac{2(\omega^2 m_1 - \omega_0^2)^2}{\omega^2[\omega_2^2 + \omega_1^2 - 2\omega_0^2 m_1 + \omega^2(m_1^2 - 1)]}\right\}$$

When $0 < \omega < \omega_1$, $\beta = -\pi$ and

$$\alpha = \cosh^{-1}\left\{\frac{2(\omega^2 m_1 - \omega_0^2)^2}{\omega^2[\omega_2^2 + \omega_1^2 - 2\omega_0^2 m_1 + \omega^2(m_1^2 - 1)]} - 1\right\}$$

When $\omega_1 < \omega < \omega_2$, $\alpha = 0$ and

$$\beta = \cos^{-1}\left\{1 - \frac{2(\omega^2 m_1 - \omega_0^2)^2}{\omega^2[\omega_2^2 + \omega_1^2 - 2\omega_0^2 m_1 + \omega^2(m_1^2 - 1)]}\right\}$$

When $\omega_{2\infty} < \omega < \infty$, $\beta = 0$ and
$\alpha =$ same formula as for $0 < \omega < \omega_1$

conditions:

$m_1 = 1$

$m_2 = \sqrt{\left(1 - \frac{\omega_1^2\infty}{\omega_0^2}\right)\left(1 - \frac{\omega_1^2\infty}{\omega_2^2}\right)}$

$m_1 = \sqrt{\left(1 - \frac{\omega_2^2\infty}{\omega_0^2}\right)\left(1 - \frac{\omega_1^2}{\omega_2^2\infty}\right)}$

$m_2 = 1$

frequency of peak α:

$\omega_1\infty = \omega_0\sqrt{\dfrac{1 - m_2^2}{\omega_2^2 + \omega_1^2 - 2\omega_0^2 m_2}}$

$\omega_2\infty = \infty$

$\omega_1\infty = 0$

$\omega_2\infty = \omega_0\sqrt{\dfrac{\omega_2^2 + \omega_1^2 - 2\omega_0^2 m_1}{1 - m_1^2}}$

design formulas — series arm:

$L_1 = L_{1k}$
$C_1 = \dfrac{C_{1k}}{m_2}$

$L_1 = L_{2k}$
$C_1 = \dfrac{C_{2k}}{m_2}\left[\dfrac{[\omega_2 - \omega_1]^2}{\omega_0^2} - \dfrac{(1 - m_2)^2}{m_2}\right]$
$L_1' = \dfrac{m_2}{1 - m_2^2}L_{2k}$

$L_1 = m_1 L_{1k}$
$C_1 = C_{1k}$

$L_1 = m_1 L_{2k}\left/\left[\dfrac{[\omega_2 - \omega_1]^2}{\omega_0^2} - \dfrac{(m_1 - 1)^2}{m_1}\right]\right.$
$C_1 = C_{2k}$
$C_1' = \dfrac{1 - m_1^2}{m_1}C_{2k}$

design formulas — shunt arm:

$L_2 = \dfrac{L_{1k}}{m_2}\left[\dfrac{[\omega_2 - \omega_1]^2}{\omega_0^2} - \dfrac{(1 - m_2)^2}{m_2}\right]$
$C_2 = C_{1k}\left[\dfrac{[\omega_2 - \omega_1]^2}{\omega_0^2} - \dfrac{(1 - m_2)^2}{m_2}\right]$
$C_2' = \dfrac{m_2}{1 - m_2^2}C_{1k}$

$L_2 = \dfrac{L_{2k}}{m_2}$
$C_2 = C_{2k}$

$L_2 = L_{1k}\left/\left[\dfrac{[\omega_2 - \omega_1]^2}{\omega_0^2} - \dfrac{(m_1 - 1)^2}{m_1}\right]\right.$
$C_2 = m_1 C_{1k}\left/\left[\dfrac{[\omega_2 - \omega_1]^2}{\omega_0^2} - \dfrac{(m_1 - 1)^2}{m_1}\right]\right.$
$L_2' = \dfrac{1 - m_1^2}{m_1}L_{1k}$

$L_2 = L_{2k}$
$C_2 = m_1 C_{2k}$

Band-pass filter design*   *continued*

type and half section	impedance characteristics
6-element series 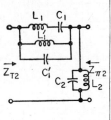	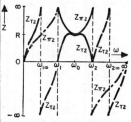 $Z_{T1} = Z_{Tk}$ $Z_{\pi 1} = \dfrac{R}{\omega(\omega_2 - \omega_1)}$ $\times \dfrac{(\omega_2{}^2 - \omega^2)(\omega^2 - \omega_1{}^2) + (\omega_0{}^2 m_2 - \omega^2 m_1)^2}{\sqrt{(\omega_2{}^2 - \omega^2)(\omega^2 - \omega_1{}^2)}}$
6-element shunt	$Z_{T2} = R^2 / Z_{\pi 1}$ $Z_{\pi 2} = Z_{\pi k}$

---

full-section attenuation α and phase β characteristics

When $\omega_1 < \omega < \omega_2$, $\alpha = 0$ and

$$\beta = \cos^{-1}\left[1 - \frac{2(\omega^2 m_1 - \omega_0{}^2 m_2)^2}{(\omega^2 m_1 - \omega_0{}^2 m_2)^2 + (\omega_2{}^2 - \omega^2)(\omega^2 - \omega_1{}^2)}\right]$$

When $\omega_2 < \omega < \omega_{2\infty}$, $\beta = \pi$ and

$$\alpha = \cosh^{-1}\left[\frac{2(\omega^2 m_1 - \omega_0{}^2 m_2)^2}{(\omega^2 m_1 - \omega_0{}^2 m_2)^2 + (\omega_2{}^2 - \omega^2)(\omega^2 - \omega_1{}^2)} + 1\right]$$

When $0 < \omega < \omega_{1\infty}$, $\beta = 0$ and

$$\alpha = \cosh^{-1}\left[1 - \frac{2(\omega^2 m_1 - \omega_0{}^2 m_2)^2}{(\omega^2 m_1 - \omega_0{}^2 m_2)^2 + (\omega_2{}^2 - \omega^2)(\omega^2 - \omega_1{}^2)}\right]$$

When $\omega_{1\infty} < \omega < \omega_1$, $\beta = -\pi$ and

$$\alpha = \cosh^{-1}\left[\frac{2(\omega^2 m_1 - \omega_0{}^2 m_2)^2}{(\omega^2 m_1 - \omega_0{}^2 m_2)^2 + (\omega_2{}^2 - \omega^2)(\omega^2 - \omega_1{}^2)} - 1\right]$$

When $\omega_{2\infty} < \omega < \infty$, $\beta = 0$ and
α = same formula as for $0 < \omega < \omega_{1\infty}$

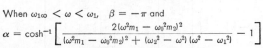

* See notations on pp. 136–137.

design formulas

series arm	shunt arm
	$L_2 = \dfrac{L_{1k}}{m_2}\left[\dfrac{(\omega_2 - \omega_1)^2}{\omega_0{}^2} - \dfrac{(m_1 - m_2)^2}{m_1 m_2}\right]$
$L_1 = m_1 L_{1k}$	$L_2' = \dfrac{1 - m_1{}^2}{m_1} L_{1k}$
$C_1 = \dfrac{C_{1k}}{m_2}$	$C_2 = \dfrac{m_1 C_{1k}}{\dfrac{(\omega_2 - \omega_1)^2}{\omega_0{}^2} - \dfrac{(m_1 - m_2)^2}{m_1 m_2}}$
	$C_2' = \dfrac{m_2}{1 - m_2{}^2} C_{1k}$
$L_1 = \dfrac{m_1 L_{2k}}{\dfrac{(\omega_2 - \omega_1)^2}{\omega_0{}^2} - \dfrac{(m_1 - m_2)^2}{m_1 m_2}}$	
$C_1 = \dfrac{C_{2k}}{m_2}\left[\dfrac{(\omega_2 - \omega_1)^2}{\omega_0{}^2} - \dfrac{(m_1 - m_2)^2}{m_1 m_2}\right]$	$L_2 = \dfrac{L_{2k}}{m_2}$
$L_1' = \dfrac{m_2}{1 - m_2{}^2} L_{2k}$	$C_2 = m_1 C_{2k}$
$C_1' = \dfrac{1 - m_1{}^2}{m_1} C_{2k}$	

conditions	frequency of peak α
$m_1 = \dfrac{g\,\dfrac{\omega_0{}^2}{\omega_{2\infty}^2} + h}{1 - \dfrac{\omega_{1\infty}^2}{\omega_{2\infty}^2}}$ $m_2 = \dfrac{g + h\,\dfrac{\omega_{1\infty}^2}{\omega_0{}^2}}{1 - \dfrac{\omega_{1\infty}^2}{\omega_{2\infty}^2}}$	$\omega_{1\infty}^2 + \omega_{2\infty}^2 = \dfrac{\omega_2{}^2 + \omega_1{}^2 - 2\omega_0{}^2 m_1 m_2}{1 - m_1{}^2}$
	$\omega_{1\infty}^2 \times \omega_{2\infty}^2 = \omega_0{}^4\left(\dfrac{1 - m_2{}^2}{1 - m_1{}^2}\right)$

Band-stop filter design

Notations

Z in ohms, α in nepers, and β in radians

$\omega_1 = $ lower cutoff angular frequency

$\omega_2 = $ upper cutoff angular frequency

$\omega_0 = \sqrt{\omega_1 \omega_2} = 1/\sqrt{L_{1k} C_{1k}}$
$= 1/\sqrt{L_{2k} C_{2k}}$

$\omega_2 - \omega_1 = $ width of stop band

$\omega_{1\infty} = $ lower angular frequency of peak attenuation

$\omega_{2\infty} = $ upper angular frequency of peak attenuation

$R = $ nominal terminating resistance

$R^2 = \dfrac{L_{1k}}{C_{2k}} = \dfrac{L_{2k}}{C_{1k}}$
$= Z_{1k} Z_{2k} = Z_{Tk} Z_{\pi k} = k^2$
$= Z_{1(\text{series-}m)}\, Z_{2(\text{shunt-}m)}$
$= Z_{2(\text{series-}m)}\, Z_{1(\text{shunt-}m)}$
$= Z_{T2}\, Z_{\pi 1}$

Band-stop filter design* continued

type and half section	impedance characteristics

Constant-k

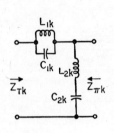

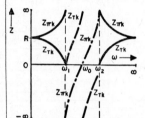

$$Z_{Tk} = \frac{R\sqrt{(\omega^2 - \omega_1{}^2)(\omega^2 - \omega_2{}^2)}}{(\omega_0{}^2 - \omega^2)}$$

$$Z_{\pi k} = \frac{R(\omega_0{}^2 - \omega^2)}{\sqrt{(\omega^2 - \omega_1{}^2)(\omega^2 - \omega_2{}^2)}}$$

For the pass bands, use $|\omega_0{}^2 - \omega^2|$ in the above formulas

Series m-derived

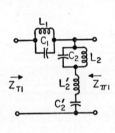

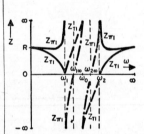

curves drawn for $m = 0.6$

$$Z_{T1} = Z_{Tk}$$

$$Z_{\pi 1} = R\left\{ \frac{1 - (1 - m^2)\left[\dfrac{\omega(\omega_2 - \omega_1)}{\omega_0{}^2 - \omega^2}\right]^2}{\sqrt{1 - \left[\dfrac{\omega(\omega_2 - \omega_1)}{\omega_0{}^2 - \omega^2}\right]^2}} \right\}$$

Shunt m-derived

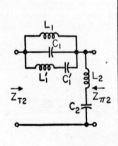

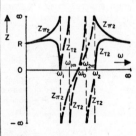

curves drawn for $m = 0.6$

$$Z_{T2} = \frac{R^2}{Z_{\pi 1}}$$

$$Z_{\pi 2} = Z_{\pi k}$$

* See notations on preceding page.

full-section attenuation α and phase β characteristics	condi-tions	freq of peak α	design formulas	
			series arm	shunt arm

When $\omega = \omega_0$
$\alpha = \infty$

When $\omega_0 < \omega < \omega_2$
$\alpha = 2\cosh^{-1}\dfrac{\omega(\omega_2 - \omega_1)}{\omega^2 - \omega_0^2}$
$\beta = -\pi$

When $\omega_2 < \omega < \infty$
$\alpha = 0$
$\beta = 2\sin^{-1}\dfrac{\omega(\omega_2 - \omega_1)}{\omega_0^2 - \omega^2}$

When $\omega_1 < \omega < \omega_0$
$\alpha = 2\cosh^{-1}\dfrac{\omega(\omega_2 - \omega_1)}{\omega_0^2 - \omega^2}$
$\beta = \pi$

When $0 < \omega < \omega_1$
$\alpha = 0$
$\beta = 2\sin^{-1}\dfrac{\omega(\omega_2 - \omega_1)}{\omega_0^2 - \omega^2}$

$\omega_0 = \sqrt{\omega_1\omega_2}$

$L_{1k} = \dfrac{R(\omega_2 - \omega_1)}{\omega_1\omega_2}$ $L_{2k} = \dfrac{R}{\omega_2 - \omega_1}$

$C_{1k} = \dfrac{1}{R(\omega_2 - \omega_1)}$ $C_{2k} = \dfrac{\omega_2 - \omega_1}{\omega_1\omega_2 R}$

---

curves drawn for $m = 0.6$

When $\omega_2 < \omega < \infty$, $\alpha = 0$ and $\beta =$ same formula as for $0 < \omega < \omega_1$

When $\omega_{2\infty} < \omega < \omega_2$, $\beta = -\pi$ and $\alpha =$ same formula as for $\omega_1 < \omega < \omega_{1\infty}$

When $0 < \omega < \omega_1$, $\alpha = 0$ and
$\beta = \cos^{-1}\left[1 - \dfrac{2\omega^2 m^2(\omega_2 - \omega_1)^2}{(\omega^2 - \omega_1^2)(\omega^2 - \omega_2^2) + \omega^2 m^2(\omega_2 - \omega_1)^2}\right]$

When $\omega_1 < \omega < \omega_{1\infty}$, $\beta = \pi$ and
$\alpha = \cosh^{-1}\left[\dfrac{2\omega^2 m^2(\omega_2 - \omega_1)^2}{(\omega^2 - \omega_1^2)(\omega^2 - \omega_2^2) + \omega^2 m^2(\omega_2 - \omega_1)^2} - 1\right]$

When $\omega_{1\infty} < \omega < \omega_{2\infty}$, $\beta = 0$ and
$\alpha = \cosh^{-1}\left[1 - \dfrac{2\omega^2 m^2(\omega_2 - \omega_1)^2}{(\omega^2 - \omega_1^2)(\omega^2 - \omega_2^2) + \omega^2 m^2(\omega_2 - \omega_1)^2}\right]$

$m = \sqrt{1 - \dfrac{(\omega_{2\infty} - \omega_{1\infty})^2}{(\omega_2 - \omega_1)^2}}$

$\omega_{1\infty}\omega_{2\infty} = \omega_0^2$

$L_1 = mL_{1k}$
$C_1 = \dfrac{C_{1k}}{m}$

$L_2 = \dfrac{1 - m^2}{m}L_{1k}$
$C_2 = \dfrac{m}{1 - m^2}C_{1k}$
$L_2' = \dfrac{L_{2k}}{m}$
$C_2' = mC_{2k}$

$L_1 = mL_{1k}$
$C_1 = \dfrac{C_{1k}}{m}$
$L_1' = \dfrac{m}{1 - m^2}L_{2k}$
$C_1' = \dfrac{1 - m^2}{m}C_{2k}$

$L_2 = \dfrac{L_{2k}}{m}$
$C_2 = mC_{2k}$

Building up a composite filter

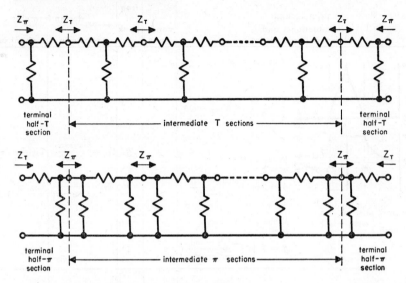

Fig. 2—Method of building up a composite filter.

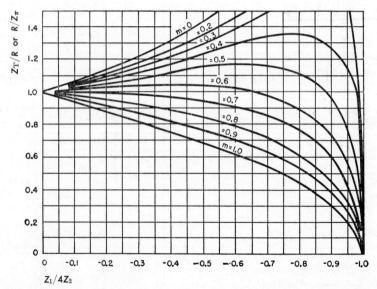

Fig. 3—Effect of design parameter *m* on the image-impedance characteristics in the pass band.

Building up a composite filter   *continued*

The intermediate sections (Fig. 2) are matched on an image-impedance basis, but the attenuation characteristics of the sections may be varied by suitably designing the series and shunt arms of each section. Thus, the frequencies attenuated only slightly by one section may be strongly attenuated by other sections. However, the image impedance will be far from constant in the passband, unless the value of m is appropriately selected. In order to have a more constant impedance at the external terminals, suitably designed half sections are added. For these terminating sections, a value of $m \approx 0.6$ is used (Fig. 3). When they are designed with the same cutoff frequencies and the same load resistance as the midsections, the image impedance will match that of the midsections.

Example of low-pass filter design

To cut off at 15 kilocycles/second; to give peak attenuation at 30 kilocycles; with a load resistance of 600 ohms; and using a constant-k midsection and an m-derived midsection. Full T-sections will be used.

Constant-k midsection

$$L_k = \frac{R}{\omega_c} = \frac{600}{(6.28)\,(15 \times 10^3)} = 6.37 \times 10^{-3} \text{ henry}$$

$$C_k = \frac{1}{\omega_c R} = \frac{1}{(6.28)\,(15 \times 10^3)\,(600)} = 0.0177 \times 10^{-6} \text{ farad}$$

$$\alpha = 2 \cosh^{-1} \frac{\omega}{\omega_c} = 2 \cosh^{-1} \frac{f}{15}$$

$$\beta = 2 \sin^{-1} \frac{\omega}{\omega_c} = 2 \sin^{-1} \frac{f}{15}$$

where α is in nepers, β in radians, and f in kilocycles.

m-derived midsection

$$m = \sqrt{1 - \omega_c^2/\omega_\infty^2} = \sqrt{1 - 15^2/30^2}$$

$$= \sqrt{0.75} = 0.866$$

$$L_1 = mL_k = 0.866\,(6.37 \times 10^{-3})$$

$$= 5.52 \times 10^{-3} \text{ henry}$$

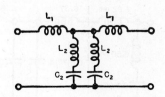

Example of low-pass filter design   *continued*

$$L_2 = \frac{1 - m^2}{m} L_k = \left[\frac{1 - (0.866)^2}{0.866} \right] (6.37 \times 10^{-3}) = 1.84 \times 10^{-3} \text{ henry}$$

$$C_2 = mC_k = 0.866 \ (0.0177 \times 10^{-6}) = 0.0153 \times 10^{-6} \text{ farad}$$

$$\alpha = \cosh^{-1} \left[1 - \frac{2m^2}{\dfrac{\omega_c^2}{\omega^2} - (1 - m^2)} \right] = \cosh^{-1} \left[1 - \frac{1.5}{\dfrac{225}{f^2} - 0.25} \right]$$

$$\beta = \cos^{-1} \left[1 - \frac{2m^2}{\dfrac{\omega_c^2}{\omega^2} - (1 - m^2)} \right] = \cos^{-1} \left[1 - \frac{1.5}{\dfrac{225}{f^2} - 0.25} \right]$$

End sections m = 0.6

$$L_1 = mL_k = 0.6 \ (6.37 \times 10^{-3})$$
$$= 3.82 \times 10^{-3} \text{ henry}$$

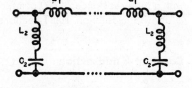

$$L_2 = \frac{1 - m^2}{m} L_k$$

$$= \left[\frac{1 - (0.6)^2}{0.6} \right] (6.37 \times 10^{-3}) = 6.80 \times 10^{-3} \text{ henry}$$

$$C_2 = mC_k = 0.6 \ (0.0177 \times 10^{-6}) = 0.0106 \times 10^{-6} \text{ farad}$$

Frequency of peak attenuation f_∞

$$f_\infty = \sqrt{\frac{f_c^2}{1 - m^2}} = \sqrt{\frac{(15 \times 10^3)^2}{1 - (0.6)^2}} = 18.75 \text{ kilocycles}$$

Filter showing individual sections

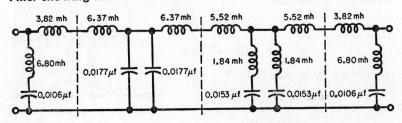

Example of low-pass filter design *continued*

Filter after combining elements

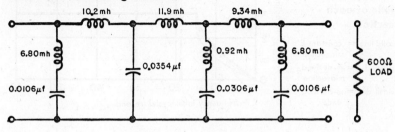

Attenuation of each section

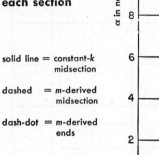

solid line = constant-*k* midsection

dashed = *m*-derived midsection

dash-dot = *m*-derived ends

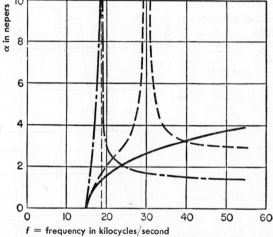

f = frequency in kilocycles/second

Attenuation of composite filter

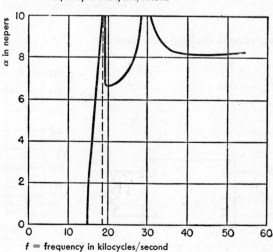

f = frequency in kilocycles/second

Example of low-pass filter design *continued*

Phase characteristic of each section

solid line = constant-*k* midsection

dashed = *m*-derived midsection

dash-dot = *m*-derived ends

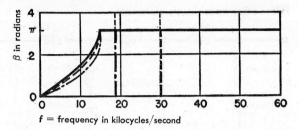

Phase characteristic of composite filter

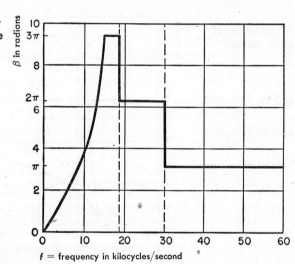

Impedance looking into filter Z_{in}

$$Z_{in} = \frac{R\left[1 - \dfrac{\omega^2}{\omega_c^2}(1 - m^2)\right]}{\sqrt{1 - \omega^2/\omega_c^2}}$$

$$= \frac{600\left[1 - 0.64\,(f/15)^2\right]}{\sqrt{1 - (f/15)^2}}$$

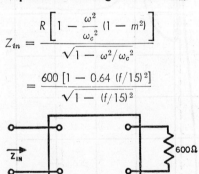

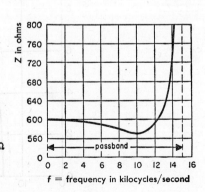

■ Attenuators

Definitions

An attenuator is a network designed to introduce a known loss when working between resistive impedances Z_1 and Z_2 to which the input and output impedances of the attenuator are matched. Either Z_1 or Z_2 may be the source and the other the load. The attenuation of such networks expressed as a power ratio is the same regardless of the direction of working.

Three forms of resistance network that may be conveniently used to realize these conditions are shown on page 158. These are the T section, the π section, and the bridged-T section. Equivalent balanced sections also are shown. Methods are given for the computation of attenuator networks, the hyperbolic expressions giving rapid solutions with the aid of tables of hyperbolic functions on pages 632 to 634. Tables of the various types of attenuators are given on pages 161 to 168.

Ladder attenuator

Ladder attenuator, Fig. 1, input switch points P_0, P_1, P_2, P_3 at shunt arms. Also intermediate point P_m tapped on series arm. May be either unbalanced, as shown, or balanced.

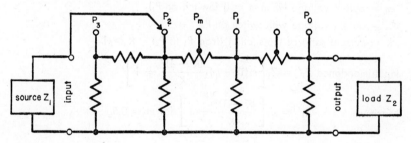

Fig. 1—Ladder attenuator.

Ladder, for design purposes, Fig. 2, is resolved into a cascade of π sections by imagining each shunt arm split into two resistors. Last section matches Z_2 to $2Z_1$. All other sections are symmetrical, matching impedances $2Z_1$, with a terminating resistor $2Z_1$ on the first section. Each section is designed for the loss required between the switch points at the ends of that section.

Input to P_0: Loss in decibels $= 10 \log_{10} \dfrac{(2Z_1 + Z_2)^2}{4Z_1 Z_2}$

Input impedance $Z_1' = \dfrac{Z_2}{2}$ $\qquad$ Output impedance $= \dfrac{Z_1 Z_2}{Z_1 + Z_2}$

Ladder attenuator *continued*

Input to P_1, P_2, or P_3: Loss in decibels = 3 + (sum of losses of π sections between input and output).   Input impedance $Z_1' = Z_1$

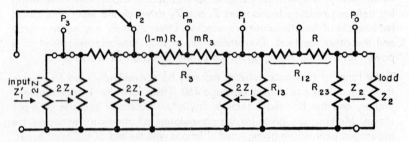

Fig. 2—Ladder attenuator resolved into a cascade of π sections.

Input to P_m (on a symmetrical π section):

$$\frac{e_0}{e_m} = \frac{1}{2} \frac{m(1-m)(K-1)^2 + 2K}{K - m(K-1)}$$

where

e_0 = output voltage when $m = 0$ (Switch on P_1)

e_m = output voltage with switch on P_m

K = current ratio of the section (from P_1 to P_2) $K > 1$

Input impedance $Z_1' = Z_1 \left[m(1-m) \dfrac{(K-1)^2}{K} + 1 \right]$

Maximum $Z_1' = Z_1 \left[\dfrac{(K-1)^2}{4K} + 1 \right]$ for $m = 0.5$.

The unsymmetrical last section may be treated as a system of voltage-dividing resistors. Solve for the resistance R from P_0 to the tap, for each value of

$$\left(\frac{\text{output voltage with input on } P_0}{\text{output voltage with input on tap}} \right)$$

A useful case

When $Z_1 = Z_2 = 500$ ohms.

Then loss on P_0 is 3.52 decibels.

Let the last section be designed for loss of 12.51 decibels. Then

Ladder attenuator   *continued*

$R_{13} = 2444$ ohms (shunted by 1000 ohms)
$R_{23} = 654$ ohms (shunted by 500 ohms)
$R_{12} = 1409$ ohms

The table shows the location of the tap and the input and output impedances for several values of loss, relative to the loss on P_0:

relative loss in decibels	tap R ohms	input impedance ohms	output impedance ohms
0	0	250	250
2	170	368	304
4	375	478	353
6	615	562	394
8	882	600	428
10	1157	577	454
12	1409	500	473

Input to P_0:   Output impedance $= 0.6\,Z$ (See Fig. 3.)

Input to P_0, P_1, P_2, or P_3: Loss in decibels $= 6 +$ (sum of losses of π sections between input and output).   Input impedance $= Z$

Input to P_m:

$$\frac{e_0}{e_m} = \frac{1}{4}\,\frac{m(1-m)(K-1)^2 + 4K}{K - m(K-1)}$$

Input impedance:

$$Z' = Z\left[\frac{m(1-m)(K-1)^2}{2K} + 1\right]$$

Maximum $Z' = Z\left[\frac{(K-1)^2}{8K} + 1\right]$ for $m = 0.5$

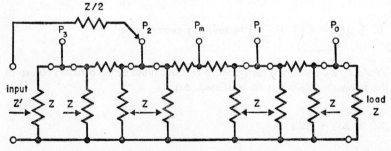

Fig. 3—A variation of the ladder attenuator, useful when $Z_1 = Z_2 = Z$. Simpler in design, with improved impedance characteristics, but having minimum insertion loss 2.5 decibels higher than attenuator of Fig. 2. All π sections are symmetrical.

Load impedance

Effect of incorrect load impedance on operation of an attenuator

In the applications of attenuators, the question frequently arises as to the effect upon the input impedance and the attenuation by the use of a load impedance which is different from that for which the network was designed. The following results apply to all resistive networks that, when operated between resistive impedances Z_1 and Z_2, present matching terminal impedances Z_1 and Z_2, respectively. The results may be derived in the general case by the application of the network theorems, and may be readily confirmed mathematically for simple specific cases such as the T section.

For the designed use of the network, let

Z_1 = input impedance of properly terminated network

Z_2 = load impedance that properly terminates the network

N = power ratio from input to output

K = current ratio from input to output

$$K = \frac{i_1}{i_2} = \sqrt{\frac{NZ_2}{Z_1}} \text{ (different in the two directions except when } Z_2 = Z_1)$$

For the actual conditions of operation, let

$$(Z_2 + \Delta Z_2) = Z_2\left(1 + \frac{\Delta Z_2}{Z_2}\right) = \text{actual load impedance}$$

$$(Z_1 + \Delta Z_1) = Z_1\left(1 + \frac{\Delta Z_1}{Z_1}\right) = \text{resulting input impedance}$$

$$(K + \Delta K) = K\left(1 + \frac{\Delta K}{K}\right) = \text{resulting current ratio}$$

While Z_1, Z_2, and K are restricted to real quantities by the assumed nature of the network, ΔZ_2 is not so restricted, e.g.,

$$\Delta Z_2 = \Delta R_2 + j\Delta X_2$$

As a consequence, ΔZ_1 and ΔK can become imaginary or complex. Furthermore, ΔZ_2 is not restricted to small values.

Load impedance   *continued*

The results for the actual conditions are

$$\frac{\Delta Z_1}{Z_1} = \frac{2 \, \Delta Z_2 / Z_2}{2N + (N - 1)\dfrac{\Delta Z_2}{Z_2}} \quad \text{and} \quad \frac{\Delta K}{K} = \left(\frac{N - 1}{2N}\right)\frac{\Delta Z_2}{Z_2}$$

Certain special cases may be cited

Case 1: For small $\Delta Z_2 / Z_2$

$$\frac{\Delta Z_1}{Z_1} = \frac{1}{N}\frac{\Delta Z_2}{Z_2} \quad \text{or} \quad \Delta Z_1 = \frac{1}{K^2}\Delta Z_2$$

$$\frac{\Delta i_2}{i_2} = -\frac{1}{2}\frac{\Delta Z_2}{Z_2}$$

but the error in insertion power loss of the attenuator is negligibly small.

Case 2: Short-circuited output

$$\frac{\Delta Z_1}{Z_1} = \frac{-2}{N + 1}$$

or input impedance $= \left(\dfrac{N - 1}{N + 1}\right) Z_1 = Z_1 \tanh \theta$

where θ is the designed attenuation in nepers.

Case 3: Open-circuited output

$$\frac{\Delta Z_1}{Z_1} = \frac{2}{N - 1}$$

or input impedance $= \left(\dfrac{N + 1}{N - 1}\right) Z_1 = Z_1 \coth \theta$

Case 4: For $N = 1$ (possible only when $Z_1 = Z_2$ and directly connected)

$$\frac{\Delta Z_1}{Z_1} = \frac{\Delta Z_2}{Z_2}$$

$$\frac{\Delta K}{K} = 0$$

Case 5: For large N

$$\frac{\Delta K}{K} = \frac{1}{2}\frac{\Delta Z_2}{Z_2}$$

Attenuator network design   see page 160 for symbols

description	configuration	
	unbalanced	**balanced**
Unbalanced T and balanced H (see Fig. 8)		
Symmetrical T and H ($Z_1 = Z_2 = Z$) (see Fig. 4)		
Minimum-loss pad matching Z_1 and Z_2 ($Z_1 > Z_2$) (see Fig. 7)		
Unbalanced π and balanced 0		
Symmetrical π and 0 ($Z_1 = Z_2 = Z$) (see Fig. 5)		
Bridged T and bridged H (see Fig. 6)		

design formulas		checking formulas
hyperbolic	**arithmetical**	**checking formulas**

hyperbolic	arithmetical	checking formulas
$R_3 = \dfrac{\sqrt{Z_1 Z_2}}{\sinh \theta}$ $R_1 = \dfrac{Z_1}{\tanh \theta} - R_3$ $R_2 = \dfrac{Z_2}{\tanh \theta} - R_3$	$R_3 = \dfrac{2\sqrt{N Z_1 Z_2}}{N-1}$ $R_1 = Z_1\left(\dfrac{N+1}{N-1}\right) - R_3$ $R_2 = Z_2\left(\dfrac{N+1}{N-1}\right) - R_3$	
$R_3 = \dfrac{Z}{\sinh \theta}$ $R_1 = Z \tanh \dfrac{\theta}{2}$	$R_3 = \dfrac{2Z\sqrt{N}}{N-1} = \dfrac{2ZK}{K^2-1}$ $\quad = \dfrac{2Z}{K - 1/K}$ $R_1 = Z\dfrac{\sqrt{N}-1}{\sqrt{N}+1} = Z\dfrac{K-1}{K+1}$ $\quad = Z[1 - 2/(K+1)]$	$R_1 R_3 = \dfrac{Z^2}{1+\cosh \theta} = Z^2\dfrac{2K}{(K+1)^2}$ $\dfrac{R_1}{R_3} = \cosh \theta - 1 = 2\sinh^2 \dfrac{\theta}{2}$ $\quad = \dfrac{(K-1)^2}{2K}$ $Z = R_1\sqrt{1 + 2\dfrac{R_3}{R_1}}$
$\cosh \theta = \sqrt{\dfrac{Z_1}{Z_2}}$ $\cosh 2\theta = 2\dfrac{Z_1}{Z_2} - 1$	$R_1 = Z_1\sqrt{1 - \dfrac{Z_2}{Z_1}}$ $R_3 = \dfrac{Z_2}{\sqrt{1 - \dfrac{Z_2}{Z_1}}}$	$R_1 R_3 = Z_1 Z_2$ $\dfrac{R_1}{R_3} = \dfrac{Z_1}{Z_2} - 1$ $N = \left(\sqrt{\dfrac{Z_1}{Z_2}} + \sqrt{\dfrac{Z_1}{Z_2} - 1}\right)^2$
$R_3 = \sqrt{Z_1 Z_2}\, \sinh \theta$ $\dfrac{1}{R_1} = \dfrac{1}{Z_1 \tanh \theta} - \dfrac{1}{R_3}$ $\dfrac{1}{R_2} = \dfrac{1}{Z_2 \tanh \theta} - \dfrac{1}{R_3}$	$R_3 = \dfrac{N-1}{2}\sqrt{\dfrac{Z_1 Z_2}{N}}$ $\dfrac{1}{R_1} = \dfrac{1}{Z_1}\left(\dfrac{N+1}{N-1}\right) - \dfrac{1}{R_3}$ $\dfrac{1}{R_2} = \dfrac{1}{Z_2}\left(\dfrac{N+1}{N-1}\right) - \dfrac{1}{R_3}$	
$R_3 = Z \sinh \theta$ $R_1 = \dfrac{Z}{\tanh \dfrac{\theta}{2}}$	$R_3 = Z\dfrac{N-1}{2\sqrt{N}} = Z\dfrac{K^2-1}{2K}$ $\quad = Z(K - 1/K)/2$ $R_1 = Z\dfrac{\sqrt{N}+1}{\sqrt{N}-1} = Z\dfrac{K+1}{K-1}$ $\quad = Z[1 + 2/(K-1)]$	$R_1 R_3 = Z^2(1+\cosh \theta) = Z^2\dfrac{(K+1)^2}{2K}$ $\dfrac{R_3}{R_1} = \cosh \theta - 1 = \dfrac{(K-1)^2}{2K}$ $Z = \dfrac{R_1}{\sqrt{1 + 2\dfrac{R_1}{R_3}}}$
	$R_1 = R_2 = Z$ $R_4 = Z(K-1)$ $R_3 = \dfrac{Z}{K-1}$	$R_3 R_4 = Z^2$ $\dfrac{R_4}{R_3} = (K-1)^2$

Four-terminal networks: The hyperbolic formulas above are valid for passive linear four-terminal networks in general, working between input and output impedances matching the respective image impedances. In this case: Z_1 and Z_2 are the image impedances; R_1, R_2 and R_3 become complex impedances; and θ is the image transfer constant. $\theta = \alpha + j\beta$, where α is the image attenuation constant and β is the image phase constant.

Attenuator network design *continued*

Symbols

Z_1 and Z_2 are the terminal impedances (resistive) to which the attenuator is matched.

N is the ratio of the power absorbed by the attenuator from the source to the power delivered to the load.

K is the ratio of the attenuator input current to the output current into the load. When $Z_1 = Z_2$, $K = \sqrt{N}$. Otherwise K is different in the two directions.

Attenuation in decibels $= 10 \log_{10} N$

Attenuation in nepers $= \theta = \frac{1}{2} \log_e N$

For a table of decibels versus power and voltage or current ratio, see page 30. Factors for converting decibels to nepers, and nepers to decibels, are given at the foot of that table.

Notes on error formulas

The formulas and figures for errors, given in Figs. 4 to 8, are based on the assumption that the attenuator is terminated approximately by its proper terminal impedances Z_1 and Z_2. They hold for deviations of the attenuator arms and load impedances up to $\pm$ 20 percent or somewhat more. The error due to each element is proportional to the deviation of the element, and the total error of the attenuator is the sum of the errors due to each of the several elements.

When any element or arm R has a reactive component ΔX in addition to a resistive error ΔR, the errors in input impedance and output current are

$$\Delta Z = A(\Delta R + j\Delta X)$$

$$\frac{\Delta i}{i} = B\left(\frac{\Delta R + j\Delta X}{R}\right)$$

where A and B are constants of proportionality for the elements in question. These constants can be determined in each case from the figures given for errors due to a resistive deviation ΔR.

The reactive component ΔX produces a quadrature component in the output current, resulting in a phase shift. However, for small values of ΔX, the error in insertion loss is negligibly small.

For the errors produced by mismatched terminal load impedance, refer to Case 1, page 157.

Symmetrical T or H attenuators

Interpolation of symmetrical T or H attenuators (Fig. 4)

Column R_1 may be interpolated linearly. Do not interpolate R_3 column. For 0 to 6 decibels interpolate the $1000/R_3$ column. Above 6 decibels, interpolate the column $\log_{10} R_3$ and determine R_3 from the result.

Fig. 4—Symmetrical T and H attenuator values. Z = 500 ohms resistive (diagram on page 158).

attenuation in decibels	series arm R_1 ohms	shunt arm R_3 ohms	$1000/R_3$	$\log_{10} R_3$
0.0	0.0	inf	0.0000	——
0.2	5.8	21,700	0.0461	——
0.4	11.5	10,850	0.0921	——
0.6	17.3	7,230	0.1383	——
0.8	23.0	5,420	0.1845	——
1.0	28.8	4,330	0.2308	——
2.0	57.3	2,152	0.465	——
3.0	85.5	1,419	0.705	——
4.0	113.1	1,048	0.954	——
5.0	140.1	822	1.216	——
6.0	166.1	669	1.494	2.826
7.0	191.2	558	——	2.747
8.0	215.3	473.1	——	2.675
9.0	238.1	405.9	——	2.608
10.0	259.7	351.4	——	2.546
12.0	299.2	268.1	——	2.428
14.0	333.7	207.8	——	2.318
16.0	363.2	162.6	——	2.211
18.0	388.2	127.9	——	2.107
20.0	409.1	101.0	——	2.004
22.0	426.4	79.94	——	1.903
24.0	440.7	63.35	——	1.802
26.0	452.3	50.24	——	1.701
28.0	461.8	39.87	——	1.601
30.0	469.3	31.65	——	1.500
35.0	482.5	17.79	——	1.250
40.0	490.1	10.00	——	1.000
50.0	496.8	3.162	——	0.500
60.0	499.0	1.000	——	0.000
80.0	499.9	0.1000	——	−1.000
100.0	500.0	0.01000	——	−2.000

Symmetrical T or H attenuators   *continued*

Errors in symmetrical T or H attenuators

Series arms R_1 and R_2 in error: Error in input impedances:

$$\Delta Z_1 = \Delta R_1 + \frac{1}{K^2} \Delta R_2$$

and

$$\Delta Z_2 = \Delta R_2 + \frac{1}{K^2} \Delta R_1$$

nominally $R_1 = R_2$
$Z_1 = Z_2$

Error in insertion loss, in decibels,

$$db = 4 \left(\frac{\Delta R_1}{Z_1} + \frac{\Delta R_2}{Z_2} \right) \text{ approximately}$$

Shunt arm R_3 in error (10 percent high)

designed loss, in decibels	error in insertion loss, in decibels	error in input impedance $100 \frac{\Delta Z}{Z}$ percent
0.2	−0.01	0.2
1	−0.05	1.0
6	−0.3	3.3
12	−0.5	3.0
20	−0.7	1.6
40	−0.8	0.2
100	−0.8	0.0

Error in input impedance:

$$\frac{\Delta Z}{Z} = 2 \frac{K-1}{K(K+1)} \frac{\Delta R_3}{R_3}$$

Error in output current:

$$\frac{\Delta i}{i} = \frac{K-1}{K+1} \frac{\Delta R_3}{R_3}$$

See Notes on page 160.

Symmetrical π and O attenuators

Interpolation of symmetrical π and O attenuators (Fig. 5).

Column R_1 may be interpolated linearly above 16 decibels, and R_3 up to 20 decibels. Otherwise interpolate the $1000/R_1$ and $\log_{10} R_3$ columns, respectively.

Fig. 5—Symmetrical π and O attenuator. Z = 500 ohms resistive (diagram, page 158).

attenuation in decibels	shunt arm R_1 ohms	$1000/R_1$	series arm R_3 ohms	$\log_{10} R_3$
0.0	∞	0.000	0.0	—
0.2	43,400	0.023	11.5	—
0.4	21,700	0.046	23.0	—
0.6	14,500	0.069	34.6	—
0.8	10,870	0.092	46.1	—
1.0	8,700	0.115	57.7	—
2.0	4,362	0.229	116.1	—
3.0	2,924	0.342	176.1	—
4.0	2,210	0.453	238.5	—
5.0	1,785	0.560	304.0	—
6.0	1,505	0.665	373.5	—
7.0	1,307	0.765	448.0	—
8.0	1,161.4	0.861	528.4	—
9.0	1,049.9	0.952	615.9	—
10.0	962.5	1.039	711.5	—
12.0	835.4	1.197	932.5	—
14.0	749.3	1.335	1,203.1	—
16.0	688.3	1.453	1,538	—
18.0	644.0	—	1,954	—
20.0	611.1	—	2,475	3.394
22.0	586.3	—	3,127	3.495
24.0	567.3	—	3,946	3.596
26.0	552.8	—	4,976	3.697
28.0	541.5	—	6,270	3.797
30.0	532.7	—	7,900	3.898
35.0	518.1	—	14,050	4.148
40.0	510.1	—	25,000	4.398
50.0	503.2	—	79,100	4.898
60.0	501.0	—	2.50×10^5	5.398
80.0	500.1	—	2.50×10^6	6.398
100.0	500.0	—	2.50×10^7	7.398

Symmetrical π and O attenuators   *continued*

Errors in symmetrical π and O attenuators

Error in input impedance:

$$\frac{\Delta Z'}{Z'} = \frac{K-1}{K+1}\left(\frac{\Delta R_1}{R_1} + \frac{1}{K^2}\frac{\Delta R_2}{R_2} + \frac{2}{K}\frac{\Delta R_3}{R_3}\right)$$

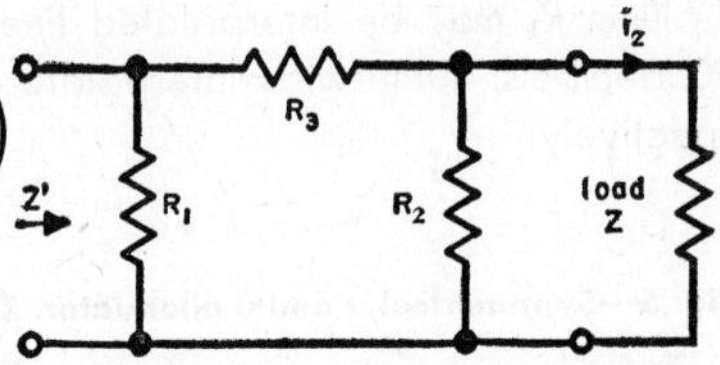

Error in insertion loss,

$$\text{decibels} = -8\,\frac{\Delta i_2}{i_2} \text{ (approximately)}$$

nominally $R_1 = R_2$ and $Z' = Z$

$$= 4\frac{K-1}{K+1}\left(-\frac{\Delta R_1}{R_1} - \frac{\Delta R_2}{R_2} + 2\frac{\Delta R_3}{R_3}\right)$$

See Notes on page 160.

Bridged T or H attenuators

Interpolation of bridged T or H attenuators *(Fig. 6)*

Bridge arm R_4: Use the formula $\log_{10}(R_4 + 500) = 2.699 + \text{decibels}/20$ for $Z = 500$ ohms. However, if preferred, the tabular values of R_4 may be interpolated linearly, between 0 and 10 decibels only.

Fig. 6—Values for bridged T or H attenuators. $Z = 500$ ohms resistive, $R_1 = R_2 = 500$ ohms (diagram on page 158).

attenuation in decibels	bridge arm R_4 ohms	shunt arm R_3 ohms	attenuation in decibels	bridge arm R_4 ohms	shunt arm R_3 ohms
0.0	0.0	∞	12.0	1,491	167.7
0.2	11.6	21,500	14.0	2,006	124.6
0.4	23.6	10,610	16.0	2,655	94.2
0.6	35.8	6,990	18.0	3,472	72.0
0.8	48.2	5,180	20.0	4,500	55.6
1.0	61.0	4,100	25.0	8,390	29.8
2.0	129.5	1,931	30.0	15,310	16.33
3.0	206.3	1,212	40.0	49,500	5.05
4.0	292.4	855	50.0	157,600	1.586
5.0	389.1	642	60.0	499,500	0.501
6.0	498	502	80.0	5.00×10^6	0.0500
7.0	619	404	100.0	50.0×10^6	0.00500
8.0	756	331	——	——	——
9.0	909	275.0	——	——	——
10.0	1,081	231.2	——	——	——

Bridged T or H attenuators   *continued*

Shunt arm R_3: Do not interpolate R_3 column. Compute R_3 by the formula $R_3 = 10^6/4R_4$ for $Z = 500$ ohms.

Note: For attenuators of 60 db and over, the bridge arm R_4 may be omitted provided a shunt arm is used having twice the resistance tabulated in the R column. (This makes the input impedance 0.1 of 1 percent high at 60 db.)

Errors in bridged T or H attenuators

Resistance of any one arm 10 percent higher than correct value

designed loss decibels	A decibels*	B percent*	C percent*
0.2	0.01	0.005	0.2
1	0.05	0.1	1.0
6	0.2	2.5	2.5
12	0.3	5.6	1.9
20	0.4	8.1	0.9
40	0.4	10	0.1
100	0.4	10	0.0

* Refer to following tabulation.

element in error (10 percent high)	error in loss	error in terminal impedance	remarks
Series arm R_1 (analogous for arm R_2)	Zero	B, for adjacent terminals	Error in impedance at opposite terminals is zero
Shunt arm R_3	$-A$	C	Loss is lower than designed loss
Bridge arm R_4	A	C	Loss is higher than designed loss

Error in input impedance:

$$\frac{\Delta Z_1}{Z_1} = \left(\frac{K-1}{K}\right)^2 \frac{\Delta R_1}{R_1} + \frac{K-1}{K^2}\left(\frac{\Delta R_3}{R_3} + \frac{\Delta R_4}{R_4}\right)$$

For $\Delta Z_2/Z_2$ use subscript 2 in formula in place of subscript 1.

Error in output current:

$$\frac{\Delta i}{i} = \frac{K-1}{2K}\left(\frac{\Delta R_3}{R_3} - \frac{\Delta R_4}{R_4}\right)$$

See Notes on page 160.

Minimum-loss pads

Interpolation of minimum-loss pads (Fig. 7)

This table may be interpolated linearly with respect to Z_1, Z_2, or Z_1/Z_2 except when Z_1/Z_2 is between 1.0 and 1.2. The accuracy of the interpolated value becomes poorer as Z_1/Z_2 passes below 2.0 toward 1.2, especially for R_3.

For other terminations

If the terminating resistances are to be Z_A and Z_B instead of Z_1 and Z_2, respectively, the procedure is as follows. Enter the table at $\dfrac{Z_1}{Z_2} = \dfrac{Z_A}{Z_B}$ and

Fig. 7—Values for minimum-loss pads matching Z_1 and Z_2, both resistive (diagram on page 158).

Z_1 ohms	Z_2 ohms	Z_1/Z_2	loss in decibels	series arm R_1 ohms	shunt arm R_3 ohms
10,000	500	20.00	18.92	9,747	513.0
8,000	500	16.00	17.92	7,746	516.4
6,000	500	12.00	16.63	5,745	522.2
5,000	500	10.00	15.79	4,743	527.0
4,000	500	8.00	14.77	3,742	534.5
3,000	500	6.00	13.42	2,739	547.7
2,500	500	5.00	12.54	2,236	559.0
2,000	500	4.00	11.44	1,732	577.4
1,500	500	3.00	9.96	1,224.7	612.4
1,200	500	2.40	8.73	916.5	654.7
1,000	500	2.00	7.66	707.1	707.1
800	500	1.60	6.19	489.9	816.5
600	500	1.20	3.77	244.9	1,224.7
500	400	1.25	4.18	223.6	894.4
500	300	1.667	6.48	316.2	474.3
500	250	2.00	7.66	353.6	353.6
500	200	2.50	8.96	387.3	258.2
500	160	3.125	10.17	412.3	194.0
500	125	4.00	11.44	433.0	144.3
500	100	5.00	12.54	447.2	111.80
500	80	6.25	13.61	458.3	87.29
500	65	7.692	14.58	466.4	69.69
500	50	10.00	15.79	474.3	52.70
500	40	12.50	16.81	479.6	41.70
500	30	16.67	18.11	484.8	30.94
500	25	20.00	18.92	487.3	25.65

Minimum-loss pads   *continued*

read the loss and the tabular values of R_1 and R_3. Then the series and shunt arms are, respectively, MR_1 and MR_3, where $M = \dfrac{Z_A}{Z_1} = \dfrac{Z_B}{Z_2}$.

Errors in minimum-loss pads

impedance ratio Z_1/Z_2	D decibels*	E percent*	F percent*
1.2	0.2	+4.1	+1.7
2.0	0.3	7.1	1.2
4.0	0.35	8.6	0.6
10.0	0.4	9.5	0.25
20.0	0.4	9.7	0.12

*Notes

Series arm R_1 10 percent high: Loss is increased by D decibels from above table. Input impedance Z_1 is increased by E percent. Input impedance Z_2 is increased by F percent.

Shunt arm R_3 10 percent high: Loss is decreased by D decibels from above table. Input impedance Z_2 is increased by E percent. Input impedance Z_1 is increased by F percent.

Errors in input impedance

$$\frac{\Delta Z_1}{Z_1} = \sqrt{1 - \frac{Z_2}{Z_1}} \left(\frac{\Delta R_1}{R_1} + \frac{1}{N} \frac{\Delta R_3}{R_3} \right)$$

$$\frac{\Delta Z_2}{Z_2} = \sqrt{1 - \frac{Z_2}{Z_1}} \left(\frac{\Delta R_3}{R_3} + \frac{1}{N} \frac{\Delta R_1}{R_1} \right)$$

Error in output current, working either direction

$$\frac{\Delta i}{i} = \frac{1}{2} \sqrt{1 - \frac{Z_2}{Z_1}} \left(\frac{\Delta R_3}{R_3} - \frac{\Delta R_1}{R_1} \right)$$

See Notes on page 160.

Miscellaneous T and H pads (Fig. 8)

Fig. 8—Values for miscellaneous T and H pads (diagram on page 158).

resistive terminations		loss decibels	attenuator arms		
Z_1 ohms	Z_2 ohms		series R_1 ohms	series R_2 ohms	shunt R_3 ohms
5,000	2,000	10	3,889	222	2,222
5,000	2,000	15	4,165	969	1,161
5,000	2,000	20	4,462	1,402	639
5,000	500	20	4,782	190.7	319.4
2,000	500	15	1,763	165.4	367.3
2,000	500	20	1,838	308.1	202.0
2,000	200	20	1,913	76.3	127.8
500	200	10	388.9	22.2	222.2
500	200	15	416.5	96.9	116.1
500	200	20	446.2	140.2	63.9
500	50	20	478.2	19.07	31.94
200	50	15	176.3	16.54	36.73
200	50	20	183.8	30.81	20.20

Errors in T and H pads

Series arms R_1 and R_2 in error: Errors in input impedances are

$$\Delta Z_1 = \Delta R_1 + \frac{1}{N}\frac{Z_1}{Z_2}\Delta R_2 \quad \text{and} \quad \Delta Z_2 = \Delta R_2 + \frac{1}{N}\frac{Z_2}{Z_1}\Delta R_1$$

Error in insertion loss, in decibels $= 4\left(\dfrac{\Delta R_1}{Z_1} + \dfrac{\Delta R_2}{Z_2}\right)$ approximately

Shunt arm R_3 in error (10 percent high)

Z_1/Z_2	designed loss decibels	error in loss decibels	error in input impedance	
			$100\,\dfrac{\Delta Z_1}{Z_1}$	$100\,\dfrac{\Delta Z_2}{Z_2}$
2.5	10	−0.4	1.1%	7.1%
2.5	15	−0.6	1.2	4.6
2.5	20	−0.7	0.9	2.8
4.0	15	−0.5	0.8	6.0
4.0	20	−0.65	0.6	3.6
10	20	−0.6	0.3	6.1

$$\frac{\Delta Z_1}{Z_1} = \frac{2}{N-1}\left(\sqrt{\frac{NZ_2}{Z_1}} + \sqrt{\frac{Z_1}{NZ_2}} - 2\right)\frac{\Delta R_3}{R_3} \quad \left\{ \begin{array}{l} \text{for } \Delta Z_2/Z_2 \text{ interchange sub-} \\ \text{scripts 1 and 2.} \end{array}\right.$$

$$\frac{\Delta i}{i} = \frac{N+1-\sqrt{N}\left(\sqrt{\dfrac{Z_1}{Z_2}} + \sqrt{\dfrac{Z_2}{Z_1}}\right)}{N-1}\frac{\Delta R_3}{R_3} \quad \left\{ \text{where } i \text{ is the output current.} \right.$$

■ Bridges and impedance measurements

Introduction

In the diagrams of bridges below, the source is shown as a generator, and the detector as a pair of headphones. The positions of these two elements may be interchanged as dictated by detailed requirements in any individual case, such as location of grounds, etc. For all but the lowest frequencies, a shielded transformer is required at either the input or output (but not usually at both) terminals of the bridge. This is shown in some of the following diagrams. The detector is chosen according to the frequency of the source. Above the middle audio frequencies, a simple radio receiver or its equivalent is essential. The source may be modulated in order to obtain an audible signal, but greater sensitivity and discrimination against interference are obtained by the use of a continuous-wave source and a heterodyne detector. An amplifier and oscilloscope or an output meter are sometimes preferred for observing nulls. In this case it is convenient to have an audible output signal available for the preliminary setup and for locating trouble, since much can be deduced from the quality of the audible signal that would not be apparent from observation of amplitude only.

Fundamental alternating-current or Wheatstone bridge

Balance condition is $Z_x = Z_s Z_a / Z_b$

Maximum sensitivity when Z_d is the conjugate of the bridge output impedance and Z_g the conjugate of its

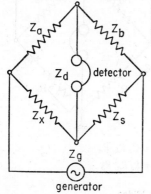

input impedance. Greatest sensitivity when bridge arms are equal, e.g., for resistive arms,

$$Z_d = Z_a = Z_b = Z_x = Z_s = Z_g$$

Bridge with double-shielded transformer

Shield on secondary may be floating, connected to either end, or to center of secondary winding. It may be in two equal parts and connected to opposite ends of the winding. In any case, its capacitance to ground must be kept to a minimum.

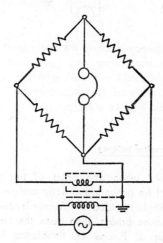

Wagner earth connection

None of the bridge elements are grounded directly. First balance bridge with switch to B. Throw switch to G and rebalance by means of R and C. Recheck bridge balance and repeat as required. The capacitor balance C is necessary only when the

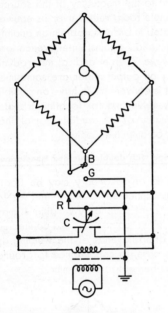

frequency is above the audio range. The transformer may have only a single shield as shown, with the capacitance of the secondary to the shield kept to a minimum.

Capacitor balance

Useful when one point of bridge must be grounded directly and only a simple shielded transformer is used. Balance bridge, then open the two arms at P and Q. Rebalance by

auxiliary capacitor C. Close P and Q and check balance.

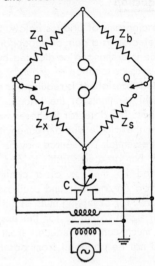

Series-resistance-capacitance bridge

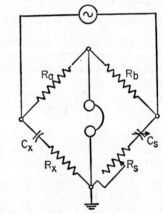

$$C_x = C_s R_b / R_a$$
$$R_x = R_s R_a / R_b$$

Wien bridge

$$\frac{C_x}{C_s} = \frac{R_b}{R_a} - \frac{R_s}{R_x}$$
$$C_s C_x = 1 / \omega^2 R_s R_x$$

Wien bridge   *continued*

For measurement of frequency, or in a frequency-selective application, if

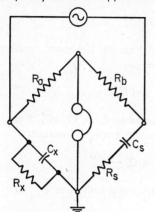

we make $C_x = C_s$, $R_x = R_s$, and $R_b = 2R_a$, then

$$f = \frac{1}{2\pi C_s R_s}$$

Owen bridge

$$L_x = C_b R_a R_d$$

$$R_x = \frac{C_b R_a}{C_d} - R_c$$

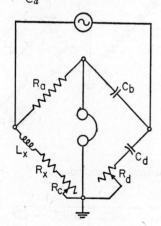

Resonance bridge

$$\omega^2 LC = 1$$

$$R_x = R_s R_a / R_b$$

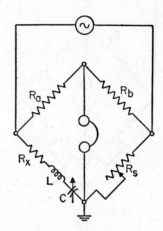

Maxwell bridge

$$L_x = R_a R_b C_s$$

$$R_x = \frac{R_a R_b}{R_s}$$

$$Q_x = \omega \frac{L_x}{R_x} = \omega C_s R_s$$

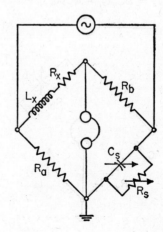

Hay bridge

For measurement of large inductance.

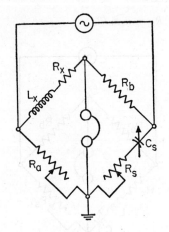

$$L_x = \frac{R_a R_b C_s}{1 + \omega^2 C_s{}^2 R_s{}^2}$$

$$Q_x = \frac{\omega L_x}{R_x} = \frac{1}{\omega C_s R_s}$$

Schering bridge

$$C_x = C_s R_b / R_a$$

$$1/Q_x = \omega C_x R_x = \omega C_b R_b$$

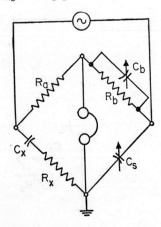

Substitution method for high impedances

Initial balance (unknown terminals x — x open):

C_s' and R_s'

Final balance (unknown connected to x — x):

C_s'' and R_s''

Then when $R_x > 10/\omega C_s'$, there results, with error < 1 percent,

$$C_x = C_s' - C_s''$$

The parallel resistance is

$$R_x = \frac{1}{\omega^2 C_s'{}^2 (R_s' - R_s'')}$$

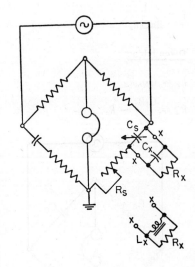

If unknown is an inductor,

$$L_x = -\frac{1}{\omega^2 C_x} = \frac{1}{\omega^2 (C_s'' - C_s')}$$

Measurement with capacitor in series with unknown

Initial balance (unknown terminals x–x short-circuited):

C'_s and R'_s

Final balance (x — x un-shorted):

C''_s and R''_s

Then the series resistance is

$$R_x = (R''_s - R'_s) R_a / R_b$$

$$C_x = \frac{R_b C'_s C''_s}{R_a (C'_s - C''_s)}$$

$$= \frac{R_b}{R_a} C'_s \left(\frac{C'_s}{C'_s - C''_s} - 1 \right)$$

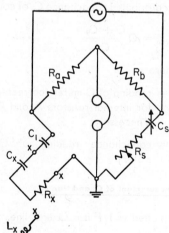

When $C''_s > C'_s$,

$$L_x = \frac{1}{\omega^2} \frac{R_a}{R_b C_s} \left(1 - \frac{C'_s}{C''_s} \right)$$

Measurement of direct capacitance

Connection of N to N' places C_{nq} across phones, and C_{np} across R_b which requires only a small readjustment of R_s.

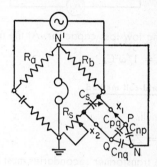

Initial balance: Lead from P disconnected from X_1 but lying as close to connected position as practical.

Final balance: Lead connected to X_1.

By the substitution method above, $C_{pq} = C'_s - C''_s$

Felici mutual-inductance balance

At the null:

$$M_x = -M_s$$

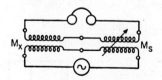

Useful at lower frequencies where capacitive reactances associated with windings are negligibly small.

Mutual-inductance capacitance balance

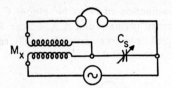

Using low-loss capacitor. At the null

$$M_x = 1/\omega^2 C_s$$

Hybrid-coil method

At null:

$$Z_1 = Z_2$$

The transformer secondaries must be accurately matched and balanced to

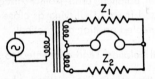

ground. Useful at audio and carrier frequencies.

Q of resonant circuit by bandwidth

For 3-decibel or half-power points. Source loosely coupled to circuit. Adjust frequency to each side of resonance, noting bandwidth when

$$v = 0.71 \times (v \text{ at resonance})$$

$$Q = \frac{(\text{resonance frequency})}{(\text{bandwidth})}$$

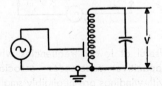

Q-meter (Boonton Radio Type 160A)

$$R_1 = 0.04 \text{ ohm}$$
$$R_2 = 100 \text{ megohms}$$
$$V = \text{vacuum-tube voltmeter}$$
$$I = \text{thermal milliammeter}$$
$$L_x R_x C_0 = \text{unknown coil plugged into COIL terminals for measurement.}$$

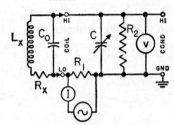

Correction of Q reading

For distributed capacitance C_0 of coil

$$Q_{\text{true}} = Q \frac{C + C_0}{C}$$

where

Q = reading of Q-meter (corrected for internal resistors R_1 and R_2 if necessary)

C = capacitance reading of Q-meter

Measurement of C_0 and true L_x

C plotted vs $1/f^2$ is a straight line.

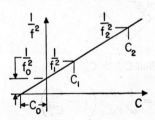

Measurement of C_0 and true L_x *continued*

L_x = true inductance

$$= \frac{1/f^2_2 - 1/f^2_1}{4\pi^2 (C_2 - C_1)}$$

C_0 = negative intercept

f_0 = natural frequency of coil

When only two readings are taken and $f_1/f_2 = 2.00$,

$$C_0 = (C_2 - 4C_1)/3$$

Measurement of admittance

Initial readings $C'Q'$ (LR_p is any suitable coil)

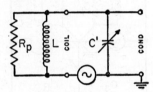

Final readings $C''Q''$

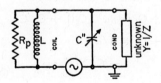

$$1/Z = Y = G + jB = 1/R_p + j\omega C$$

Then

$$C = C' - C''$$

$$\frac{1}{Q} = \frac{G}{\omega C}$$

$$= \frac{C'}{C}\left(\frac{1000}{Q''} - \frac{1000}{Q'}\right) \times 10^{-3}$$

If Z is inductive, $C'' > C'$

Measurement of impedances lower than those directly measurable

For the initial reading, $C'Q'$, COND terminals are open.

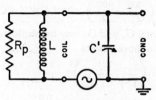

On second reading, $C''Q''$, a capacitive divider C_aC_b is connected to the COND terminals.

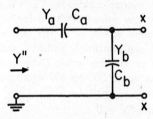

Final reading, $C'''Q'''$, unknown connected to $x-x$.

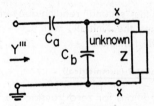

$$Y_a = G_a + j\omega C_a \quad Y_b = G_b + j\omega C_b$$

G_a and G_b not shown in diagrams.

Then the unknown impedance is

$$Z = \left(\frac{Y_a}{Y_a + Y_b}\right)^2 \frac{1}{Y''' - Y''}$$

$$- \frac{1}{Y_a + Y_b} \text{ ohms}$$

where, with capacitance in micro-microfarads and $\omega = 2\pi \times$ (frequency in megacycles/second):

Measurement of impedances lower than those directly measurable *continued*

$$\frac{1}{Y''' - Y''} =$$

$$\frac{10^6/\omega}{C'\left(\dfrac{1000}{Q'''} - \dfrac{1000}{Q''}\right) \times 10^{-3} + j(C'' - C''')}$$

Usually G_a and G_b may be neglected, when there results

$$Z = \left(\frac{1}{1 + C_b/C_a}\right)^2 \frac{1}{Y''' - Y''}$$

$$+ j \frac{10^6}{\omega(C_a + C_b)} \text{ ohms}$$

For many measurements, C_a may be 100 micromicrofarads. $C_b = 0$ for very low values of Z and for highly reactive values of Z. For unknowns that are principally resistive and of low or medium value, C_b may take sizes up to 300 to 500 micromicrofarads.

When $C_b = 0$

$$Z = \frac{1}{Y''' - Y''} + j \frac{10^6}{\omega C_a} \text{ ohms}$$

and the "second" reading above becomes the "initial", with $C' = C''$ in the formulas.

Parallel-T (symmetrical)

Conditions for zero transfer are

$$\omega^2 C_1 C_2 = 2/R_2{}^2$$
$$\omega^2 C_1{}^2 = 1/2R_1 R_2$$
$$C_2 R_2 = 4 C_1 R_1$$

Use any two of these three equations.

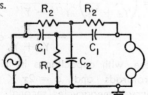

When used as a frequency-selective network, if we make $R_2 = 2R_1$ and $C_2 = 2C_1$ then

$$f = 1/2\pi C_1 R_2 = 1/2\pi C_2 R_1$$

Twin-T admittance-measuring circuit

(General Radio Co. Type 821-A)

This circuit may be used for measuring admittances in the range somewhat exceeding 400 kilocycles to 40 megacycles. It is applicable to the special measuring techniques described above for the Q-meter.

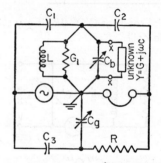

Conditions for null in output

$$G + G_i = R\omega^2 C_1 C_2 (1 + C_g/C_3)$$
$$C + C_b = 1/\omega^2 L$$
$$- C_1 C_2 \left(\frac{1}{C_1} + \frac{1}{C_2} + \frac{1}{C_3}\right)$$

With the unknown disconnected, call the initial balance C_b' and C_g'.

With unknown connected, final balance is C_b'' and C_g''.

Then the components of the unknown $Y = G + j\omega C$ are

$$C = C_b' - C_b''$$
$$G = \frac{R\omega^2 C_1 C_2}{C_3}(C_g'' - C_g')$$

■ Rectifiers and filters

Rectifier basic circuits

Half-wave rectifier (Fig. 1): Most applications are for low-power direct conversion of the type necessary in small ac-dc radio receivers (without an intermediary transformer), and often with the use of a metallic rectifier. Not generally used in high-power circuits due to the low frequency of the ripple voltage and a large direct-current polarization effect in the transformer, if used.

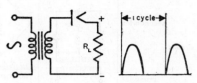

Fig. 1—Half-wave single-phase rectifier.

Full-wave rectifier (Fig. 2): Extensively used due to higher frequency of ripple voltage and absence of appreciable direct-current polarization of transformer core because transformer-secondary halves are balanced.

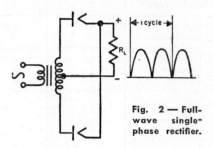

Fig. 2 — Full-wave single-phase rectifier.

Bridge rectifier (Fig. 3): Frequently used with metallic-rectifier elements; may operate by direct conversion or through a transformer. Compared to full-wave rectifiers, has greater transformer utilization, but requires twice the number of rectifier elements and has twice the rectifier-element voltage drop. If tubes are used, three well-insulated filament-transformer secondaries are required.

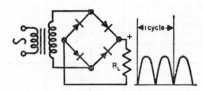

Fig. 3—Bridge rectifier.

Voltage multiplier (Fig. 4): May be used with or without a line transformer. Without the transformer, it develops sufficiently high output voltage for low-power equipment; however, lack of electrical insulation from the power line may be objectionable. May also be used for obtaining high voltages from a transformer having relatively low step-up ratio.

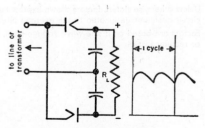

Fig. 4—Voltage-doubler rectifier.

Typical power rectifier circuit connections and circuit data

types of circuits	rectifier	single-phase full-wave	single-phase full-wave (bridge)	3-phase half-wave	3-phase half-wave
	transformer	single-phase center-tap	single-phase	delta-wye	delta-zig zag
circuits	secondaries				
	primaries				
Number of phases of supply		1	1	3	3
Number of tubes*		2	4	3	3
Ripple voltage		0.48	0.48	0.18	0.18
Ripple frequency		2f	2f	3f	3f
Line voltage		1.11	1.11	0.855	0.855
Line current		1	1	0.816	0.816
Line power factor†		0.90	0.90	0.826	0.826
Trans primary volts per leg		1.11	1.11	0.855	0.855
Trans primary amperes per leg		1	1	0.471	0.471
Trans primary kva		1.11	1.11	1.21	1.21
Trans average kva		1.34	1.11	1.35	1.46
Trans secondary volts per leg		1.11(A)	1.11	0.855	0.493(A)
Trans secondary amperes per leg		0.707	1	0.577	0.577
Transformer secondary kva		1.57	1.11	1.48	1.71
Peak inverse voltage per tube		3.14	1.57	2.09	2.09
Peak current per tube		1	1	1	1
Average current per tube		0.5	0.5	0.333	0.333

Unless otherwise stated, factors shown express the ratio of the root-mean-square value of the circuit quantities designated to the average direct-current-output values of the rectifier.

Factors are based on a sine-wave voltage input, infinite-impedance choke, and no transformer or rectifier losses.

6-phase half-wave	6-phase half-wave	6-phase (double 3-phase) half-wave	3-phase full-wave	3-phase full-wave
delta-star	delta-6-phase fork	delta-double wye with balance coil	delta-wye	delta-delta
3	3	3	3	3
6	6	6	6	6
0.042	0.042	0.042	0.042	0.042
6f	6f	6f	6f	6f
0.740	0.428	0.855	0.428	0.740
0.816	1.41	0.707	1.41	0.816
0.955	0.955	0.955	0.955	0.955
0.740	0.428	0.855	0.428	0.740
0.577	0.816	0.408	0.816	0.471
1.28	1.05	1.05	1.05	1.05
1.55	1.42	1.26	1.05	1.05
0.740(A)	0.428(A)	0.855(A)	0.428	0.740
0.408	{ 0.577 (B) } { 0.408 (C) }	0.289	0.816	0.471
1.81	1.79	1.48	1.05	1.05
2.09	2.09	2.42	1.05	1.05
1	1	0.5	1	1
0.167	0.167	0.167	0.333	0.333

* These circuit factors are equally applicable to tube or metallic-plate rectifying elements.

† Line power factor = direct-current output watts/line volt-amperes.

Grid-controlled gaseous rectifiers

Grid-controlled rectifiers are used to obtain closely controlled voltages and currents. They are commonly used in the power supplies of high-power radio transmitters. For low voltages, gas-filled tubes, such as argon (those that are unaffected by temperature changes) are used. For higher voltages, mercury-vapor tubes are used to avoid flash-back (conduction of current when plate is negative). These circuits permit large power to be handled, with smooth and stable control of voltage, and permit the control of short-circuit currents through the load by automatic interruption of the rectifier output for a period sufficient to permit short-circuit arcs to clear, followed by immediate reapplication of voltage.

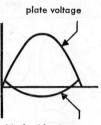

Fig. 5 — Critical grid voltage versus plate voltage.

In a thyratron, the grid has a one-way control of conduction, and serves to fire the tube at the instant that it acquires a critical voltage. Relationship of the critical voltage to the plate voltage is shown in Fig. 5. Once the tube is fired, current flow is generally determined by the external circuit conditions; the grid then has no control, and plate current can be stopped only when the plate voltage drops to zero.

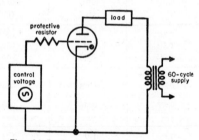

Fig. 6—Basic thyratron circuit. The grid voltage has direct- and alternating-current components.

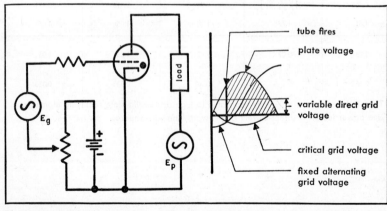

Fig. 7—Control of plate-current conduction period by means of variable direct grid voltage. E_g lags E_p by 90 degrees.

Grid-controlled gaseous rectifiers   *continued*

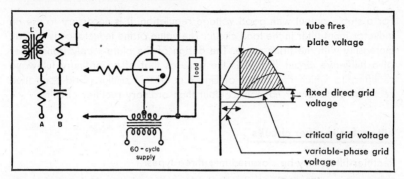

Fig. 8—Control of plate-current conduction period by fixed direct grid voltage (not indicated in schematic) and alternating grid voltage of variable phase. Either inductance-resistance or capacitance-resistance phase-shift networks (A and B, respectively) may be used. L may be a variable inductor of the saturable-reactor type.

Basic circuit

The basic circuit of a thyratron with alternating-current plate and grid excitation is shown in Fig. 6. The average plate current may be controlled by maintaining

a. A variable direct grid voltage plus a fixed alternating grid voltage that lags the plate voltage by 90 degrees (Fig. 7).

b. A fixed direct grid voltage plus an alternating grid voltage of variable phase (Fig. 8).

Phase shifting

The phase of the grid voltage may be shifted with respect to the plate voltage by the methods illustrated in Figs. 8 and 9.

a. Varying the indicated resistor.

b. Variation of the inductance of the saturable reactor.

c. Varying the capacitor.

On multiphase circuits, a phase-shifting transformer may be used.

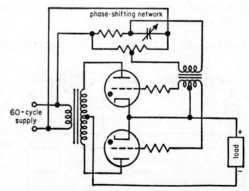

Fig. 9—Full-wave thyratron rectifier. The capacitor is the variable element in the phase-shifting network, and hence gives control of output voltage.

Grid-controlled gaseous rectifiers   *continued*

For a stable output with good voltage regulation, it is necessary to use an inductor-input filter in the load circuit. The value of the inductance is critical, increasing with the firing angle. The design of the plate-supply transformer of a full-wave circuit (Fig. 9) is the same as that of an ordinary full-wave rectifier, to which the circuit of Fig. 9 is closely similar. Grid-controlled rectifiers yield larger harmonic output than ordinary rectifier circuits.

Filters for rectifier circuits

Rectifier filters may be classified into three types:

Inductor input (Fig. 10): Have good voltage regulation, high transformer-utilization factor, and low rectifier peak currents, but also give relatively low output voltage.

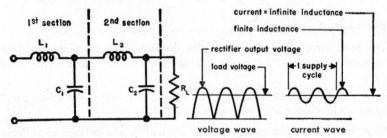

Fig. 10—Inductor-input filter.

Capacitor input (Fig. 11): Have high output voltage, but poor regulation, poor transformer-utilization factor, and high peak currents. Used mostly in radio receivers.

Resistor input (Fig. 12): Used for low-current applications.

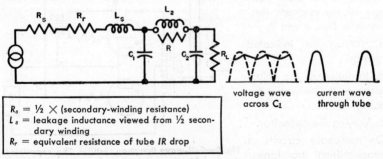

$R_s = \frac{1}{2} \times$ (secondary-winding resistance)
$L_s = $ leakage inductance viewed from $\frac{1}{2}$ secondary winding
$R_r = $ equivalent resistance of tube IR drop

Fig. 11—Capacitor-input filter. C_1 is the input capacitor.

Filters for rectifier circuits   *continued*

Design of inductor-input filters

The constants of the first section (Fig. 10) are determined from the following considerations:

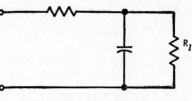

Fig. 12—Resistor-input filter.

a. There must be sufficient inductance to insure continuous operation of rectifiers and good voltage regulation. Increasing this critical value of inductance by a 25-percent safety factor, the minimum value becomes

$$L_{min} = \frac{K}{f_s} R_l \text{ henries} \tag{1}$$

where

f_s = frequency of source in cycles/second

R_l = maximum value of total load resistance in ohms

K = 0.060 for full-wave single-phase circuits

= 0.0057 for full-wave two-phase circuits

= 0.0017 for full-wave three-phase circuits

At 60 cycles, single-phase full-wave,

$$L_{min} = R_l/1000 \text{ henries} \tag{1a}$$

b. The LC product must exceed a certain minimum, to insure a required ripple factor

$$r = \frac{E_r}{E_{dc}} = \frac{\sqrt{2}}{p^2-1} \frac{10^6}{(2\pi f_s p)^2 L_1 C_1} = \frac{K'}{L_1 C_1} \tag{2}$$

where, except for single-phase half-wave,

p = effective number of phases of rectifier

E_r = root-mean-square ripple voltage appearing across C_1

E_{dc} = direct-current voltage on C_1

L_1 is in henries and C_1 in microfarads.

For single-phase full-wave, $p = 2$ and

$$r = \frac{0.83}{L_1 C_1} \left(\frac{60}{f_s}\right)^2 \tag{2a}$$

Filters for rectifier circuits *continued*

For three-phase, full-wave, $p = 6$ and

$$r = (0.0079/L_1 C_1)(60/f_s)^2 \qquad \text{(2b)}$$

Equations (1) and (2) define the constants L_1 and C_1 of the filter, in terms of the load resistor R_l and allowable ripple factor r.

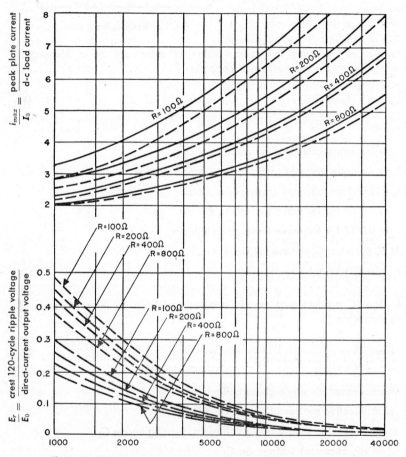

effective load resistance = actual load resistance plus filter-choke resistance in ohms

Reprinted from "*Radio Engineers Handbook*" by F. E Terman,
1st ed., p. 672, 1943; by permission, McGraw-Hill Book Co., N. Y.

$R = R_s + R_r$ (see Fig. 11)

——————— input capacitance = ∞

— — —   = 8 μf

— — — —   = 4 μf

Fig. 13—Performance of capacitor-input filter for 60-cycle full-wave rectifier, assuming negligible leakage-inductance effect.

Filters for rectifier circuits *continued*

Swinging chokes: Swinging chokes have inductances that vary with the load current. When the load resistance varies through a wide range, a swinging choke, with a bleeder resistor R_b (10,000 to 20,000 ohms) connected across the filter output, is used to guarantee efficient operation; i.e., $L_{min} = R_l'/1000$ for all loads, where $R_l' = (R_l R_b)/(R_l + R_b)$. Swinging chokes are economical due to their smaller relative size, and result in adequate filtering in many cases.

Second section: For further reduction of ripple voltage E_{r1}, a smoothing section (Fig. 10) may be added, and will result in output ripple voltage E_{r2}:

$$E_{r2}/E_{r1} \approx 1/(2\pi f_r)^2 L_2 C_2 \tag{3}$$

where f_r = ripple frequency

Design of capacitor-input filters

The constants of the input capacitor (Fig. 11) are determined from:

a. Degree of filtering required.

$$r = \frac{E_r}{E_{dc}} = \frac{\sqrt{2}}{2\pi f_r C_1 R_l} = \frac{0.00188}{C_1 R_l}\left(\frac{120}{f_r}\right) \tag{4}$$

where $C_1 R_l$ is in microfarads $\times$ megohms, or farads $\times$ ohms.

b. A maximum-allowable C_1 so as not to exceed the maximum allowable peak-current rating of the rectifier.

Unlike the inductor-input filter, the source impedance (transformer and rectifier) affects output direct-current and ripple voltages, and the peak currents. The equivalent network is shown in Fig. 11.

Neglecting leakage inductance, the peak output ripple voltage E_{r1} (across the capacitor) and the peak plate current for varying effective load resistance are given in Fig. 13. If the load current is small, there may be no need to add the L-section consisting of an inductor and a second capacitor. Otherwise, with the completion of an $L_2 C_2$ or RC_2 section (Fig. 11), greater filtering is obtained, the peak output-ripple voltage E_{r2} being given by (3) or

$$E_{r2}/E_{r1} \approx 1/\omega R C_2 \tag{5}$$

respectively.

■ Iron-core transformers and reactors

General

Iron-core transformers are, with few exceptions, closely coupled circuits for transmitting alternating-current energy and matching impedances. The equivalent circuit of a generalized transformer is shown in Fig. 1.

Major transformer types used in electronics

Power transformers

Rectifier plate and/or filament: Operate from a source of nearly zero impedance and at a single frequency.

Vibrator power supply: Permit the operation of radio receivers from direct-current sources, such as automobile batteries, when used in conjunction with vibrator inverters.

Scott connection: Serve to transmit power from 2-phase to 3-phase systems, or vice-versa.

Autotransformer: Is a special case of the usual isolation type in that a part of the primary and secondary windings are physically common. The size, voltage regulation, and leakage inductance of an autotransformer are, for a given rating, less than those for an isolation-type transformer handling the same power.

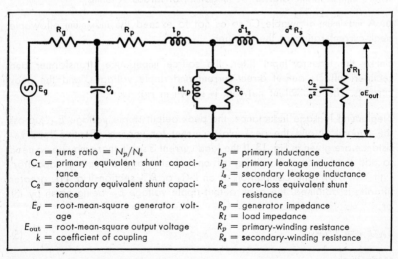

$$a = \text{turns ratio} = N_p/N_s$$
C_1 = primary equivalent shunt capacitance
C_2 = secondary equivalent shunt capacitance
E_g = root-mean-square generator voltage
E_{out} = root-mean-square output voltage
k = coefficient of coupling

L_p = primary inductance
l_p = primary leakage inductance
l_s = secondary leakage inductance
R_c = core-loss equivalent shunt resistance
R_g = generator impedance
R_l = load impedance
R_p = primary-winding resistance
R_s = secondary-winding resistance

Fig. 1—Equivalent network of a transformer.

Major transformer types used in electronics   *continued*

Audio-frequency transformers

Match impedances and transmit audio frequencies.

Output: Couple the plate(s) of an amplifier to an output load.

Input or interstage: Couple a magnetic pickup, microphone, or plate of a tube to the grid of another tube.

Driver: Couple the plate(s) of a driver stage (preamplifier) to the grid(s) of an amplifier stage where grid current is drawn.

Modulation: Couple the plate(s) of an audio-output stage to the grid or plate of a modulated amplifier.

High-frequency transformers

Match impedances and transmit a band of frequencies in the carrier or higher-frequency ranges.

Power-line carrier-amplifier: Couple different stages, or couple input and output stages to the line.

Intermediate-frequency: Are coupled tuned circuits used in receiver intermediate-frequency amplifiers to pass a band of frequencies (these units may, or may not have magnetic cores).

Pulse: Transform energy from a pulse generator to the impedance level of a load with, or without, phase inversion. Also serve as interstage coupling or inverting devices in pulse amplifiers. Pulse transformers may be used to obtain low-level pulses of a certain repetition rate in regenerative-pulse-generating circuits (blocking oscillators).

Sawtooth-amplifier: Provide a linear sweep to the horizontal plates of a cathode-ray oscilloscope.

Major electronic reactor types

Filter: Smooth out ripple voltage in direct-current supplies. Here, swinging chokes are the most economical design in providing adequate filtering, in most cases, with but a single filtering section.

Audio-frequency: Supply plate current to a vacuum tube in parallel with the output circuit.

Radio-frequency: Pass direct current and present high impedance at the high frequencies.

Wave-filter: Used as filter components to aid in the selection or rejection of certain frequencies.

Special nonlinear transformers and reactors

These make use of nonlinear properties of magnetic cores by operating near the knee of the magnetization curve.

Peaking transformers: Produce steeply peaked waveforms, for firing thyratrons.

Saturable-reactor elements: Used in tuned circuits; generate pulses by virtue of their saturation during a fraction of each half cycle.

Saturable reactors: Serve to regulate voltage, current, or phase in conjunction with glow-discharge tubes of the thyratron type. Used as voltage-regulating devices with dry-type rectifiers. Also used in mechanical vibrator rectifiers and magnetic amplifiers.

Design of power transformers for rectifiers

The equivalent circuit of a power transformer is shown in Fig. 2.

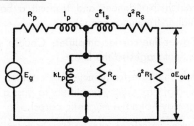

a. Determine total output volt-amperes, and compute the primary and secondary currents from

$$E_p I_p \times 0.9 = \frac{1}{\eta}\left[(E_s I_{dc})_{pl} K + (EI)_{fil} \right]$$

$$I_s = K' I_{dc}$$

Fig. 2—Equivalent network of a power transformer. I_p and I_s may be neglected when there are no strict requirements on voltage regulation.

where the numeric 0.9 is the power factor, and the efficiency η and the K, K' factors are listed in Figs. 3 and 4. $E_p I_p$ is the input volt-amperes, I_{dc} refers to the total direct-current component drawn by the supply; and

Fig. 3—Factors K and K' for various rectifier supplies.

Fig. 4—Efficiency of various sizes of power supplies. *

filter	K	K'	watts output	approximate efficiency in percent
Full-wave:			20	70
Capacitor input	0.717	1.06	30	75
Reactor input	0.5	0.707	40	80
Half-wave:			80	85
Capacitor input	1.4	2.2	100	86
Reactor input	1.06	1.4	200	90

* From "Radio Components Handbook," Technical Advertising Associates; Cheltenham, Pa., May, 1948: p. 92.

Design of power transformers for rectifiers   *continued*

the subscripts *pl* and *fil* refer to the volt-amperes drawn from the plate-supply and filament-supply (if present) windings, respectively. E_s is the root-mean-square voltage applied to the plate of a rectifier element. In a full-wave circuit, this would be half of the total secondary voltage.

b. Compute the size of wire of each winding, on the basis of current densities given by

For 60-cycle sealed units,

$$\text{amperes/inch}^2 = 2470 - 585 \log W_{out}$$

or, inches diameter $\approx 1.13 \sqrt{\dfrac{I \text{ (in amperes)}}{2470 - 585 \log W_{out}}}$

For 60-cycle open units, uncased,

$$\text{amperes/inch}^2 = 2920 - 610 \log W_{out}$$

or, inches diameter $\approx 1.13 \sqrt{\dfrac{I \text{ (in amperes)}}{2920 - 610 \log W_{out}}}$

Fig. 5—Equivalent LI^2 **and** EI **ratings of power transformers:** B_m = **flux density in gauss;** EI = **volt-amperes. This table gives the maximum values of** LI^2 **and** EI **ratings at 60 and 400 cycles for various size cores. Ratings are based on a 50-degree-centigrade rise above ambient. These values can be reduced to obtain a smaller temperature rise.** EI **ratings are based on a two-winding transformer with normal operating voltage. When three or more windings are required, the** EI **ratings should be decreased slightly.**

	at 60 cycles		at 400 cycles			tongue width of E	stack height	amperes per
LI^2	EI	B_m*	EI	B_m*	EI-type punchings	in inches	in inches	inch²
0.0195	3.9	14,000	9.5	5000	21	$\frac{1}{2}$	$\frac{1}{2}$	3200
0.0288	5.8	14,000	15.0	4900	625	$\frac{5}{8}$	$\frac{5}{8}$	2700
0.067	13.0	14,000	30.0	4700	75	$\frac{3}{4}$	$\frac{3}{4}$	2560
0.088	17.0	14,000	38.0	4600	75	$\frac{3}{4}$	1	2560
0.111	24.0	13,500	50.0	4500	11	$\frac{7}{8}$	$\frac{7}{8}$	2330
0.200	37.0	13,000	80.0	4200	12	1	1	2130
0.300	54.0	13,000	110.0	4000	12	1	$1\frac{1}{2}$	2030
0.480	82.0	12,500	180.0	3900	125	$1\frac{1}{4}$	$1\frac{1}{4}$	1800
0.675	110.0	12,000	230.0	3900	125	$1\frac{1}{4}$	$1\frac{3}{4}$	1770
0.850	145.0	12,000	325.0	3700	13	$1\frac{1}{2}$	$1\frac{1}{2}$	1600
1.37	195.0	11,000	420.0	3500	13	$1\frac{1}{2}$	2	1500
3.70	525.0	10,500	1100.0	3200	19	$1\frac{1}{4}$	$1\frac{3}{4}$	1220

From "Radio Components Handbook," Technical Advertising Associates; Cheltenham, Pa.; May, 1948: see p. 92.

* B_m refers to 29-gauge silicon steel.

continued **Design of power transformers for rectifiers**

Fig. 6—Wire table for transformer design. The resistance R_T at any temperature T is given by $R_T = \dfrac{234.5+T}{234.5+t} \times r$, where t = reference temperature of winding, and r = resistance of winding at temperature t.

AWG B&S gauge	diameter in inches			turns per inch (formvar)	space factor	ohms per 1000 ft†	pounds per 1000 ft	margin m in inches	interlayer insulation‡ t	AWG B&S gauge
	bare	single formvar*	double formvar							
10	0.1019	0.1039	0.1055	8	90	0.9989	31.43	0.25	0.010K	10
11	0.0907	0.0927	0.0942	9	90	1.260	24.92	0.25	0.010K	11
12	0.0808	0.0827	0.0842	10	90	1.588	19.77	0.25	0.010K	12
13	0.0719	0.0738	0.0753	12	90	2.003	15.68	0.25	0.010K	13
14	0.0641	0.0659	0.0673	13	90	2.525	12.43	0.25	0.010K	14
15	0.0571	0.0588	0.0602	15	90	3.184	9.858	0.25	0.010K	15
16	0.0508	0.0524	0.0538	17	90	4.016	7.818	0.1875	0.010K	16
17	0.0453	0.0469	0.0482	19	90	5.064	6.200	0.1875	0.007K	17
18	0.0403	0.0418	0.0431	21	90	6.385	4.917	0.1875	0.007K	18
19	0.0359	0.0374	0.0386	23	90	8.051	3.899	0.1562	0.007K	19
20	0.0320	0.0334	0.0346	26	90	10.15	3.092	0.1562	0.005K	20
21	0.0285	0.0299	0.0310	30	90	12.80	2.452	0.1562	0.005K	21
22	0.0253	0.0266	0.0277	33	90	16.14	1.945	0.125	0.003K	22
23	0.0226	0.0239	0.0249	37	90	20.36	1.542	0.125	0.003K	23
24	0.0201	0.0213	0.0223	42	90	25.67	1.223	0.125	0.002G	24
25	0.0179	0.0190	0.0200	47	90	32.37	0.9699	0.125	0.002G	25
26	0.0159	0.0169	0.0179	52	89	40.81	0.7692	0.125	0.002G	26
27	0.0142	0.0152	0.0161	57	89	51.47	0.6100	0.125	0.002G	27
28	0.0126	0.0135	0.0145	64	89	64.90	0.4837	0.125	0.0015G	28
29	0.0113	0.0122	0.0131	71	89	81.83	0.3836	0.125	0.0015G	29
30	0.0100	0.0109	0.0116	80	89	103.2	0.3042	0.125	0.0015G	30
31	0.0089	0.0097	0.0104	88	88	130.1	0.2413	0.125	0.0015G	31
32	0.0080	0.0088	0.0094	98	88	164.1	0.1913	0.0937	0.0013G	32
33	0.0071	0.0079	0.0084	110	88	206.9	0.1517	0.0937	0.0013G	33
34	0.0063	0.0070	0.0075	124	88	260.9	0.1203	0.0937	0.001G	34
35	0.0056	0.0062	0.0067	140	88	329.0	0.0954	0.0937	0.001G	35
36	0.0050	0.0056	0.0060	155	87	414.8	0.0757	0.0937	0.001G	36
37	0.0045	0.0050	0.0054	170	87	523.1	0.0600	0.0937	0.001G	37
38	0.0040	0.0045	0.0048	193	87	659.6	0.0476	0.0625	0.001G	38
39	0.0035	0.0040	0.0042	215	86	831.8	0.0377	0.0625	0.0007G	39
40	0.0031	0.0036	0.0038	239	86	1049	0.0299	0.0625	0.0007G	40

*Dimensions very nearly the same as for enamelled wire.
†Values are at 20 degrees centigrade.
‡K = kraft paper, G = glassine.

Additional data on wire will be found on pp. 40–45 and p. 74.

Design of power transformers for rectifiers   continued

c. Compute, roughly, the net core area

$$A_c = \frac{W_{out}}{5.58} \sqrt{\frac{60}{f}} \text{ inches}^2$$

where f is in cycles (see also Fig. 5). Select a lamination and core size from the manufacturer's data book that will nearly meet the space requirements, and provide core area for a flux density B_m not to exceed a limiting value (10,000 gauss for 29-gauge 4-percent silicon steel, at 60 cycles) under normal operating conditions.

d. Compute the primary turns N_p from the transformer equation

$$E_p = 4.44 \, f N_p A_c B_m \times 10^{-8}$$

and the secondary turns

$$N_s = 1.05 (E_s/E_p) N_p$$

(this allows 5 percent for IR drop of windings).

e. Calculate the number of turns per layer that can be placed in the lamination window space, deducting from the latter the margin space given in Fig. 6 (see also Fig. 7).

f. From (d) and (e) compute the number of layers n_l for each winding. Use interlayer insulation of thickness t as given in Fig. 6, except that the minimum allowance should be 40 volts/mil dielectric strength.

g. Calculate the coil-built a:

$$a = 1.1[n_l(D + t) - t + t_c]$$

for each winding from (b) and (f), where D = diameter of insulated wire and t_c = thickness of insulation under and over the winding; the numeric 1.1 allows for a 10-percent bulge factor. The total coil-built should not exceed 85–90 percent of the window width. (Note: Insulation over the core may vary from 0.025 to 0.050 inches for core-builts of $\frac{1}{2}$ to 2 inches.)

h. Compute the mean length per turn (MLT), of each winding, from the geometry of core and windings. Compute length of each winding N(MLT)

i. Calculate the resistance of each winding from (h) and Fig. 6, and determine IR drop and I^2R loss for each winding.

j. Make corrections, if required, in the number of turns of the windings to allow for the IR drops, so as to have the required E_s:

$$E_s = (E_p - I_p R_p) N_s/N_p - I_s R_s$$

Design of power transformers for rectifiers   *continued*

k. Compute core losses from weight of core and the table on core materials, Fig. 8.

l. Determine the percent efficiency η and voltage regulation (vr) from

$$\eta = \frac{W_{out} \times 100}{W_{out} + (\text{core loss}) + (\text{copper loss})}$$

$$(vr) = \frac{I_s[R_s + (N_s/N_p)^2 R_p]}{E_s}$$

m. For a more accurate evaluation of voltage regulation, determine leakage-reactance drop $= I_{dc}\omega l_{sc}/2\pi$, and add to the above (vr) the value of $(I_{dc}\omega l_{sc})/2\pi E_{dc}$. Here, l_{sc} = leakage inductance viewed from the secondary; see "Methods of winding transformers", p. 205 to evaluate I_{sc}.

n. Bring out all terminal leads using the wire of the coil, insulated with suitable sleevings, for all sizes of wire heavier than 21; and by using 7–30 stranded and insulated wire for smaller sizes.

High-frequency power transformers: For use in rectification may be designed similarly to low-frequency units. Of interest are units that may use Ferroxcube-III cores having practically no eddy-current losses.

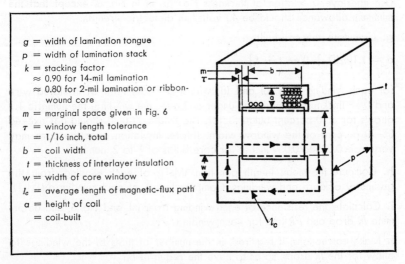

g = width of lamination tongue
p = width of lamination stack
k = stacking factor
  ≈ 0.90 for 14-mil lamination
  ≈ 0.80 for 2-mil lamination or ribbon-wound core
m = marginal space given in Fig. 6
τ = window length tolerance
  $= 1/16$ inch, total
b = coil width
t = thickness of interlayer insulation
w = width of core window
l_c = average length of magnetic-flux path
a = height of coil
  = coil-built

Fig. 7—Dimensions relating to the design of a transformer coil-built and core. Core area $A_c = (gp)k$.

continued **Design of power transformers for rectifiers**

Fig. 8—Core materials for low- and medium-frequency transformers.

alloy	initial permeability μ_0	maximum permeability μ_m	saturation induction B_s in gauss*	coercive force in oersteds	specific resistivity in microhms/centimeter	core losses in watts/pound (at $B_m = 10{,}000$)	gauge in mils	chief uses
4-percent silicon steel	400	10,000	12,000	0.6	60	0.6 at 60 cycles	14	Small power and audio transformers, chokes and saturable reactors
Hipersil	1,500	40,000	17,000	0.1	48	0.33–0.44 at 60 cycles	14	Larger power and wider-range audio transformers and chokes, and saturable reactors
						3.8 at 400 cycles	5	400–800-cycle power transformers
						1.25 at 800 cycles ($B_m = 4{,}000$)	2	High-frequency and pulse transformers
Hiperco	600	10,000	24,000	0.4	—	4 at 60 cycles ($B_m = 20{,}000$)	14	Small power transformers for aircraft equipment
Hipernik	4,000	80,000	15,000	0.05	35	0.36 at 60 cycles	14	
Allegheny 4750†	4,000	40,000	15,000	0.07	52	—	—	Audio transformers with better characteristics; low- and high-voltage levels
Monimax	3,200	38,000	14,000	0.15	80	1.7 at 400 cycles	4	400–800-cycle power transformers
Sinimax	4,600	30,000	11,000	0.1	90	1.7 at 400 cycles	6	400–800-cycle power transformers
Mumetal	20,000	110,000	7,200	0.03	60	—	—	Low-voltage-level, high-fidelity transformers
4-79 molybdenum-permalloy‡	20,000	80,000	8,500	0.05	57	—	—	Low-voltage-level, high-fidelity transformers
Ferroxcube-III	600	—	2,500	—	10^8	—	—	High-frequency power and pulse transformers

Data mostly from: R. M. Bozorth, "Magnetism," *Reviews of Modern Physics*, v. 19, p. 42; January, 1947.

* These B_s values may be termed useful saturation values of induction, in contradistinction with the true saturation values B_s, which may be considerably higher (such as for 4-percent silicon steel, $B_s \approx 20{,}000$). For these high B_s values, the exciting current and core losses would become prohibitive, due to very low permeabilities.

† Carpenter 49 alloy is approximately the equivalent of Allegheny 4750.

‡ Carpenter Hymu is the approximate equivalent of Western Electric Company's 4-79 Molybdenum-permalloy.

Design of filter reactors for rectifiers and plate-current supply

These reactors carry direct current and are provided with suitable air-gaps. Optimum design data may be obtained from Hanna curves, Fig. 9. These curves relate direct-current energy stored in core per unit volume, LI_{dc}^2/V to magnetizing field NI_{dc}/l_c (where l_c = average length of flux path in core), for an appropriate air-gap. Heating is seldom a factor, but direct-current-resistance requirements affect the design; however, the transformer equivalent volt-ampere ratings of chokes (Fig. 5) should be useful in determining their sizes.

As an example, take the design of a choke that is to have an inductance of 10 henries with a superimposed direct current of 0.225 amperes, and a direct-current resistance $\leqslant$ 125 ohms. This reactor shall be used for suppressing harmonics of 60 cycles, where the alternating-current ripple voltage (2nd harmonic) is about 35 volts.

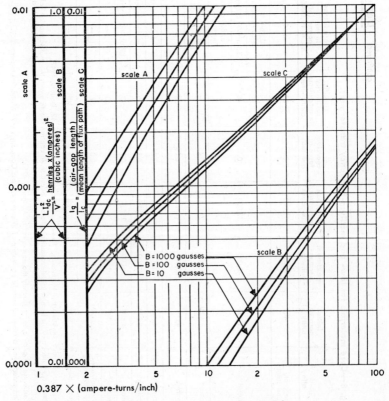

Fig. 9—Hanna curves for 4-percent silicon-steel core material.

Design of filter reactors for rectifiers   continued

a. $LI^2 = 0.51$. Based on data of Fig. 5, try 4-percent silicon-steel core, type EI–125 punchings, with a core-built of 1.5 inches. From manufacturer's data, volume = 13.7 inches^3; $l_c = 7.5$ inches; $A_c = 1.69$ inches^2.

b. Compute $LI_{dc}^2/V = 0.037$; from Fig. 9, $NI_{dc}/l_c = 85$; hence, by substitution, $N = 2840$ turns. Also, gap ratio $l_g/l_c = 0.003$, or, total gap $l_g = 22$ mils.

Alternating-current flux density $B_m = \dfrac{E \times 10^8}{4.44fNA_c} = 210$

c. Calculate from the geometry of the core, the mean length/turn, (MLT) = 0.65 feet, and the length of coil = N(MLT) = 1840 feet, which is to have a maximum direct-current resistance of 125 ohms. Hence, R_{dc}/N(MLT) = 0.068 ohms/foot. From Fig. 6, the nearest size is No. 28.

d. Now see if 1840 turns of No. 28 single-Formex wire will fit in the window space of the core. (Determine turns per layer, number of layers, and coil-built, as explained in the design of power transformers.)

e. This is an actual coil design; in case lamination window space is too small (or too large) change stack of laminations, or size of lamination, so that the coil meets the electrical requirements, and the total coil-built ≈ 0.85 to $0.90 \times$ (window width).

Note: To allow for manufacturing variations in permeability of cores and resistance of wires, use at least 10-percent tolerance.

Design of wave-filter reactors

These must have high Q values to enable sharp cutoff, or high attenuation at frequencies immediately off the pass-band. Data on high-Q cores is given in table on cores, Fig. 10. Nicalloy and Hymu (or their equivalents) are listed primarily for low frequencies, and should be used only with suitable gaps to minimize losses and insure stability of inductance and effective resistance for small magnetizing fields. Maximum Q is obtained when

(copper loss) $\approx$ (core loss)

The inductance is given by

$$L \approx \frac{1.25N^2A_c}{l_g + l_c/\mu_0} 10^{-8} \quad \text{henries}$$

where dimensions are in centimeters and μ_0 = initial permeability.

When using molybdenum-permalloy-dust toroidal cores, the inductance is given by

$$L \approx \frac{1.25N^2A_c}{l_c} \mu_{ef} \times 10^{-8} \qquad \text{for } \mu_{ef} = 125$$

Fig. 10—Characteristics of core materials for high-Q coils.

alloy		initial permeability μ_0	resistivity in microhms/centimeter	hysteresis coefficient‡ (a $\times 10^6$)	residual coefficient‡ (c $\times 10^6$)	eddy-current coefficient‡ (e $\times 10^9$)	gauge in mils	uses (frequencies in kilocycles)
4-percent silicon steel		400	60	120	75	870	14	Rectifier filters
Nicalloy*		3,500	45	0.4	14	1550	14	Wave filters up to 0.1–0.2
						284	6	Wave filters up to 10
Hymu*		20,000	55	0.05	0.05	950	14	Wave filters up to 0.1–0.2
						175	6	Wave filters up to 10
2–81 molybdenum-permalloy dust‡		125	1 ohm/cm	1.6	30	19	—	Wave filters 0.2 to 7
		60	—	3.2	50	10	—	Wave filters 5–20
		26	—	6.9	96	7.7	—	Wave filters 15–60
		14	—	11.4	143	7.1	—	Wave filters 40–150
Carbonyl types	C	55	—	9	80	7	—	Wave filters
	P	26	—	3.4	220	27	—	Wave filters
	Th	16	—	2.5	80	8	—	Wave filters 40–high
Ferroxcube–III†		600	50 ohms/cm	3.0	40 at 10 kc / 120 at 100 kc / 630 at 1000 kc	—	—	—

*The toroidal 2–81-percent molybdenum-permalloy dust cores yield higher Q than laminated Hymu or Nicalloy (provided with suitable air-gaps) at frequencies above 200 cycles.

†Has a temperature coefficient of inductance of about 0.15 percent/degree between 10 and 40 degrees centigrade, and a Curie temperature = 120 degrees centigrade.

‡Data on molybdenum-permalloy dust and definition of constants a, c, and e are from an article by V. E. Legg, and F. J. Given, "Compressed Powdered Molybdenum-Permalloy for High-Quality Inductance Coils," *Bell System Technical Journal,* v. 19, pp. 385–406; July, 1940:

$R_c/fL = \mu_0(aB_m + c) + \mu_0 ef$

where R_c = resistance due to core loss, in ohms.

Design of wave-filter reactors   *continued*

$$L \approx 0.85 \frac{1.25N^2A_c}{l_c} \mu_{ef} \times 10^{-8} \quad \text{for } \mu_{ef} = 65$$

Ferroxcube-III cores may be used only if cognizance is taken of their high temperature instability (0.15 percent/degree centigrade, between 10 and 40 degrees) and their low Curie temperature of 120 degrees centigrade. Suitable gaps would reduce core losses, improve Q, and insure stability of constants for varying alternating voltage; and also (to some extent) for varying temperatures.

Design of audio-frequency transformers

Important parameters are: generator and load impedances R_g, R_l, respectively, generator voltage E_g, frequency band to be transmitted, efficiency (output transformers only), harmonic distortion, and operating voltages (for adequate insulation).

At mid-frequencies: The relative low- and high-frequency responses are taken with reference to mid-frequencies, where

$$\frac{aE_{out}}{E_g} = \frac{1}{(1 + R_s/R_l) + R_1/a^2R_l}$$

At low frequencies: The equivalent unity-ratio network of a transformer becomes approximately as shown in Fig. 11:

$$\text{Amplitude} = \frac{1}{\sqrt{1 + (R'_{par}/X_m)^2}}$$

$$\text{Phase angle} = \tan^{-1}\frac{R'_{par}}{X_m}$$

where

$$R'_{par} = \frac{R_1R_2a^2}{R_1 + R_2a^2}$$

$$R_1 = R_g + R_p$$

$$R_2 = R_l + R_s$$

$$X_m = 2\pi f L_p$$

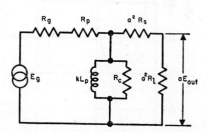

Fig. 11—Equivalent network of an audio-frequency transformer at low frequencies. $R_1 = R_g + R_p$ and $R_2 = R_s + R_l$. In a good output transformer, R_p, R_s, and R_c may be neglected. In input or interstage transformers, R_c may be omitted.

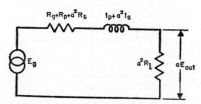

Fig. 12—Equivalent network of an audio-frequency transformer at high frequencies, neglecting the effect of the winding shunt capacitances. Primary short-circuit inductance $l_{scp} = l_p + a^2l_s$.

Design of audio-frequency transformers *continued*

At high frequencies: Neglecting the effect of winding and other capacitances (as in low-impedance-level output transformers), the equivalent unity-ratio network becomes approximately as in Fig. 12:

$$\text{Amplitude} = \frac{1}{\sqrt{1 + (X_l/R'_{se})^2}}$$

$$\text{Phase angle} = \tan^{-1} \frac{X_l}{R'_{se}}$$

where $R'_{se} = R_1 + R_2 a^2$ and $X_l = 2\pi f l_{sc}$

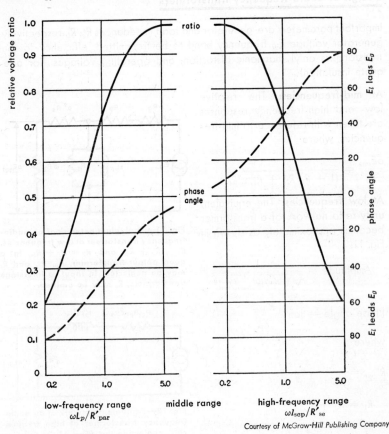

Courtesy of McGraw-Hill Publishing Company

Fig. 13—Universal frequency- and phase-response characteristics of output transformers.

Design of audio-frequency transformers   *continued*

These low- and high-frequency responses are shown on the curves of Fig. 13.

If at high frequencies, the effect of winding and other capacitances is appreciable, the equivalent network on a 1:1-turns-ratio basis becomes as shown in Fig. 14. The relative high-frequency response of this network is given by

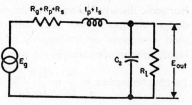

$$\frac{(R_1 + R_2)/R_2}{\sqrt{\left(\dfrac{R_1}{X_c} + \dfrac{X_l}{R_l}\right)^2 + \left(\dfrac{X_l}{X_c} - \dfrac{R_g}{R_l} - 1\right)^2}}$$

Fig. 14—Equivalent network of a 1:1-turns-ratio audio-frequency transformer at high frequencies when effect of winding shunt capacitances is appreciable. In a step-up transformer, $C_2 =$ equivalent shunt capacitances of both windings. In a step-down transformer, C_2 shunts both leakage inductances and R_2.

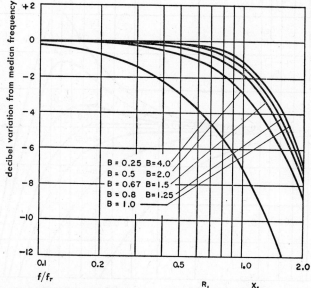

Reprinted from "*Electronic Transformers and Circuits,*" by R. Lee, 1st ed., p. 122, 1947; by permission, John Wiley & Sons, N. Y.

Fig. 15—Transformer characteristics at high frequencies for matched impedances. At frequency f_r, $X_l = X_c$ and $B = X_c/R_l$.

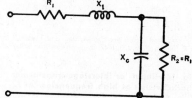

Design of audio-frequency transformers   *continued*

This high-frequency response is plotted in Figs. 15 and 16 for $R_1 = R_2$ (matched impedances), and $R_2 = \infty$ (input and interstage transformers).

Harmonic distortion: Requirements may constitute a deciding factor in the design of transformers. Such distortion is caused by either variations in load impedance or nonlinearity of magnetizing current. The percent harmonic voltage appearing in the output of a loaded transformer is given by*

$$\text{Percent harmonics} = \frac{E_h}{E_f} = \frac{I_h}{I_f}\frac{R'_{\text{par}}}{X_m}\left(1 - \frac{R'_{\text{par}}}{4X_m}\right)$$

where $100\, I_h/I_f$ = percent of harmonic current measured with zero-impedance source (values are given in Fig. 17 for 4-percent silicon-steel core).

*N. Partridge, "Harmonic Distortion in Audio-Frequency Transformers," *Wireless Engineer,* v. 19; September, October, and November, 1942.

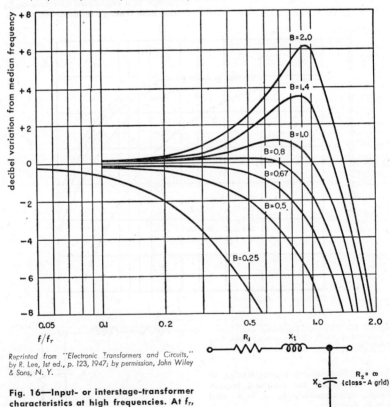

Reprinted from "Electronic Transformers and Circuits," by R. Lee, 1st ed., p. 123, 1947; by permission, John Wiley & Sons, N. Y.

Fig. 16—Input- or interstage-transformer characteristics at high frequencies. At f_r, $X_l = X_c$ and $B = X_c/R_1$.

Example of audio-output-transformer design

This transformer is to operate from a 4000-ohm impedance; to deliver 5 watts to a matched load of 10 ohms; to transmit frequencies of 60 to 15,000 cycles with a V_{out}/V_{in} ratio of 71 percent of that at mid-frequencies (400 cycles); and the harmonic distortion is to be less than 2 percent. (See Figs. 11 and 12.)

a. We have: $E_s = \sqrt{W_{out}R_l} = 7.1$ volts

$$I_s = W_{out}/E_s = 0.7 \text{ amperes}$$

$$a = \sqrt{R_g/R_l} = 20$$

Then

$I_p \approx 1.1 \, I_s/a = 0.039$ amperes, and $E_p \approx 1.1 \, aE_s = 156$

b. To evaluate the required primary inductance to transmit the lowest frequency of 60 cycles, determine $R'_{se} = R_1 + a^2R_2$ and $R'_{par} = \dfrac{R_1R_2a^2}{R_1 + R_2a^2}$, where $R_1 = R_g + R_p$ and $R_2 = R_l + R_s$. We choose winding resistances $R_s = R_p/a^2 \approx 0.05R_l = 0.5$

(for a copper efficiency $= \dfrac{R_la^2 \times 100}{(R_l + R_s)a^2 + R_p} = 91$ percent). Then,

$R'_{se} = 2R_1 = 8400$ ohms, and $R'_{par} = R_1/2 = 2100$ ohms.

c. In order to meet the frequency-response requirements, we must have, according to Fig. 13, $\dfrac{\omega_{low}L_p}{R'_{par}} = 1 = \dfrac{\omega_{high}l_{sep}}{R'_{se}}$, which yield

$L_p \approx 5.8$ henries and $l_{sep} = 0.093$ henries

Fig. 17—Harmonics produced by various flux densities B_m in a 4-percent silicon-steel-core audio transformer.

B_m	percent 3rd harmonic	percent 5th harmonic
100	4	1.0
500	7	1.5
1,000	9	2.0
3,000	15	2.5
5,000	20	3.0
10,000	30	5.0

Example of audio-output-transformer design *continued*

d. Harmonic distortion is usually a more important factor in determining the minimum inductance of output transformers than is the attenuation requirement at low frequencies. Compute now the number of turns and inductance for an assumed $B_m = 5000$ for 4-percent silicon-steel core with type EI–12 punchings in square stack. Here, A_c (net) $= 5.8$ centimeters^2, $l_c = 15.25$ centimeters, and $\mu_{ac} \approx 5000$. See Fig. 18.

$$N_p = \frac{E_p \times 10^8}{4.44 f A_c B_m} = 2020$$

$$N_s = 1.1 N_p/a = 111$$

$$L_p \approx \frac{1.25 N_p^2 \mu_{ac} A_c}{l_c} \times 10^{-8} = 97 \text{ henries}$$

At 60 cycles, $X_m = \omega L_p = 36{,}600$ and $R'_{par}/X_m \approx 0.06$.

From values of I_h/I_f for 4-percent silicon-steel (See Fig. 17):

$$\frac{E_h}{E_f} = \frac{I_h}{I_f}\frac{R'_{par}}{X_m}\left(1 - \frac{R'_{par}}{4X_m}\right) \approx 0.012 \text{ or } 1.2 \text{ percent}$$

e. Now see if core window is large enough to fit windings. Assuming a simple method of winding (secondary over the primary), compute from geometry of core the approximate (MLT), for each winding.

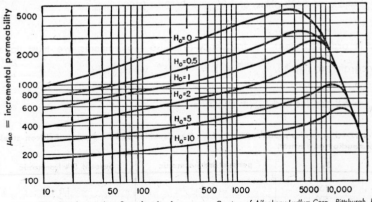

B_m = alternating flux density in gausses *Courtesy of Allegheny-Ludlum Corp., Pittsburgh, Pa.*

Fig. 18—Incremental permeability μ_{ac} characteristics of Allegheny audio-transformer "A" sheet steel at 60 cycles/second. No. 29 U.S. gauge, L–7 standard laminations stacked 100 percent, interleaved. This is 4-percent silicon-steel core material. H_0 = magnetizing field in oersteds.

Example of audio-output-transformer design   *continued*

For the primary, (MLT) $\approx$ 0.42 feet and N_p(MLT) $\approx$ 850 feet.

For the secondary, (MLT) $\approx$ 0.58 feet and N_s(MLT) $\approx$ 65 feet.

For the primary, then, the size of wire is obtained from R_p/N_p(MLT) = 0.236 ohms/foot; and from Fig. 6, use No. 33.

For the secondary, R_s/N_s(MLT) $\approx$ 0.008, and size of wire is No. 18.

f. Compute the turns/layer, number of layers, and total coil-built, as for power transformers. For an efficient design,

(total coil-built) $\approx$ (0.85 to 0.90) $\times$ (window width)

g. To determine if leakage inductance is within the required limit of (c) above, evaluate

$$l_{sc} = \frac{10.6 N_p{}^2 (MLT)(2nc + a)}{n^2 b \times 10^9} = 0.036 \text{ henries}$$

which is less than the limit 0.093 henries of (c). The symbols of this equation are defined in Fig. 19. If leakage inductance is high, interleave windings as indicated under "Methods of winding transformers", p. 205.

Example of audio-input-transformer design

This transformer must couple a 500-ohm line to the grids of 2 tubes in class-A push-pull. Attenuation to be flat to 0.5 decibels over 100 to 15,000 cycles; step-up = 1:10; and input to primary is 2 volts.

a. Use Allegheny 4750 material for high μ_0 (4000) due to low input voltage. Interleave primary between halves of secondary. Use No. 40 wire for secondary. For interwinding insulation use 0.010 paper. Use winding-space tolerance of 10 percent.

b. Total secondary load resistance $= R'_{par} = \dfrac{a^2 R_1 R_2}{a^2 R_1 + R_2} = a^2 R_1$
$$= 500 \times 10^2 = 50,000 \text{ ohms}$$

From universal-frequency-response curves of Fig. 13 for 0.5 decibel down at 100 cycles (voltage ratio = 0.95),

$\dfrac{\omega_{low} L_s}{R'_{par}} = 3$, or $L_s \approx 240$ henries

c. Try Allegheny type EI–68 punchings, square stack. Here, A_c = 3.05 centimeters, l_c = 10.5 centimeters, and window dimensions = $\frac{11}{32} \times 1\frac{1}{32}$ inches,

Example of audio-input-transformer design   *continued*

interleaved singly: $l_g = 0.0005$. From formula $L = \dfrac{1.25N^2A_c}{l_g + l_c/\mu_0} \times 10^{-8}$ and above constants, compute

$N_s = 4400$
$N_p = N_s/a = 440$

d. Choose size of wire for primary winding, so that $R_p \approx 0.1R_g = 50$ ohms. From geometry of core, (MLT) ≈ 0.29 feet; also, R_p/N_p (MLT) $= 0.392$, or No. 35 wire $(D = 0.0062$ for No. 35F$)$.

e. Turns per layer of primary $= 0.9b/d = 110$; number of layers $n_p = N_p/110 = 4$; turns per layer of secondary $0.9b/d = 200$; number of layers $n_s = N_s/200 = 22$.

f. Secondary leakage inductance

$$l_{scs} = \frac{10.6N^2_s(\text{MLT})(2nc + a) \times 10^{-9}}{n^2b} = 0.35 \text{ henries}$$

g. Secondary effective layer-to-layer capacitance

$$C_e = \frac{4C_l}{3n_l}\left(1 - \frac{1}{n_l}\right)$$

(see Fig. 19) where $C_l = 0.225A\epsilon/t = 1770$ micromicrofarads. Substituting this value of C_l into above expression of C_e, we find

$C_e = 107$ micromicrofarads

h. Winding-to-core capacitance $= 0.225A\epsilon/t \approx 63$ micromicrofarads (using 0.030-inch insulation between winding and core). Assuming tube and stray capacitances total 30 micromicrofarads, total secondary capacitance

$C_s \approx 200$ micromicrofarads

i. Series-resonance frequency of l_{sc} and C_s is

$$f_r = \frac{1}{2\pi\sqrt{l_{sc}C_s}} = 19,200 \text{ cycles,}$$

and X_c/R_1 at f_r is $1/2\pi f_r C_s R_1 = 0.83$; at 15,000 cycles, $f/f_r = 0.78$.

From Fig. 16, decibels variation from median frequency is seen to be less than 0.5.

If it is required to extend the frequency range, use Mumetal core material for its higher μ_0 (20,000). This will reduce the primary turns, the leakage inductance, and the winding shunt capacitance.

Methods of winding transformers

Most common methods of winding transformers are shown in Fig. 19. Leakage inductance is reduced by interleaving, i.e., by dividing the primary or secondary coil in two sections, and placing the other winding between the two sections. Interleaving may be accomplished by concentric and by coaxial windings, as shown on Figs. 19B and C; reduction of leakage inductance may be seen from formula

$$l_{sc} = \frac{10.6 N^2 (MLT) (2nc + a)}{n^2 b \times 10^9} \text{ henries}$$

(dimensions in inches) to be the same for both Figs. 19B and C.

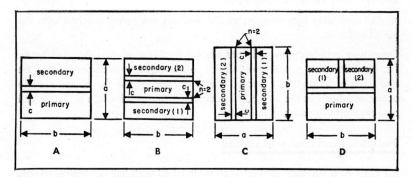

Fig. 19—Methods of winding transformers.

Effective interlayer capacitance of a winding may be reduced by sectionalizing it as shown in D. This can be seen from the formula

$$C_e = \frac{4C_l}{3n_l}\left(1 - \frac{1}{n_l}\right) \text{ micromicrofarads}$$

where

C_l = capacitance of one layer to another
n_l = number of layers

$$C_l = \frac{0.225 A \epsilon}{t} \text{ micromicrofarads}$$

where

A = area of winding layer
  = (MLT)b inches^2
t = thickness of interlayer insulation in inches
ϵ = dielectric constant
  $\approx$ 3 for paper

Temperature and humidity

The average life expectancies of class-A and class-B insulated transformers are given by*

Class A: $\log t = 8.7 - 0.038T$

Class B: $\log t = 10 - 0.038T$

where t = time in hours and T = temperature in degrees centigrade.

For class-A insulation (organic materials), operating-temperature limits are set at 95 degrees.

For class-B insulation (inorganic: glass, mica, asbestos), operating temperature limits are set at 125 degrees.

Higher operating temperatures of 200 degrees are being reached with the use of silicones.

Open-type constructions will naturally be cooler than the enclosed types. To eliminate the detrimental effects of humidity, transformers may be enclosed in hermetically sealed cans, or surrounded by some suitable compound (such as the Intelin 211 compound) that will insulate all leads and prevent moisture conduction as well.

Dielectric insulation and corona

For class-A, a maximum dielectric strength of 40 volts/mil is considered safe for small thicknesses of insulation. At high operating voltages, due regard should be paid to corona, which starts at about 1250 volts and is then of greater importance than dielectric strength in causing failure. 60-cycle root-mean-square corona voltage may be given by, approximately,

$$\log \frac{V \text{ (in volts)}}{800} = \frac{2}{3} \log (100t)$$

where t = total insulation thickness in inches. This may be used as a guide in determining the thickness of insulation. With the use of some new varnishes that require no solvents, but solidify by polymerization, the bubbles present in the usual varnishes are eliminated, and much higher operating voltages and, hence, reduction in the size of high-voltage units may be obtained. Fosterite, and some polyesters, such as the Intelin 211 compound, belong in this group. In the design of high-voltage transformers, the creepage distance required between wire and core may necessitate the use of insulating channels covering the high-voltage coil, or taping of the latter. For units operating at 10 kilovolts or higher, oil insulation will greatly reduce creepage and, hence, size of the transformer.

*R. Lee, "Fibrous Glass Insulation in Radio Apparatus," *Electronics*, vol. 12, pp. 33–34; October, 1939.

Saturable reactors and magnetic amplifiers

A saturable reactor (S.R.) is one in which the core, or part of it, operates near the knee of the magnetization curve, and the impedance of the

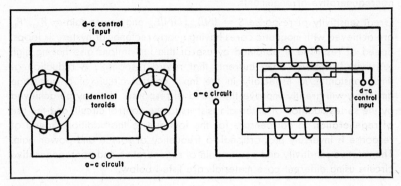

Fig. 20—Saturable-reactor connections.

alternating-current windings is varied by a direct (or slowly varying) current in the control windings, in which no voltage is induced by the alternating-current windings. Typical connections are shown in Fig. 20.

A magnetic amplifier has an essential component, the saturable reactor(s), and also has rectifier(s), load, and possibly other elements. Similar to vacuum-tube amplifiers, magnetic amplifiers may be used in non-regenerative or regenerative circuits, as shown in Fig. 21.

Regenerative- (positive-) type amplifiers have increased sensitivities to changes in the control current, are responsive to the polarity of the input signals, and usually require, for the minimum output at zero-signal input, fixed negative-bias winding(s). The maximum output obtainable from

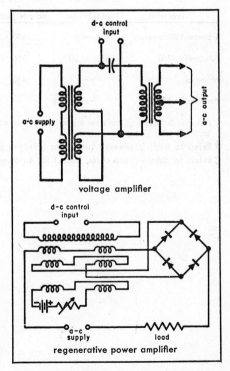

Fig. 21—Magnetic-amplifier connections.

Saturable reactors and magnetic amplifiers   *continued*

a magnetic amplifier depends on the size and properties of the core material and the value of the load; it is substantially the same for regenerative or nonregenerative arrangements.

Great sensitivity of response $S = (NI)_{out}/(NI)_{in}$ and power gain $= P_{out}/P_{in}$ are achieved with magnetic cores having nearly rectangular hysteresis loops. Speed of response is obtained by use of thin laminations also having high resistivity (to reduce eddy currents that retard response). A reduction of time constant L/R, especially in the input control circuit of a multistage amplifier, will greatly improve the speed of response. This may be achieved by the series addition of external resistors to the control circuit, and the use of regeneration to compensate for the loss due to this addition. Speed of response is inversely proportional to frequency of source and power gain. The relative sensitivity and power gain of regenerative and nonregenerative circuits using different core materials are listed below.

material	nonregenerative		regenerative
	sensitivity	power gain†	sensitivity‡
4-percent silicon steel*	$(S_1) = 5$	150	$5(S_1) = 25$
Allegheny 4750	$(S_2) = 20$	350	$50(S_2) = 40 \times 5(S_1) = 1000$
Mumetal	—	450	$2.5 \times 50(S_2) = 2500$
Permenorm 5000Z	—	—	$25 \times 50(S_2) = 25,000$

* Data for 4-percent silicon steel are for singly interleaved laminations (effective gap ≈ 0.0005 inch).

† Refers to singly interleaved laminations (effective gap ≈ 0.0005 inch).

‡ Refers to ribbon-wound cores, except for 4-percent silicon-steel core.

■ Electron tubes

General data*

Cathode emission

The cathode of an electron tube is the primary source of the electron stream. Available emission from the cathode must be at least equal to the sum of the instantaneous peak currents drawn by all of the electrodes. Maximum current of which a cathode is capable at the operating temperature is known as the saturation current and is normally taken as the value at which the current first fails to increase as the three-halves power of the voltage causing the current to flow. Thoriated-tungsten filaments for continuous-wave operation are usually assigned an available emission of approximately one-half the saturation value; oxide-coated emitters do not have a well-defined saturation point and are designed empirically. In the following table the figures refer to the saturation current.

Commonly used cathode materials

type	efficiency in milliamperes/ watt	specific emission I_s in amperes/ centimeter^2	emissivity in watts/ centimeter^2	operating temp in degrees Kelvin	ratio hot/cold resistance
Bright tungsten (W)	5–10	0.25–0.7	70–84	2500–2600	14/1
Thoriated tungsten (Th-W)	40–100	0.5–3.0	26–28	1950–2000	10/1
Tantalum (Ta)	10–20	0.5–1.2	48–60	2380–2480	6/1
Oxide coated (Ba-Ca-Sr)	50–150	0.5–2.5	5–10	1100–1250	2.5 to 5.5/1

Operation of cathodes: Thoriated-tungsten and oxide-coated emitters should be operated close to specified voltage. A customary allowable voltage deviation is ±5 percent. Bright-tungsten emitters may be operated at the minimum voltage that will supply required emission as determined by power-output and distortion measurements. Life of a bright-tungsten emitter will be lengthened by lowering the operating temperature. Fig. 1 shows the relationship between filament voltage and temperature, life, and emission in a typical case.

Mechanical stresses in filaments due to the magnetic field of the heating current are proportional to I_f^2. Current flow through a cold filament should be limited to 150 percent of the normal operating value for large tubes, and

* J. Millman, and S. Seely, "Electronics," 1st ed., McGraw-Hill Book Company, New York, New York; 1941. K. R. Spangenberg, "Vacuum Tubes," 1st ed., McGraw-Hill Book Company, New York, New York; 1948.

210

General data   *continued*

250 percent for medium types. Excessive starting current may easily warp or break a filament.

Thoriated-tungsten filaments may sometimes be restored to useful activity by applying filament voltage (only) in accordance with one of the following schedules.

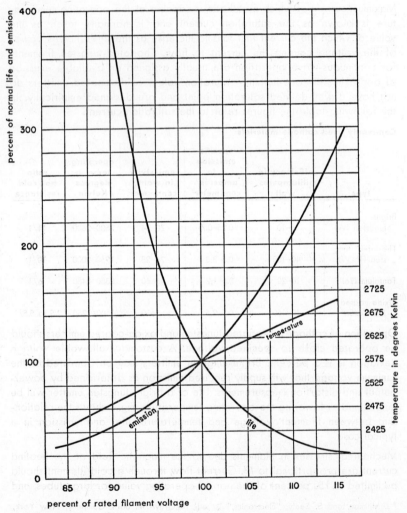

Fig. 1—Effect of change in filament voltage on the temperature, life, and emission of a bright-tungsten filament (based on 2575-degree-Kelvin normal temperature).

General data   *continued*

a. Normal filament voltage for several hours or overnight.

b. If the emission fails to respond; at 30 percent above normal for 10 minutes, then at normal for 20 to 30 minutes.

c. In extreme cases, when a and b have failed to give results, and at the risk of burning out the filament; at 75 percent above normal for 3 minutes followed by schedule b.

Electrode dissipation

Typical operating data for common types of cooling

type	average cooling-surface temperature in degrees centigrade	specific dissipation in watts/centimeter^2 of cooling surface	cooling-medium supply
Radiation	400–1000	4–10	
Water	30–150	30–110	0.25–0.5 gallons/minute/ kilowatt
Forced-air	150–200	0.5–1	50–150 feet^3/minute/ kilowatt

In computing cooling-medium flow, a minimum velocity sufficient to insure turbulent flow at the dissipating surface must be maintained. The figures for specific dissipation apply to clean cooling surfaces and may be reduced to a small fraction of the values shown by heat-insulating coatings such as scale or dust.

Operating temperature of a radiation-cooled surface for a given dissipation is determined by the relative total emissivity of the anode material. Temperature and dissipation are related by the expression,

$$P = \epsilon_t \sigma (T^4 - T_0^4) \times 10^{-7}$$

where

P = radiated power in watts/centimeter^2

ϵ_t = total thermal emissivity of the surface

σ = Stefan-Boltzmann constant

   = 5.72×10^{-12} watt-centimeters^{-2} × degrees Kelvin^{-4}

T = temperature of radiating surface in degrees Kelvin

T_0 = temperature of surroundings in degrees Kelvin

Total thermal emissivity varies with the degree of roughness of the surface of the material, and the temperature. Values for typical surfaces are as follows:

General data   *continued*

Total thermal emissivity ϵ_t of electron-tube materials

material	temperature in degrees Kelvin	total thermal emissivity
Aluminum	450	0.1
Anode graphite	1000	0.9
Copper	300	0.07
Molybdenum	1300	0.13
Molybdenum, quartz-blasted	1300	0.5
Nickel	600	0.09
Tantalum	1400	0.18
Tungsten	2600	0.30

Except where noted, the surface of the metals is as normally produced.

Dissipation and temperature rise for water cooling

$$P = 264\, Q_W (T_2 - T_1)$$

where

P = power in watts
Q_W = flow in gallons/minute
T_2, T_1 = outlet and inlet water temperatures in degrees Kelvin, respectively

Dissipation and temperature rise for forced-air cooling

$$P = 169\, Q_A \left(\frac{T_2}{T_1} - 1 \right)$$

where Q_A = air flow in feet^3/minute, other quantities as above. Fig. 2 shows the method of measuring air flow and temperature rise in forced-air-cooled systems. A water manometer is used to determine the static pressure against which the blower must deliver the required air flow. Air velocity and outlet air temperature must be weighted over the cross-section of the air stream.

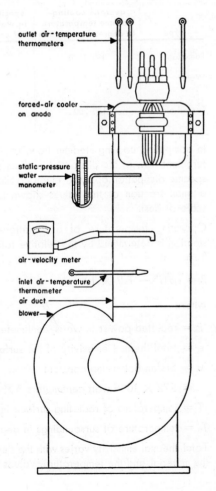

outlet air-temperature thermometers

forced-air cooler on anode

static-pressure water manometer

air-velocity meter

inlet air-temperature thermometer
air duct
blower

Fig. 2—Measurement of air flow and temperature rise in a forced-air-cooled system is shown at the right.

General data   *continued*

Grid temperature: Operation of grids at excessive temperatures will result in one or more harmful effects; liberation of gas, high primary (thermal) emission, contamination of the other electrodes by deposition of grid material, and melting of the grid may occur. Grid-current ratings should not be exceeded, even for short periods.

Noise in tubes*

Noise figure F: Is defined as the ratio of the available signal/noise ratio at the signal-generator (input) terminals to the available signal/noise ratio at the output terminals. A more detailed discussion of noise figure will be found in the chapter "Radio noise and interference."

Shot effect: Is noise due to random emission, is less pronounced in space-charge-limited than in temperature-limited tubes.

Flicker effect: Due to variations in the activity of the cathode, is most common in oxide-coated emitters.

Collision ionization: Causes noise when ionized gas atoms or molecules liberate bursts of electrons on striking the cathode.

Partition noise: Caused by random division of current between electrodes.

Induced noise: Caused by ultra-high-frequency components of the random space-charge fluctuations.

Miscellaneous noises: Due to microphonics, hum, leakage, charges on insulators, and poor contacts.

Nomenclature

Application of the standard nomenclature† to a typical electron-tube circuit is shown in Fig. 3. A typical oscillogram is given in Fig. 4 to illustrate the designation of the various components of a current. By logical extension of these principles, any tube, circuit, or electrical quantity may be covered.

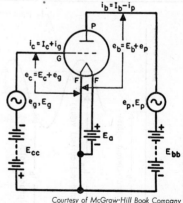

Courtesy of McGraw-Hill Book Company

Fig. 3—Typical electron-tube circuit.

* B. J. Thompson, D. O. North, and W. A. Harris, "Fluctuations in Space-Charge-Limited Currents at Moderately High Frequencies," *RCA Review:* Part I—January, 1940; Part II—July, 1940; Part III—October, 1940; Part IV—January, 1941; Part V—April, 1941.

† "Standards on Abbreviations, Graphical Symbols, Letter Symbols, and Mathematical Signs," The Institute of Radio Engineers; 1948.

Nomenclature   *continued*

e_c = instantaneous total grid voltage
e_b = instantaneous total plate voltage
i_c = instantaneous total grid current
E_c = average or quiescent value of grid voltage
E_b = average or quiescent value of plate voltage
I_c = average or quiescent value of grid current
e_g = instantaneous value of varying component of grid voltage
e_p = instantaneous value of varying component of plate voltage
i_g = instantaneous value of varying component of grid current
E_g = effective or maximum value of varying component of grid voltage
E_p = effective or maximum value of varying component of plate voltage
I_g = effective or maximum value of varying component of grid current
I_f = filament or heater current
I_s = total electron emission from cathode
C_{gp} = grid-plate direct capacitance
C_{gk} = grid-cathode direct capacitance
C_{pk} = plate-cathode direct capacitance
θ_p = plate-current conduction angle
r_l = external plate load resistance
r_p = variational (a-c) plate resistance

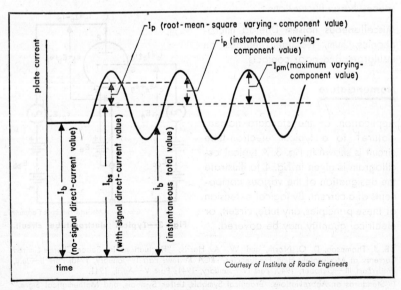

Courtesy of Institute of Radio Engineers

Fig. 4—Nomenclature of the various components of a current.

Low- and medium-frequency tubes

This section applies particularly to triodes and multigrid tubes operated at frequencies where electron-inertia effects are negligible.

Terminology

Space-charge grid: Placed adjacent to the cathode and positively biased to reduce the limiting effect of space charge on the current through the tube.

Control grid: Ordinarily placed between the cathode and the anode, for use as a control electrode.

Screen grid: Placed between the control grid and the anode, and usually maintained at a fixed positive potential, for the purpose of reducing the electrostatic influence of the anode in the space between the screen grid and the cathode.

Suppressor grid: Interposed between two electrodes (usually the screen grid and plate), both positive with respect to the cathode, in order to prevent the passage of secondary electrons from one to the other.

Anode: Electrode to which a principal electron stream flows.

Electron emission: The liberation of electrons from an electrode into the surrounding space. Quantitatively, it is the rate at which electrons are emitted from an electrode.

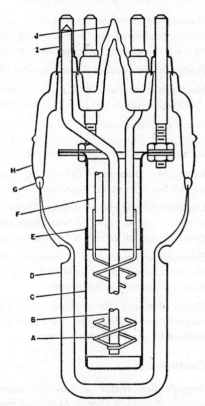

Fig. 5—Electrode arrangement of a small external-anode triode. Overall length is $4\frac{1}{16}$ inches. A—filament, B—filament central-support rod, C—grid wires, D—anode, E—grid-support sleeve, F—filament-leg support rods, G—metal-to-glass seal, H—glass envelope, I—filament and grid terminals, J—exhaust tubulation.

Low- and medium-frequency tubes   *continued*

Thermionic emission: Electron or ion emission due directly to the temperature of the emitter. Thermionic electron emission is also known as primary emission.

Secondary emission: Electron emission due directly to impact by electrons or ions.

Grid emission: Electron or ion emission from a grid.

Perveance: Ratio of the current, expressed in amperes, to the $\frac{3}{2}$ power of the potential expressed in volts.

Electrode admittance: The quotient of the alternating component of the electrode current by the alternating component of the electrode voltage, all other electrode voltages being maintained constant.

Electrode impedance: The reciprocal of the electrode admittance.

Electrode characteristic: A relation, usually shown by a graph, between an electrode voltage and current, other electrode voltages maintained constant.

Transfer characteristic: A relation, usually shown by a graph, between the voltage of one electrode and the current to another electrode, all other voltages being maintained constant.

Electrode capacitance: The capacitance of one electrode to all other electrodes connected together.

Constant-current characteristics: Show the relation, usually by a graph, between the voltages on two electrodes for constant specified current to one of them, all other voltages being maintained constant.

Electronic efficiency: Of a vacuum-tube oscillator or amplifier, is the electromagnetic power delivered by the electron stream divided by the power contained in the stream.

Circuit efficiency: Of a vacuum-tube oscillator or amplifier, is the electromagnetic power delivered to the load divided by the electromagnetic power received from the electron stream.

Coefficients

Amplification factor μ: Ratio of incremental plate voltage to control-electrode voltage change at a fixed plate current with constant voltage on other electrodes

$$\mu = \left[\frac{\delta e_b}{\delta e_{c1}}\right]_{I_b} \left.\begin{array}{c} \\ E_{c2} \text{------------} E_{cn} \\ r_l = 0 \end{array}\right\} \text{constant}$$

Low- and medium-frequency tubes *continued*

Transconductance s_m: Ratio of incremental plate current to control-electrode voltage change at constant voltage on other electrodes

$$s_m = \left[\frac{\delta i_b}{\delta e_{c1}} \right] E_b, E_{c2}\text{------------}E_{cn} \text{ constant}$$
$$r_l = 0$$

When electrodes are plate and control grid, the ratio is the mutual conductance, g_m

$$g_m = \frac{\mu}{r_p}$$

Variational (a-c) plate resistance r_p: Ratio of incremental plate voltage to current change at constant voltage on other electrodes

$$r_p = \left[\frac{\delta e_b}{\delta i_b} \right] E_{c1}\text{------------}E_{cn} \text{ constant}$$
$$r_l = 0$$

Total (d-c) plate resistance R_p: Ratio of total plate voltage to current for constant voltage on other electrodes

$$R_p = \left[\frac{E_b}{I_b} \right] E_{c1}\text{------------}E_{cn} \text{ constant}$$
$$r_l = 0$$

A useful approximation of these coefficients may be obtained from a family of anode characteristics, Fig. 6.

Amplification factor $\mu = \dfrac{e_{b2} - e_{b1}}{e_{c2} - e_{c1}}$

Mutual conductance $g_m = \dfrac{i_{b2} - i_{b1}}{e_{c2} - e_{c1}}$

Total plate resistance $R_p = \dfrac{e_{b2}}{i_{b2}}$

Variational plate resistance $r_p = \dfrac{e_{b2} - e_{b1}}{i_{b2} - i_{b1}}$

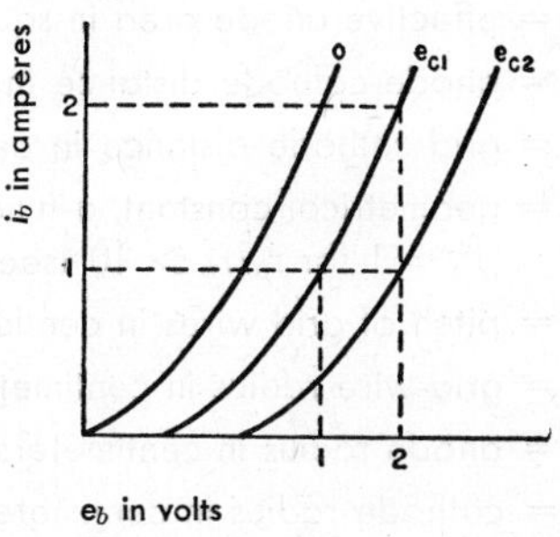

Fig. 6—Graphical method of determining coefficients.

Low- and medium-frequency tubes   *continued*

Formulas

For unipotential cathode and negligible saturation of cathode emission

function	parallel-plane cathode and anode	cylindrical cathode and anode
Diode anode current (amperes)	$G_1 e_b^{\frac{3}{2}}$	$G_1 e_b^{\frac{3}{2}}$
Triode anode current (amperes)	$G_2 \left(\dfrac{e_b + \mu e_c}{1 + \mu} \right)^{\frac{3}{2}}$	$G_2 \left(\dfrac{e_b + \mu e_c}{1 + \mu} \right)^{\frac{3}{2}}$
Diode perveance G_1	$2.3 \times 10^{-6} \dfrac{A_b}{d_b^{\,2}}$	$2.3 \times 10^{-6} \dfrac{A_b}{\beta^2 r_b^{\,2}}$
Triode perveance G_2	$2.3 \times 10^{-6} \dfrac{A_b}{d_b d_c}$	$2.3 \times 10^{-6} \dfrac{A_b}{\beta^2 r_b r_c}$
Amplification factor μ	$\dfrac{2.7\, d_c \left(\dfrac{d_b}{d_c} - 1 \right)}{\rho \log \dfrac{\rho}{2\pi r_g}}$	$\dfrac{2\pi d_c}{\rho} \dfrac{\log \dfrac{d_b}{d_c}}{\log \dfrac{\rho}{2\pi r_g}}$
Mutual conductance g_m	$1.5 G_2 \dfrac{\mu}{\mu + 1} \sqrt{E'_g}$ $E'_g = \dfrac{E_b + \mu E_c}{1 + \mu}$	$1.5 G_2 \dfrac{\mu}{\mu + 1} \sqrt{E'_g}$ $E'_g = \dfrac{E_b + \mu E_c}{1 + \mu}$

where

A_b = effective anode area in square centimeters

d_b = anode-cathode distance in centimeters

d_c = grid-cathode distance in centimeters

β = geometrical constant, a function of ratio of anode-to-cathode radius; $\beta^2 \approx 1$ for $r_b/r_k > 10$ (see curve Fig. 7)

ρ = pitch of grid wires in centimeters

r_g = grid-wire radius in centimeters

r_b = anode radius in centimeters

r_k = cathode radius in centimeters

r_c = grid radius in centimeters

Note: These formulas are based on theoretical considerations and do not provide accurate results for practical structures; however, they give a fair idea of the relationship between the tube geometry and the constants of the tube.

Low- and medium-frequency tubes *continued*

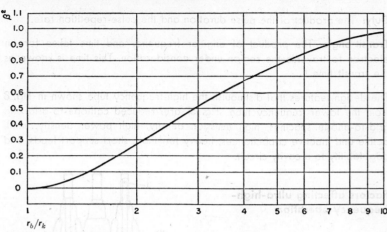

Fig. 7—Values of β^2 for values of $r_b/r_k < 10$.

High-frequency triodes and multigrid tubes*

When the operating frequency is increased, the operation of triodes and multigrid tubes is affected by electron-inertia effects. The poor microwave performance of these tubes has fostered the development of other types of tubes for use as oscillators and amplifiers at microwave frequencies. The three principal varieties are the magnetron, the klystron, and the traveling-wave amplifier.

Terminology

The definitions of the previous section apply in addition to those given below:

Pulse: Momentary flow of energy of such short time duration that it may be considered as an isolated phenomenon.

Pulse operation: Method of operation in which the energy is delivered in pulses.

Coherent-pulse operation: Method of pulse operation in which the phase of the radio-frequency wave is maintained through successive pulses.

R-F pulse duration: Time interval between the points at which the amplitude of the envelope of the radio-frequency pulse is 70.7 percent of the maximum amplitude of the envelope.

* D. R. Hamilton, J. K. Knipp, and J. B. H. Kuper, "Klystrons and Microwave Triodes," 1st ed., McGraw-Hill Book Company, New York, New York; 1948.

High-frequency triodes and multigrid tubes *continued*

Duty: The product of the pulse duration and the pulse-repetition rate.

Transit angle: The product of angular frequency and time taken for an electron to traverse the region under consideration. This time is known as the transit time.

The design features that distinguish the high-frequency tube shown in Fig. 8 from the lower-frequency tube (Fig. 5) are: reduced cathode-to-grid and grid-to-anode spacings, high emission density, high power density, small active and inactive capacitances, heavy terminals, short support leads, and adaptability to a cavity circuit.

Factors affecting ultra-high-frequency operation

Electron inertia: The theory of electron-inertia effects in small-signal tubes has been formulated;[*] no comparable complete theory is now available for large-signal tubes.

When the transit time of the electrons from cathode to anode is an appreciable fraction of one radio-frequency cycle:

a. Input conductance due to re-action of electrons with the varying field from the grid becomes appreciable. This conductance, which increases as the square of the frequency, results in lowered gain, an increase in driving-power requirement, and loading of the input circuit.

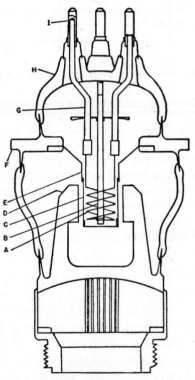

Fig. 8—Electrode arrangement of external-anode ultra-high-frequency triode. Overall length is 4 9/16 inches. A—filament, B—filament central-support rod, C—grid wires, D—anode, E—grid-support cone, F—grid terminal flange, G—filament-leg support rods, H—glass envelope, I—filament terminals.

* A. G. Clavier, "Effect of Electron Transit-Time in Valves," *L'Onde Electrique*, v. 16, pp. 145–149; March, 1937: also, A. G. Clavier, "The Influence of Time of Transit of Electrons in Thermionic Valves," *Bulletin de la Societe Francaise des Electriciens*, v. 19, pp. 79–91; January, 1939. F. B. Llewellyn, "Electron-Inertia Effects," 1st ed., Cambridge University Press, London; 1941.

High-frequency triodes and multigrid tubes *continued*

b. Grid-anode transit time introduces a phase lag between grid voltage and anode current. In oscillators, the problem of compensating for the phase lag by design and adjustment of a feedback circuit becomes difficult. Efficiency is reduced in both oscillators and amplifiers.

c. Distortion of the current pulse in the grid-anode space increases the anode-current conduction angle and lowers the efficiency.

Electrode admittances: In amplifiers, the effect of cathode-lead inductance is to introduce a conductance component in the grid circuit. This effect is serious in small-signal amplifiers because the loading of the input circuit by the conductance current limits the gain of the stage. Cathode-grid and grid-anode capacitive reactances are of small magnitude at ultra-high frequencies. Heavy currents flow as a result of these reactances and tubes must be designed to carry the currents without serious loss. Coaxial cavities are often used in the circuits to resonate with the tube reactances and to minimize resistive and radiation losses. Two circuit difficulties arise as operating frequencies increase:

a. The cavities become physically impossible as they tend to take the dimensions of the tube itself.

b. Cavity Q varies inversely as the square root of the frequency, which makes the attainment of an optimum Q a limiting factor.

Scaling factors: For a family of similar tubes, the dimensionless magnitudes such as efficiency are constant when the parameter

$$\phi = fd/V^{\frac{1}{2}}$$

is constant, where

f = frequency in megacycles

d = cathode-to-anode distance in centimeters

V = anode voltage in volts

Based upon this relationship and similar considerations, it is possible to derive a series of factors that determine how operating conditions will vary as the operating frequency or the physical dimensions are varied (see table, p. 222). If the tube is to be scaled exactly, all dimensions will be reduced inversely as the frequency is increased, and operating conditions will be as given in the "size-frequency scaling" column. If the dimensions of the tube are to be changed, but the operating frequency is to be maintained, operation will be as in the "size scaling" column. If the dimensions are to be maintained, but the operating frequency changed, operating conditions will be as in the "frequency scaling" column. These factors apply in general to all types of tubes.

High-frequency triodes and multigrid tubes *continued*

Scaling factors for ultra-high-frequency tubes

quantity	ratio	size-frequency scaling	size scaling	frequency scaling
Voltage	V_2/V_1	1	d^2	f^2
Field	E_2/E_1	f	d	f^2
Current	I_2/I_1	1	d^3	f^3
Current density	J_2/J_1	f^2	d	f^3
Power	P_2/P_1	1	d^5	f^5
Power density	h_2/h_1	f^2	d^3	f^5
Conductance	G_2/G_1	1	d	f
Magnetic-flux density	B_2/B_1	f	1	f

d = ratio of scaled to original dimensions
f = ratio of original to scaled frequency

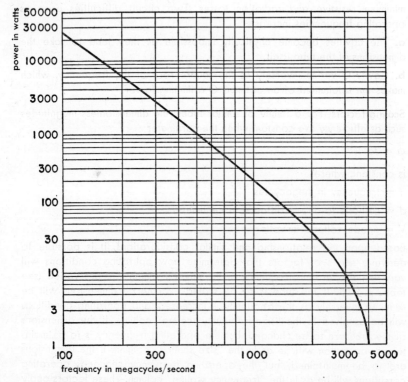

Fig. 9—Maximum ultra-high-frequency continuous-wave power obtainable from a single triode or tetrode. These data are based on present knowledge and techniques.

High-frequency triodes and multigrid tubes *continued*

With present knowledge and techniques, it has been possible to reach certain values of power with conventional tubes in the ultra- and super-high-frequency regions. The approximate maximum values that have been obtained are plotted in Fig. 9.

Positive-grid tubes

Specially designed triodes have been operated with positive grid and negative anode to produce oscillations in the microwave region. Such tubes utilize an oscillating space charge produced by acceleration of electrons through the positive grid toward a negative reflecting anode. This principle has been used to generate oscillations at wavelengths down to one centimeter. A typical tube is shown in Fig. 10.

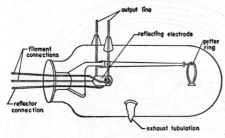

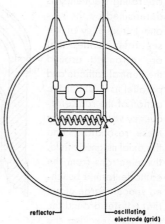

Fig. 10—Construction of a positive-grid tube. Electrode arrangement is shown at the right.

Low power output and low efficiency have hitherto limited their wide application. As local oscillators, positive-grid tubes possess the advantage of a relatively long and linear frequency vs. anode-voltage characteristic. A frequency variation of ± 25 megacycles at 3000 megacycles is obtainable.

Magnetrons*

A magnetron is a high-vacuum tube containing a cathode and an anode, the latter usually divided into two or more segments, in which tube a constant magnetic field modifies the space-charge distribution and the current-

* G. B. Collins, "Microwave Magnetrons," v. 6, Radiation Laboratory Series, 1st ed., McGraw-Hill Book Company, New York, New York; 1948. J. B. Fisk, H. D. Hagstrum, and P. L. Hartman, "The Magnetron as a Generator of Centimeter Waves," *Bell System Technical Journal*, v. 25, pp. 167–348; April, 1946.

Magnetrons   *continued*

voltage relations. In modern usage, the term "magnetron" refers to the magnetron oscillator in which the interaction of the electronic space charge with a resonant system converts direct-current power into alternating-current power.

Many forms of magnetrons have been made in the past and several kinds of operation have been employed. The type of tube that is now almost universally employed is the multicavity magnetron generating traveling-wave oscillations. It possesses the advantages of good efficiency at high frequencies, capability of high outputs either in pulsed or continuous-wave operation, moderate magnetic-field requirements, and good stability of operation. The basic structure of a typical magnetron is shown in Fig. 11.

In this type of tube, the operating frequency is determined by the resonant frequency of the separate cavities that are arranged around the central cathode and parallel to it. Under the action of the radio-frequency voltages across these resonators, and the axial magnetic field, the electrons from the cathode form a bunched space-charge cloud that rotates around the tube axis, exciting the cavities and maintaining their voltages. Direct current is fed into the tube and radio-frequency output is brought out through a suitable transmission line or

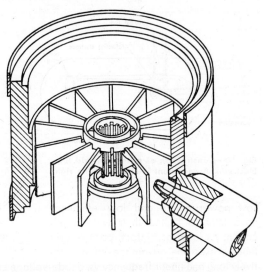

Fig. 11—Basic structure of a typical multicavity centimeter-wave magnetron. The cathode is not shown.

wave guide, usually coupled to one of the resonator cavities. The tube operates most efficiently when in the π mode, that is, in such a fashion that the phase difference between the voltages across each adjacent resonator is 180 degrees. Since other modes of operation are possible, it is often desirable to provide means for suppressing them; a common method is to strap alternate anode segments together conductively, so that large circulating currents flow in the unwanted modes of operation, thus damping them.

Magnetrons *continued*

Terminology

Many of the definitions given in previous sections apply.

Anode strap: Metallic connector between selected anode segments of a multicavity magnetron.

Interaction space: Region between anode and cathode.

End spaces: In a multicavity magnetron, the two cavities at either end of the anode block terminating all of the anode-block cavity resonators.

End shields: Limit the interaction space in the direction of the magnetic field.

Magnet gap: Space between the pole faces of the magnet.

Mode number *n* (magnetron): The number of radians of phase shift in going once around the anode, divided by 2π. Thus, n can have integral values 1, 2, 3, ... , $N/2$, where N is the number of anode segments.

π mode: Of a multicavity magnetron, is the mode of resonance for which the phase difference between any two adjacent anode segments is π radians. For an N-cavity magnetron, the π mode has the mode number $N/2$.

Frequency pulling: Of an oscillator, is the change in the generated frequency caused by a change of the load impedance.

Pulling figure: Of an oscillator, is the difference in megacycles/second between the maximum and minimum frequencies of oscillation obtained when the phase angle of the load-impedance reflection coefficient varies through 360 degrees, while the absolute value of this coefficient is constant and equal to 0.20.

Frequency pushing: Of an oscillator, is the change in frequency due to change in anode current (or in anode voltage).

Pushing figure: Of an oscillator, is the rate of frequency pushing in megacycles/second/ampere (or megacycles/second/volt).

Q: Of a specific mode of resonance of a system, is 2π times the ratio of the stored electromagnetic energy to the energy dissipated per cycle when the system is excited in this mode.

Unloaded Q: Of a specific mode of resonance of a system, is the Q of the mode when there is no external coupling to it.

Loaded Q: Of a specific mode of resonance of a system, is the Q when there is external coupling to that mode. Note: When the system is connected to the load by means of a transmission line, the loaded Q is customarily determined when the line is terminated in its characteristic impedance.

External Q: The reciprocal of the difference between the reciprocals of the loaded and unloaded Q's.

Magnetrons *continued*

Performance data

The performance data for a magnetron is usually given in terms of two diagrams, the performance chart and the Rieke diagram.

Performance chart: Is a plot of anode current along the abscissa and anode voltage along the ordinate of rectangular-coordinate paper. For a fixed typical tube load, pulse duration, pulse-repetition rate, and setting of the tuner of tunable tubes, lines of constant magnetic field, power output, efficiency, and frequency, may be plotted over the complete operating range of the tube. Regions of unsatisfactory operation are indicated by cross hatching. For tunable tubes, it is customary to show performance charts for more than one setting of the tuner. In the case of magnetrons with attached magnets, curves showing the variation of anode voltage, efficiency, frequency, and power output with change in anode current are given. A typical chart for a magnetron having eight resonators is given in Fig. 12.

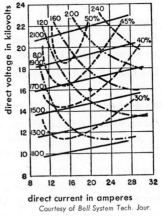

direct current in amperes
Courtesy of Bell System Tech. Jour.

———— constant field in gausses
— · — constant output in kilowatts
— — — constant overall efficiency
● typical operating point

Fig. 12—Performance chart for pulsed magnetron.

Rieke diagram: Shows the variation of power output, anode voltage, efficiency, and frequency with changes in the voltage standing-wave ratio and phase angle of the load for fixed typical operating conditions such as magnetic field, anode current, pulse duration, pulse-repetition rate, and the setting of the tuner for tunable tubes. The Rieke diagram is plotted on polar coordinates, the radial coordinate being the reflection coefficient measured in the line joining the tube to the load and the angular coordinate being the angular distance of the voltage standing-wave minimum from a suitable reference plane on the output terminal. On the Rieke diagram, lines of constant frequency, anode voltage, efficiency, and output may be drawn (Fig. 13).

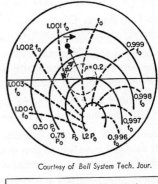

Courtesy of Bell System Tech. Jour.

———— · constant power output
— — — constant frequency

Fig. 13—Rieke diagram.

Magnetrons   continued

Design data

The design of a new magnetron is usually begun by scaling from an existing magnetron having similar characteristics. Normalized operating parameters have been defined in such a way that a family of magnetrons scaled from the same parent have the same electronic efficiency for like values of $I/\mathcal{J}$, $V/\mathcal{V}$, and $B/\mathcal{B}$,

where the normalized parameters $\mathcal{J}$, $\mathcal{V}$, and $\mathcal{B}$ for the π mode are

$$\mathcal{J} = \frac{2\pi a_1}{(1 - \sigma^2)^2 (1/\sigma + 1)} \frac{m}{e} \left(\frac{4\pi c}{N\lambda}\right)^3 r_a^2 \epsilon_0 h$$

$$= \frac{8440 a_1}{(1 - \sigma^2)(1/\sigma + 1)} \left(\frac{4\pi r_a}{N\lambda}\right)^3 \frac{h}{r_a} \text{ amperes}$$

$$\mathcal{V} = \frac{1}{2}\frac{m}{e}\left(\frac{4\pi c}{N\lambda}\right)^2 r_a^2 = 253{,}000 \left(\frac{4\pi r_a}{N\lambda}\right)^2 \text{ volts}$$

$$\mathcal{B} = 2\frac{m}{e}\left(\frac{4\pi c}{N\lambda}\right)\frac{1}{(1 - \sigma^2)} = \frac{42{,}400}{N\lambda(1 - \sigma^2)} \text{ gausses}$$

where

a_1 = a slowly varying function of r_a/r_c approximately equal to one in the range of interest

r_a = radius of anode in meters

r_c = radius of cathode in meters

h = anode height in meters

N = number of resonators

n = mode number

λ = wave length in meters

m = mass of an electron in kilograms

e = charge on an electron in coulombs

c = velocity of light in free space in meters/second

ϵ_0 = permittivity of free space

and I, V, and B are the operating conditions. Scaling may be done in any direction or in several directions at the same time. For reasonable performance it has been found empirically that

Magnetrons *continued*

$$\frac{V}{\upsilon} \geqslant 6, \quad \frac{B}{\mathcal{B}} \geqslant 4, \quad \text{and} \quad \frac{1}{3} < \frac{I}{\mathcal{J}} < 3$$

The minimum voltage required for oscillation has been named the "Hartree" voltage and is given by

$$V_H = \upsilon \left(2\frac{B}{\mathcal{B}} - 1 \right)$$

Slater's rule gives the relation between cathode and anode radius as

$$\sigma = \frac{r_c}{r_a} \approx \frac{N-4}{N+4}$$

Magnetrons for pulsed operation have been built to deliver peak powers varying from 3 megawatts at 10 centimeters to 100 kilowatts at one centimeter. Continuous-wave magnetrons having outputs ranging from one kilowatt at 10 centimeters to a few watts at 1 centimeter have been produced. Operation efficiencies up to 60 percent at 10 centimeters are obtained, falling to 30 percent at 1 centimeter.

Klystrons*

A klystron is a vacuum tube in which the distinguishing features are the modulation or periodic variation of the longitudinal velocity of an electron stream without appreciable variation of its convection current, and the subsequent conversion of this velocity modulation into convection-current modulation by the process of bunching.

In the usual form of klystron, a beam of electrons passes through the interaction gap of an input resonator where additional acceleration is given to each electron by the voltage across the gap. The sign and magnitude of this acceleration depends upon the magnitude and phase of the voltage at the instant the electron crosses the gap. The stream of electrons thus modulated in velocity then passes through a radio-frequency-field-free drift space where the velocity modulation is converted into density modulation. At the end of the drift space, the electron stream passes through the interaction gap of an output resonator which is excited by the density-modulated, or bunched beam. By applying a signal to the input resonator and a load to the output resonator, amplifier action may be obtained. This amplification takes place because of the conversion of a portion of the

* D. R. Hamilton, J. K. Knipp, and J. B. H. Kuper, "Klystrons and Microwave Triodes," 1st ed., McGraw-Hill Book Company, New York, New York; 1948. J. R. Pierce, and W. G. Shepherd, "Reflex Oscillators," *Bell System Technical Journal*, v. 26, pp. 460–681; July, 1947.

Klystrons _continued_

direct-current beam energy into radio-frequency energy that is abstracted by the output resonator. If some of the output is coupled back to the input cavity in the proper energy phase, oscillations may be obtained. A schematic of a typical structure is shown in Fig. 14.

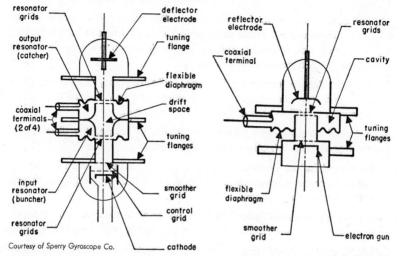

Courtesy of Sperry Gyroscope Co.

Fig. 14—Diagram of a 2-cavity klystron.   **Fig. 15—Diagram of a reflex klystron.**

A variation of the basic klystron tube that has advantages as an oscillator is the reflex klystron. In this tube, the electron stream, after being velocity modulated in the interaction gap of a cavity, enters a retarding-field region where it is reversed in direction and returned through the original resonator gap. While in the retarding-field region, the velocity-modulated beam is bunched. By proper proportioning of dimensions and retarding voltage, the bunches return in the proper phase to deliver energy to the resonator and oscillations may be sustained. A typical structure is shown in Fig. 15.

Frequency of operation is determined by the frequency to which the resonators are tuned, and the repeller voltage. Since the reflex klystron has only a single resonator, the tuning procedure is simplified. This advantage and the possibility of using the repeller voltage for automatic frequency control or frequency-modulation purposes accounts for its widespread use.

Terminology

Many of the definitions given in the previous sections apply.

Cavity resonator: Any region bounded by conducting walls within which resonant electromagnetic fields may be excited.

Klystrons *continued*

Interaction gap: Region between electrodes in which the electron stream interacts with a radio-frequency field.

Input gap: Gap in which the initial velocity modulation of the electron stream is produced. This gap is also known as the buncher gap.

Output gap: Gap in which variations in the convection current of the electron stream are subjected to opposing electric fields in such a manner as to extract usable radio-frequency power from the electron beam. This gap is also known as the catcher gap.

Drift space: Region relatively free of radio-frequency fields where a convection-current modulation of an electron stream arises as a result of the existence of differences in the electron velocities.

Reflector: Electrode whose primary function is to reverse the direction of an electron stream. It is also called a repeller.

Velocity modulation: Process whereby a periodic time variation in velocity is impressed on an electron stream; also, the condition existing in the stream subsequent to such a process.

Convection-current modulation: Periodic variation in the convection current passing any one point, or the process of producing such a variation.

Bunching: Any process that introduces a radio-frequency convection-current component into a velocity-modulated electron stream as a direct result of the variation in electron transit time that the velocity modulation produces.

Reflex bunching: Type of bunching that occurs when the velocity-modulated electron stream is made to reverse its direction by means of an opposing direct-current field.

Beam-coupling coefficient: Ratio of the amplitude of the velocity modulation produced by a gap, expressed in volts, to the radio-frequency gap voltage.

Cavity impedance: The impedance of the cavity which appears across the gap.

Mode number (klystron): Number of whole cycles that a mean-speed electron remains in the drift space of a reflex klystron.

Electron transit time: For a reflex klystron, is $N + \frac{3}{4}$ cycles, where N is the mode number.

Performance data

The performance data for a reflex klystron is usually given in terms of a *Reflector* (or *Repeller*) *characteristic chart*. This chart displays power output

Klystrons *continued*

and frequency deviation as a function of reflector voltage. Usually information is given on four modes. This chart is also called a *Reflector mode chart*. A typical chart is shown in Fig. 16.

Klystrons find use as amplifiers, oscillators, and frequency multipliers. In the latter service, the output resonator is tuned to a harmonic of the input-resonator frequency. Klystron amplifiers have been developed for frequencies from 1000 to 5000 megacycles with output powers up to 750 watts and power gains to 1500.

Pulsed 2-cavity oscillators have been built with a power output of 10 kilowatts and an efficiency of 20 percent at 3000 megacycles.

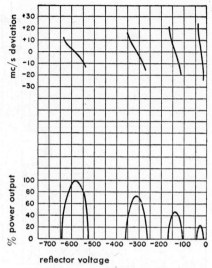

Courtesy of Sperry Gyroscope Co.

Fig. 16—Klystron reflector characteristic chart.

Reflex klystrons with the following characteristics have been developed

frequency in megacycles	power output in watts	efficiency in percent	operating beam voltage
3000	0.150	2.3	300
5000	12	8	1200
9000	0.030	0.5	300

Klystron frequency multipliers from 300 to 5100 megacycles have been built with output powers in the tens of milliwatts and efficiencies in the neighborhood of $\frac{1}{2}$ percent.

Traveling-wave tubes*

Traveling-wave tubes are a relatively new class of tubes useful as amplifiers in the ultra-high- and super-high-frequency ranges. They depend on the

---

* R. Kompfner, "The Traveling-Wave Tube as Amplifier at Microwaves," *Proceedings of the I.R.E.*, v. 35, pp. 124–127; February, 1947. J. R. Pierce, "Theory of the Beam-Type Traveling-Wave Tube," *Proceedings of the I.R.E.*, v. 35, pp. 111–123; February, 1947.

Traveling-wave tubes *continued*

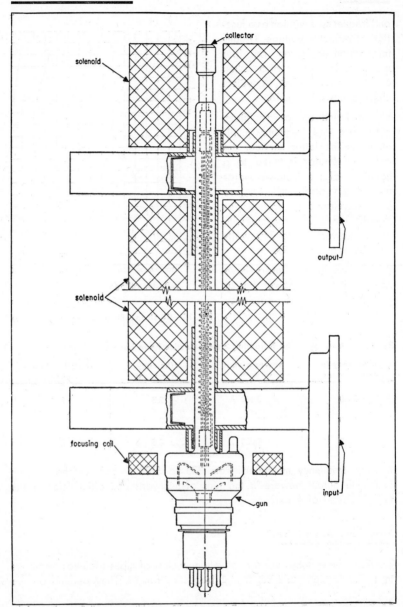

Fig. 17—Diagram of a traveling-wave amplifier. The electron beam travels from bottom to top through the center of the helix. Microwave input and output signals are coupled through the rectangular wave guides. Impedance of the wave guides is matched to that of the helix by means of the movable shorting stubs.

Traveling-wave tubes   *continued*

interaction of a longitudinal electron beam with a wave-propagating structure.

By virtue of the distributed interaction of the wave and the electron stream, traveling-wave tubes do not suffer the gain–bandwidth limitation of ordinary thermionic tubes. The bandwidth is most easily characterized by a percentage of the center frequency, 20 percent being not uncommon. An essential feature of traveling-wave tubes is the approximate synchronism between the speed of the electron stream and the wave on the propagating structure. Practical considerations require low voltages and hence wave guides with phase velocities v of the order of 0.1c, where c is the velocity of light.

The best-known type of traveling-wave tube uses a helix as the slow-wave guide, Fig. 17. Such a tube gives gains as high as 23 decibels over a bandwidth of 800 megacycles around a center frequency of 4000 megacycles. These amplifiers are limited in output and operate at very low efficiencies, but such limitations are not fundamental.

The gain of a traveling-wave tube is given approximately by

$$G = -9 + 47.3\,CN$$

in decibels for a lossless helix, where

$$N = \frac{l}{\lambda_0} \times \frac{c}{v}$$

$$C = \left(\frac{E_z^2}{(\omega/v)^2 P} \times \frac{I_0}{8V_0} \right)^{\frac{1}{3}}$$

where

l = length of the helix

I_0 = beam current

V_0 = beam voltage

and $E_z^2/(\omega/v)^2 P$ is a normalized wave impedance that may be defined in a number of ways. For lossy helices, the gain is given approximately by

$$G = -9 + 47.3\,CN - L/3 \text{ decibels}$$

where L is the cold insertion loss of the helix. The maximum output power is given approximately by $P_{out} \approx CI_0V_0$. Commonly, C is of the order of 0.02 to 0.04 in helix traveling-wave tubes.

Gas tubes*

A gas tube is a vacuum tube in which the pressure of the contained gas or vapor is such as to affect substantially the electrical characteristics of the tube. The presence of gas allows the formation of positive ions that effectively neutralize the electron space charge and allow large currents to flow at low voltages. Construction of a typical gas triode is shown in Fig. 18.

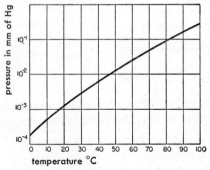

Fig. 18—Electrode arrangement of a typical gas triode. A—heater, B—cathode, C—grid, D—anode, E—glass envelope, F—anode terminal, G—heater, cathode, and grid terminal pins.

Terminology

Critical grid voltage: Instantaneous value of the grid voltage when the anode current starts to flow.

Critical grid current: Instantaneous value of the grid current when the anode current starts to flow.

Control characteristic: A relation, usually shown by a graph, between critical grid voltage and anode voltage.

Deionization time: Time required after anode-current interruption for the grid to regain control.

Cathode-heating time: Time required for the cathode to attain operating temperature with normal voltage applied to the heating element.

Tube-heating time: In a mercury-vapor tube, is the time required for the coolest portion of the tube to attain operating temperature.

Mercury-vapor rectifier tubes

In mercury-vapor tubes, the source of the vapor is usually a reservoir of liquid mercury. Since the vapor pressure of this mercury is a function of the temperature of the condensed mercury, the operating characteristics are dependent upon the temperature (Figs. 19 and 20).

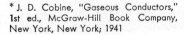

Fig. 19—Dependence of mercury-vapor pressure on temperature.

* J. D. Cobine, "Gaseous Conductors," 1st ed., McGraw-Hill Book Company, New York, New York; 1941

Gas tubes   *continued*

Operation below the minimum temperature recommended by the manufacturer results in excessive internal voltage drop. This in turn results in destructive bombardment of the cathode (in hot-cathode tubes) by mercury ions.

Operation above the maximum temperature recommended by the manufacturer results in a decrease in the peak-inverse voltage that the tube can withstand.

Pool-cathode rectifiers: Wherein electron supply is from a cathode spot on a pool of mercury, are affected only to the extent that low temperatures increase the internal voltage drop and decrease the efficiency.

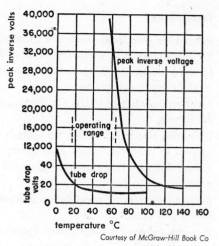

Courtesy of McGraw-Hill Book Co

Fig. 20—Tube drop and arcback voltages as a function of the condensed mercury temperature in a hot-cathode mercury-vapor tube.

Hot-cathode gas-rectifier tubes

These tubes approximate their mercury-vapor counterparts in physical form and operating characteristics. Generally, the internal voltage drop is higher, and the peak-inverse-voltage rating is lower than in mercury-vapor tubes. Their operating characteristics are substantially independent of the temperature of the gas.

Ionizing voltages for various gases

Argon	15.4	Hydrogen	15.9	Nitrogen	16.7
Carbon monoxide	14.2	Mercury	10.4	Oxygen	13.5
Helium	24.6	Neon	21.5	Water vapor	13.2

Cathode-ray tubes*

A cathode-ray tube is a vacuum tube in which an electron beam, deflected by applied electric and/or magnetic fields, indicates by a trace on a fluorescent screen the instantaneous value of the actuating voltages and/or currents.

* K. R. Spangenberg, "Vacuum Tubes," 1st ed., McGraw-Hill Book Company, New York, New York; 1948.

Cathode-ray tubes *continued*

Terminology

Modulating electrode: Electrode to which potential is applied to control the beam current. It is also known as grid or control electrode.

Focusing electrode: Controls the cross-sectional area of the electron beam in electrostatic-focus tubes.

Accelerating electrode: Used to increase the velocity of the electrons in the beam.

Deflecting electrodes (deflecting plates): Electrodes to which a potential is applied to produce angular displacement of the beam.

Cut-off voltage: Negative grid potential at which beam current becomes zero.

Control characteristic (modulation characteristic): A curve of beam current versus grid potential.

Focusing voltage: In electrostatic-focus tubes, the voltage at which the spot comes to a focus.

Focusing current or focusing ampere turns: In magnetic-focus tubes, the current required through a given focus coil located at a given point on the tube to bring the spot into focus.

Deflection factor: In electrostatic-focus tubes, the voltage required between a pair of deflection plates to produce unit deflection. Value usually is expressed in direct-current volts/inch.

Deflection factor: In magnetic-focus tubes, the current required through a definite deflection yoke at a definite point on the tube to produce unit deflection. Value usually is expressed in milliamperes/inch.

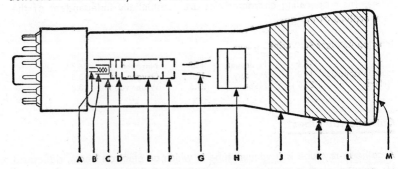

Fig. 21—Electrode arrangement of typical electrostatic focus and deflection cathode-ray tube. A—heater, B—cathode, C—control electrode, D—screen grid or pre-accelerator, E—focusing electrode, F—accelerating electrode, G—deflection-plate pair, H—deflection-plate pair, J—conductive coating connected to accelerating electrode, K—intensifier-electrode terminal, L—intensifier electrode (conductive coating on glass), M—fluorescent screen.

Cathode-ray tubes   *continued*

Deflection sensitivity: The reciprocal of the deflection factor. Value is expressed in inches/volt for electrostatic-deflection tubes.

Formulas

Electrostatic deflection: Is proportional to the deflection voltage, inversely proportional to the accelerating voltage, and deflection is in the direction of the applied field (Fig. 22). For structures using straight and parallel deflection plates, it is given by

$$D = \frac{E_d L l}{2 E_a A}$$

where

D = deflection in centimeters
E_a = accelerating voltage
E_d = deflection voltage
l = length of deflecting plates or deflecting field in centimeters
L = length from center of deflecting field to screen in centimeters
A = separation of plates

Fig. 22—Electrostatic deflection.

Electromagnetic deflection: Is proportional to the flux or the current in the coil, inversely proportional to the square root of the accelerating voltage, and deflection is at right angles to the direction of the applied field (Fig. 23).

Deflection is given by

$$D = \frac{0.3 L l H}{\sqrt{E_a}}$$

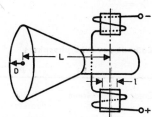

where H = flux density in gauss
l = length of deflecting field in centimeters

Fig. 23—Magnetic deflection.

Deflection sensitivity: Is linear up to frequency where the phase of the deflecting voltage begins to reverse before an electron has reached the end of the deflecting field. Beyond this frequency, sensitivity drops off, reaching zero and then passing through a series of maxima and minima as $n = 1, 2, 3, \ldots$. Each succeeding maximum is of smaller magnitude.

$$D_{zero} = n\lambda \, v/c$$

$$D_{max} = (2n - 1) \frac{\lambda}{2} \frac{v}{c}$$

Cathode-ray tubes   *continued*

where

D = deflection in centimeters
v = electron velocity in centimeters/second
c = speed of light $(3 \times 10^{10}$ centimeters/second)
λ = free-space wavelength in centimeters

Magnetic focusing: There is more than one value of current that will focus. Best focus is at minimum value. For an average coil

$$IN = 220\sqrt{\frac{V_0 d}{f}}$$

IN = ampere turns
V_0 = accelerating voltage in kilovolts
d = mean diameter of coil
f = focal length

d and f are in the same units. A well-designed, shielded coil will require fewer ampere turns.

Example of good shield design (Fig. 24):

$$X = \frac{d_1}{20}$$

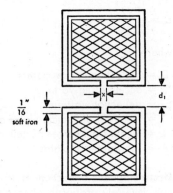

Fig. 24—Magnetic focusing.

Cathode-ray-tube phosphors

	P1	P2	P4	P5	P7	P11
Color	Green	Blue fluorescence; green phosphorescence	White	Blue	Blue fluorescence; yellow phosphorescence	Blue
Spectral range in Angstrom units	5740–4850	4280–6080	3980–6880	3470–6100	4140–6210	3770–5690
Spectral peak in Angstrom units	5220	4550; 5300	4600–5550	4280	4500; 5700	4400
Persistence	Medium—30 milliseconds for decay to 10 percent	Long	Medium	Very short—15 microseconds for decay to 10 percent	Long	Short—60 microseconds for decay to 10 percent

Armed Services preferred list of electron tubes

Receiving

filament voltage	diodes	diode-triodes	triodes	twin triodes	pentodes remote	pentodes sharp	converters	klystrons	power output	tuning indicators	rectifiers
1.4	1A3			3A5	1T4	1U4, 1U5	1R5		3B4, 3S4, 3V4		1Z2
5.0											5U4G, 5Y3GT
6.3	2B22, 6AL5	6AT6, 6BF6	2C40, 6C4, 6F4, 6J4	2C51, 6AS7G, 6J6, 6N7GT, 6SL7GT, 12AT7, 12AU7, 12AX7	6BA6, 6BD6, 6SG7, 6SK7, 9003	6AC7, 6AG5, 6AH6, 6AK5, 6AS6, 6AU6, 6SH7, 6SJ7, 5656	6BE6, 6SB7Y	2K22, 2K25, 2K26, 2K28, 2K29, 2K41, 2K45, 2K50, 2K54, 2K55	2E30, 6AG7, 6AK6, 6AN5, 6AQ5, 6B4G, 6L6GA, 6V6GT, 6Y6G	6E5	6X4, 6X5GT
25 or over — Only types for 28 volts anode-supply operation		26C6				26A6	26D6		25L6GT, 26A7GT		25Z6GT

miscellaneous

cathode ray	voltage regulators	crystals	phototubes
2BP1	0A2	1N21B	1P30
3DP1A	0B2	1N23B	1P37
3JP11, 7, 12	0A3	1N25	1P39
5CP11A, 7A, 12	0C3	1N26	1P40
5FP7(A, 14)	0D3	1N31	927
5JP1A	5651	1N32	
5SP1(1, 7)		1N43	
7BP7A			
10KP7			
12DP7A			

Transmitting

triodes	tetrodes	twin tetrodes	rectifiers vacuum	rectifiers gas	grid control	clipper tubes	gas switching ATR	gas switching TR	pulse modulation	magnetrons
2C43, 9C21, 9C22, 100TH, 250TH, 450TH, 811, 880, 893A, 893AR, 5667	4D21, 5D22, 807	829B, 832A	2X2A, 3B24W, 5R4GY, 371B, 836, 1616, 8020	0Z4A, 3B28, 4B26, 4B32, 6C, 16B	2D21, 6D4, C6J, 393A, 394A, 884	3B29, 4B31, 719A	1B35, 1B36, 1B37, 1B44, 1B51, 1B52, 1B53, 1B56, 1B57	1B26, 1B27, 1B32, 1B50, 1B60	3D21A, 3C45, 3E29, 4C35, 5C22, 6C21	2J30-34, 2J48, 2J51, 2J58, 2J61A-62A, 3J21, 4J51, 4J52, 4J54-59, 5J26, 5586, 5657

From "Armed Services Preferred Parts Lists (Electronic Components)," Armed Services Electro Standards Agency, Fort Monmouth, New Jersey; April 1, 1949.

■ Amplifiers and oscillators

Classification

It is common practice to differentiate between types of vacuum-tube circuits, particularly amplifiers, on the basis of the operating regime of the tube.

Class-A: Grid bias and alternating grid voltages such that plate current flows continuously throughout electrical cycle $(\theta_p = 360$ degrees).

Class-AB: Grid bias and alternating grid voltages such that plate current flows appreciably more than half but less than entire electrical cycle $(360° > \theta_p > 180°)$.

Class-B: Grid bias close to cut-off such that plate current flows only during approximately half of electrical cycle $(\theta_p \approx 180°)$.

Class-C: Grid bias appreciably greater than cut-off so that plate current flows for appreciably less than half of electrical cycle $(\theta_p < 180°)$.

A further classification between circuits in which positive grid current is conducted during some portion of the cycle, and those in which it is not, is denoted by subscripts 2 and 1, respectively. Thus a class-AB$_2$ amplifier operates with a positive swing of the alternating grid voltage such that positive electronic current is conducted, and accordingly in-phase power is required to drive the tube.

General design

For quickly estimating the performance of a tube from catalog data, or for predicting the characteristics needed for a given application, the ratios given below may be used.

The table gives correlating data for typical operation of tubes in the various amplifier classifications. From the table, knowing the maximum ratings of a tube, the maximum power output, currents, voltages, and corresponding load

Typical amplifier operating data. Maximum signal conditions—per tube

function	class A	class B a-f (p-p)	class B r-f	class C r-f
Plate efficiency η (percent)	20–30	35–65	60–70	65–85
Peak instantaneous to d-c plate current ratio $^M i_b/I_b$	1.5–2	3.1	3.1	3.1–4.5
RMS alternating to d-c plate current ratio I_p/I_b	0.5–0.7	1.1	1.1	1.1–1.2
RMS alternating to d-c plate voltage ratio E_p/E_b	0.3–0.5	0.5–0.6	0.5–0.6	0.5–0.6
D-C to peak instantaneous grid current $I_c/^M i_c$		0.25–0.1	0.25–0.1	0.15–0.1

General design   *continued*

impedance may be estimated. Thus, taking for example, a type F-124-A water-cooled transmitting tube as a class-C radio-frequency power amplifier and oscillator—the constant-current characteristics of which are shown in Fig. 1—published maximum ratings are as follows:

D-C plate voltage $E_b = 20,000$ volts
D-C grid voltage $E_c = 3,000$ volts
D-C plate current $I_b = 7$ amperes
R-F grid current $I_g = 50$ amperes
Plate input $P_i = 135,000$ watts
Plate dissipation $P_p = 40,000$ watts

Maximum conditions may be estimated as follows:

For $\eta = 75$ percent $\quad P_i = 135,000$ watts $\quad E_b = 20,000$ volts

Power output $P_0 = \eta P_i = 100,000$ watts

Average d-c plate current $I_b = P_i/E_b = 6.7$ amperes

From tabulated typical ratio $^M i_b/I_b = 4$, instantaneous peak plate current $^M i_b = 4 I_b = 27$ amperes*

The rms alternating plate-current component, taking ratio $I_p/I_b = 1.2$, $I_p = 1.2\, I_b = 8$ amperes

The rms value of the alternating plate-voltage component from the ratio $E_p/E_b = 0.6$ is $E_p = 0.6\, E_b = 12,000$ volts.

The approximate operating load resistance r_l is now found from

$r_l = E_p/I_p = 1500$ ohms

An estimate of the grid drive power required may be obtained by reference to the constant-current characteristics of the tube and determination of the peak instantaneous positive grid current $^M i_c$ and the corresponding instantaneous total grid voltage $^M e_c$. Taking the value of grid bias E_c for the given operating condition, the peak alternating grid drive voltage is

$$^M E_g = (^M e_c - E_c)$$

from which the peak instantaneous grid drive power is

$$^M P_c = {}^M E_g \, {}^M i_c$$

---

* In this discussion, the superscript M indicates the use of the maximum or peak value of the varying component, i.e., $^M i_b =$ maximum or peak value of the alternating component of the plate current.

General design *continued*

An approximation to the average grid drive power P_g, necessarily rough due to neglect of negative grid current, is obtained from the typical ratio

$$\frac{I_c}{^M i_c} = 0.2$$

of d-c to peak value of grid current, giving

$$P_g = I_c E_g = 0.2\,{}^M i_c E_g \text{ watts}$$

Plate dissipation P_p may be checked with published values since

$$P_p = P_i - P_0$$

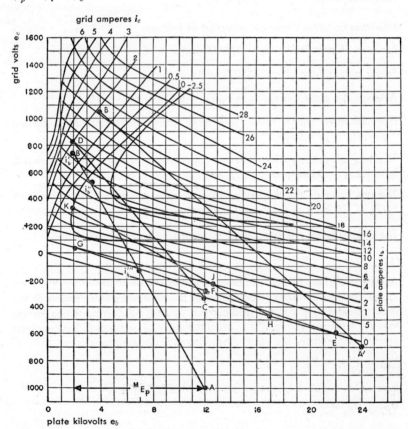

Fig. 1—Constant-current characteristics with typical load lines AB—class C, CD—class B, EFG—class A, and HJK—class AB.

General design *continued*

It should be borne in mind that combinations of published maximum ratings as well as each individual maximum rating must be observed. Thus, for example in this case, the maximum d-c plate operating voltage of 20,000 volts does not permit operation at the maximum d-c plate current of 7 amperes since this exceeds the maximum plate input rating of 135,000 watts.

Plate load resistance r_l may be connected directly in the tube plate circuit, as in the resistance-coupled amplifier, through impedance-matching elements as in audio-frequency transformer coupling, or effectively represented by a loaded parallel-resonant circuit as in most radio-frequency amplifiers. In any case, calculated values apply only to effectively resistive loads, such as are normally closely approximated in radio-frequency amplifiers. With appreciably reactive loads, operating currents and voltages will in general be quite different and their precise calculation is quite difficult.

The physical load resistance present in any given set-up may be measured by audio-frequency or radio-frequency bridge methods. In many cases, the proper value of r_l is ascertained experimentally as in radio-frequency amplifiers that are tuned to the proper minimum d-c plate current. Conversely, if the circuit is to be matched to the tube, r_l is determined directly as in a resistance-coupled amplifier or as

$$r_l = N^2 r_s$$

in the case of a transformer-coupled stage, where N is the primary-to-secondary voltage transformation ratio. In a parallel-resonant circuit in which the output resistance r_s is connected directly in one of the reactance legs,

$$r_l = \frac{X^2}{r_s} = \frac{L}{C r_s} = QX$$

where X is the leg reactance at resonance (ohms), and L and C are leg inductance in henries and capacitance in farads, respectively;

$$Q = \frac{X}{r_s}$$

Graphical design methods

When accurate operating data are required, more precise methods must be used. Because of the nonlinear nature of tube characteristics, graphical methods usually are most convenient and rapid. Examples of such methods are given below.

A comparison of the operating regimes of class A, AB, B, and C amplifiers is given in the constant-current characteristics graph of Fig. 1. The lines

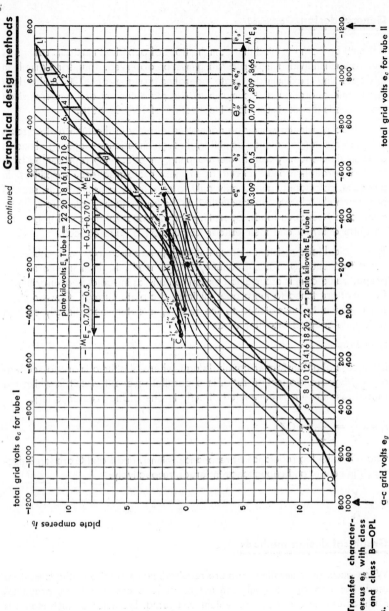

Graphical design methods — continued

Fig. 2—Transfer characteristics i_b versus e_b with class A_2—CKF and class B—OPL load lines.

Graphical design methods   *continued*

corresponding to the different classes of operation are each the locus of instantaneous grid e_c and plate e_b voltages, corresponding to their respective load impedances.

For radio-frequency amplifiers and oscillators having tuned circuits giving an effectively resistive load, plate and grid tube and load alternating voltages are sinusoidal and in phase (disregarding transit time), and the loci become straight lines.

For amplifiers having nonresonant resistive loads, the loci are in general nonlinear except in the distortionless case of linear tube characteristics (constant r_p), for which they are again straight lines.

Thus, for determination of radio-frequency performance, the constant-current chart is convenient. For solution of audio-frequency problems, however, it is more convenient to use the $(i_b - e_c)$ transfer characteristics of Fig. 2 on which a dynamic load line may be constructed.

Methods for calculation of the most important cases are given below.

Class-C radio-frequency amplifier or oscillator

Draw straight line from A to B (Fig. 1) corresponding to chosen d-c operating plate and grid voltages, and to desired peak alternating plate and grid voltage excursions. The projection of AB on the horizontal axis thus corresponds to ^ME_p. Using Chaffee's 11-point method of harmonic analysis, lay out on AB points:

$$e_p' = {}^ME_p \qquad e_p'' = 0.866\,{}^ME_p \qquad e_p''' = 0.5\,{}^ME_p$$

to each of which correspond instantaneous plate currents i_b', i_b'' and i_b''' and instantaneous grid currents i_c', i_c'' and i_c'''. The operating currents are obtained from the following expressions:

$$I_b = \frac{1}{12}\,[i_b' + 2\,i_b'' + 2\,i_b'''] \qquad I_c = \frac{1}{12}\,[i_c' + 2\,i_c'' + 2\,i_c''']$$

$$^MI_p = \frac{1}{6}\,[i_b' + 1.73\,i_b'' + i_b'''] \qquad {}^MI_g = \frac{1}{6}\,[i_c' + 1.73\,i_c'' + i_c''']$$

Substitution of the above in the following give the desired operating data

Power output $P_0 = \dfrac{{}^ME_p\,{}^MI_p}{2}$

Power input $P_i = E_b\,I_b$

Average grid excitation power $= \dfrac{{}^ME_g\,{}^MI_g}{2}$

Graphical design methods   *continued*

Peak grid excitation power $= {}^{M}E_g\, i'_c$

Plate load resistance $r_l = \dfrac{{}^{M}E_p}{{}^{M}I_p}$

Grid bias resistance $R_c = \dfrac{E_c}{I_c}$

Plate efficiency $\eta = \dfrac{P_0}{P_i}$

Plate dissipation $P_p = P_i - P_0$

The above procedure may also be applied to plate-modulated class-C amplifiers. Taking the above data as applying to carrier conditions, the analysis is repeated for $^{crest}E_b = 2E_b$ and $^{crest}P_0 = 4P_0$ keeping r_l constant. After a cut-and-try method has given a peak solution, it will often be found that combination fixed and self grid biasing as well as grid modulation is indicated to obtain linear operation.

To illustrate the preceding exposition, a typical amplifier calculation is given below:

Operating requirements (carrier condition)

$E_b = 12{,}000$ volts $P_0 = 25{,}000$ watts $\eta = 75$ percent

Preliminary calculation (refer to table below)

Class-C r-f amplifier data for 100-percent plate modulation.

symbol	preliminary carrier	detailed carrier	detailed crest
E_b (volts)	12,000	12,000	24,000
$^{M}E_p$ (volts)	10,000	10,000	20,000
E_c (volts)	—	−1,000	−700
$^{M}E_g$ (volts)	—	1,740	1,740
I_b (amp)	2.9	2.8	6.4
$^{M}I_p$ (amp)	4.9	5.1	10.2
I_c (amp)	—	0.125	0.083
$^{M}I_g$ (amp)	—	0.255	0.183
P_i (watts)	35,000	33,600	154,000
P_0 (watts)	25,000	25,500	102,000
P_g (watts)	—	220	160
η (percent)	75	76	66
r_l (ohms)	2,060	1,960	1,960
R_c (ohms)	—	7,100	7,100
E_{cc} (volts)	—	−110	−110

Graphical design methods   *continued*

$$\frac{E_p}{E_b} = 0.6$$

$$E_p = 0.6 \times 12{,}000 = 7200 \text{ volts}$$

$${}^M E_p = 1.41 \times 7200 = 10{,}000 \text{ volts}$$

$$I_p = \frac{P_o}{E_p}$$

$$I_p = \frac{25{,}000}{7200} = 3.48 \text{ amperes}$$

$${}^M I_p = 4.9 \text{ amperes}$$

$$\frac{I_p}{I_b} = 1.2$$

$$I_b = \frac{3.48}{1.2} = 2.9 \text{ amperes}$$

$$P_i = 12{,}000 \times 2.9 = 35{,}000 \text{ watts}$$

$$\frac{{}^M i_b}{I_b} = 4.5$$

$${}^M i_b = 4.5 \times 2.9 = 13.0 \text{ amperes}$$

$$r_l = \frac{E_p}{I_p} = \frac{7200}{3.48} = 2060 \text{ ohms}$$

Complete calculation

Lay out carrier operating line, AB on constant-current graph, Fig. **1**, using values of E_b, ${}^M E_p$, and ${}^M i_b$ from preliminary calculated data. Operating carrier bias voltage, E_c, is chosen somewhat greater than twice cutoff value, 1000 volts, to locate point A.

The following data are taken along AB:

$i_b' = 13$ amp	$i_c' = 1.7$ amp	$E_c = -1000$ volts
$i_b'' = 10$ amp	$i_c'' = -0.1$ amp	$e_c' = 740$ volts
$i_b''' = 0.3$ amp	$i_c''' = 0$ amp	${}^M E_p = 10{,}000$ volts

From the formulas, complete carrier data as follows are calculated:

$$ {}^M I_p = \frac{1}{6}[13 + 1.73 \times 10 + 0.3] = 5.1 \text{ amp} $$

$$ P_0 = \frac{10{,}000 \times 5.1}{2} = 25{,}500 \text{ watts} $$

$$ I_b = \frac{1}{12}[13 + 2 \times 10 + 2 \times 0.3] = 2.8 \text{ amp} $$

$$ P_i = 12{,}000 \times 2.8 = 33{,}600 \text{ watts} $$

Graphical design methods   continued

$$\eta = \frac{25,500}{33,600} \times 100 = 76 \text{ percent}$$

$$r_l = \frac{10,000}{5.1} = 1960 \text{ ohms}$$

$$I_c = \frac{1}{12} [1.7 + 2 \, (-0.1)] = 0.125 \text{ amp}$$

$$^M I_g = \frac{1}{6} [1.7 + 1.7 \, (-0.1)] = 0.255 \text{ amp}$$

$$P_g = \frac{1740 \times 0.255}{2} = 220 \text{ watts}$$

Operating data at 100-percent positive modulation crests are now calculated knowing that here

$$E_b = 24,000 \text{ volts} \qquad r_l = 1960 \text{ ohms}$$

and for undistorted operation

$$P_0 = 4 \times 25,500 = 102,000 \text{ watts} \qquad ^M E_p = 20,000 \text{ volts}$$

The crest operating line A′B′ is now located by trial so as to satisfy the above conditions, using the same formulas and method as for the carrier condition.

It is seen that in order to obtain full-crest power output, in addition to doubling the alternating plate voltage, the peak plate current must be increased. This is accomplished by reducing the crest bias voltage with resultant increase of current conduction period, but lower plate efficiency.

The effect of grid secondary emission to lower the crest grid current is taken advantage of to obtain the reduced grid-resistance voltage drop required. By use of combination fixed and grid resistance bias proper variation of the total bias is obtained. The value of grid resistance required is given by

$$R_c = \frac{- [E_c - {}^{\text{crest}}E_c]}{I_c - {}^{\text{crest}}I_c}$$

and the value of fixed bias by

$$E_{cc} = E_c - (I_c R_c)$$

Calculations at carrier and positive crest together with the condition of zero output at negative crest give sufficiently complete data for most purposes. If accurate calculation of audio-frequency harmonic distortion is necessary, the above method may be applied to the additional points required.

Graphical design methods   *continued*

Class-B radio-frequency amplifiers

A rapid approximate method is to determine by inspection from the tube $(i_b - e_b)$ characteristics the instantaneous current, i'_b and voltage e'_b corresponding to peak alternating voltage swing from operating voltage E_b.

A-C plate current $^M I_p = \dfrac{i'_b}{2}$

D-C plate current $I_b = \dfrac{i'_b}{\pi}$

A-C plate voltage $^M E_p = E_b - e'_b$

Power output $P_0 = \dfrac{(E_b - e'_b)\, i'_b}{4}$

Power input $P_i = \dfrac{E_b i'_b}{\pi}$

Plate efficiency $\eta = \dfrac{\pi}{4}\left(1 - \dfrac{e'_b}{E_b}\right)$

Thus $\eta \approx 0.6$ for the usual crest value of $^M E_p \approx 0.8\, E_b$.

The same method of analysis used for the class-C amplifier may also be used in this case. The carrier and crest condition calculations, however, are now made from the same E_b, the carrier condition corresponding to an alternating-voltage amplitude of $^M E_p/2$ such as to give the desired carrier power output.

For greater accuracy than the simple check of carrier and crest conditions, the radio-frequency plate currents $^M I_p{}'$, $^M I_p{}''$, $^M I_p{}'''$, $^M I_p{}^\circ$, $- {}^M I_p{}'''$, $- {}^M I_p{}''$, and $- {}^M I_p{}'$ may be calculated for seven corresponding selected points of the audio-frequency modulation envelope $+ {}^M E_g$, $+ 0.707\, {}^M E_g$, $+ 0.5\, {}^M E_g$, 0, $-0.5 {}^M E_g$, $- 0.707 {}^M E_g$, and $- {}^M E_g$, where the negative signs denote values in the negative half of the modulation cycle. Designating

$S' = {}^M I'_p + (- {}^M I'_p)$
$D' = {}^M I'_p - (- {}^M I'_p)$, etc.,

the fundamental and harmonic components of the output audio-frequency current are obtained as

$$^M I_{p1} = \frac{S'}{4} + \frac{S''}{2\sqrt{2}} \ \text{(fundamental)} \qquad\qquad ^M I_{p2} = \frac{5\, D'}{24} + \frac{D''}{4} - \frac{D'''}{3}$$

Graphical design methods   *continued*

$$^{M}I_{p3} = \frac{S'}{6} - \frac{S'''}{3}$$

$$^{M}I_{p4} = \frac{D'}{8} - \frac{D''}{4}$$

$$^{M}I_{p5} = \frac{S'}{12} - \frac{S''}{2\sqrt{2}} + \frac{S'''}{3}$$

$$^{M}I_{p6} = \frac{D'}{24} - \frac{D''}{4} + \frac{D'''}{3}$$

This detailed method of calculation of audio-frequency harmonic distortion may, of course, also be applied to calculation of the class-C modulated amplifier, as well as to the class-A modulated amplifier.

Class-A and AB audio-frequency amplifiers

Approximate formulas assuming linear tube characteristics:

Maximum undistorted power output $^{M}P_0 = \dfrac{^{M}E_p \, ^{M}I_p}{2}$

when plate load resistance $r_l = r_p \left[\dfrac{E_c}{\dfrac{^{M}E_p}{\mu} - E_c} - 1 \right]$

and

negative grid bias $E_c = \dfrac{^{M}E_p}{\mu} \left(\dfrac{r_l + r_p}{r_l + 2r_p} \right)$

giving

maximum plate efficiency $\eta = \dfrac{^{M}E_p \, ^{M}I_p}{8E_b \, I_b}$

Maximum maximum undistorted power output $^{MM}P_0 = \dfrac{^{M}E^2_p}{16 \, r_p}$

when

$$r_l = 2 \, r_p \qquad E_c = \frac{3}{4} \frac{^{M}E_p}{\mu}$$

An exact analysis may be obtained by use of a dynamic load line laid out on the transfer characteristics of the tube. Such a line is CKF of Fig. 2 which is constructed about operating point K for a given load resistance r_l from the following relation:

$$i_b^S = \frac{e_b^R - e_b^S}{r_l} + i_b^R$$

where

R, S, etc., are successive conveniently spaced construction points.

Graphical design methods   *continued*

Using the seven-point method of harmonic analysis, plot instantaneous plate currents i_b', i_b'', i_b''', i_b, $-i_b'''$, $-i_b''$, and $-i_b'$ corresponding to $+{}^M E_g$, $+0.707{}^M E_g$, $+0.5{}^M E_g$, 0, $-0.5{}^M E_g$, $-0.707{}^M E_g$, and $-{}^M E_g$, where 0 corresponds to the operating point K. In addition to the formulas given under class-B radio-frequency amplifiers:

$$I_b \text{ average} = I_b + \frac{D'}{8} + \frac{D''}{4}$$

from which complete data may be calculated.

Class-AB and B audio-frequency amplifiers

Approximate formulas assuming linear tube characteristics give (referring to Fig. 1, line CD) for a class-B audio-frequency amplifier:

$${}^M I_p = i_b'$$

$$P_o = \frac{{}^M E_p \, {}^M I_p}{2}$$

$$P_i = \frac{2}{\pi} E_b \, {}^M I_p$$

$$\eta = \frac{\pi}{4} \frac{{}^M E_p}{E_b}$$

$$R_{pp} = 4 \frac{{}^M E_p}{i'_b} = 4 r_l$$

Again an exact solution may be derived by use of the dynamic load line JKL on the $(i_b - e_c)$ characteristic of Fig. 2. This line is calculated about the operating point K for the given r_l (in the same way as for the class-A case). However, since two tubes operate in phase opposition in this case, an identical dynamic load line MNO represents the other half cycle, laid out about the operating bias abscissa point but in the opposite direction (see Fig. 2).

Algebraic addition of instantaneous current values of the two tubes at each value of e_c gives the composite dynamic characteristic for the two tubes OPL. Inasmuch as this curve is symmetrical about point P, it may be analyzed for harmonics along a single half-curve PL by the Mouromtseff 5-point method. A straight line is drawn from P to L and ordinate plate-current differences a, b, c, d, f between this line and curve, corresponding to e_g'', e_g''', e_g^{IV}, e_g^{V}, and e_g^{VI}, are measured. Ordinate distances measured upward from curve PL are taken positive.

Graphical design methods   *continued*

Fundamental and harmonic current amplitudes and power are found from the following formulas:

$$^{M}I_{p1} = i'_b - {^{M}I_{p3}} + {^{M}I_{p5}} - {^{M}I_{p7}} + {^{M}I_{p9}} - {^{M}I_{p11}}$$

$$^{M}I_{p3} = 0.4475 \ (b + f) + \frac{d}{3} - 0.578 \ d - \frac{1}{2} {^{M}I_{p5}}$$

$$^{M}I_{p5} = 0.4 \ (a - f)$$

$$^{M}I_{p7} = 0.4475 \ (b + f) - {^{M}I_{p3}} + 0.5 \ {^{M}I_{p5}}$$

$$^{M}I_{p9} = {^{M}I_{p3}} - \frac{2}{3} \ d$$

$$^{M}I_{p11} = 0.707c - {^{M}I_{p3}} + {^{M}I_{p5}}.$$

Even harmonics are not present due to dynamic characteristic symmetry. The direct-current and power-input values are found by the 7-point analysis from curve PL and doubled for two tubes.

Classification of amplifier circuits

The classification of amplifiers in classes A, B, and C is based on the operating conditions of the tube.

Another classification can be used, based on the type of circuits associated with the tube.

A tube can be considered as a four-terminal network with two input terminals and two output terminals. One of the input terminals and one of the output terminals are usually common; this common junction or point is usually called "ground".

When the common point is connected to the filament or cathode of the tube, we can speak of a grounded-cathode circuit. It is the most conventional type of vacuum-tube circuit. When the common point is the grid, we can speak of a grounded-grid circuit, and when the common point is the plate or anode, we can speak of the grounded-anode circuit.

This last type of circuit is most commonly known by the name of *cathode follower*.

A fourth and most general class of circuit is obtained when the common point or ground is not directly connected to any of the three electrodes of the tube. This is the condition encountered at u-h-f where the series impedances of the internal tube leads make it impossible to ground any of them. It is also encountered in such special types of circuits as the *phase-splitter*, in which the impedance from plate to ground and the impedance from cathode to ground are made equal in order to obtain an output between plate and cathode balanced with respect to ground.

Classification of amplifier circuits   *continued*

	grounded-cathode	grounded-grid	grounded-plate or cathode-follower
Circuit schematic			
Equivalent circuit, a-c component, class-A operation			
Voltage gain, γ for output load impedance $= Z_2$ $$\gamma = \frac{E_2}{E_1}$$	neglecting C_{gp} $$\gamma = \frac{-\mu Z_2}{r_p + Z_2}$$ $$= -g_m \frac{r_p Z_2}{r_p + Z_2}$$ (Z_2 includes C_{pk})	neglecting C_{pk} $$\gamma = (1+\mu)\,\frac{Z_2}{r_p + Z_2}$$ (Z_2 includes C_{gp})	neglecting C_{gk} $$\gamma = \frac{\mu Z_2}{r_p + (1+\mu) Z_2}$$ (Z_2 includes C_{pk})
Input admittance $$Y_1 = \frac{I_1}{E_1}$$	$Y_1 = j\omega[C_{gk} + (1-\gamma)C_{gp}]$	$Y_1 = j\omega[C_{gk} + (1-\gamma)C_{pk}] + \dfrac{1+\mu}{r_p + Z_2}$	$Y_1 = j\omega[C_{gp} + (1-\gamma)C_{gk}]$
Equivalent generator seen by load at output terminals	neglecting C_{gp}	neglecting C_{pk}	neglecting C_{gk}

Classification of amplifier circuits   *continued*

Design information for the first three classifications is given in the table on page 253, where

Z_2 = load impedance to which output terminals of amplifier are connected

E_1 = rms driving voltage across input terminals of amplifier

E_2 = rms output voltage across load impedance Z_2

I_1 = rms current at input terminals of amplifier

γ = voltage gain of amplifier = E_2/E_1

Y_1 = input admittance to input terminals of amplifier = I_1/E_1

ω = $2\pi \times$ (frequency of excitation voltage E_1)

$j = \sqrt{-1}$

and the remaining notation is in accordance with the nomenclature of pages 213 and 214.

Cathode-follower data

General characteristics

a. High-impedance input, low-impedance output.

b. Input and output have one side grounded.

c. Good wideband frequency and phase response.

d. Output is in phase with input.

e. Voltage gain or transfer is always less than **one**.

f. A power gain can be obtained.

g. Input capacitance is reduced.

General case

$$\text{Transfer} = \frac{E_{out}}{E_{in}} = \frac{g_m R_L}{g_m R_L + 1} \approx g_m Z_r$$

Z_r = resultant cathode-to-ground impedance = R_{out} in parallel with R_L

R_{out} = output resistance of tube

$$= \frac{R_p}{\mu + 1} \text{ or approximately } \frac{1}{g_m}$$

g_m = transconductance in mhos
   (1000 micromhos = 0.001 mhos)

R_L = total load resistance

$$\text{Input capacitance} = C_{gp} + \frac{C_{gk}}{1 + g_m R_L}$$

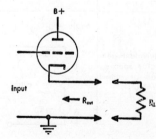

Cathode-follower data *continued*

Specific cases

a. To match the characteristic impedance of the transmission line, R_{out} must equal Z_0. The transfer is approximately 0.5.

b. If R_{out} is less than Z_0, add resistor R_c' in series so that $R_c' = Z_0 - R_{out}$. The transfer is approximately 0.5.

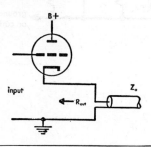

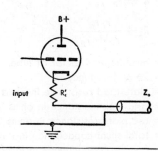

c. If R_{out} is greater than Z_0 add resistor R_c in parallel so that

$$R_c = \frac{Z_0 R_{out}}{R_{out} - Z_0}$$

$$\text{Transfer} = \frac{g_m Z_0}{2}$$

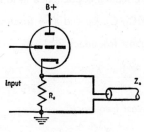

Note: Normal operating bias must be provided. For coupling a high impedance into a low-impedance transmission line, for maximum transfer choose a tube with a high g_m.

Resistance-coupled audio-amplifier design

Stage gain: At

medium frequencies $= A_m = \dfrac{\mu R}{R + R_p}$

high frequencies $= A_h = \dfrac{A_m}{\sqrt{1 + \omega^2 C_1^2 r^2}}$

low frequencies* $= A_l = \dfrac{A_m}{\sqrt{1 + \dfrac{1}{\omega^2 C_2^2 \rho^2}}}$

* The low-frequency stage gain also is affected by the values of the cathode bypass capacitor and the screen bypass capacitor.

Resistance-coupled audio-amplifier design *continued*

where

$$R = \frac{r_l R_2}{r_l + R_2}$$

$$r = \frac{R r_p}{R + r_p}$$

$$\rho = R_2 + \frac{r_l r_p}{r_l + r_p}$$

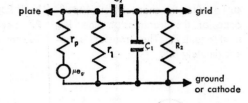

μ = amplification factor of tube
$\omega = 2\pi \times$ frequency
r_l = plate-load resistance in ohms
R_2 = grid-leak resistance in ohms
r_p = a-c plate resistance in ohms
C_1 = total shunt capacitance in farads
C_2 = coupling capacitance in farads

Given C_1, C_2, R_2, and X = fractional response required.

At highest frequency

$$r = \frac{\sqrt{1 - X^2}}{\omega C_1 X} \qquad R = \frac{r\, r_p}{r_p - r} \qquad r_l = \frac{R R_2}{R_2 - R}$$

At lowest frequency*

$$C_2 = \frac{X}{\omega \rho \sqrt{1 - X^2}}$$

Negative feedback

The following quantities are functions of frequency with respect to magnitude and phase:

E, N, and D = signal, noise, and distortion output voltage with feedback
e, n, and d = signal, noise, and distortion output voltage without feedback

$\qquad A$ = voltage amplification of amplifier at a given frequency
$\qquad \beta$ = fraction of output voltage fed back; for usual negative feedback, β is negative
$\qquad \phi$ = phase shift of amplifier and feedback circuit at a given frequency

* The low-frequency stage gain also is affected by the values of the cathode bypass capacitor and the screen bypass capacitor.

Negative feedback *continued*

Reduction in gain caused by feedback

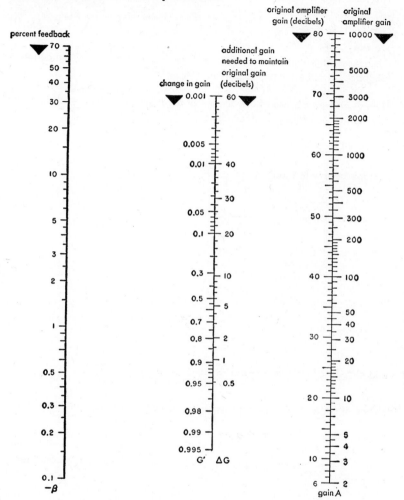

Fig. 3—In negative-feedback amplifier consider-ations β, expressed as a percentage, has a negative value. A line across the β and A scales intersects the center scale to indicate change in gain. It also indicates the amount, in decibels, the input must be increased to maintain original output.

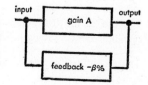

Negative feedback *continued*

The total output voltage with feedback **is**

$$E + N + D = e + \frac{n}{1 - A\beta} + \frac{d}{1 - A\beta} \qquad (1)$$

It is assumed that the input signal to the amplifier is increased when negative feedback is applied, keeping $E = e$.

$(1 - A\beta)$ is a measure of the amount of feedback. By definition, the amount of feedback expressed in decibels is

$$20 \log_{10} | 1 - A\beta | \qquad (2)$$

$$\text{Voltage gain with feedback} = \frac{A}{1 - A\beta} \qquad (3)$$

$$\text{and change of gain} = \frac{1}{1 - A\beta} \qquad (4)$$

If the amount of feedback is large, i.e., $- A\beta \gg 1$,

voltage gain becomes $- 1/\beta$ and so is independent of A. $\qquad (5)$

In the general case when ϕ is not restricted to 0 or π

$$\text{the voltage gain} = \frac{A}{\sqrt{1 + | A\beta |^2 - 2 | A\beta | \cos \phi}} \qquad (6)$$

$$\text{and change of gain} = \frac{1}{\sqrt{1 + | A\beta |^2 - 2 | A\beta | \cos \phi}} \qquad (7)$$

Hence if $|A\beta| \gg 1$, the expression is substantially independent of ϕ.

On the polar diagram relating $(A\beta)$ and ϕ (Nyquist diagram), the system is unstable if the point (1, 0) is enclosed by the curve. Examples of Nyquist diagrams for feedback amplifiers will be found in the chapter on "Servo mechanisms".

Feedback amplifier with single beam-power tube

The use of the foregoing negative feedback formulas is illustrated by the amplifier circuit shown in Fig. 4.

The amplifier consists of an output stage using a 6V6-G beam-power tetrode with feedback, driven by a resistance-coupled stage using a 6J7-G

Negative feedback   *continued*

in a pentode connection. Except for resistors R_1 and R_2 which supply the feedback voltage, the circuit constants and tube characteristics are taken from published data.

The fraction of the output voltage to be fed back is determined by specifying that the total harmonic distortion is not to exceed 4 percent. The plate supply voltage is taken as 250 volts. At this voltage, the 6V6-G has 8-percent

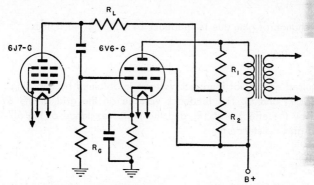

Fig. 4—Feedback amplifier with single beam-power tube.

total harmonic distortion. From equation (1), it is seen that the distortion output voltage with feedback is

$$D = \frac{d}{1 - A\beta}$$

This may be written as

$$1 - A\beta = \frac{d}{D}$$

where

$$\frac{d}{D} = \frac{8}{4} = 2 \qquad 1 - A\beta = 2 \qquad \beta = -\frac{1}{A}$$

and where A = the voltage amplification of the amplifier without feedback.

The peak a-f voltage output of the 6V6-G under the assumed conditions is

$$E_o = \sqrt{4.5 \times 5000 \times 2} = 212 \text{ volts}$$

This voltage is obtained with a peak a-f grid voltage of 12.5 volts so that the voltage gain of this stage without feedback is

$$A = \frac{212}{12.5} = 17$$

Negative feedback *continued*

Hence $\beta = -\dfrac{1}{A} = -\dfrac{1}{17} = -0.0589$ or 5.9 percent, approximately.

The voltage gain of the output stage with feedback is computed from equation (3) as follows

$$A' = \frac{A}{1 - A\beta} = \frac{17}{2} = 8.5$$

and the change of gain due to feedback by equation (4) is thus

$$\frac{1}{1 - A\beta} = 0.5$$

The required amount of feedback voltage is obtained by choosing suitable values for R_1 and R_2. The feedback voltage on the grid of the 6V6-G is reduced by the effect of R_g, R_L and the plate resistance of the 6J7-G. The effective grid resistance is

$$R_g' = \frac{R_g\, r_p}{R_g + r_p}$$

where $R_g = 0.5$ megohm.

This is the maximum allowable resistance in the grid circuit of the 6V6-G with cathode bias.

$r_p = 4$ megohms $=$ the plate resistance of the 6J7-G tube

$$R_g' = \frac{4 \times 0.5}{4 + 0.5} = 0.445 \text{ megohm}$$

The fraction of the feedback voltage across R_2 that appears at the grid of the 6V6-G is

$$\frac{R_g'}{R_g' + R_L} = \frac{0.445}{0.445 + 0.25} = 0.64$$

where $R_L = 0.25$ megohm.

Thus the voltage across R_2 to give the required feedback must be

$$\frac{5.9}{0.64} = 9.2 \text{ percent of the output voltage.}$$

This voltage will be obtained if $R_1 = 50,000$ ohms and $R_2 = 5000$ ohms. This resistance combination gives a feedback voltage ratio of

$$\frac{5000 \times 100}{50,000 + 5000} = 9.1 \text{ percent of the output voltage}$$

Negative feedback *continued*

In a transformer-coupled output stage, the effect of phase shift on the gain with feedback does not become appreciable until a noticeable decrease in gain without feedback also occurs. In the high-frequency range, a phase shift of 25 degrees lagging is accompanied by a 10-percent decrease in gain. For this frequency, the gain with feedback is computed from (6).

$$A' = \frac{A}{\sqrt{1 + |A\beta|^2 - 2|A\beta|\cos\phi}}$$

where $A = 15.3$, $\phi = 155°$, $\cos\phi = -0.906$, $\beta = 0.059$.

$$A' = \frac{15.3}{\sqrt{1 + |0.9|^2 + 2|0.9|0.906}} = \frac{15.3}{\sqrt{3.44}} = \frac{15.3}{1.85} = 8.27$$

The change of gain with feedback is computed from (7).

$$\frac{1}{\sqrt{1 + |A\beta|^2 - 2|A\beta|\cos\phi}} = \frac{1}{1.85} = 0.541$$

If this gain with feedback is compared with the value of 8.5 for the case of no phase shift, it is seen that the effect of frequency on the gain is only 2.7 percent with feedback compared to 10 percent without feedback.

The change of gain with feedback is 0.541 times the gain without feedback whereas in the frequency range where there is no phase shift, the corresponding value is 0.5. This quantity is 0.511 when there is phase shift but no decrease of gain without feedback.

Distortion

A rapid indication of the harmonic content of an alternating source is given by the *distortion factor* which is expressed as a percentage.

$$\left(\begin{matrix}\text{Distortion} \\ \text{factor}\end{matrix}\right) = \sqrt{\frac{\text{(sum of squares of amplitudes of harmonics)}}{\text{(square of amplitude of fundamental)}}} \times 100 \text{ percent}$$

If this factor is reasonably small, say less than 10 percent, the error involved in measuring it,

$$\sqrt{\frac{\text{(sum of squares of amplitudes of harmonics)}}{\text{(sum of squares of amplitudes of fundamental and harmonics)}}} \times 100 \text{ percent}$$

is also small. This latter is measured by the *distortion-factor meter*.

Capacitive-differentiation amplifiers

Capacitive-differentiation systems employ a series-RC circuit (Fig. 5) with the output voltage e_2 taken across R_2. The latter includes the resistance of the load, which is assumed to have a negligible reactive component compared to R_2. In many applications the circuit time constant $RC \ll T$, where T is the period of the input pulse e_1. Thus, transients constitute a minor part of the response, which is essentially a steady-state phenomenon within the time domain of the pulse.

Differential equation

$$e_1 = e_c + RC \frac{de_c}{dt}$$

where $R = R_1 + R_2$. Then

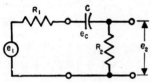

Fig. 5—Capacitive differentiation.

$$e_2 = R_2C \frac{de_c}{dt} = \frac{R_2}{R} (e_1 - e_c)$$

When the rise and decay times of the pulse are each $\gg RC$,

$$e_2 \approx R_2C \frac{de_1}{dt}$$

Trapezoidal input pulse

When T_1, T_2, and T_3 are each much greater than RC, the output response e_2 is approximately rectangular, as shown in Fig. 6.

$$E_{21} = E_1R_2C/T_1$$

$$E_{23} = -E_1R_2C/T_3$$

More accurately, for any value of T, but for widely spaced input pulses,

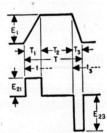

Fig. 6—Trapezoidal input pulse and principal response.

If $\quad 0 < t < T_1$: $e_{21} = \dfrac{E_1R_2C}{T_1}\left[1 - \exp\left(-\dfrac{t}{RC}\right)\right]$

$T_1 < t < (T_1 + T_2)$: $e_{22} = \dfrac{E_1R_2C}{T_1}\left[\exp\left(\dfrac{T_1}{RC}\right) - 1\right]\exp\left(-\dfrac{t}{RC}\right)$

Note: $\quad \exp\left(-\dfrac{t}{RC}\right) = \epsilon^{-t/RC}$

Capacitive-differentiation amplifiers *continued*

$$(T_1 + T_2) < t < T: \quad e_{23} = -\frac{E_1 R_2 C}{T_3}\left\{1 - \left\{\frac{T_3}{T_1}\left[\exp\left(\frac{T_1}{RC}\right) - 1\right]\right.\right.$$
$$\left.\left. + \exp\left(\frac{T_1 + T_2}{RC}\right)\right\} \exp\left(-\frac{t}{RC}\right)\right\}$$

$$t > T: \quad e_{2x} = \frac{E_1 R_2 C}{T_3}\left\{\frac{T_3}{T_1}\left[\exp\left(\frac{T_1}{RC}\right) - 1\right]\right.$$
$$\left. + \exp\left(\frac{T_1 + T_2}{RC}\right) - \exp\left(\frac{T}{RC}\right)\right\} \exp\left(-\frac{t}{RC}\right)$$

$$= A \exp\left(-\frac{t}{RC}\right)$$

when $T_2 \gg RC$: $\quad e_{23} = -\frac{E_1 R_2 C}{T_3}\left[1 - \exp\left(-\frac{t_3}{RC}\right)\right]$

For a long train of identical pulses repeated at regular intervals of T_r between starting points of adjacent pulses, add to each of the above (e_{21}, e_{22}, e_{23}, and e_{2x}) a term

$$e_{20} = \frac{A}{\exp\left(\dfrac{T_r}{RC}\right) - 1} \exp\left(-\frac{t}{RC}\right)$$

where A is defined in the expression for e_{2x} above.

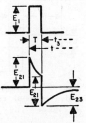

Fig. 7—Single rectangular pulse and response for T much shorter than in Fig. 6.

Rectangular input pulse

Fig. 7 is a special case of Fig. 6, with $T_1 = T_3 = 0$.

$$0 < t < T: \quad e_{21} = \frac{R_2}{R} E_1 \exp\left(-\frac{t}{RC}\right) = E_{21} \exp\left(-\frac{t}{RC}\right)$$

$$t > T: \quad e_{23} = -\frac{R_2}{R} E_1 \left[\exp\left(\frac{T}{RC}\right) - 1\right] \exp\left(-\frac{t}{RC}\right)$$

$$= E_{23} \exp\left(-\frac{t_3}{RC}\right)$$

where $E_{23} = -\frac{R_2}{R} E_1 \left[1 - \exp\left(-\frac{T}{RC}\right)\right]$

Capacitive-differentiation amplifiers   *continued*

Triangular input pulse

Fig. 8 is a special case of the trapezoidal pulse, with $T_2 = 0$. The total
output amplitude is approximately

$$|E_{21}| + |E_{23}| = |E_1| R_2 C \frac{T_1 + T_3}{T_1 T_3}$$

which is a maximum

when $T_1 = T_3$.

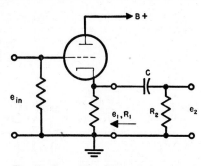

Fig. 9—Capacitive-differentiation circuit with cathode-follower source.

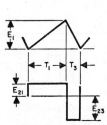

Fig. 8 — Triangular pulse—special case of Fig. 6.

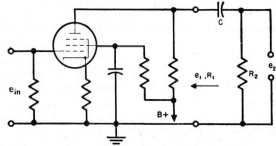

Fig. 10—Capacitive-differentiation circuit with plate-circuit source.

Schematic diagrams

Two capacitive-differentiation circuits using vacuum tubes as driving sources are given in Figs. 9 and 10.

Capacitive-integration amplifiers

Capacitive-integration circuits employ a series-RC circuit (Fig. 11) with the output voltage e_2 taken across capacitor C. The load admittance is accounted for by including its capacitance in C; while its shunt resistance is combined with R_1 and R_2 to form a voltage divider treated by Thevenin's theorem. In contrast with capacitive differentiation, time constant $RC \gg T$ in many applications. Thus, the output voltage is composed mostly of the early part of a transient response to the input voltage wave. For a long repeated train of identical input pulses, this repeated transient response becomes steady-state.

Capacitive-integration amplifiers *continued*

Circuit equations

$$e_1 = e_2 + RC \frac{de_2}{dt}$$

where $R = R_1 + R_2$.

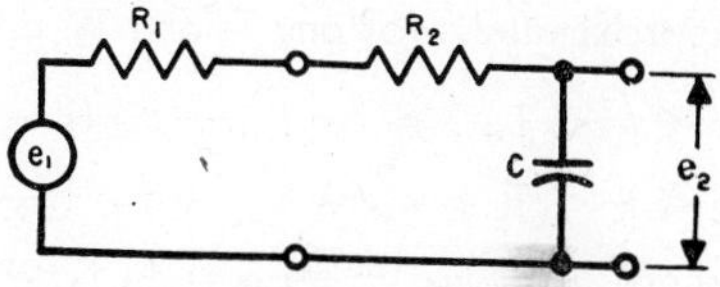

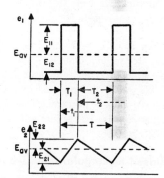

Fig. 11—Capacitive integration.

When $t \ll RC$ and E_{20} is very small compared to the amplitude of e_1,

$$e_2 \approx E_{20} + \frac{1}{RC} \int_0^t e_1 \, dt$$

where E_{20} = value of e_2 at time $t = 0$.

Rectangular input-wave train

See Fig. 12.

$$E_{av} = \frac{1}{T} \int_0^T e_1 \, dt$$

Then

$$E_{11} T_1 + E_{12} T_2 = 0$$

Fig. 12—Rectangular input-wave train at top. Below, output wave on an exaggerated voltage scale.

After equilibrium or steady-state has been established,

$$e_{21} = E_{av} + E_{11} \left[1 - \exp \left(- \frac{t_1}{RC} \right) \right] + E_{21} \exp \left(- \frac{t_1}{RC} \right)$$

$$e_{22} = E_{av} + E_{12} \left[1 - \exp \left(- \frac{t_2}{RC} \right) \right] + E_{22} \exp \left(- \frac{t_2}{RC} \right)$$

If the steady-state has not been established at time $t_1 = 0$, add to e_2 the term

$$(E_{20} - E_{av} - E_{21}) \exp \left(- \frac{t_1}{RC} \right)$$

When $T_1 = T_2 = T/2$, then

$$E_{11} = -E_{12} = E_1$$
$$E_2 = E_{22} = -E_{21} = E_1 \tanh \, (T/4RC)$$

Capacitive-integration amplifiers   *continued*

Approximately, for any T_1 and T_2, provided $T \ll RC$,

$$0 < t_1 < T_1: \quad e_{21} = E_{av} - E_2 (1 - 2t_1/T_1)$$

$$0 < t_2 < T_2: \quad e_{22} = E_{av} + E_2 (1 - 2t_2/T_2)$$

where $E_2 = E_{22} = -E_{21} = E_{11}T_1/2RC$

$$= -E_{12}T_2/2RC$$

Error: Due to assuming a linear output-voltage wave (Fig. 13) is

$$E_\Delta/E_2 \approx T/8RC$$

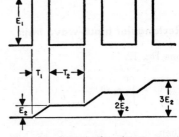

Fig. 13—Error E_Δ from assuming a linear output (dashed line).

when $T_1 = T_2 = T/2$. The error in E_2 due to setting $\tanh (T/4RC) = T/4RC$ is comparatively negligible. When $T/RC = 0.7$, the approximate error in E_2 is only 1 percent. However, the error E_Δ is 1 percent of E_2 when $T/RC = 0.08$.

Biased rectangular input wave

In Fig. 14, when $(T_1 + T_2) \ll RC$, and $E_{20} = 0$ at $t = 0$, the output voltage approximates a series of steps.

$$E_2 = E_1 T_1/RC$$

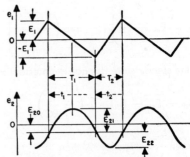

Fig. 14—Rectangular input wave gives stepped output.

Triangular input wave

In Fig. 15, when $(T_1 + T_2) \ll RC$, and after the steady-state has been established, then, approximately,

$0 < t_1 < T_1$:

$$e_{21} = E_{20} + E_{21} - 4E_{21}\left(\frac{t_1}{T_1} - \frac{1}{2}\right)$$

$0 < t_2 < T_2$:

$$e_{22} = E_{20} + E_{22} - 4E_{22}\left(\frac{t_2}{T_2} - \frac{1}{2}\right)$$

where

$$E_{20} = E_1 (T_2 - T_1)/6RC$$

$$E_{21} = E_1 T_1/4RC$$

$$E_{22} = -E_1 T_2/4RC$$

Fig. 15—Triangular input wave at top. Below, parabolic output wave on an exaggerated voltage scale.

Capacitive-integration amplifiers   *continued*

Schematic diagrams

Two capacitive-integration circuits using vacuum tubes as sources are given in Figs. 16 and 17.

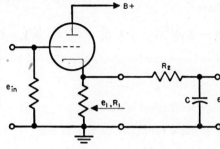

Fig. 16 (right)—Capacitive-integration circuit with cathode-follower source.

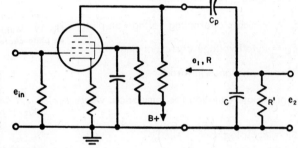

Fig. 17 (right)— Capacitive-integration circuit with plate-circuit source.
$C_p \gg C$ and $R' \gg R$

Nonsinusoidal generators

Free-running zero-bias symmetrical multivibrator

Exact equation for semiperiod (Figs. 18 and 19):

$$\mathcal{I}_1 = \left(R_{g1} + \frac{R_{l2} r_p}{R_{l2} + r_p} \right) C_1 \log_e \frac{E_b - E_m}{E_x}$$

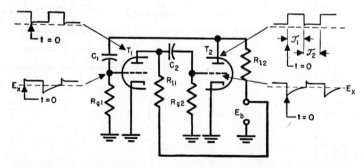

Fig. 18—Schematic diagram of symmetrical multivibrator and voltage waveforms on tube elements.

Nonsinusoidal generators *continued*

where

$$\Im = \Im_1 + \Im_2 = 1/f, \; \Im_1 = \Im_2, \; R_{g1} = R_{g2}, \; C_1 = C_2.$$

f = repetition frequency in cycles/second

$\Im$ = period in seconds

$\Im_1$ = semiperiod in seconds

r_p = plate resistance of tube in ohms

E_b = plate-supply voltage

E_m = minimum alternating voltage on plate

E_x = cutoff voltage corresponding to E_b

C = capacitance in farads

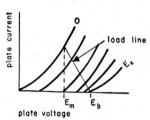

Fig. 19—Multivibrator potentials on plate-characteristic curve.

Approximate equation for semiperiod, where $R_{g1} \gg \dfrac{R_{l2}r_p}{R_{l2} + r_p}$, is

$$\Im_1 = R_{g1}C_1 \log_e \left(\frac{E_b - E_m}{E_x} \right)$$

Equation for buildup time is

$$\Im_B = 4(R_l + r_p)C = 98 \text{ percent of peak value}$$

Free-running zero-bias unsymmetrical multivibrator

See symmetrical multivibrator for circuit and terminology; the wave forms are given in Fig. 20.

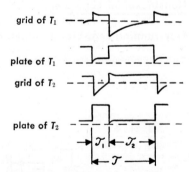

Fig. 20 — Unsymmetrical multivibrator waveforms.

Equations for fractional periods are

$$\Im_1 = \left(R_{g1} + \frac{R_{l2}r_p}{R_{l2} + r_p} \right) C_1 \log_e \left(\frac{E_{b2} - E_{m2}}{E_{x1}} \right)$$

$$\Im_2 = \left(R_{g2} + \frac{R_{l1}r_p}{R_{l1} + r_p} \right) C_2 \log_e \left(\frac{E_{b1} - E_{m1}}{E_{x2}} \right)$$

$$\Im = \Im_1 + \Im_2 = 1/f$$

Nonsinusoidal generators   *continued*

Free-running positive-bias multivibrator

Equations for fractional period (Fig. 21) are

$$\Im_1 = \left(R_{g1} + \frac{R_{l2}r_p}{R_{l2} + r_p}\right) C_1 \log_e\left(\frac{E_{b2} - E_{m2} + E_{c1}}{E_{c1} + E_{x1}}\right)$$

$$\Im_2 = \left(R_{g2} + \frac{R_{l1}r_p}{R_{l1} + r_p}\right) C_2 \log_e\left(\frac{E_{b1} - E_{m1} + E_{c2}}{E_{c2} + E_{x2}}\right)$$

where

$$\Im = \Im_1 + \Im_2 = 1/f$$

E_c = positive bias voltage

R_c = bias control

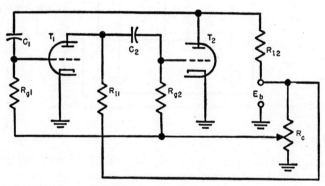

Fig. 21—Free-running positive-bias multivibrator.

Driven (one-shot) multivibrator

Circuit is given in Fig. 22. Equations are

$$f_{mv} = f_s$$

f_{mv} = multivibrator frequency in cycles/second

f_s = synchronizing frequency in cycles/second

Conditions of operation are

$$f_s > f_n \quad \text{or} \quad \Im_s < \Im_n$$

Nonsinusoidal generators   *continued*

where

f_n = free-running frequency in cycles/second

$\mathcal{T}_s$ = synchronizing period in seconds

$\mathcal{T}_n$ = free-running period in seconds

$$\mathcal{T}_{n2} = R_{g2}C \log_e \left(\frac{E_{b1} - E_{m1} + E_{c2}}{E_{c2} + E_{x2}} \right)$$

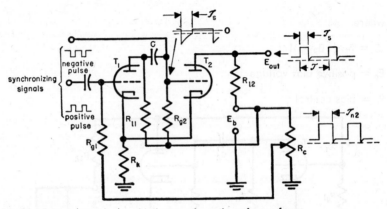

Fig. 22—Driven (one-shot) multivibrator schematic and waveforms.

Phantastron*

The phantastron circuit is a time-delay device of the multivibrator type having high-accuracy possibilities. A negative pulse of about 30-volts amplitude is applied at the input, and the circuit produces a delayed positive output pulse at the cathode of the 6SA7. The amount of delay is determined by the setting of the calibrated delay-control potentiometer, delay being linearly proportional to the output voltage of this potentiometer to within ±0.5 microsecond. At any one setting of the delay control, the long-time variation in time delay is about half of the above figure.

Maximum time delay $\approx R_g C_g (E_{\max} - E_{\min})/E_b$

where $E_{\max}$ is the maximum value of the control voltage, $E_{\min}$ is the minimum control voltage resulting in delay (40 to 60 volts), and E_b is the plate-supply voltage.

Minimum delay $\approx 0.02 \times$ (maximum delay)

* R. N. Close, and M. T. Lebenbaum, "Design of Phantastron Time-Delay Circuits," *Electronics,* vol. 21, pp. 100–107; April, 1948.

Nonsinusoidal generators *continued*

For the circuit shown, E_{max} = 225 volts, E_{min} = 50 volts, and delay range is 60 to 3000 microseconds.

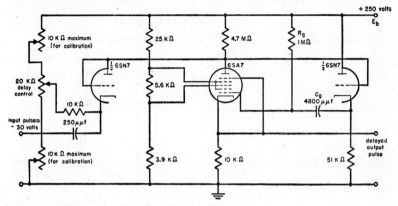

Fig. 23—Schematic of a typical phantastron delay network.

Free-running blocking oscillator

Conditions for blocking

$$E_1/E_0 < 1 - \epsilon^{1/af - \theta}$$

where

E_0 = peak grid volts

E_1 = positive portion of grid swing in volts

E_c = grid bias in volts

f = frequency in cycles/second

α = grid time constant in seconds

ϵ = 2.718 = base of natural logs

θ = decrement of wave

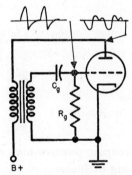

Fig. 24—Free-running blocking oscillator—schematic and waveforms.

a. Use strong feedback
= E_0 is high

b. Use large grid time constant
= α is large

c. Use high decrement (high losses)
= θ is high

Pulse width is $\mathfrak{I}_1 \approx 2\sqrt{LC}$

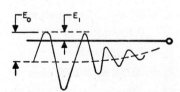

Fig. 25—Blocking-oscillator grid voltage.

Nonsinusoidal generators   *continued*

where

$\mathfrak{I}_1$ = pulse width in seconds

 L = magnetizing inductance of transformer in henries

 C = interwinding capacitance of transformer in farads

$$L = M \frac{n_1}{n_2}$$

where

 M = mutual inductance between windings

n_1/n_2 = turns ratio of transformer

Repetition frequency

$$\mathfrak{I}_2 \approx \frac{1}{f} \approx R_g C_g \log_e \frac{E_b + E_g}{E_b + E_x}$$

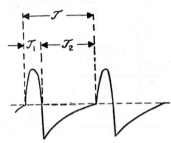

Fig. 26—Blocking oscillator pulse waveform.

where

$\mathfrak{I}_2 \gg \mathfrak{I}_1$

 f = repetition frequency in cycles/second

E_b = plate-supply voltage

E_g = maximum negative grid voltage

E_x = grid cutoff in volts

$\mathfrak{I} = \mathfrak{I}_1 + \mathfrak{I}_2 = 1/f$

Free-running positive-bias wide-frequency-range blocking oscillator

Typical circuit values are

 R = 0.5 to 5 megohms

 C = 50 micromicrofarads to 0.1 microfarads

R_k = 10 to 200 ohms

R_b = 50,000 to 250,000 ohms

$\triangle f$ = 100 cycles to 100 kilocycles

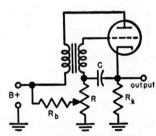

Fig. 27 — Free-running positive-bias blocking oscillator.

Nonsinusoidal generators   *continued*

Synchronized blocking oscillator

Operating conditions (Fig. 28) are

$$f_n < f_s \text{ or } T_n > T_s$$

where

f_n = free-running frequency in cycles/
second

f_s = synchronizing frequency in cycles/
second

T_n = free-running period in seconds

T_s = synchronizing period in seconds

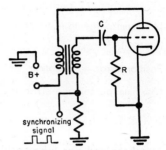

Fig. 28—Synchronized blocking oscillator.

Driven blocking oscillator

Operating conditions (Fig. 29) are

a. Tube off unless positive voltage is applied to grid.

b. Signal input controls repetition frequency.

c. E_c is a high negative bias.

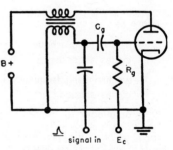

Fig. 29—Driven blocking oscillator.

Free-running gas-tube oscillator

Equation for period (Fig. 30)

$$\Im = \alpha RC \left(1 + \alpha/2\right)$$

where

$\Im$ = period in cycles/second

$$\alpha = \frac{E_i - E_x}{E - E_x}$$

E_i = ignition voltage

E_x = extinction voltage

E = plate-supply voltage

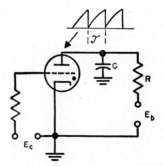

Fig. 30—Free-running gas-tube oscillator.

Nonsinusoidal generators *continued*

Velocity error = change in velocity of cathode-ray-tube spot over trace period.

Maximum percentage error = $\alpha \times 100$

if $\alpha \ll 1$.

Position error = deviation of cathode-ray-tube trace from linearity.

Maximum percentage error = $\dfrac{\alpha}{8} \times 100$

if $\alpha \ll 1$.

Synchronized gas-tube oscillator

Conditions for synchronization (Fig. 31) are

$$f_s = N f_n$$

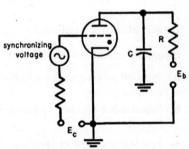

where

f_n = free-running frequency in cycles/second

f_s = synchronizing frequency in cycles/second

N = an integer

For $f_s \neq N f_n$, the maximum δf_n before slipping is given by

$$\frac{E_0}{E_s} \frac{\delta f_n}{f_s} = 1$$

Fig. 31—Synchronized gas-tube oscillator.

where

$\delta f_n = f_n - f_s$

E_0 = free-running ignition voltage

E_s = synchronizing voltage referred to plate circuit

■ Modulation

Introduction

The process of modulation of a radio-frequency carrier $y = A(t) \cos \gamma(t)$ is treated under two main headings as follows:

a. Modification of its amplitude $A(t)$

b. Modification of its phase $\gamma(t)$

For a harmonic oscillation, $\gamma(t)$ is replaced by $(\omega t + \phi)$, so that

$$y = A(t) \cos(\omega t + \phi) = A(t) \cos \psi(t)$$

A is the amplitude. The whole argument of the cosine $\psi(t)$ is the phase.

Amplitude modulation

In amplitude modulation (Fig. 1), ω is constant. The signal intelligence $f(t)$ is made to control the amplitude parameter of the carrier by the relation

$$A(t) = [A_0 + a\, f(t)]$$
$$= A_0[1 + m_a\, f(t)]$$

where

$\psi(t) = \omega t + \phi$

ω = angular carrier frequency

ϕ = carrier phase constant

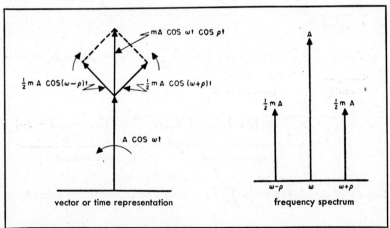

vector or time representation   frequency spectrum

Fig. 1—Sideband and vector representation of amplitude modulation for a single sinusoidal modulation frequency ($a \cos pt$).

Amplitude modulation *continued*

A_0 = amplitude of the unmodulated carrier

a = maximum amplitude of modulating function

$f(t)$ = generally, a continuous function of time representing the signal; $0 \leqslant f(t) \leqslant 1$

$m_a = a/A_0$ = degree of amplitude modulation; $0 \leqslant m_a < 1$

$y = A_0 [1 + m_a f(t)] \cos (\omega_0 t + \phi)$

For a signal $f(t)$ represented by a sum of sinusoidal components

$$f(t) = \sum_{K=1}^{K=M} a_K \cos (\rho_K t + \theta_K)$$

where ρ_K is the angular frequency of the modulating signal and θ_K is the constant part of its phase.

Assuming the system is linear, each frequency component ρ_K gives rise to a pair of sidebands $(\omega + \rho_K)$ and $(\omega - \rho_K)$ symmetrically located about the carrier frequency ω.

$$y = A_0 \left[1 + \frac{1}{A_0} \sum_{K=1}^{K=M} a_K \cos (\rho_K t + \theta_K) \right] \cos (\omega t + \phi)$$

The constant component of the carrier phase ϕ is dropped for simplification.

$$y = \underbrace{A_0 \cos (\omega_0 t)}_{\text{carrier}} + \underbrace{(\cos \omega_0 t) \left[\sum_{K=1}^{K=M} a_K \cos (\rho_K t + \theta_K) \right]}_{\text{modulation vectors}}$$

$$= \underbrace{A_0 \cos \omega_0 t}_{\text{carrier}} + \underbrace{\frac{a_1}{2} \cos [(\omega_0 + \rho_1) t + \theta_1]}_{\text{upper sideband}} + \underbrace{\frac{a_1}{2} \cos [(\omega_0 - \rho_1) t - \theta_1]}_{\text{lower sideband}} + \cdots$$

$$+ \underbrace{\frac{a_m}{2} \cos [(\omega_0 + \rho_m) t + \theta_m]}_{\text{upper sideband}} + \underbrace{\frac{a_m}{2} \cos [(\omega_0 - \rho_m) t - \theta_m]}_{\text{lower sideband}}$$

Degree of modulation $= \dfrac{1}{A_0} \displaystyle\sum_{K=1}^{K=m} a_K$ for ρ's not harmonically related.

Percent modulation $= \dfrac{\text{(crest ampl)} - \text{(trough ampl)}}{\text{(crest ampl)} + \text{(trough ampl)}} \times 100$

Amplitude modulation   *continued*

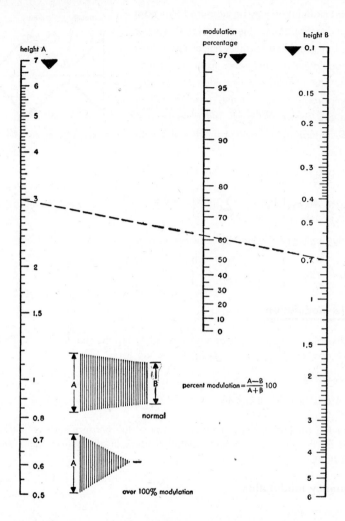

percent modulation = $\dfrac{A-B}{A+B}$ 100

To determine the modulation percentage from an oscillogram of type illustrated apply measurements A and B to scales A and B and read percentage from center scale. Any units of measurement may be used.

Example: A = 3 inches, B = 0.7 inches = 62-percent modulation.

Fig. 2—Modulation percentage from oscillograms.

Amplitude modulation   *continued*

Percent modulation may be measured by means of an oscilloscope, the modulated carrier wave being applied to the vertical plates and the modulating voltage wave to the horizontal plates. The resulting trapezoidal pattern and a nomograph for computing percent modulation are shown in Fig. 2. The dimensions A

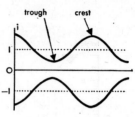

and B in that figure are proportional to the crest amplitude and trough amplitude, respectively.

Peak voltage at crest for ρ's not harmonically related:

$$A_{\text{crest}} = A_{0,\text{ rms}} \left[1 + \frac{1}{A_0} \sum_{K=1}^{K=m} a_K \right] \times \sqrt{2}$$

Effective value of the modulated wave in general:

$$A_{\text{eff}} = A_{0,\text{ rms}} \left[1 + \frac{1}{A_0^2} \sum_{K=1}^{K=m} a_K^2 \right]^{\frac{1}{2}}$$

Angle modulation

All sinusoidal angle modulations derived from the harmonic oscillation $y = A \cos(\omega t + \phi)$ can be expressed in the form

$$y = A \cos \psi(t)$$
$$= A \cos(\omega_0 t + \Delta\theta \cos \rho t)$$

where the oscillating component $\Delta\theta \cos \rho t$ of the phase excursion is determined by the type of angular modulation used. In all angle modulations A is constant.

Frequency modulation

$$y = A_0 \cos \psi(t)$$

The signal intelligence $f(t)$ is made to control the instantaneous frequency parameter of the carrier by the relation

$$\omega(t) = \omega_0 + \Delta\omega f(t)$$
$$= \frac{d\psi(t)}{dt}$$

Angle modulation   *continued*

where

$\omega(t)$ = instantaneous frequency

    = $d\psi(t)/dt$

$\psi(t)$ = $\int \omega(t)\ dt$

ω_0 = frequency of unmodulated carrier

$\Delta\omega$ = maximum instantaneous frequency excursion from ω_0

For single-frequency modulation $f(t) = \cos pt$,

$$y = A \cos\left(\omega_0 t + \frac{\Delta\omega}{p}\sin pt\right)$$

$\Delta\omega/p = \Delta\theta$ (in radians) is the modulation index. The phase excursion $\Delta\theta$ is inversely proportional to the modulating frequency p. In general for broadcast applications, $\Delta\omega \ll \omega_0$ and $\Delta\theta \gg 1$.

Phase modulation

$$y = A_0 \cos \psi(t)$$

The signal intelligence $f(t)$ is made to control the instantaneous phase excursions of the carrier by the relation $\delta\theta = \Delta\theta\ f(t)$.

$$\psi(t) = [\omega_0 t + \Delta\theta\ f(t)] = \int_0^t \omega(t)\ dt$$

$$y = A \cos[\omega_0 t + \Delta\theta\ f(t)]$$

For sinusoidal modulation $f(t) = \cos pt$,

$$y = A \cos(\omega_0 t + \Delta\theta \cos pt)$$

Maximum phase excursion is independent of the modulating frequency p.

The instantaneous frequency of the phase-modulated wave is given by the derivative of its total phase:

$$\omega(t) = d\psi(t)/dt = (\omega_0 - p\Delta\theta \sin pt)$$

$$\delta\omega = \omega(t) - \omega_0 = -p\Delta\theta \sin pt$$

Maximum frequency excursion $\Delta\omega = -p\Delta\theta$ is proportional to the modulation frequency p.

Angle modulation   *continued*

Sideband energy distribution in angle modulation

$$y = A \cos (\omega_0 t + \Delta\theta \cos pt)$$

for $\Delta\theta \ll 0.2$ and a single sinusoidal modulation. See Fig. 3.

$$y = A(\underbrace{\cos \omega_0 t}_{\text{carrier}} - \underbrace{\Delta\theta \cos pt \sin \omega_0 t}_{\text{modulation vector}})$$

$$= A \left[\underbrace{\cos \omega_0 t}_{\text{carrier}} - \underbrace{\frac{\Delta\theta}{2} \sin (\omega_0 + p)t}_{\text{upper sideband}} - \underbrace{\frac{\Delta\theta}{2} \sin (\omega_0 - p)t}_{\text{lower sideband}} \right]$$

Frequency spectrum of angle modulation

No restrictions on $\Delta\theta$.

$$y = A \cos (\omega_0 t + \Delta\theta \cos pt)$$

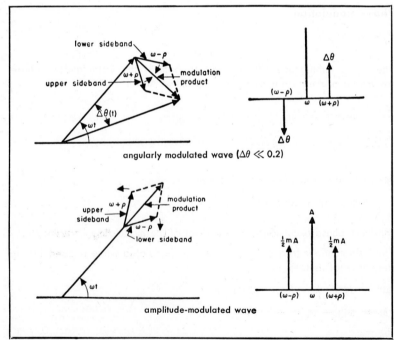

angularly modulated wave ($\Delta\theta \ll 0.2$)

amplitude-modulated wave

Fig. 3—Sideband and modulation vector representation of angle modulation for $\Delta\theta \ll 0.2$ as well as for amplitude modulation.

Angle modulation *continued*

$$y = A[J_0(\Delta\theta) \cos \omega_0 t - 2J_1(\Delta\theta) \cos pt \sin \omega_0 t$$
$$+ 2J_2(\Delta\theta) \sin 2pt \cos \omega_0 t$$
$$- 2J_3(\Delta\theta) \sin 3pt \sin \omega_0 t$$
$$+ \ldots \ldots \ldots \ldots]$$

This gives the carrier modulation vectors. See Fig. 4.

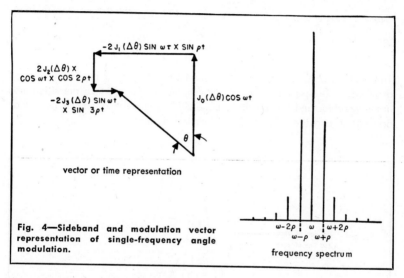

Fig. 4—Sideband and modulation vector representation of single-frequency angle modulation.

The sideband frequencies are given by

$$y = A\{J_0(\Delta\theta) \cos \omega_0 t - J_1(\Delta\theta)[\sin (\omega_0 + p)t + \sin (\omega_0 - p)t]$$
$$+ J_2(\Delta\theta)[\sin (\omega_0 + 2p)t + \sin (\omega_0 - 2p)t]$$
$$- J_3(\Delta\theta)[\sin (\omega_0 + 3p)t + \sin (\omega_0 - 3p)t]\}$$

Here, $J_n(\Delta\theta)$ is the Bessel function of the first kind and nth order with argument $\Delta\theta$. An expansion of $J_n(\Delta\theta)$ in a series is given on page 614, tables of Bessel functions are on pages 636 to 639; and a 3-dimensional representation of Bessel functions is given in Fig. 5. The carrier and sideband amplitudes are oscillating functions of $\Delta\theta$:

Carrier vanishes for $\Delta\theta$ radians = 2.40; 5.52; 8.65 + $n\pi$

First sideband vanishes for $\Delta\theta$ radians = 3.83; 7.02; 10.17; 13.32 + $n\pi$

The property of vanishing carrier is used frequently in the measurement of $\Delta\omega$ in frequency modulation. This follows from $\Delta\omega = (\Delta\theta)(\rho)$. Knowing $\Delta\theta$ and ρ, $\Delta\omega$ is computed.

Angle modulation *continued*

The approximate number of important sidebands and the corresponding bandwidth necessary for transmission are as follows, where $f = p/2\pi$ and $\Delta f = \Delta\omega/2\pi$,

m_f	5	10	20
Signal frequency f	$0.2 \Delta f$	$0.1 \Delta f$	$0.05 \Delta f$
Number of pairs of sidebands	7	13	23
Bandwidth	14 f	26 f	46 f
	2.8 Δf	2.6 Δf	2.3 Δf

This table is based on neglecting sidebands in the outer regions where all amplitudes are less than $0.02A_0$. The amplitude below which the sidebands are neglected, and the resultant bandwidth, will depend on the particular application and the quality of transmission desired.

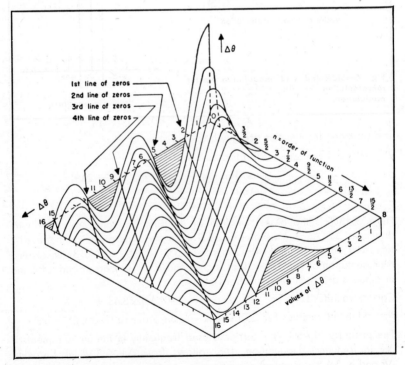

Fig. 5—3-dimensional representation of Bessel functions.

Interference and noise in AM and FM

Interference rejection in amplitude and frequency modulations

Simplest case of interference; two unmodulated carriers:

e_0 = desired signal

$\qquad = E_0 \sin \omega_0 t$

e_1 = interfering signal

$\qquad = E_1 \sin \omega_1 t$

The vectorial addition of these two results in a voltage that has both amplitude and frequency modulation.

Amplitude-modulation interference

E_t = resultant voltage

$$\approx E_0 \left[1 + \frac{E_1}{E_0} \cos (\omega_1 - \omega_0 t) \right] \text{ for } E_1 \ll E_0$$

The interference results in the amplitude modulation of the original carrier by a beat frequency equal to $(\omega_0 - \omega_1)$ having a modulation index equal to E_1/E_0.

Frequency-modulation interference

$\omega(t)$ = resultant instantaneous frequency

$$= \omega_0 + \frac{E_1}{E} (\omega_1 - \omega_0) \cos (\omega_1 - \omega_0) t \text{ for } E_1 \ll E_0$$

$$\Delta \omega_1 = \omega(t) - \omega_0 = \frac{E_1}{E} (\omega_1 - \omega_0) \cos (\omega_1 - \omega_0) t$$

The interference results in frequency modulation of the original carrier by a beat frequency equal to $(\omega_0 - \omega_1)$ having a frequency-modulation index equal to $E_1(\omega_1 - \omega_0)/E\Delta\omega$

$$\left(\frac{\text{interference amplitude modulation}}{\text{interference frequency modulation}} \right) = \frac{\Delta \omega}{(\omega_1 - \omega_0)}$$

where $\Delta \omega$ is the desired frequency deviation.

Interference and noise in AM and FM   *continued*

Noise reduction in frequency modulation

The noise-suppressing properties of frequency modulation apply when the signal carrier level at the frequency discriminator is greater than the noise level. When the noise level exceeds the carrier signal level, the noise suppresses the signal. For a given amount of noise at a receiver there is a sharp threshold level of frequency-modulation signal above which the noise is suppressed and below which the signal is suppressed. This threshold has been defined as the improvement threshold. For the condition where the threshold level is exceeded:

Random noise: Assuming the receivers have uniform gain in the pass band, the resultant noise is proportional to the square of the voltage components over the spectrum of noise frequencies:

$$\left(\frac{\text{F-M signal/random-noise ratio}}{\text{A-M signal/random-noise ratio}}\right) = \sqrt{3}\,\frac{\Delta\omega}{\rho} = \sqrt{3}\,\Delta\theta$$

Impulse noise: Noise voltages add directly:

$$\left(\frac{\text{F-M signal/impulse-noise ratio}}{\text{A-M signal/impulse-noise ratio}}\right) = 2\,\frac{\Delta\omega}{\rho} = 2\,\Delta\theta$$

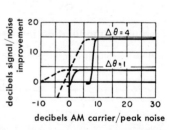

Fig. 6—Improvement threshold for frequency modulation. Deviation $\Delta\theta$ affects amount of signal required to reach threshold and also amount of noise suppression obtained. Solid line shows peak, and dotted line the root-mean-square noise in the output.
Courtesy of McGraw-Hill Book Company

The carrier signal required to reach the improvement threshold depends on the frequency deviation of the incoming signal. The greater the deviation, the greater the signal required to reach the improvement threshold, but the greater the noise suppression, once this level is reached. Fig. 6 illustrates this characteristic.

In amplitude modulation, the presence of the carrier increases the background noise in a receiver. In frequency modulation, the presence of the carrier decreases the background noise, since the carrier effectively suppresses it.

Pulse modulation

Pulse-modulation methods

There are four general classes of pulse-modulation methods:

a. Modulation methods in which the values of instantaneous samples of the modulating wave are caused to modulate the time of occurrence of some characteristic of a pulse carrier. (This class has been called pulse-time modulation, or PTM.)

b. A second class in which the values of the instantaneous samples of the modulating wave are caused to modulate the amplitude of a pulse carrier with the time of occurrence of the individual pulses being fixed.

c. That class in which the modulating wave is sampled, quantized, and coded. (This method has been called pulse-code modulation, or PCM.)

d. The class that includes composite methods combining the modulation characteristics of the aforementioned classes.

Class a

Pulse-position modulation (PPM): Pulse-time modulation (PTM) in which the value of each instantaneous sample of a modulating wave is caused to modulate the position.

Pulse-duration modulation (PDM): Pulse-time modulation in which the value of each instantaneous sample of the modulating wave is caused to modulate the duration of a pulse. Also called pulse-width modulation (PWM).

Pulse-frequency modulation (PFM): Modulation in which the modulating wave is used to frequency-modulate a carrier wave consisting of a series of direct-current pulses.

Additional methods: Which include modified-time-reference and pulse-shape modulation.

Class b

Pulse-amplitude modulation (PAM): Used when the modulating wave is caused to amplitude-modulate a pulse carrier. Forms of this type of modulation include unidirectional PAM and bidirectional PAM.

Class c

Binary pulse-code modulation (PCM): Pulse-code modulation in which the code for each element of information consists of one of two distinct kinds or values, such as pulses and spaces.

Pulse modulation   *continued*

Ternary pulse-code modulation (PCM): Pulse-code modulation in which the code for each element of information consists of any one of three distinct kinds or values, such as positive pulses, negative pulses, and spaces.

N-ary pulse-code modulation (PCM): Pulse-code modulation in which the code for each element of information consists of any one of N distinct kinds or values.

Terminology

Pulse: A single disturbance characterized by the rise and decay in time or space, or both, of a quantity whose value is normally constant.

Unidirectional pulses: Single-polarity pulses that all rise in the same direction.

Bidirectional pulses: Pulses some of which rise in one direction and the remainder in the other direction.

Pulse duration: Equal to the duration of rectangular pulses whose energy and peak power equal those of the pulse in question.

Pulse-rise time: The time required for the instantaneous amplitude to go from 10 percent to 90 percent of the peak value.

Pulse-decay time: The time required for the instantaneous amplitude to go from 90 percent to 10 percent of the peak value.

Transducer: A device by means of which energy can flow from one or more transmission systems to one or more other transmission systems.

Clipper: A transducer that gives output only when the input exceeds the critical value.

Limiter: A transducer whose output is constant for all inputs above a critical value.

Time gate: A transducer that gives output only during chosen time intervals.

Improvement threshold: In pulse-modulation systems, the condition that exists when the ratio of peak-pulse voltage to peak-noise voltage exceeds 2 after selection and before any nonlinear process such as amplitude clipping and limiting.

Quantization: A process wherein the complete range of instantaneous values of a wave is divided into a finite number of smaller subranges, each of which is represented by an assigned or quantized value within the subranges.

Code: A plan for representing each of a finite number of values as a particularly arrangement of discrete events.

Code element: One of the discrete events in a code.

Pulse modulation   *continued*

Code character: A particular arrangement of code elements used in a code to represent a single value.

Baud: The unit of signaling speed equal to the number of code elements per second.

Level: The number by which a given subrange of a quantized signal may be identified.

Pulse regeneration: The process of replacing each code element by a new element standardized in timing and magnitude.

Quantization distortion: The inherent distortion introduced in the process of quantization. This is sometimes referred to as quantization noise.

Sampling

The modulation is impressed on the pulses by the process known as sampling, wherein the amplitude of the modulating signal is determined at the time of occurrence of the pulse. A characteristic of the pulse, such as its time position or amplitude, is then affected by the signal amplitude at that instant. This process, for the several types of modulations, is illustrated in Fig. 7.

The minimum ratio of sampling frequency f_p to modulating frequency bandwidth $(f_h - f_l)$, where f_h and f_l are the high- and low-frequency limits of the modulating-frequency band, respectively, is given by

$$f_p/(f_h - f_l) = 2$$

In practice, a larger ratio is utilized to permit the sampling components to be separated from the voice components with an economical filter. Consequently, a ratio of about 2.5 is used.

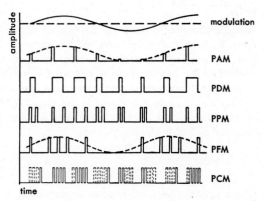

Fig. 7—Pulse trains of single channels for various pulse systems, showing effect of modulation on amplitude and time-spacing of subcarrier pulses. The modulating signal is at the top.

Pulse bandwidth

The bandwidth necessary to transmit a video pulse

Pulse modulation   *continued*

train is determined by the rise and decay times of the pulse. This bandwidth F_v is approximately given by

$$F_v \approx 1/2t_r$$

where t_r is the rise or decay time, whichever is the smaller.

The radio-frequency bandwidth F_R is then

$$F_R \approx 1/t_r$$

for amplitude-keyed radio-frequency carrier. Bandwidth is

$$F_R \approx \frac{1}{t_r}(m + 1)$$

for frequency-keyed radio-frequency carrier where m is the index of modulation.

Signal-to-noise ratio

The signal/noise improvement factors (NIF) for the pulse subcarrier are as follows:

Pulse-amplitude modulation: If the minimum bandwidth, is used for transmission of PAM pulses, the signal/noise ratio at the receiver output is equal to that at the input to the receiver. The improvement factor is therefore unity.

Pulse-position modulation: By the use of wider bandwidths, an improvement in the signal/noise ratio at the receiver output may be obtained. This improvement is similar to that obtained by frequency modulation applied to a continuous-wave carrier. Since PPM is a constant-amplitude method of transmission, amplitude noise variations may be removed by limiting and clipping the pulses in the receiver. An improvement threshold is then established at which the signal/noise power ratio s/n at the receiver output is closely given by

$$s/n = 160(F_v t_m)^2 \frac{f_p}{f_h - f_l}$$

where t_m is the peak modulation displacement.

Pulse-code modulation: The output signal/noise ratio is extremely large after the improvement threshold is exceeded. However, because of the random nature of noise peaks, the exact threshold is indeterminate. The output

Pulse modulation   *continued*

signal/noise ratio in decibels can be closely given in terms of the input power ratio by

(decibels output s/n) $\approx$ 2.2 $\times$ (input s/n)

for a binary-PCM system.

For N-ary codes of orders greater than 2, the (NIF) is less than that for the binary code, and decreases with larger values of N.

The overall radio-frequency-transmission signal/noise ratio is determined by the product of the transmission and the pulse-subcarrier improvement factors. To calculate the overall output s/n ratio, the pulse-subcarrier signal/noise ratio is first determined using the radio-frequency modulation-improvement formula. This value of pulse s/n is substituted as the input s/n in the above equations.

Quantization

In generating pulse-code modulation, the process of quantization is introduced to enable the transformation of the sampled signal amplitude into a pulse code. This process divides the signal amplitude into a number of discrete levels. Quantization introduces a type of distortion that, because of its random nature, resembles noise. This distortion varies with the number of levels used to quantize the signal. The percent distortion D is given by

$$D = \frac{1}{\sqrt{6}\,L} \times 100$$

where L is the number of levels on one side of the zero axis.

Time-division multiplex

Pulse modulation is commonly used in time-division-multiplex systems. Because of the time space available between the modulated pulses, other pulses corresponding to other signal channels can be inserted if they are

Fig. 8—Time-multiplex train of subcarrier pulses for 8 channels and marker pulse *M* for synchronization of receiver with transmitter.

Pulse modulation   *continued*

in frequency synchronism. A multiplex train of pulses is shown in Fig. 8. It is common practice to use a channel or a portion of a channel for synchronization between the transmitter and the receiver. This pulse is shown as M in Fig. 8. This synchronizing pulse may be separated from the signal-carrying pulses by giving it some unique characteristic such as modulation at a submultiple of the sampling rate, wider duration, or by using two or more pulses with a fixed spacing.

An important characteristic of a multiplex system is the interchannel crosstalk. Such crosstalk can be kept to a reasonably low value by preventing excessive carryover between channel pulses.

Crosstalk between channels in a pulse-code-modulation system will arise if the carryover from the last pulse of a channel does not decay to one-half or less of the amplitude of the pulse at the time of the next channel.

For pulse-amplitude modulation, the requirement is more severe, since the crosstalk is directly proportional to the amplitude of the decaying pulse at the time of occurrence of the following channel. Thus if the pulse decays over a time T in an exponential manner, such as might be caused by transmission through a resistance-capacitance network, the crosstalk ratio is then

$$\text{crosstalk ratio} = \exp\left[2\pi F_v T\right]$$

where F_v is measured at the 3-decibel point.

For pulse-position modulation, the crosstalk ratio under the same conditions is

$$\text{crosstalk ratio} = \frac{\exp\left[2\pi F_v T\right]}{\sinh\left(2\pi F_v t_m\right)} \frac{t_m}{t_r}$$

■ Fourier waveform analysis

Real form of Fourier series

For functions defined in the interval $-\pi$ to $+\pi$ or 0 to 2π, as illustrated below,

$$f(x) = \frac{A_0}{2} + \sum_{n=1}^{n=\infty} (A_n \cos nx + B_n \sin nx) \quad x \text{ in radians} \tag{1}$$

$$= \frac{A_0}{2} + \sum_{n=1}^{n=\infty} C_n \cos (nx + \phi_n) \tag{2}$$

where

$$C_n = \sqrt{A_n^2 + B_n^2}$$

$$\phi_n = \tan^{-1} (-B_n/A_n)$$

The coefficients A_0, A_n, and B_n are determined by

$$A_0 = \frac{1}{\pi} \int_{-\pi}^{\pi} f(x) \, dx \qquad = \frac{1}{\pi} \int_0^{2\pi} f(x) \, dx \tag{3}$$

$$A_n = \frac{1}{\pi} \int_{-\pi}^{\pi} f(x) \cos nx \, dx = \frac{1}{\pi} \int_0^{2\pi} f(x) \cos nx \, dx \tag{4}$$

$$B_n = \frac{1}{\pi} \int_{-\pi}^{\pi} f(x) \sin nx \, dx = \frac{1}{\pi} \int_0^{2\pi} f(x) \sin nx \, dx \tag{5}$$

Arbitrary expansion interval

For functions defined in the intervals $-T/2$ to $+T/2$ or from 0 to T instead of from $-\pi$ to $+\pi$ or 0 to 2π, the Fourier expansion is given by

$$f(x) = \frac{A_0}{2} + \sum_{n=1}^{n=\infty} \left(A_n \cos 2n \frac{\pi}{T} x + B_n \sin 2n \frac{\pi}{T} x \right)$$

and the coefficients by

$$A_n = \frac{2}{T} \int_{-T/2}^{T/2} f(x) \cos \frac{2n\pi x}{T} \, dx = \frac{2}{T} \int_0^T f(x) \cos \frac{2n\pi x}{T} \, dx$$

$$B_n = \frac{2}{T} \int_{-T/2}^{T/2} f(x) \sin \frac{2n\pi x}{T} \, dx = \frac{2}{T} \int_0^T f(x) \sin \frac{2n\pi x}{T} \, dx$$

Complex form of Fourier series

For functions defined in the interval $-\pi$ to $+\pi$,

$$f(x) = \sum_{n=-\infty}^{n=+\infty} D_n e^{inx} \tag{6}$$

where

$$D_n = \frac{A_n - jB_n}{2}$$

$$D_{-n} = \frac{A_n + jB_n}{2}$$

$$D_0 = \frac{A_0}{2}$$

The summation is over negative as well as positive integral values of n, including zero.

$$D_n = \frac{1}{2\pi} \int_{-\pi}^{+\pi} f(x)\, e^{-inx}\, dx \tag{7}$$

where n takes on all positive and negative integral values including zero.

For the arbitrary expansion interval $-T/2$ to $T/2$ or 0 to T

$$f(x) = \sum_{n=-\infty}^{n=+\infty} D_n \exp\left[j\frac{2n\pi x}{T}\right]$$

$$D_n = \frac{1}{T} \int_0^T f(x) \exp\left[-j\frac{2n\pi x}{T}\right] dx$$

Periodic functions

When the function $f(x)$, such as shown in the illustration on page 291 is periodic, i.e., every value of the function is repeated after each 2π interval, then the Fourier expansions will continue to be valid throughout the whole range in which the functions are periodic.

Odd and even functions

If $f(x)$ is an odd function, i.e.,

$$f(x) = -f(-x)$$

Odd and even functions   *continued*

then all the coefficients of the cosine terms (A_n) vanish and the Fourier series consists of sine terms alone.

If $f(x)$ is an even function, i.e.,

$$f(x) = f(-x)$$

then all the coefficients of the sine terms (B_n) vanish and the Fourier series consists of cosine terms alone, and a possible constant.

The Fourier expansions of functions in general include both cosine and sine terms. Every function capable of Fourier expansion consists of the sum of an even and an odd part:

$$f(x) = \underbrace{\frac{A_0}{2} + \sum_{n=1}^{n=\infty} A_n \cos nx}_{\text{even}} + \underbrace{\sum_{n=1}^{n=\infty} B_n \sin nx}_{\text{odd}}$$

To separate a general function $f(x)$ into its odd and even parts, use

$$f(x) \equiv \underbrace{\frac{f(x) + f(-x)}{2}}_{\text{even}} + \underbrace{\frac{f(x) - f(-x)}{2}}_{\text{odd}}$$

Whenever possible choose the origin so that the function to be expanded is either odd or even.

Odd or even harmonics

An odd or even function may contain odd or even harmonics. The condition that causes a function $f(x)$ of period 2π to have only odd harmonics in its Fourier expansion is

$$f(x) = -f(x + \pi)$$

The condition that causes a function $f(x)$ of period 2π to have only even harmonics in the Fourier expansion is

$$f(x) = f(x + \pi)$$

To separate a general function $f(x)$ into its odd and even harmonics use

$$f(x) \equiv \underbrace{\frac{f(x) + f(x + \pi)}{2}}_{\text{even harmonics}} + \underbrace{\frac{f(x) - f(x + \pi)}{2}}_{\text{odd harmonics}}$$

Odd or even harmonics *continued*

A periodic function may sometimes be changed from odd to even, and vice versa, but the presence of particular odd or even harmonics is unchanged by such a shift.

Graphical solution

If the function to be analyzed is not known analytically, a solution of the Fourier integral may be approximated by graphical means.

The period of the function is divided into a number of ordinates as indicated by the graph.

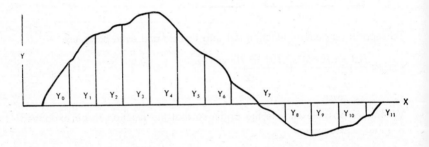

The values of these ordinates are recorded and the following computations made:

	Y_0	Y_1	Y_2	Y_3	Y_4	Y_5	Y_6	(8)
		Y_{11}	Y_{10}	Y_9	Y_8	Y_7		
Sum	S_0	S_1	S_2	S_3	S_4	S_5	S_6	
Difference		d_1	d_2	d_3	d_4	d_5		

The sum terms are arranged as follows:

	S_0	S_1	S_2	S_3	(9)
	S_6	S_5	S_4		
Sum	$\overline{S_0}$	$\overline{S_1}$	$\overline{S_2}$	$\overline{S_3}$	
Difference	D_0	D_1	D_2		

	$\overline{S_0}$	$\overline{S_1}$	(10)
	$\overline{S_2}$	$\overline{S_3}$	
	$\overline{S_7}$	$\overline{S_8}$	

Graphical solution   *continued*

The difference terms are as follows:

	d_1	d_2	d_3	(11)
	d_5	d_4		
Sum	$\overline{S_4}$	$\overline{S_5}$	$\overline{S_6}$	
Difference	D_3	D_4		

	(12)
$\overline{S_4}$	D_0
$\overline{S_6}$	D_2
D_5	D_6

The coefficients of the Fourier series are now obtained as follows, where A_0 equals the average value, the $B_{1....n}$ expressions represent the coefficients of the cosine terms, and the $A_{1.....n}$ expressions represent the coefficients of the sine terms:

$$B_0 = \frac{\overline{S_7} + \overline{S_8}}{12} \qquad (13)$$

$$B_1 = \frac{D_0 + 0.866\, D_1 + 0.5\, D_2}{6} \qquad (14)$$

$$B_2 = \frac{\overline{S_0} + 0.5\, \overline{S_1} - 0.5\, \overline{S_2} - \overline{S_3}}{6} \qquad (15)$$

$$B_3 = \frac{D_6}{6} \qquad (16)$$

$$B_4 = \frac{\overline{S_0} - 0.5\, \overline{S_1} - 0.5\, \overline{S_2} + \overline{S_3}}{6} \qquad (17)$$

$$B_5 = \frac{D_0 - 0.866\, D_1 + 0.5\, D_2}{6} \qquad (18)$$

$$B_6 = \frac{\overline{S_7} - \overline{S_8}}{12} \qquad (19)$$

Also

$$A_1 = \frac{0.5\, \overline{S_4} + 0.866\, \overline{S_5} + \overline{S_6}}{6} \qquad (20)$$

$$A_2 = \frac{0.866\,(D_3 + D_4)}{6} \qquad (21)$$

$$A_3 = \frac{D_5}{6} \qquad (22)$$

Graphical solution   *continued*

$$A_4 = \frac{0.866 \ (D_3 - D_4)}{6} \tag{23}$$

$$A_5 = \frac{0.5 \ \overline{S_4} - 0.866 \ \overline{S_5} + \overline{S_6}}{6} \tag{24}$$

Analyses of commonly encountered waveforms

The following analyses include the time function, the corresponding frequency function, and the coefficients of the Fourier series for all harmonics (nth order). The symbols used are

A = pulse amplitude

T = period

t_0 = pulse width

t_1 = pulse build-up time

t_2 = pulse decay time

n = order of harmonic

C_n = amplitude of nth harmonic

θ_n = phase angle of nth harmonic

A_{av} = average value of function

$$= \frac{1}{T} \int_0^T y(t) \ dt$$

A_{rms} = root-mean-square value of function

$$= \left\{ \frac{1}{T} \int_0^T [y(t)]^2 \ dt \right\}^{\frac{1}{2}}$$

The frequency function is a plot of the envelope of the amplitudes C_n of the harmonics versus frequency $F = 1/T$, with $1 \leqslant n \leqslant \infty$. The direct-current term is shown by A_{av}. The ratio $n = F/f_0 = t_0/T$ determines the number of harmonics that lie between $F = 0$ and $nF/f_0 = 1$.

As an example, consider a rectangular pulse where $A_{av} = A/4$ and $A_{rms} = A/2$. Then,

$$C_n = 2A_{av} \left(\frac{\sin \frac{\pi n F}{f_0}}{\pi n F / f_0} \right) = 2A_{av} \left(\frac{\sin \frac{\pi n}{4}}{\pi n / 4} \right)$$

Analyses of commonly encountered waveforms *continued*

It is seen that the even harmonics disappear. The amplitude coefficients may be read directly from the graph of the frequency function for the rectangular pulse.

n	nF/f_0	C_n/A_{av}	amplitudes
1	0.25	1.8	$C_1 = 0.45\ A$
2	0.50	1.35	$C_2 = 0.34\ A$
3	0.75	0.64	$C_3 = 0.16\ A$
4	1.00	0	$C_4 = 0$
etc			

The frequency function for this case is as shown at right.

Alternatively, the graph (as shown below) for the $(\sin x)/x$ function, where $y(x)$ is even, may be used to evaluate the amplitude coefficients.

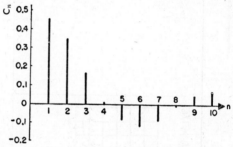

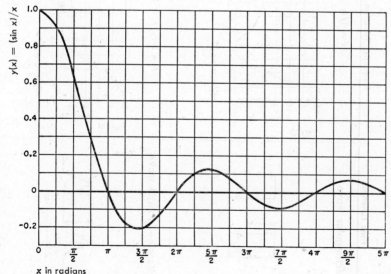

x in radians

continued

Analyses of commonly encountered waveforms

time function	frequency function	equations
Rectangular wave	$F = 1/T; \ f_0 = 1/t_0$ $nF/f_0 = nt_0/T$	$A_{av} = A \, t_0/T$ $A_{rms} = A\sqrt{t_0/T}$ $C_n = 2A_{av}\left(\dfrac{\sin \pi \, \dfrac{nt_0}{T}}{\pi n t_0/T}\right)$ $= 2A_{av}\left(\dfrac{\sin \pi \, \dfrac{nF}{f_0}}{\pi n F/f_0}\right)$
Isosceles-triangle wave	$F = 1/T; \ f_1 = 1/t_1 = 2f_0$ $nF/f_1 = nt_1/T$	$A_{av} = A \, t_1/T$ $A_{rms} = A\sqrt{2t_1/3T}$ $C_n = 2A_{av}\left(\dfrac{\sin \pi \, \dfrac{nt_1}{T}}{\pi n t_1/T}\right)^2$ $= 2A_{av}\left(\dfrac{\sin \pi \, \dfrac{nF}{f_1}}{\pi n F/f_1}\right)^2$

Sawtooth wave

$F = 1/T$; $f_0 = 1/t_0$

C_n/A_{av}

$nF/f_0 = nt_0/T$

$$A_{av} = \frac{A}{2}\frac{t_0}{T} \qquad A_{rms} = A\sqrt{\frac{t_0}{3T}}$$

$$C_n = \frac{4A_{av}}{\left(\frac{2\pi n t_0}{T}\right)^2}\left[2\left(1 - \cos\frac{2\pi n t_0}{T}\right) + \frac{2\pi n t_0}{T}\left(\frac{2\pi n t_0}{T} - 2\sin\frac{2\pi n t_0}{T}\right)\right]^{\frac{1}{2}}$$

$$= \frac{4A_{av}}{\left(2\pi\frac{nF}{f_0}\right)^2}\left[2\left(1 - \cos 2\pi\frac{nF}{f_0}\right) + 2\pi\frac{nF}{f_0}\left(2\pi\frac{nF}{f_0} - 2\sin 2\pi\frac{nF}{f_0}\right)\right]^{\frac{1}{2}}$$

If t_0 is small,

$$C_n = \frac{2A_{av}}{\pi nF/f_0}\left(\frac{\sin\pi\frac{nF}{f_0}}{\pi nF/f_0} - 1\right)$$

Clipped sawtooth wave

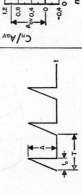

$F/f_0 = t_0/T = 1$

C_n/A_{av}

$$A_{av} = \frac{A}{2}$$

$$A_{rms} = \frac{A}{\sqrt{3}}$$

$$C_n = -2A_{av}\left(\frac{\cos\pi n}{\pi n}\right)$$

continued

Analyses of commonly encountered waveforms

time function	frequency function	equations

Half sine wave

$F = 1/T;\ f_0 = 1/t_0$

$\dfrac{nF}{f_0} = \dfrac{nt_0}{T}$

$$A_{av} = \frac{2A}{\pi}\frac{t_0}{T} \qquad A_{rms} = A\sqrt{\frac{t_0}{2T}}$$

$$C_n = \frac{\pi}{2}A_{av}\left[\frac{\sin\frac{\pi}{2}\left(1-\frac{2nt_0}{T}\right)}{\frac{\pi}{2}\left(1-\frac{2nt_0}{T}\right)} + \frac{\sin\frac{\pi}{2}\left(1+\frac{2nt_0}{T}\right)}{\frac{\pi}{2}\left(1+\frac{2nt_0}{T}\right)}\right]$$

$$= \frac{\pi}{2}A_{av}\left[\frac{\sin\frac{\pi}{2}\left(1-\frac{2nF}{f_0}\right)}{\frac{\pi}{2}\left(1-\frac{2nF}{f_0}\right)} + \frac{\sin\frac{\pi}{2}\left(1+\frac{2nF}{f_0}\right)}{\frac{\pi}{2}\left(1+\frac{2nF}{f_0}\right)}\right]$$

Full sine wave

$F = 1/T;\ f_0 = 1/t_0$

$\dfrac{nF}{f_0} = \dfrac{nt_0}{T}$

$$A_{av} = \frac{A}{2}\frac{t_0}{T} \qquad A_{rms} = \frac{A}{2}\sqrt{\frac{3t_0}{2T}}$$

$$C_n = A_{av}\left[\frac{\sin\pi\frac{nt_0}{T}}{2\,\pi\frac{nt_0}{T}} + \frac{\sin\pi\left(1-\frac{nt_0}{T}\right)}{\pi\left(1-\frac{nt_0}{T}\right)} + \frac{\sin\pi\left(1+\frac{nt_0}{T}\right)}{\pi\left(1+\frac{nt_0}{T}\right)}\right]$$

$$= A_{av}\left[\frac{\sin\pi\frac{nF}{f_0}}{2\,\frac{nF}{f_0}} + \frac{\sin\pi\left(1-\frac{nF}{f_0}\right)}{\pi\left(1-\frac{nF}{f_0}\right)} + \frac{\sin\pi\left(1+\frac{nF}{f_0}\right)}{\pi\left(1+\frac{nF}{f_0}\right)}\right]$$

Full-wave-rectified sine wave

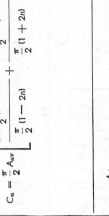

$F/f_0 = t_0/T = 1$

$$A_{av} = \frac{2}{\pi} A$$

$$A_{rms} = \frac{A}{\sqrt{2}}$$

$$C_n = \frac{\pi}{2} A_{av} \left[\frac{\sin^2 \frac{\pi}{2}(1-2n)}{\frac{\pi}{2}(1-2n)} + \frac{\sin^2 \frac{\pi}{2}(1+2n)}{\frac{\pi}{2}(1+2n)} \right]$$

Critically damped exponential wave

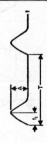

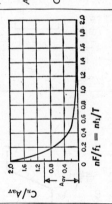

$F = 1/T;\ f_1 = 1/t_1$

$$y(t) = \frac{A\epsilon}{t_1} t\epsilon^{-t/t_1} \quad \text{for } T > 10t_1, \text{ where } \epsilon = 2.718$$

$$A_{av} = \frac{A\epsilon t_1}{T}$$

$$A_{rms} = \frac{A\epsilon}{2} \sqrt{\frac{t_1}{T}}$$

$$C_n = 2A_{av} \left[\frac{1}{1 + \left(2\pi \frac{nt_1}{T}\right)^2} \right] = 2A_{av} \left[\frac{1}{1 + \left(2\pi \frac{nF}{f_1}\right)^2} \right]$$

$$= 2A_{av} \cos^2 \frac{\theta_n}{2}$$

$$\frac{\theta_n}{2} = \tan^{-1}\left(2\pi \frac{nt_1}{T}\right) = \tan^{-1}\left(2\pi \frac{nF}{f_1}\right)$$

Analyses of commonly encountered waveforms

continued

time function	equations
Symmetrical trapezoid wave 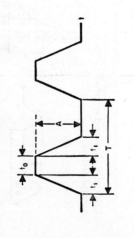	$A_{av} = A \dfrac{t_0 + t_1}{T}$ $\qquad A_{rms} = A \sqrt{\dfrac{3t_0 + 2t_1}{3T}}$ $C_n = 2A_{av}\left[\dfrac{\sin \pi \frac{nt_1}{T}}{\pi \frac{nt_1}{T}}\right]\left[\dfrac{\sin \pi \frac{n(t_0 + t_1)}{T}}{\pi \frac{n(t_0 + t_1)}{T}}\right]$ $= 2A_{av}\left[\dfrac{\sin \pi \frac{nF}{f_1}}{\frac{nF}{f_1}}\right]\left[\dfrac{\sin \pi nF\left(\frac{1}{f_0} + \frac{1}{f_1}\right)}{\pi nF\left(\frac{1}{f_0} + \frac{1}{f_1}\right)}\right]$
Unsymmetrical trapezoid wave 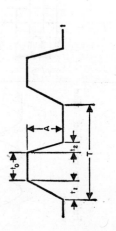	$A_{av} = \dfrac{A}{T}\left[t_0 + \dfrac{t_1}{2} + \dfrac{t_2}{2}\right]$ If $t_1 \approx t_2$ $\qquad A_{rms} = A \sqrt{\dfrac{3t_0 + t_1 + t_2}{3T}}$ $C_n = 2A_{av}\left[\dfrac{\sin \pi \frac{nt_1}{T}}{\pi \frac{nt_1}{T}}\right]\left[\dfrac{\sin \pi \frac{n(t_2 - t_1)}{T}}{\pi \frac{n(t_2 - t_1)}{T}}\right]\left[\dfrac{\sin \pi \frac{n(t_0 + t_1)}{T}}{\pi \frac{n(t_0 + t_1)}{T}}\right]$ $= 2A_{av}\left[\dfrac{\sin \pi \frac{nF}{f_1}}{\pi \frac{nF}{f_1}}\right]\left[\dfrac{\sin \pi nF\left(\frac{1}{f_0} + \frac{1}{f_1}\right)}{\pi nF\left(\frac{1}{f_0} + \frac{1}{f_1}\right)}\right]\left[\dfrac{\sin \pi nF\left(\frac{1}{f_2} - \frac{1}{f_1}\right)}{\pi nF\left(\frac{1}{f_2} - \frac{1}{f_1}\right)}\right]$

Fractional sine wave

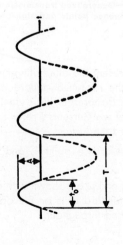

$$A_{av} = \frac{A\left(\sin\pi\frac{t_0}{T} - \pi\frac{t_0}{T}\cos\pi\frac{t_0}{T}\right)}{\pi\left(1 - \cos\pi\frac{t_0}{T}\right)}$$

$$A_{rms} = \frac{A}{\left(1 - \cos\pi\frac{t_0}{T}\right)}\left[\frac{1}{2\pi}\left(\pi\frac{t_0}{T} + \frac{1}{2}\sin 2\pi\frac{t_0}{T} - 4\cos\pi\frac{t_0}{T}\sin\pi\frac{t_0}{T} + 2\pi\frac{t_0}{T}\cos^2\pi\frac{t_0}{T}\right)\right]$$

$$C_n = \frac{A_{av}\,\pi\frac{t_0}{T}}{n\left(\sin\pi\frac{t_0}{T} - \pi\frac{t_0}{T}\cos\pi\frac{t_0}{T}\right)}\left[\frac{\sin\pi(n-1)\frac{t_0}{T}}{\pi(n-1)\frac{t_0}{T}} - \frac{\sin\pi(n+1)\frac{t_0}{T}}{\pi(n+1)\frac{t_0}{T}}\right]$$

$$= \frac{A_{av}\,\pi\frac{F}{f_0}}{n\left(\sin\pi\frac{F}{f_0} - \pi\frac{F}{f_0}\cos\pi\frac{F}{f_0}\right)}\left[\frac{\sin\pi(n-1)\frac{F}{f_0}}{\pi(n-1)\frac{F}{f_0}} - \frac{\sin\pi(n+1)\frac{F}{f_0}}{\pi(n+1)\frac{F}{f_0}}\right]$$

Sawtooth wave

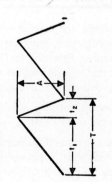

$$A_{av} = \frac{A}{2} \qquad A_{rms} = \frac{A}{\sqrt{3}}$$

$$C_n = \frac{2A_{av}}{\pi^2 n^2 \frac{t_1}{T}}\left(1 - \frac{t_1}{T}\right)\sin\pi\frac{t_1}{T}$$

$$= \frac{2A_{av}}{\pi^2 n^2 \frac{F}{f_1}}\left(1 - \frac{F}{f_1}\right)\sin\pi\frac{F}{f_1}$$

■ Transmission lines

General

The formulas compiled below apply to transmission lines in the steady state. They give the voltage, impedance, etc., at a point 2 on the line with respect to the values at a reference point 1 (Fig. 1). Point 2 may be either on the source side or on the load side of 1, provided in the latter case, that a minus sign is placed before x and θ in the formulas. The minus sign may then be cleared through the hyperbolic or circular functions; thus,

$$\sinh(-\gamma x) = -\sinh \gamma x, \text{ etc.}$$

The formulas for small attenuation are obtained by neglecting the terms $\alpha^2 x^2$ and higher powers in the expansions of ϵ^{ax}, etc. Thus, when

$$\alpha x = \frac{\alpha}{\beta} \theta = 0.1 \text{ neper}$$

(or about 1 decibel), the error in the approximate formulas is of the order of 1 percent.

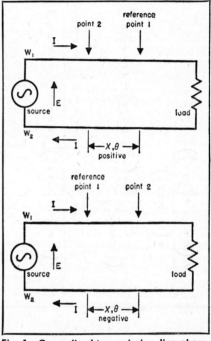

Fig. 1—Generalized transmission line showing reference points and sign conventions.

Symbols and sign conventions

Voltage and current symbols usually represent the alternating-current complex sinusoid, with magnitude equal to the root-mean-square value of the quantity. Referring to Fig. 1, all voltages E represent the potential of conductor w_1 with respect to the potential of w_2. Currents I refer to current in w_1, and are positive when flowing toward the load.

Symbols carrying subscript 1 refer to reference point 1, and subscript 2 to the other point, 2.

Certain quantities, namely C, c, f, L, T, v, and ω are shown with an optional set of units in parentheses. Either the standard units or the optional units may be used, provided the same set is used throughout.

Symbols and sign conventions   *continued*

B_m = susceptive component of Y_m in mhos

C = capacitance of line in farads/unit length (microfarads/unit length)

c = velocity of light in units of length/second (units of length/microsecond)

E = voltage (root-mean-square complex sinusoid) in volts

$_fE$ = voltage of forward wave, traveling toward load

$_rE$ = voltage of reflected wave

$|E_{flat}|$ = root-mean-square voltage when standing-wave ratio = 1.0

$|E_{max}|$ = root-mean-square voltage at crest of standing wave

$|E_{min}|$ = root-mean-square voltage at trough of standing wave

e = instantaneous voltage

f = frequency in cycles/second (megacycles/second)

G = conductance of line in mhos/unit length

G_m = conductive component of Y_m in mhos

$g_a = Y_a/Y_0$ = normalized admittance at voltage standing-wave maximum

$g_b = Y_b/Y_0$ = normalized admittance at voltage standing-wave minimum

I = current (root-mean-square complex sinusoid) in amperes

$_fI$ = current of forward wave, traveling toward load

$_rI$ = current of reflected wave

i = instantaneous current

L = inductance of line in henries/unit length (microhenries/unit length)

P = power in watts

$(pf) = G/\omega C$ = power factor of dielectric

R = resistance of line in ohms/unit length

R_m = resistive component of Z_m in ohms

$r_a = Z_a/Z_0$ = normalized impedance at voltage standing-wave maximum

$r_b = Z_b/Z_0$ = normalized impedance at voltage standing-wave minimum

306

(swr) = voltage standing-wave ratio

T = delay of line in seconds/unit length (microseconds/unit length)

v = phase velocity of propagation in units of length/second (units of length/microsecond)

X_m = reactive component of Z_m in ohms

x = distance between points 1 and 2 in units of length (see Fig. 1 regarding signs)

$Y_1 = G_1 + jB_1 = 1/Z_1$ = admittance in mhos looking toward load from point 1

$Y_0 = G_0 + jB_0 = 1/Z_0$ = characteristic admittance of line in mhos

$Z_1 = R_1 + jX_1$ = impedance in ohms looking toward load from point 1

$Z_0 = R_0 + jX_0$ = characteristic impedance of line in ohms

Z_{oc} = input impedance of a line open-circuited at the far end

Z_{sc} = input impedance of a line short-circuited at the far end

α = attenuation constant = nepers/unit length
$= 0.1151 \times$ decibels/unit length

β = phase constant in radians/unit length

$\Gamma = |\Gamma| \underline{/2\psi}$ = reflection coefficient

$\gamma = \alpha + j\beta$ = propagation constant

ϵ = base of natural logarithms = 2.718; or dielectric constant of medium (relative to air), according to context

η = efficiency (fractional)

$\theta = \beta x$ = electrical length or angle of line in radians

$\theta° = 57.3\theta$ = electrical angle of line in degrees

λ = wavelength in units of length

λ_0 = wavelength in free space

ϕ = time phase angle of complex voltage at voltage standing-wave maximum

ψ = half the angle of the reflection coefficient = electrical angle to nearest voltage standing-wave maximum toward source

$\omega = 2\pi f$ = angular velocity in radians/second (radians/microsecond)

Fundamental quantities and line parameters

$$dE/dx = (R + j\omega L)I$$
$$d^2E/dx^2 = \gamma^2 E$$
$$dI/dx = (G + j\omega C)E$$
$$d^2I/dx^2 = \gamma^2 I$$
$$\gamma = \alpha + j\beta = \sqrt{(R + j\omega L)(G + j\omega C)}$$
$$= j\omega\sqrt{LC}\sqrt{(1 - jR/\omega L)(1 - jG/\omega C)}$$
$$\alpha = \{\tfrac{1}{2}[\sqrt{(R^2 + \omega^2 L^2)(G^2 + \omega^2 C^2)} + RG - \omega^2 LC]\}^{\frac{1}{2}}$$
$$\beta = \{\tfrac{1}{2}[\sqrt{(R^2 + \omega^2 L^2)(G^2 + \omega^2 C^2)} - RG + \omega^2 LC]\}^{\frac{1}{2}}$$
$$\gamma x = \alpha x + j\beta x = \frac{\alpha}{\beta}\theta + j\theta$$
$$\theta = \beta x = 2\pi x/\lambda = 2\pi fTx$$
$$\theta° = 57.3\theta = 360 x/\lambda = 360 fTx$$
$$Z_0 = \frac{1}{Y_0} = \sqrt{\frac{R + j\omega L}{G + j\omega C}} = \sqrt{\frac{L}{C}} \times \sqrt{\frac{1 - jR/\omega L}{1 - jG/\omega C}} = R_0\left(1 + j\frac{X_0}{R_0}\right)$$
$$Y_0 = 1/Z_0 = G_0(1 + j B_0/G_0)$$
$$1/T = v = f\lambda = \omega/\beta$$
$$\beta = \omega/v = \omega T = 2\pi/\lambda$$

a. Special case—distortionless line: when $R/L = G/C$, the quantities Z_0 and α are independent of frequency

$$X_0 = 0$$
$$\alpha = R/R_0$$
$$Z_0 = R_0 + j0 = \sqrt{L/C}$$
$$\beta = \omega\sqrt{LC}$$

b. For small attenuation: $R/\omega L$ and $G/\omega C$ are small

$$\gamma = j\omega\sqrt{LC}\left[1 - j\left(\frac{R}{2\omega L} + \frac{G}{2\omega C}\right)\right] = j\beta\left(1 - j\frac{\alpha}{\beta}\right)$$
$$\beta = \omega\sqrt{LC}$$
$$T = 1/v = \sqrt{LC}$$
$$\frac{\alpha}{\beta} = \frac{R}{2\omega L} + \frac{G}{2\omega C} = \frac{R}{2\omega L} + \frac{(pf)}{2} = \text{attenuation in nepers/ radian}$$

Fundamental quantities and line parameters   *continued*

$$\alpha = \frac{R}{2}\sqrt{\frac{C}{L}} + \frac{G}{2}\sqrt{\frac{L}{C}} = \frac{R}{2R_0} + \pi\frac{(pf)}{\lambda} = \frac{R}{2R_0} + \frac{(pf)\beta}{2}$$

where R and G vary with frequency, while L, C, and (pf) are nearly independent of frequency.

$$Z_0 = \frac{1}{Y_0} = \sqrt{\frac{L}{C}}\left[1 - j\left(\frac{R}{2\omega L} - \frac{G}{2\omega C}\right)\right] = R_0\left(1 + j\frac{X_0}{R_0}\right)$$

$$= \frac{1}{G_0(1 + j\,B_0/G_0)} = \frac{1}{G_0}\left(1 - j\frac{B_0}{G_0}\right)$$

$$R_0 = 1/G_0 = \sqrt{L/C}$$

$$\frac{B_0}{G_0} = -\frac{X_0}{R_0} = \frac{R}{2\omega L} - \frac{(pf)}{2}$$

$$X_0 = -\frac{R}{2\omega\sqrt{LC}} + \frac{G}{2\omega C}\sqrt{\frac{L}{C}} = -\frac{R\lambda}{4\pi} + \frac{(pf)}{2}R_0$$

$$\left.\begin{array}{l} L = 1.016\,R_0\sqrt{\epsilon} \times 10^{-3}\ \text{microhenries/foot} \\[4pt] \quad = \tfrac{1}{3}R_0\sqrt{\epsilon} \times 10^{-4}\ \text{microhenries/centimeter} \\[4pt] C = 1.016\,\dfrac{\sqrt{\epsilon}}{R_0} \times 10^{-3}\ \text{microfarads/foot} \\[4pt] \quad = \dfrac{\sqrt{\epsilon}}{3R_0} \times 10^{-4}\ \text{microfarads/centimeter} \\[4pt] v/c = 1/\sqrt{\epsilon} \\[4pt] \lambda = \lambda_0\,v/c = c/f\sqrt{\epsilon} \end{array}\right\} \begin{array}{l} \epsilon = \text{ dielectric constant} \\ \quad\ \text{relative to air} \end{array}$$

Voltages and currents

$$E_2 = {_f}E_2 + {_r}E_2 = {_f}E_1\epsilon^{\gamma x} + {_r}E_1\epsilon^{-\gamma x} = E_1\left(\frac{Z_1 + Z_0}{2Z_1}\epsilon^{\gamma x} + \frac{Z_1 - Z_0}{2Z_1}\epsilon^{-\gamma x}\right)$$

$$= \frac{E_1 + I_1 Z_0}{2}\epsilon^{\gamma x} + \frac{E_1 - I_1 Z_0}{2}\epsilon^{-\gamma x}$$

$$= E_1\left[\cosh\gamma x + (Z_0/Z_1)\sinh\gamma x\right] = E_1\cosh\gamma x + I_1 Z_0\sinh\gamma x$$

$$= \frac{E_1}{1 + \Gamma_1}\left(\epsilon^{\gamma x} + \Gamma_1\epsilon^{-\gamma x}\right)$$

Voltages and currents *continued*

$$I_2 = {}_fI_2 + {}_rI_2 = {}_fI_1\epsilon^{\gamma x} + {}_rI_1\epsilon^{-\gamma x} = Y_0({}_fE_1\epsilon^{\gamma x} - {}_rE_1\epsilon^{-\gamma x})$$

$$= I_1\left(\frac{Z_0 + Z_1}{2Z_0}\epsilon^{\gamma x} + \frac{Z_0 - Z_1}{2Z_0}\epsilon^{-\gamma x}\right) = \frac{I_1 + E_1Y_0}{2}\epsilon^{\gamma x} + \frac{I_1 - E_1Y_0}{2}\epsilon^{-\gamma x}$$

$$= I_1\left(\cosh \gamma x + \frac{Z_1}{Z_0}\sinh \gamma x\right)$$

$$= I_1\cosh \gamma x + E_1Y_0\sinh \gamma x = \frac{I_1}{1 - \Gamma_1}(\epsilon^{\gamma x} - \Gamma_1\epsilon^{-\gamma x})$$

a. When point No. 1 is at a voltage maximum or minimum; x' is measured from voltage maximum and x'' from voltage minimum:

$$E_2 = E_{max}\left[\cosh \gamma x' + \frac{1}{(swr)}\sinh \gamma x'\right]$$

$$= E_{min}[\cosh \gamma x'' + (swr)\sinh \gamma x'']$$

$$I_2 = I_{max}\left[\cosh \gamma x' + \frac{1}{(swr)}\sinh \gamma x'\right]$$

$$= I_{min}[\cosh \gamma x'' + (swr)\sinh \gamma x'']$$

When attenuation is neglected:

$$E_2 = E_{max}\left[\cos \theta' + j\frac{1}{(swr)}\sin \theta'\right]$$

$$= E_{min}[\cos \theta'' + j(swr)\sin \theta'']$$

b. Letting Z_l = impedance of load, l = distance from load to No. 1, and x_l = distance from load to No. 2:

$$E_2 = E_1\frac{\cosh \gamma x_l + (Z_0/Z_l)\sinh \gamma x_l}{\cosh \gamma l + (Z_0/Z_l)\sinh \gamma l}$$

$$I_2 = I_1\frac{\cosh \gamma x_l + (Z_l/Z_0)\sinh \gamma x_l}{\cosh \gamma l + (Z_l/Z_0)\sinh \gamma l}$$

c. $e_2 = \sqrt{2}\,|{}_fE_1|\epsilon^{\alpha x}\sin\left(\omega t + 2\pi\frac{x}{\lambda} - \psi_1 + \phi\right)$

$$+ \sqrt{2}\,|{}_rE_1|\,\epsilon^{-\alpha x}\sin\left(\omega t - 2\pi\frac{x}{\lambda} + \psi_1 + \phi\right)$$

Voltages and currents *continued*

$$i_2 = \sqrt{2}\,|{}_fI_1|\,\epsilon^{\alpha x} \sin\left(\omega t + 2\pi\frac{x}{\lambda} - \psi_1 + \phi + \tan^{-1}\frac{B_0}{G_0}\right) + \sqrt{2}\,|{}_rI_1|\epsilon^{-\alpha x} \sin\left(\omega t - 2\pi\frac{x}{\lambda} + \psi_1 + \phi + \tan^{-1}\frac{B_0}{G_0}\right)$$

d. For small attenuation:

$$E_2 = E_1\left[\left(1 + \frac{Z_0}{Z_1}\alpha x\right)\cos\theta + j\left(\frac{Z_0}{Z_1} + \alpha x\right)\sin\theta\right]$$

$$I_2 = I_1\left[\left(1 + \frac{Z_1}{Z_0}\alpha x\right)\cos\theta + j\left(\frac{Z_1}{Z_0} + \alpha x\right)\sin\theta\right]$$

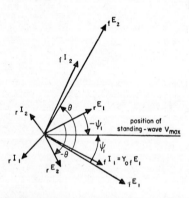

Fig. 2—Diagram of complex voltages and currents at two fixed points on a line with considerable attenuation. (Diagram rotates counterclockwise with time.)

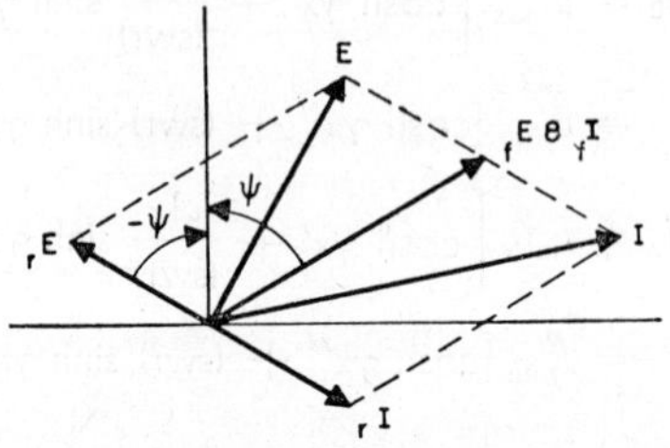

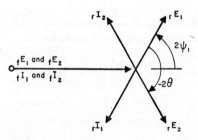

Fig. 3—Voltages and currents at time t=0 at a point ψ electrical degrees toward the load from a voltage standing-wave maximum.

Fig. 4—Abbreviated diagram of a line with zero attenuation.

e. When attenuation is neglected:

$$\begin{aligned} E_2 &= E_1\cos\theta + jI_1Z_0\sin\theta \\ &= E_1[\cos\theta + j(Y_1/Y_0)\sin\theta] \\ &= {}_fE_1\epsilon^{j\theta} + {}_rE_1\epsilon^{-j\theta} \end{aligned}$$

$$\begin{aligned} I_2 &= I_1\cos\theta + jE_1Y_0\sin\theta = I_1[\cos\theta + j(Z_1/Z_0)\sin\theta] \\ &= Y_0({}_fE_1\epsilon^{j\theta} - {}_rE_1\epsilon^{-j\theta}) \end{aligned}$$

Impedances and admittances

$$\frac{Z_2}{Z_0} = \frac{Z_1 \cosh \gamma x + Z_0 \sinh \gamma x}{Z_0 \cosh \gamma x + Z_1 \sinh \gamma x}$$

$$\frac{Y_2}{Y_0} = \frac{Y_1 \cosh \gamma x + Y_0 \sinh \gamma x}{Y_0 \cosh \gamma x + Y_1 \sinh \gamma x}$$

a. When $Z_2 = $ load impedance Z_l, and $-x = $ distance l from No. 1 to load:

$$\frac{Z_l}{Z_0} = \frac{Z_1 \cosh \gamma l - Z_0 \sinh \gamma l}{Z_0 \cosh \gamma l - Z_1 \sinh \gamma l}$$

b. The input impedance of a line at a position of maximum or minimum voltage has the same phase angle as the characteristic impedance:

$$\frac{Z_1}{Z_0} = \frac{Z_b}{Z_0} = \frac{Y_0}{Y_b} = r_b + j0 = \frac{1}{(\text{swr})} \text{ at a voltage minimum (current maximum)}.$$

$$\frac{Y_1}{Y_0} = \frac{Y_a}{Z_0} = \frac{Z_0}{Z_a} = g_a + j0 = \frac{1}{(\text{swr})} \text{ at a voltage maximum (current minimum)}.$$

c. When attenuation is small:

$$\frac{Z_2}{Z_0} = \frac{\left(\dfrac{Z_1}{Z_0} + \alpha x\right) + j\left(1 + \dfrac{Z_1}{Z_0}\alpha x\right)\tan\theta}{\left(1 + \dfrac{Z_1}{Z_0}\alpha x\right) + j\left(\dfrac{Z_1}{Z_0} + \alpha x\right)\tan\theta}$$

For admittances, replace Z_0, Z_1, and Z_2 by Y_0, Y_1, and Y_2, respectively.

When A and B are real:

$$\frac{A \pm jB \tan\theta}{B \pm jA \tan\theta} = \frac{2AB \pm j(B^2 - A^2)\sin 2\theta}{(B^2 + A^2) + (B^2 - A^2)\cos 2\theta}$$

d. When attenuation is neglected:

$$\frac{Z_2}{Z_0} = \frac{Z_1/Z_0 + j\tan\theta}{1 + j(Z_1/Z_0)\tan\theta} = \frac{1 - j(Z_1/Z_0)\cot\theta}{Z_1/Z_0 - j\cot\theta}$$

and similarly for admittances.

e. When attenuation $\alpha x = \theta\alpha/\beta$ is small and (swr) is large (say >10):

For θ measured from a voltage minimum

Impedances and admittances   *continued*

$$\frac{Z_2}{Z_0} = \left(r_b + \frac{\alpha}{\beta}\theta\right)(1 + \tan^2\theta) + j\tan\theta = \left(r_b + \frac{\alpha}{\beta}\theta\right)\frac{1}{\cos^2\theta} + j\tan\theta$$

(See Note 1)

$$\frac{Z_0}{Z_2} = \frac{Y_2}{Y_0} = \left(r_b + \frac{\alpha}{\beta}\theta\right)(1 + \cot^2\theta) - j\cot\theta$$

$$= \left(r_b + \frac{\alpha}{\beta}\theta\right)\frac{1}{\sin^2\theta} - j\cot\theta$$

(See Note 2)

For θ measured from a voltage maximum

$$\frac{Z_0}{Z_2} = \frac{Y_2}{Y_0} = \left(g_a + \frac{\alpha}{\beta}\theta\right)(1 + \tan^2\theta) + j\tan\theta \qquad \text{(See Note 1)}$$

$$\frac{Z_2}{Z_0} = \left(g_a + \frac{\alpha}{\beta}\theta\right)(1 + \cot^2\theta) - j\cot\theta \qquad \text{(See Note 2)}$$

Note 1: Not valid when $\theta \approx \pi/2$, $3\pi/2$, etc., due to approximation in denominator $1 + (r_b + \theta\alpha/\beta)^2 \tan^2\theta = 1$ (or with g_a in place of r_b).

Note 2: Not valid when $\theta \approx 0$, π, 2π, etc., due to approximation in denominator $1 + (r_b + \theta\alpha/\beta)^2 \cot^2\theta = 1$ (or with g_a in place of r_b). For open- or short-circuited line, valid at $\theta = 0$.

f. When x is an integral multiple of $\lambda/2$ or $\lambda/4$. For $x = n\lambda/2$, or $\theta = n\pi$,

$$\frac{Z_2}{Z_0} = \frac{\dfrac{Z_1}{Z_0} + \tanh n\pi\dfrac{\alpha}{\beta}}{1 + \dfrac{Z_1}{Z_0}\tanh n\pi\dfrac{\alpha}{\beta}}$$

For $x = n\lambda/2 + \lambda/4$, or $\theta = (n + \frac{1}{2})\pi$

$$\frac{Z_2}{Z_0} = \frac{1 + \dfrac{Z_1}{Z_0}\tanh(n + \frac{1}{2})\pi\dfrac{\alpha}{\beta}}{\dfrac{Z_1}{Z_0} + \tanh(n + \frac{1}{2})\pi\dfrac{\alpha}{\beta}}$$

g. For small attenuation, with any standing-wave ratio: For $x = n\lambda/2$, or $\theta = n\pi$, where n is an integer

$$\frac{Z_2}{Z_0} = \frac{\dfrac{Z_1}{Z_0} + n\pi\dfrac{\alpha}{\beta}}{1 + \dfrac{Z_1}{Z_0}n\pi\dfrac{\alpha}{\beta}}$$

Impedances and admittances   *continued*

$$g_{a2} = \frac{g_{a1} + \alpha n\lambda/2}{1 + g_{a1}\alpha n\lambda/2} = \frac{1}{(\text{swr})_2}$$

For $x = (n + \tfrac{1}{2})\lambda/2$, or $\theta = (n + \tfrac{1}{2})\pi$, where n is an integer

$$\frac{Z_2}{Z_0} = \frac{1 + \dfrac{Z_1}{Z_0}(n + \tfrac{1}{2})\alpha\dfrac{\lambda}{2}}{\dfrac{Z_1}{Z_0} + (n + \tfrac{1}{2})\alpha\dfrac{\lambda}{2}}$$

$$g_{b2} = \frac{1 + g_{a1}(n + \tfrac{1}{2})\dfrac{\alpha}{\beta}\pi}{g_{a1} + (n + \tfrac{1}{2})\dfrac{\alpha}{\beta}\pi} = (\text{swr})_2$$

Subscript a refers to the voltage-maximum point and b to the voltage minimum. In the above formulas, the subscripts a and b may be interchanged, and/or r may be substituted in place of g.

Lines open- or short-circuited at the far end

Point No. 1 is the open- or short-circuited end of the line, from which x and θ are measured.

a. Voltages and currents:

Use formulas of "Voltages and currents" section p. 308 with the following conditions

Open-circuited line: $\Gamma_1 = 1.00\,\underline{/0°} = 1.00;$ $_rE_1 = {}_fE_1 = E_1/2;$
$_rI_1 = -{}_fI_1;$ $I_1 = 0;$ $Z_1 = \infty.$
Short-circuited line: $\Gamma_1 = 1.00\,\underline{/180°} = -1.00;$ $_rE_1 = -{}_fE_1;$
$E_1 = 0;$ $_rI_1 = {}_fI_1 = I_1/2;$ $Z_1 = 0.$

b. Impedances and admittances:

$Z_{oc} = Z_0 \coth \gamma x$

$Z_{sc} = Z_0 \tanh \gamma x$

$Y_{oc} = Y_0 \tanh \gamma x$

$Y_{sc} = Y_0 \coth \gamma x$

Lines open- or short-circuited at the far end *continued*

c. For small attenuation:

Use formulas for large (swr) in paragraph e, pp. 311–312, with the following conditions

Open-circuited line: $g_a = 0$

Short-circuited line: $r_b = 0$

d. When attenuation is neglected:

$Z_{oc} = -jR_0 \cot \theta$

$Z_{sc} = jR_0 \tan \theta$

$Y_{oc} = jG_0 \tan \theta$

$Y_{sc} = -jG_0 \cot \theta$

e. Relationships between Z_{oc} and Z_{sc}:

$$\sqrt{Z_{oc}Z_{sc}} = Z_0$$

$$\pm\sqrt{Z_{sc}/Z_{oc}} = \tanh \gamma x \approx \frac{\alpha}{\beta} \theta (1 + \tan^2 \theta) + j \tan \theta = \frac{\alpha\theta}{\beta \cos^2 \theta} + j \tan \theta$$

$$\approx j \tan \theta \left[1 - j\frac{\alpha}{\beta} \theta (\tan \theta + \cot \theta) \right] = j \tan \theta \left(1 - j\frac{\alpha}{\beta} \frac{2\theta}{\sin 2\theta} \right)$$

Note: Above approximations not valid for $\theta \approx \pi/2$, $3\pi/2$, etc.

$$\pm\sqrt{Z_{oc}/Z_{sc}} = \coth \gamma x \approx \frac{\alpha}{\beta} \theta (1 + \cot^2 \theta) - j \cot \theta = \frac{\alpha\theta}{\beta \sin^2 \theta} - j \cot \theta$$

$$\approx -j \cot \theta \left[1 + j\frac{\alpha}{\beta} \theta (\tan \theta + \cot \theta) \right] = - j \cot \theta \left(1 + j\frac{\alpha}{\beta} \frac{2\theta}{\sin 2\theta} \right)$$

Note: Above approximations not valid for $\theta \approx \pi$, 2π, etc.

f. When attenuation is small (except for $\theta \approx n\pi/2$, $n = 1, 2, 3 \ldots$):

$$\pm\sqrt{\frac{Z_{sc}}{Z_{oc}}} = \pm\sqrt{\frac{Y_{oc}}{Y_{sc}}} = \pm j \sqrt{-\frac{C_{oc}}{C_{sc}}} \left[1 - j\frac{1}{2} \left(\frac{G_{oc}}{\omega C_{oc}} - \frac{G_{sc}}{\omega C_{sc}} \right) \right]$$

Where $Y_{oc} = G_{oc} + j\omega C_{oc}$ and $Y_{sc} = G_{sc} + j\omega C_{sc}$. The $+$ sign is to be used before the radical when C_{oc} is positive, and the $-$ sign when C_{oc} is negative.

Lines open- or short-circuited at the far end *continued*

g. $R/|X|$ component of input impedance of low-attenuation nonresonant line:

Short-circuited line (except when $\theta \approx \pi/2, 3\pi/2$, etc.)

$$\frac{R_2}{|X_2|} = \frac{G_2}{|B_2|} = \left| \frac{\alpha}{\beta} \theta (\tan \theta + \cot \theta) + \frac{B_0}{G_0} \right| = \left| \frac{\alpha}{\beta} \frac{2\theta}{\sin 2\theta} + \frac{B_0}{G_0} \right|$$

Open-circuited line (except when $\theta \approx \pi, 2\pi$, etc.)

$$\frac{R_2}{|X_2|} = \frac{G_2}{|B_2|} = \left| \frac{\alpha}{\beta} \theta (\tan \theta + \cot \theta) - \frac{B_0}{G_0} \right| = \left| \frac{\alpha}{\beta} \frac{2\theta}{\sin 2\theta} - \frac{B_0}{G_0} \right|$$

h. Input admittance and lumped-circuit equivalent of resonant low-loss lines:

$\theta = n\pi/2 =$ length of line at resonance frequency f_0

$n = 1, 2, 3 \ldots$ even or odd as stated in Fig. 5

θ_1 or $\pi/2 - \theta_1$ is electrical length at f_0 from end of line to tap point

The admittance looking into the line at the tap point θ_1 is approximately

$$Y = G + jB = \frac{n\pi Y_0}{2 \sin^2 \theta_1} \left(\frac{\alpha}{\beta} + j \frac{\Delta f}{f_0} \right) = \frac{n\pi Y_0}{4 \sin^2 \theta_1} \left(\frac{1}{Q} + j \frac{2\Delta f}{f_0} \right)$$

provided $\Delta f/f_0 = (f - f_0)/f_0$ is small. Formula not valid when

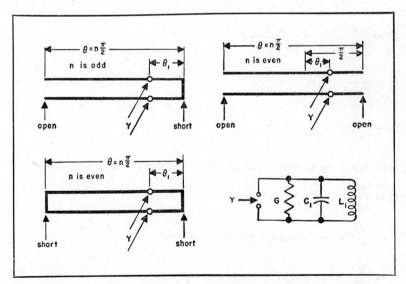

Fig. 5—Resonant low-loss transmission lines and their equivalent lumped circuit.

Lines open- or short-circuited at the far end   *continued*

$\theta_1 = 0$, π, 2π, etc. A further condition for its accuracy is that

$$\left| \theta \frac{\Delta f}{f_0} \cot \theta_1 \right| \ll 1.0$$

Such a resonant line is approximately equivalent to a lumped *LCG* parallel circuit, where

$$\omega_0{}^2 L_1 C_1 = (2\pi f_0)^2 L_1 C_1 = 1$$

Admittance of the equivalent **circuit is**

$$Y = G + j\left(\omega C_1 - \frac{1}{\omega L_1} \right)$$

$$\approx \omega_0 C_1 \left(\frac{1}{Q} + j\frac{2\Delta f}{f_0} \right)$$

Then, subject to the conditions stated above,

$$L_1 = \frac{4 \sin^2 \theta_1}{n\pi\omega_0 Y_0}$$

$$C_1 = \frac{n\pi Y_0}{4\omega_0 \sin^2 \theta_1} = \frac{nY_0}{8f_0 \sin^2 \theta_1}$$

$$G = \frac{n\pi Y_0}{2 \sin^2 \theta_1} \frac{\alpha}{\beta} = \frac{n\pi Y_0}{4Q \sin^2 \theta_1}$$

$$Q = \frac{\omega_0 C_1}{G} = \frac{1}{\omega_0 L_1 G} = \frac{\beta}{2\alpha}$$

Referring to the section above on "Fundamental quantities", page 307,

$$Q = \frac{\beta}{2\alpha}$$

$$= \frac{\omega L}{R} \quad \text{when dielectric losses are negligible}$$

$$= \frac{1}{(pf)} \quad \text{when conductor losses are negligible} \\ \text{compared to dielectric losses}$$

Lines open- or short-circuited at the far end   *continued*

Example: Find the equivalent circuit of a resonant $\lambda/4$ line shorted at one end, open at the other, if the line has a characteristic impedance of 70 ohms, a measured Q of 1000, is tapped at a point 10 electrical degrees from the shorted end, and is resonant at 200 megacycles.

From the data,

$Y_0 = 1/70$, $Q = 1000$, $\theta_1 = 10°$, $\sin \theta_1 = 0.174$, $\omega_0 = 12.57 \times 10^8$, and $n = 1$; therefore

$$L_1 = \frac{4(0.174)^2}{\pi(12.57) \times 10^8/70} = 2.15 \times 10^{-9} \text{ henry, or 2.15 millimicrohenries}$$

$$C_1 = \frac{\pi/70}{4(12.57) \times 10^8 (0.174)^2} = 2.95 \times 10^{-10} \text{ farad, or 295 micromicro-farads}$$

$$G = \frac{\pi/70}{4(1000)(0.174)^2} = 3.70 \times 10^{-4} \text{ mho, or 370 micromhos}$$

Reflection coefficient, standing-wave ratio, and power

$$\Gamma_1 = \frac{rE_1}{fE_1} = -\frac{rI_1}{fI_1} = \frac{Z_1 - Z_0}{Z_1 + Z_0} = \frac{Y_0 - Y_1}{Y_0 + Y_1} = |\Gamma_1| \underline{/2\psi_1}$$

where ψ_1 is the electrical angle to the nearest voltage maximum on the generator side of point No. 1 (Figs. 2, 3, and 4).

$$\Gamma_2 = \Gamma_1 \epsilon^{-2ax} \underline{/-2\theta}$$

$$|\Gamma_2| = |\Gamma_1|/10^{db/10}$$

$$Z_1 = \frac{E_1}{I_1} = \frac{fE_1 + rE_1}{fI_1 + rI_1} = Z_0 \frac{1 + \Gamma_1}{1 - \Gamma_1}$$

$$\frac{Z_2}{Z_0} = \frac{1 + \Gamma_2}{1 - \Gamma_2} = \frac{1 + |\Gamma_1| \underline{/2\psi_1 - 2\theta}}{1 - |\Gamma_1| \underline{/2\psi_1 - 2\theta}} \quad \text{(neglecting attenuation)}$$

$$(\text{swr}) = \left|\frac{E_{max}}{E_{min}}\right| = \left|\frac{I_{max}}{I_{min}}\right| = \left|\frac{fE| + |rE}{fE| - |rE}\right| = \left|\frac{fI| + |rI}{fI| - |rI}\right|$$

$$= \frac{1 + |\Gamma|}{1 - |\Gamma|} = r_a = \frac{1}{g_a} = g_b = \frac{1}{r_b}$$

$$|\Gamma| = \frac{(\text{swr}) - 1}{(\text{swr}) + 1}$$

Reflection coefficient, standing-wave ratio, and power   *continued*

a. When the angle X_0/R_0 of the surge impedance is negligibly small, the net power flowing toward the load is given by

$$P_1 = G_0(|_f E_1|^2 - |_r E_1|^2) = |_f E_1|^2 G_0(1 - |\Gamma_1|^2) = |E_{max} E_{min}|/R_0$$

where $|E|$ is the root-mean-square voltage.

$$P_2 = |_f E_1|^2 G_0(\epsilon^{2(\alpha/\beta)\theta} - |\Gamma_1| \epsilon^{-2(\alpha/\beta)\theta})$$

b. Efficiency:

$$\eta = \frac{P_1}{P_2} = \frac{1 - |\Gamma_1|^2}{\epsilon^{2(\alpha/\beta)\theta} - |\Gamma_1|^2 \epsilon^{-2(\alpha/\beta)\theta}}$$

When the load matches the line, $\Gamma_1 = 0$ and

$$\eta_{max} = \epsilon^{-2(\alpha/\beta)\theta}$$

For any load,

$$\eta = \frac{1 - |\Gamma_1|^2}{1 - |\Gamma_1|^2 \eta_{max}^2} \eta_{max}$$

c. Attenuation in nepers $= \frac{1}{2} \log_\epsilon \frac{P_2}{P_1} = 0.1151 \times$ (attenuation in decibels)

For a matched line, attenuation $= (\alpha/\beta)\theta = \alpha x$ nepers.

Attenuation in decibels $= 10 \log_{10} \frac{P_2}{P_1} = 8.686 \times$ (attenuation in nepers)

When $2(\alpha/\beta)\theta$ is small,

$$\frac{P_2}{P_1} = 1 + 2\frac{\alpha}{\beta}\theta \frac{1 + |\Gamma_1|^2}{1 - |\Gamma_1|^2}$$ and

$$\text{decibels/wavelength} = 10 \log_{10}\left(1 + 4\pi \frac{\alpha}{\beta} \frac{1 + |\Gamma_1|^2}{1 - |\Gamma_1|^2}\right)$$

d. For the same power flowing in a line with standing waves as in a matched, or "flat," line:

$$P = |E_{flat}|^2/R_0$$

$$|E_{max}| = |E_{flat}| \sqrt{(swr)}$$

$$|E_{min}| = |E_{flat}|/\sqrt{(swr)}$$

Reflection coefficient, standing-wave ratio, and power   *continued*

$$|_fE| = \frac{|E_{\text{flat}}|}{2}\left[\sqrt{\text{(swr)}} + \frac{1}{\sqrt{\text{(swr)}}}\right]$$

$$|_rE| = \frac{|E_{\text{flat}}|}{2}\left[\sqrt{\text{(swr)}} - \frac{1}{\sqrt{\text{(swr)}}}\right]$$

When the loss is small, so that (swr) is nearly constant over the entire length,

$$\frac{\text{(power loss)}}{\text{(loss for flat line)}} \approx \tfrac{1}{2}\left[\text{(swr)} + \frac{1}{\text{(swr)}}\right]$$

e. When a load is connected to a generator through a line, the generator output impedance being equal to the Z_0 of the line, then, for any load impedance,

$$\frac{P}{P_m} = 1 - |\Gamma|^2 = \frac{4\,\text{(swr)}}{[1 + \text{(swr)}]^2}$$

where

$P =$ power delivered to the load

$P_m =$ power that would be delivered to a load impedance matching the line

Γ and (swr) are the values at the load.

Attenuation and resistance of transmission lines
at ultra-high frequencies

$$A = 4.35\,\frac{R_t}{R_0} + 2.78\,\sqrt{\epsilon}\ \text{(pf)}\ f = \text{attenuation in decibels per 100 feet}$$

where

$R_t =$ total line resistance in ohms per 100 feet

(pf) $=$ power factor of dielectric medium

$f =$ frequency in megacycles

$$R_t = 0.1\left(\frac{1}{d} + \frac{1}{D}\right)\sqrt{f} \qquad \text{for copper coaxial line}$$

$$= \frac{0.2}{d}\sqrt{f} \qquad \text{for copper two-wire open line}$$

$d =$ diameter of conductors (coaxial line center conductor) in inches

$D =$ diameter of inner surface of outer coaxial conductor in inches

Measurement of impedance with slotted line

Symbols

Z_0 = characteristic impedance of line

Z = impedance of load (the unknown)

Z_1 = impedance at first V_{min}

k = velocity factor

= (velocity on line) / (velocity in free space)

λ = wavelength on line

χ = distance from load to first V_{min}

(swr) = V_{max}/V_{min}

$\theta° = 180 \dfrac{\chi}{\lambda/2} = 0.0120 \, f\chi/k$

where f is in megacycles and χ in centimeters.

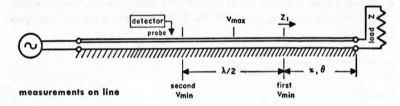

measurements on line

Procedure

Measure $\lambda/2$, χ, V_{max}, and V_{min}

Determine

$Z_1/Z_0 = 1/(swr) = V_{min}/V_{max}$

(wavelengths toward load) = $\chi/\lambda = 0.5\chi/(\lambda/2)$

Then Z/Z_0 may be found on an impedance chart. For example, suppose

$V_{min}/V_{max} = 0.60$ and $\chi/\lambda = 0.40$

Refer to the chart, such as the Smith chart reproduced in part here. Lay off with slider or dividers the distance on the vertical axis from the center point (marked 1.0) to 0.60. Pass around the circumference of the chart in a counterclockwise direction from the starting point 0 to the position 0.40, toward the load. Read off the resistance and reactance components of the normalized load impedance Z/Z_0 at the point of the dividers. Then it is found that

$Z = Z_0(0.77 + j0.39)$

Similarly, there may be found the admittance of the load. Determine

$Y_1/Y_0 = V_{max}/V_{min} = 1.67$

Measurement of impedance with slotted line   *continued*

in the above example. Now pass around the chart counterclockwise through $\chi/\lambda = 0.40$, starting at 0.25 and ending at 0.15. Read off the components of the normalized admittance.

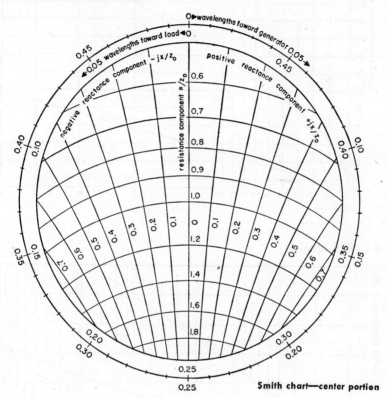

Smith chart—center portion

$$Y = \frac{1}{Z} = \frac{1}{Z_0}(1.03 - j0.53)$$

Alternatively, these results may be computed as follows:

$$Z = R_s + jX_s = Z_0 \frac{1 - j(\text{swr})\tan\theta}{(\text{swr}) - i\tan\theta} = Z_0 \frac{2(\text{swr}) - j[(\text{swr})^2 - 1]\sin 2\theta}{[(\text{swr})^2 + 1] + [(\text{swr})^2 - 1]\cos 2\theta}$$

$$Y = G + jB = \frac{1}{Z} = \frac{1}{R_p} - j\frac{1}{X_p} = Y_0 \frac{2(\text{swr}) + j[(\text{swr})^2 - 1]\sin 2\theta}{[(\text{swr})^2 + 1] - [(\text{swr})^2 - 1]\cos 2\theta}$$

where R_s and X_s are the series components of Z, while R_p and X_p are the parallel components.

Surge impedance of uniform lines

0 to 210 ohms

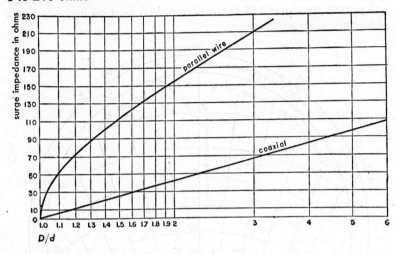

0 to 700 ohms

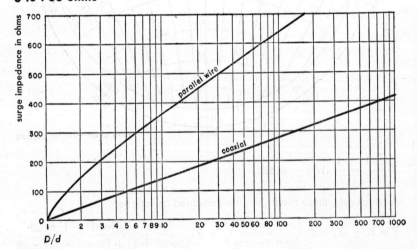

$$Z_0 = 120 \cosh^{-1} \frac{D}{d}$$

For $D \gg d$

$$Z_0 \approx 276 \log_{10} \frac{2D}{d}$$

parallel wires in air

$$Z_0 = \frac{138}{\sqrt{\epsilon}} \log_{10} \frac{D}{d}$$

Curve is for
$\epsilon = 1.00$

coaxial

Transmission-line data

type of line	characteristic impedance
A. single coaxial line 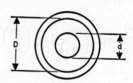	$Z_0 = \dfrac{138}{\sqrt{\epsilon}} \log_{10} \dfrac{D}{d}$ $= \dfrac{60}{\sqrt{\epsilon}} \log_e \dfrac{D}{d}$ ϵ = dielectric constant = 1 in air
B. balanced shielded line 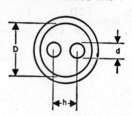	For $D \gg d$, $h \gg d$, $Z_0 \approx \dfrac{276}{\sqrt{\epsilon}} \log_{10} \left[2v \dfrac{1 - \sigma^2}{1 + \sigma^2} \right]$ $\approx \dfrac{120}{\sqrt{\epsilon}} \log_e \left[2v \dfrac{1 - \sigma^2}{1 + \sigma^2} \right]$ $v = \dfrac{h}{d} \qquad \sigma = \dfrac{h}{D}$
C. beads—dielectric ϵ_1 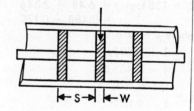	For cases (A) and (B), if ceramic beads are used at frequent intervals—call new surge impedance Z_0' $Z_0' = \dfrac{Z_0}{\sqrt{1 + \left(\dfrac{\epsilon_1}{\epsilon} - 1 \right) \dfrac{W}{S}}}$
D. open two-wire line in air 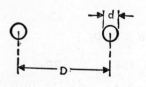	$Z_0 = 120 \cosh^{-1} \dfrac{D}{d}$ $\approx 276 \log_{10} \dfrac{2D}{d}$ $\approx 120 \log_e \dfrac{2D}{d}$

324

type of line	characteristic impedance
E. wires in parallel, near ground 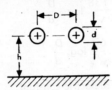	For $d \ll D, h,$ $$Z_0 = \frac{69}{\sqrt{\epsilon}} \log_{10}\left[\frac{4h}{d}\sqrt{1 + \left(\frac{2h}{D}\right)^2}\right]$$
F. balanced, near ground 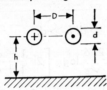	For $d \ll D, h,$ $$Z_0 = \frac{276}{\sqrt{\epsilon}} \log_{10}\left[\frac{2D}{d}\frac{1}{\sqrt{1 + (D/2h)^2}}\right]$$
G. single wire, near ground 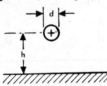	For $d \ll h,$ $$Z_0 = \frac{138}{\sqrt{\epsilon}} \log_{10}\frac{4h}{d}$$
H. single wire, square enclosure 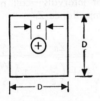	$Z_0 = 138 \log_{10}\rho + 6.48 - 2.34A$ $- 0.48B - 0.12C$ where $\rho = D/d$ $$A = \frac{1 + 0.405\rho^{-4}}{1 - 0.405\rho^{-4}}$$ $$B = \frac{1 + 0.163\rho^{-8}}{1 - 0.163\rho^{-8}}$$ $$C = \frac{1 + 0.067\rho^{-12}}{1 - 0.067\rho^{-12}}$$
I. balanced 4-wire 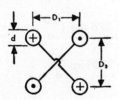	For $d \ll D_1, D_2$ $$Z_0 = \frac{138}{\sqrt{\epsilon}} \log_{10}\frac{2D_2}{d\sqrt{1 + (D_2/D_1)^2}}$$

Transmission-line data *continued*

type of line	characteristic impedance

J. parallel-strip line

$$\frac{w}{l} < 0.1$$

$$Z_0 \approx 377 \frac{w}{l}$$

K. five-wire line

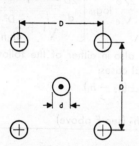

For $d \ll D$,

$$Z_0 = \frac{172}{\sqrt{\epsilon}} \log_{10} \frac{D}{0.875d}$$

L. wires in parallel—sheath return

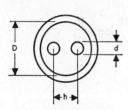

For $d \ll D, h,$

$$Z_0 = \frac{69}{\sqrt{\epsilon}} \log_{10} \left[\frac{\nu}{2\sigma^2} (1 - \sigma^4) \right]$$

$$\sigma = h/D$$

$$\nu = h/d$$

M. air coaxial with dielectric sup-
porting wedge

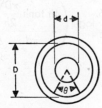

$$Z_0 \approx \frac{138 \log_{10} (D/d)}{\sqrt{1 + (\epsilon - 1)(\theta/360)}}$$

ϵ = dielectric constant of wedge

θ = wedge angle in degrees

Transmission-line data   *continued*

type of line	characteristic impedance

N. balanced 2-wire — unequal diameters

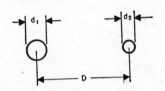

For $d_1, d_2 \ll D$,

$$Z_0 = \frac{276}{\sqrt{\epsilon}} \log_{10} \frac{2D}{\sqrt{d_1 d_2}}$$

O. balanced 2-wire near ground

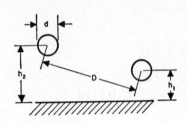

For $d \ll D, h_1, h_2$,

$$Z_0 = \frac{276}{\sqrt{\epsilon}} \log_{10} \left[\frac{2D}{d} \frac{1}{\sqrt{1 + \frac{D^2}{4h_1 h_2}}} \right]$$

Holds also in either of the following special cases:

$D = \pm(h_2 - h_1)$

or

$h_1 = h_2$ (see F above)

P. single wire between grounded parallel planes—ground return

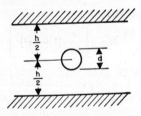

For $\dfrac{d}{h} < 0.75$,

$$Z_0 = \frac{138}{\sqrt{\epsilon}} \log_{10} \frac{4h}{\pi d}$$

Q. balanced line between grounded parallel planes

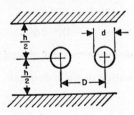

For $d \ll D, h$,

$$Z_0 = \frac{276}{\sqrt{\epsilon}} \log_{10} \left(\frac{4h \tanh \frac{\pi D}{2h}}{\pi d} \right)$$

Transmission-line data *continued*

type of line	characteristic impedance
R. balanced line between grounded parallel planes 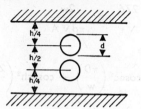	For $d \ll h$, $$Z_0 = \frac{276}{\sqrt{\epsilon}} \log_{10} \frac{2h}{\pi d}$$
S. single wire in trough 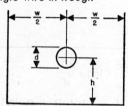	For $d \ll h, w$, $$Z_0 = \frac{138}{\sqrt{\epsilon}} \log_{10} \left[\frac{4w \tanh \dfrac{\pi h}{w}}{\pi d} \right]$$
T. balanced 2-wire line in rectangular enclosure 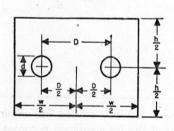	For $d \ll D, w, h$, $$Z_0 = \frac{276}{\sqrt{\epsilon}} \left\{ \log_{10} \left[\frac{4h \tanh \dfrac{\pi D}{2h}}{\pi d} \right] - \sum_{m=1}^{\infty} \log_{10} \left[\frac{1 + u_m^2}{1 - v_m^2} \right] \right\}$$ where $$u_m = \frac{\sinh \dfrac{\pi D}{2h}}{\cosh \dfrac{m\pi w}{2h}} \qquad v_m = \frac{\sinh \dfrac{\pi D}{2h}}{\sinh \dfrac{m\pi w}{2h}}$$
U. eccentric line 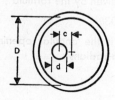	For $d \ll D$, $$Z_0 = \frac{138}{\sqrt{\epsilon}} \log_{10} \left\{ \frac{D}{d} \left[1 - \left(\frac{2c}{D} \right)^2 \right] \right\}$$ For $c/D \ll 1$ this is the Z_0 of type A diminished by approximately $$\frac{240}{\sqrt{\epsilon}} \left(\frac{c}{D} \right)^2 \text{ ohms}$$

Transmission-line data   *continued*

type of line	characteristic impedance
V. balanced 2-wire line in semi-infinite enclosure 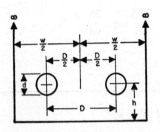	For $d \ll D, w, h,$ $$Z_0 = \frac{276}{\sqrt{\epsilon}} \log_{10} \frac{2w}{\pi d \sqrt{A}}$$ where $$A = \operatorname{cosec}^2\left(\frac{\pi D}{w}\right) + \operatorname{cosech}^2\left(\frac{2\pi h}{w}\right)$$
W. outer wires grounded, inner wires balanced to ground 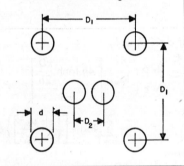	$$Z_0 = \frac{276}{\sqrt{\epsilon}} \left\{ \log_{10} \frac{2D_2}{d} - \frac{\left[\log_{10} \frac{1 + (1 + D_2/D_1)^2}{1 + (1 - D_2/D_1)^2} \right]^2}{\log_{10} \frac{2D\sqrt{2}}{d}} \right\}$$
X. slotted air line	When a slot is introduced into an air coaxial line for measuring purposes, the increase in characteristic impedance in ohms, compared with a normal coaxial line, is less than a quantity given by the formula $$\Delta Z = 0.03\theta^2$$ where θ is the angular opening of the slot in radians

Transmission-line attenuation due to load mismatch

Let W_t = power delivered to line by transmitter

W_l = power delivered to load by line

Then $A = 10 \log_{10} W_t/W_l$ decibels

A reduces to A_0 when the load impedance equals the characteristic impedance of the line.

A_0 = normal attenuation (matched)

A = total attenuation (mismatched) e.g., power loss in line, not reflection loss

ρ = standing-wave ratio $V_{\max}/V_{\min}$ at the load

Example: Find the attenuation at 200 megacycles in a 200-foot length of RG–8/U cable terminated to give a voltage standing-wave ratio of 3:1.

From the chart on page 338, the normal attenuation of RG–8/U cable at 200 megacycles is 3.1 decibels per 100 feet, or 6.2 decibels for 200 feet. Referring to the chart below, the added attenuation $(A - A_0)$ due to mismatch for $A_0 = 6.2$ and $\rho = 3$ is approximately 1.2 decibels. The total attenuation A is therefore $6.2 + 1.2 = 7.4$ decibels.

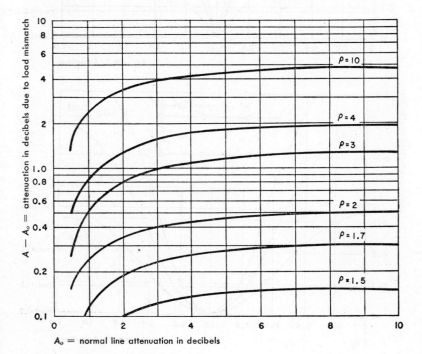

A_0 = normal line attenuation in decibels

Quarter-wave matching sections

The accompanying figures show how voltage-reflection coefficient or standing-wave ratio (swr) vary with frequency f when quarter-wave matching lines are inserted between a line of characteristic impedance Z_0 and a load of resistance R. f_0 is the frequency for which the matching sections are exactly one-quarter wavelength ($\lambda/4$) long.

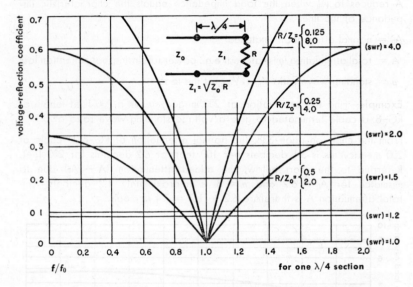

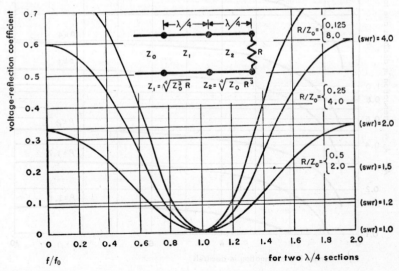

Impedance matching with shorted stub

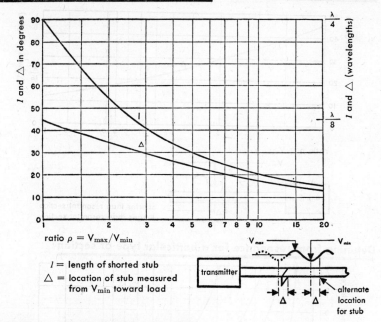

l = length of shorted stub
$\triangle$ = location of stub measured
from V_{min} toward load

Impedance matching with open stub

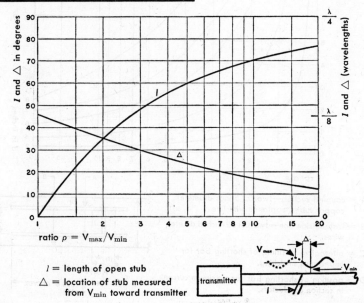

l = length of open stub
$\triangle$ = location of stub measured
from V_{min} toward transmitter

Impedance matching with coupled section

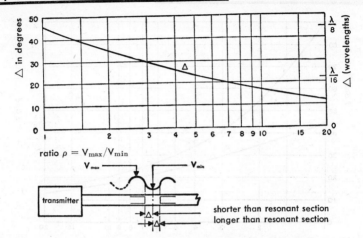

ratio $\rho = V_{max}/V_{min}$

Detuning from resonance for a particular type of section

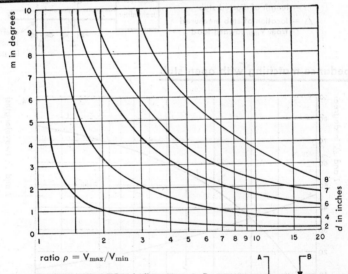

ratio $\rho = V_{max}/V_{min}$

A = coupled section—two 0.75-inch diameter copper tubes, coplanar with line.

B = transmission line—two 0.162-inch diameter wires.

C = alternative positions of shorting bar for impedance matching.

D = position of shorting bar for maximum current in section conductors.

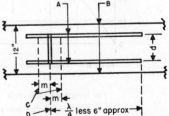

Length of transmission line

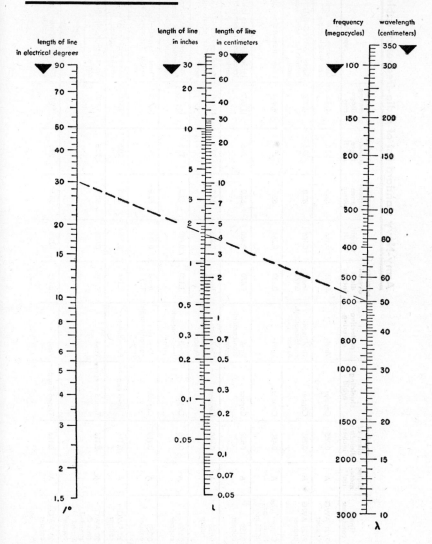

This chart gives the actual length of line in centimeters and inches when given the length in electrical degrees and the frequency, provided the velocity of propagation on the transmission line is equal to that in free space. The length is given on the L-scale intersection by a line between λ and $l°$, where $l° = \dfrac{360\ L \text{ in centimeters}}{\lambda \text{ in centimeters}}$

Example: $f = 600$ megacycles, $l° = 30$, Length $L = 1.64$ inches or 4.2 centimeters.

Army-Navy standard list of radio-frequency cables

class of cables		Army-Navy type number	inner conductor	dielec material*	nominal diam of dielectric inches	shielding braid	protective covering	nominal overall diam inches	weight lb/ft	nominal impedance ohms	nominal capacitance μμf/ft	maximum operating voltage rms	remarks
50-55 ohms	Single braid	RG-8/U	7/21 AWG copper	A	0.285	Copper	Vinyl	0.405	0.106	52.0	29.5	4,000	General-purpose medium-size flexible cable
		RG-10/U	7/21 AWG copper	A	0.285	Copper	Vinyl (non-contaminating). Armor	(max) 0.475	0.146	52.0	29.5	4,000	Same as RG-8/U armored for naval equipment
		RG-16/U	Copper tube. Nom. diam. 0.125 in.	A	0.460	Copper	Vinyl	0.630	0.254	52.0	29.5	6,000	Power-transmission cable
		RG-17/U	0.188 copper	A	0.680	Copper	Vinyl (non-contaminating)	0.870	0.460	52.0	29.5	11,000	Large high-power low-attenuation transmission cable
		RG-18/U	0.188 copper	A	0.680	Copper	Vinyl (non-contaminating). Armor	(max) 0.945	0.585	52.0	29.5	11,000	Same as RG-17/U armored for naval equipment
		RG-19/U	0.250 copper	A	0.910	Copper	Vinyl (non-contaminating)	1.120	0.740	52.0	29.5	14,000	Very large high-power low-attenuation transmission cable
		RG-20/U	0.250 copper	A	0.910	Copper	Vinyl (non-contaminating). Armor	(max) 1.195	0.925	52.0	29.5	14,000	Same as RG-19/U armored for naval equipment
		RG-29/U	20 AWG copper	A	0.116	Tinned copper	Polyethylene	0.184	0.0194	53.5	28.5	1,900	Same as RG-58/U; polyethylene jacket
		RG-58A/U	20 AWG class C stranded tinned copper	A	0.116	Tinned copper	Vinyl	0.195	0.025	52.0	28.5	1,900	Small-size highly flexible cable
		RG-58/U	20 AWG copper	A	0.116	Tinned Copper	Vinyl	0.195	0.025	53.5	28.5	1,900	General-purpose small-size flexible cable

continued

Army-Navy standard list of radio-frequency cables

class of cables		Army-Navy type number	inner conductor	dielec material*	nominal diam of dielectric inches	shielding braid	protective covering	nominal overall diam inches	weight lb/ft	nominal impedance ohms	nominal capacitance μμf/ft	maximum operating voltage rms	remarks
50-55 ohms cont.	Double braid	RG-5/U	16 AWG copper	A	0.185	Copper	Vinyl	0.332	0.087	52.5	28.5	3,000	Small microwave cable
		RG-9A/U	7/21 AWG silvered copper	A	0.280	Silvered copper	Vinyl (non-contaminating)	0.420	0.122	51.0	30.0	4,000	Same as RG-9/U with high attenuation stability
		RG-9/U	7/21 AWG silvered copper	A	0.280	Inner—silver coated copper. Outer—copper	Vinyl (non-contaminating)	0.420	0.150	51.0	30.0	4,000	Medium-size low-level-circuit cable
		RG-14/U	10 AWG copper	A	0.370	Copper	Vinyl (non-contaminating)	0.545	0.216	52.0	29.5	5,500	General-purpose semi-flexible power transmission cable
		RG-38/U	17 AWG tinned copper	C	0.196	Tinned copper	Polyethylene	0.312	0.110	52.5	38.0	1,000	High-loss flexible cable
		RG-55/U	20 AWG copper	A	0.116	Tinned copper	Polyethylene	(max) 0.206	0.034	53.5	28.5	1,900	Small-size flexible cable
		RG-74/U	10 AWG copper	A	0.370	Copper	Vinyl (non-contaminating). Armor	0.615	0.310	52.0	29.5	5,500	Same as RG-14/U armored for naval equipment
55-60 ohms	Single braid	RG-54A/U	7/0.0152 copper	A	0.178	Tinned copper	Polyethylene	0.250	0.0580	58.0	26.5	3,000	Small-size flexible cable with light-weight jacket
70-80 ohms	Single braid	RG-59/U	22 AWG copperweld	A	0.146	Copper	Vinyl	0.242	0.032	73.0	21.0	2,300	General-purpose small-size video cable
		RG-11/U	7/26 AWG tinned copper	A	0.285	Copper	Vinyl	0.405	0.096	75.0	20.5	4,000	Medium-size, flexible video and communication cable
		RG-12/U	7/26 AWG tinned copper	A	0.285	Copper	Vinyl (non-contaminating). Armor	0.475	0.141	75.0	20.5	4,000	Same as RG-11/U armored for naval equipment
		RG-34/U	7/21 AWG copper	A	0.455	Copper	Vinyl	0.625	0.215	71.0	21.5	5,200	Medium-size flexible communication cable

*Notes on dielectric materials: A—Stabilized polyethylene. B—Polymeric resin mixture. C—Synthetic rubber compound. D—layer of synthetic rubber dielectric between thin layers o conducting rubber. E—inner layer conducting rubber, center layer synthetic rubber, outer layer red insulating synthetic rubber.

continued

Army-Navy standard list of radio-frequency cables

class of cables		Army-Navy type number	inner conductor	dielec material*	nominal diam of dielectric inches	shielding braid	protective covering	nominal overall diam inches	weight lb/ft	nominal impedance ohms	nominal capacitance μμf/ft	maximum operating voltage rms	remarks
70–80 ohms cont.	Single braid cont.	RG-35/U	9 AWG copper	A	0.680	Copper	Vinyl (non-contaminating). Armor	0.945	0.439	71.0	21.5	10,000	large-size video cable
	Double braid	RG-6/U	21 AWG copperweld	A	0.185	Inner—silver coated copper. Outer—copper	Vinyl (non-contaminating)	0.332	0.082	76.0	20.0	2,700	Small size video and I-F cable
		RG-13/U	7/26 AWG tinned copper	A	0.280	Copper	Vinyl	0.420	0.126	74.0	20.5	4,000	I-F cable
		RG-15/U	15 AWG copperweld	A	0.370	Copper	Vinyl	0.545	0.181	76.0	20.0	5,000	Medium-size video cable
		RG-39/U	22 AWG tinned copperweld	C	0.196	Tinned copper	Polyethylene	0.312	0.100	72.5	28.0	1,000	High-loss video cable
		RG-40/U	22 AWG tinned copperweld	C	0.196	Tinned copper	Synthetic rubber	0.420	0.150	72.5	28.0	1,000	High-loss video cable
Cables of special characteristics	Twin conductor	RG-22/U	2 cond. 7/0.0152 copper	A	0.285	Single—tinned copper	Vinyl	0.405	0.107	95.0	16.0	1,000	Small size twin-conductor cable
		RG-23/U	2 cond. 7/21 AWG copper	A	0.380	Copper—individual inner; common outer	Vinyl	0.650 × 0.945	0.367	125.0	12.0	3,000	Balanced twin-coaxial cable
		RG-57/U	2 cond.I 7/21 AWG copper	A	0.472	Single—tinned copper	Vinyl	0.625	0.225	95.0	17.0	3,000	large size twin-conductor cable
	High attenuation	RG-21/U	16 AWG resistance wire	A	0.185	Inner—silver-coated copper. Outer—copper	Vinyl (non-contaminating)	0.332	0.087	53.0	29.0	2,700	Special attenuating cable with small temperature coefficient of attenuation
		RG-42/U	21 AWG high-resistance wire	A	0.196	2 braids—silvered copper	Vinyl (non-contaminating)	0.342	0.120	78.0	20.0	2,700	Attenuating cable with small temperature coeff. of attenuation

continued

Army-Navy standard list of radio-frequency cables

class of cables	Army-Navy type number	inner conductor	dielec material*	nominal diam of dielectric inches	shielding braid	protective covering	nominal overall diam inches	weight lb/ft	nominal impedance ohms	nominal capacitance μμf/ft	maximum operating voltage rms	remarks
High impedance	RG-65/U	No. 32 Formex F helix diam 0.128 in.	A	0.285	Single—copper	Vinyl	0.405	0.096	950	44.0	1,000	High-impedance video cable. High delay
Low capacitance / Single braid	RG-7/U	19 AWG copper	A or B	0.250	Copper	Vinyl	0.370	0.0763	90–105	12.5 Max. 14.0	1,000	Medium-size low-capacitance air-spaced cable
	RG-62/U	22 AWG copperweld	A or B	0.146	Copper	Vinyl	0.242	0.0382	93.0	13.5 max 14.5	750	Small-size low-capacitance air-spaced cable
	RG-63/U	22 AWG copperweld	A or B	0.285	Copper	Vinyl	0.405	0.0832	125	10.0 max 11.0	1,000	Medium-size low-capacitance air-spaced cable
Double braid	RG-71/U	22 AWG copperweld	A	0.146	Inner—plain copper. Outer—tinned copper	Polyethylene	0.250	0.0457	93.0	13.5 max 14.5	750	Small-size low-capacitance air-spaced cable for I-F purposes
Pulse applications / Single braid	RG-26A/U	19/0.0117 tinned copper	E	0.288	Tinned copper	Synthetic rubber, Armor	0.505	0.168†	48.0	50.0	8,000 (peak)	Medium-size armored pulse cable
	RG-27/U	19/0.0185 tinned copper	D	0.455‡	Tinned copper	Vinyl and armor	(max) 0.675	0.304	48.0	50.0	15,000 (peak)	large-size pulse cable armored for naval equipment
Double braid	RG-25A/U	19/0.0117 tinned copper	E	0.288	Tinned copper	Synthetic rubber	0.505	0.183†	48.0	50.0	8,000 (peak)	Medium-size pulse cable
	RG-28/U	19/0.0185 tinned copper	D	0.455‡	Inner—tinned copper. Outer—galvanized steel	Synthetic rubber	0.805	0.370	48.0	50.0	15,000 (peak)	Large-size pulse cable
	RG-64A/U	19/0.0117 tinned copper	E	0.288	Tinned copper	Synthetic rubber	0.475	0.162†	48.0	50.0	8,000 (peak)	Medium-size pulse cable
Twisting application / Single braid	RG-41/U	16/30 AWG tinned copper	C	0.250	Tinned copper	Neoprene	0.425	0.150	67.5	27.0	3,000	Special-twist cable

*Notes on dielectric materials: A—Stabilized polyethylene. B—Polymeric resin mixture. C—Synthetic rubber compound. D—Layer of synthetic rubber dielectric between thin layers of conducting rubber. E—Inner layer conducting rubber, center layer synthetic rubber, outer layer red insulating synthetic rubber.
†Data courtesy of Okonite Company.
‡This value is the diameter over the outer layer of conducting rubber.

Attenuation of A-N cables versus frequency

The charts below refer to cables listed in the Army–Navy standard list of radio-frequency cables. The numbers on the charts represent the RG– /U designation of the cables.

For example, the curve labeled "55, 58, 29" is the attenuation curve for cables RG–55/U, RG–58/U, and RG–29/U.

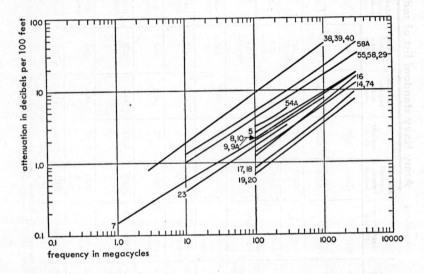

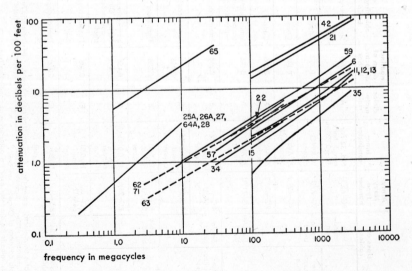

■ Wave guides and resonators

Propagation of electromagnetic waves in hollow wave guides

For propagation of energy at microwave frequencies through a hollow metal tube under fixed conditions, a number of different types of waves are available, namely:

TE waves: Transverse-electric waves, sometimes called H waves, characterized by the fact that the electric vector (E vector) is always perpendicular to the direction of propagation. This means that

$$E_x \equiv 0$$

where x is the direction of propagation.

TM waves: Transverse-magnetic waves, also called E waves, characterized by the fact that the magnetic vector (H vector) is always perpendicular to the direction of propagation.

This means that

$$H_x \equiv 0$$

where x is the direction of propagation.

Note—TEM waves: Transverse-electromagnetic waves. These waves are characterized by the fact that both the electric vector (E vector) and the magnetic vector (H vector) are perpendicular to the direction of propagation. This means that

$$E_x = H_x = 0$$

where x is the direction of propagation. This is the mode commonly excited in coaxial and open-wire lines. It cannot be propagated in a wave guide.

The solutions for the field configurations in wave guides are characterized by the presence of the integers n and m which can take on separate values from 0 or 1 to infinity. Only a limited number of these different n,m modes can be propagated, depending on the dimensions of the guide and the frequency of excitation. For each mode there is a definite lower limit or cutoff frequency below which the wave is incapable of being propagated. Thus, a wave guide is seen to exhibit definite properties of a high-pass filter.

The propagation constant $\gamma_{n,m}$ determines the amplitude and phase of each component of the wave as it is propagated along the length of the guide. With $x =$ (direction of propagation) and $\omega = 2\pi \times$ (frequency), the factor for each component is

$$\exp[j\omega t - \gamma_{n,m}x]$$

Propagation of electromagnetic waves in hollow wave guides *continued*

Thus, if $\gamma_{n,m}$ is real, the phase of each component is constant, but the amplitude decreases exponentially with x. When $\gamma_{n,m}$ is real, it is said that no propagation takes place. The frequency is considered below cutoff. Actually, propagation with high attenuation does take place for a small distance, and a short length of guide below cutoff is often used as a calibrated attenuator.

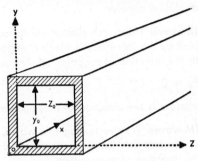

When $\gamma_{n,m}$ is imaginary, the amplitude of each component remains constant, but the phase varies with x. Hence, propagation takes place. $\gamma_{n,m}$ is a pure imaginary only in a lossless guide. In the practical case, $\gamma_{n,m}$ usually has both a real part, which is the attenuation constant, and an imaginary part, which is the phase propagation constant.

Fig. 1—Rectangular wave guide.

Rectangular wave guides

Fig. 1 shows a rectangular wave guide and a rectangular system of coordinates, disposed so that the origin falls on one of the corners of the wave guide; x is the direction of propagation along the guide, and the cross-sectional dimensions are y_o and z_o.

For the case of perfect conductivity of the guide walls with a nonconducting interior dielectric (usually air), the equations for the $TM_{n,m}$ or $E_{n,m}$ waves in the dielectric are:

$$E_x = A \sin\left(\frac{n\pi}{y_o} y\right) \sin\left(\frac{m\pi}{z_o} z\right) e^{j\omega t - \gamma_{n,m} x}$$

$$E_y = -A \frac{\gamma_{n,m}}{\gamma^2_{n,m} + \omega^2 \mu_k \epsilon_k} \left(\frac{n\pi}{y_o}\right) \cos\left(\frac{n\pi}{y_o} y\right) \sin\left(\frac{m\pi}{z_o} z\right) e^{j\omega t - \gamma_{n,m} x}$$

$$E_z = -A \frac{\gamma_{n,m}}{\gamma^2_{n,m} + \omega^2 \mu_k \epsilon_k} \left(\frac{m\pi}{z_o}\right) \sin\left(\frac{n\pi}{y_o} y\right) \cos\left(\frac{m\pi}{z_o} z\right) e^{j\omega t - \gamma_{n,m} x}$$

$$H_x = 0$$

$$H_y = A \frac{j\omega \epsilon_k}{\gamma^2_{n,m} + \omega^2 \mu_k \epsilon_k} \left(\frac{m\pi}{z_o}\right) \sin\left(\frac{n\pi}{y_o} y\right) \cos\left(\frac{m\pi}{z_o} z\right) e^{j\omega t - \gamma_{n,m} x}$$

$$H_z = -A \frac{j\omega \epsilon_k}{\gamma^2_{n,m} + \omega^2 \mu_k \epsilon_k} \left(\frac{n\pi}{y_o}\right) \cos\left(\frac{n\pi}{y_o} y\right) \sin\left(\frac{m\pi}{z_o} z\right) e^{j\omega t - \gamma_{n,m} x}$$

Rectangular wave guides continued

where ϵ_k is the dielectric constant and μ_k the permeability of the dielectric material in meter-kilogram-second (rationalized) units.

Constant A is determined solely by the exciting voltage. It has both amplitude and phase. Integers n and m may individually take values from 1 to infinity. No TM waves of the 0,0 type or 0,1 type are possible in a rectangular guide so that neither n nor m may be 0.

Equations for the $TE_{n,m}$ waves or $H_{n,m}$ waves in a dielectric are:

$$H_x = B \cos\left(\frac{n\pi}{y_o}y\right)\cos\left(\frac{m\pi}{z_o}z\right)e^{j\omega t - \gamma_{n,m}x}$$

$$H_y = B \frac{\gamma_{n,m}}{\gamma^2_{n,m} + \omega^2\mu_k\epsilon_k}\left(\frac{n\pi}{y_o}\right)\sin\left(\frac{n\pi}{y_o}y\right)\cos\left(\frac{m\pi}{z_o}z\right)e^{j\omega t - \gamma_{n,m}x}$$

$$H_z = B \frac{\gamma_{n,m}}{\gamma^2_{n,m} + \omega^2\mu_k\epsilon_k}\left(\frac{m\pi}{z_o}\right)\cos\left(\frac{n\pi}{y_o}y\right)\sin\left(\frac{m\pi}{z_o}z\right)e^{j\omega t - \gamma_{n,m}x}$$

$$E_x \equiv 0$$

$$E_y = B \frac{j\omega\mu_k}{\gamma^2_{n,m} + \omega^2\mu_k\epsilon_k}\left(\frac{m\pi}{z_o}\right)\cos\left(\frac{n\pi}{y_o}y\right)\sin\left(\frac{m\pi}{z_o}z\right)e^{j\omega t - \gamma_{n,m}x}$$

$$E_z = -B \frac{j\omega\mu_k}{\gamma^2_{n,m} + \omega^2\mu_k\epsilon_k}\left(\frac{n\pi}{y_o}\right)\sin\left(\frac{n\pi}{y_o}y\right)\cos\left(\frac{m\pi}{z_o}z\right)e^{j\omega t - \gamma_{n,m}x}$$

where ϵ_k is the dielectric constant and μ_k the permeability of the dielectric material in meter-kilogram-second (rationalized) units.

Constant B depends only on the original exciting voltage and has both magnitude and phase; n and m individually may assume any integer value from 0 to infinity. The 0,0 type of wave where both n and m are 0 is not possible, but all other combinations are.

As stated previously, propagation only takes place when the propagation constant $\gamma_{n,m}$ is imaginary;

$$\gamma_{n,m} = \sqrt{\left(\frac{n\pi}{y_o}\right)^2 + \left(\frac{m\pi}{z_o}\right)^2 - \omega^2\mu_k\epsilon_k}$$

This means, for any n,m mode, propagation takes place when

$$\omega^2\mu_k\epsilon_k > \left(\frac{n\pi}{y_o}\right)^2 + \left(\frac{m\pi}{z_o}\right)^2$$

Rectangular wave guides   *continued*

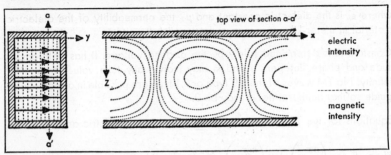

Fig. 2—Field configuration for TE$_{0,1}$ wave.

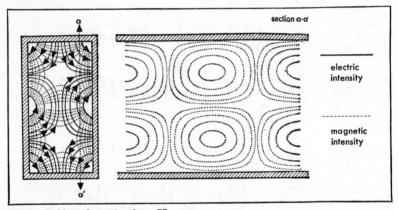

Fig. 3—Field configuration for a TE$_{1,2}$ wave.

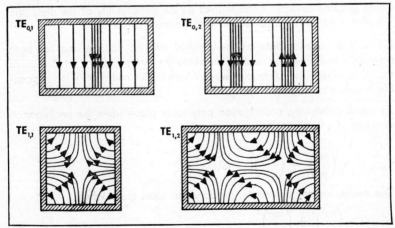

Fig. 4—Characteristic *E* lines for TE waves.

Rectangular wave guides   *continued*

or, in terms of frequency f and velocity of light c, when

$$f > \frac{c}{2\pi\sqrt{\mu_1 \epsilon_1}}\sqrt{\left(\frac{n\pi}{y_o}\right)^2 + \left(\frac{m\pi}{z_o}\right)^2}$$

where μ_1 and ϵ_1 are the relative permeability and relative dielectric constant, respectively, of the dielectric material with respect to free space.

The wavelength in the wave guide is always greater than the wavelength in an unbounded medium. If λ is the wavelength in free space, the wavelength in the guide for the n,m mode with air as a dielectric is

$$\lambda_{g(n,m)} = \frac{\lambda}{\sqrt{1 - \left(\frac{n\lambda}{2y_o}\right)^2 - \left(\frac{m\lambda}{2z_o}\right)^2}}$$

The phase velocity within the guide is also always greater than in an unbounded medium. The phase velocity v and group velocity u are related by the following equation:

$$u = \frac{c^2}{v}$$

where the phase velocity is given by $v = c\lambda_g/\lambda$ and the group velocity is the velocity of propagation of the energy.

To couple energy into wave guides, it is necessary to understand the configuration of the characteristic electric and magnetic lines. Fig. 2 illustrates the field configuration for a $TE_{0,1}$ wave. Fig. 3 shows the instantaneous field configuration for a higher mode, a $TE_{1,2}$ wave.

In Fig. 4 are shown only the characteristic E lines for the $TE_{0,1}$, $TE_{0,2}$, $TE_{1,1}$ and $TE_{1,2}$ waves. The arrows on the lines indicate their instantaneous relative directions. In order to excite a TE wave, it is necessary to insert a probe to coincide with the direction of the E lines. Thus, for a $TE_{0,1}$ wave, a single probe projecting from the side of the guide parallel to the E lines would be sufficient to couple into it. Several means of coupling from a coaxial line to a rectangular wave guide to excite the $TE_{0,1}$ mode are shown in Fig. 5. With structures such as these, it is possible to make the standing-wave ratio due to the junction less than 1.15 over a 10- to 15-percent frequency band.

Fig. 6 shows the instantaneous configuration of a $TM_{1,1}$ wave; Fig. 7, the instantaneous field configuration for a $TM_{1,2}$ wave. Coupling to this type of wave may be accomplished by inserting a probe, which is parallel to the E lines, or by means of a loop so oriented as to link the lines of flux.

Rectangular wave guides *continued*

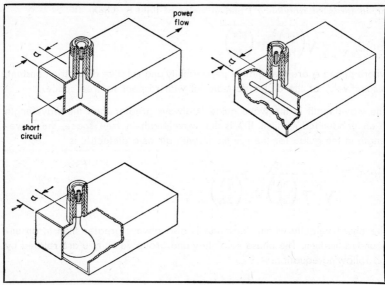

Fig. 5—Methods of coupling to TE$_{0,1}$ mode (a $\approx \lambda_g/4$).

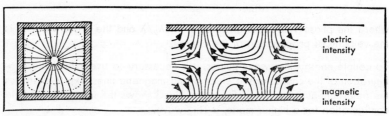

electric
intensity

- - - - - - - - - -

magnetic
intensity

Fig. 6—Instantaneous field configuration for a TM$_{1,1}$ wave.

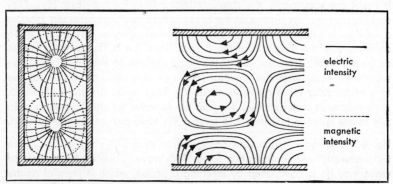

electric
intensity

- - - - - - - - - -

magnetic
intensity

Fig. 7—Instantaneous field configuration for a TM$_{1,2}$ wave.

Circular wave guides

The usual coordinate system is ρ, θ, z, where ρ is in the radial direction; θ is the angle; z is in the longitudinal direction.

TM waves (E waves): $H_z \equiv 0$

$$E_z = A J_n (k_{n,m} \rho) \cos n\theta \, e^{j\omega t - \gamma_{n,m} z}$$

By the boundary conditions, $E_z = 0$ when $\rho = a$, the radius of the guide. Thus, the only permissible values of k are those for which $J_n (k_{n,m} a) = 0$ because E_z must be zero at the boundary.

The numbers n, m take on all integral values from zero to infinity. The waves are seen to be characterized by the numbers, n and m, where n gives the order of the bessel functions, and m gives the order of the root of J_n $(k_{n,m} a)$. The bessel function has an infinite number of roots, so that there are an infinite number of k's that make $J_n (k_{n,m} a) = 0$.

The other components of the electric vector E_θ and E_ρ are related to E_z as are H_θ and H_ρ.

TE waves (H waves): $E_z \equiv 0$

$$H_z = B J_n (k_{n,m} \rho) \cos n\theta \, e^{j\omega t - \gamma_{n,m} z}$$

H_ρ, H_θ, E_ρ, E_θ, are all related to H_z.

Again n takes on integral values from zero to infinity. The boundary condition $E_\theta = 0$ when $\rho = a$ still applies. To satisfy this condition k must be such as to make $J'_n (k_{n,m} a)$ equal to zero [where the superscript indicates the derivative of $J_n (k_{n,m} a)$]. It is seen that m takes on values from 1 to infinity since there are an infinite number of roots of $J'_n (k_{n,m} a)$.

For circular wave guides, the cut-off frequency for the n,m mode is

$$f_{cn,m} = c \, k_{n,m}/2\pi$$

where c = velocity of light and $k_{n,m}$ is evaluated from the roots of the bessel functions

$$k_{n,m} = U_{n,m}/a \quad \text{or} \quad U'_{n,m}/a$$

where a = radius of guide or pipe and $U_{n,m}$ is the root of the particular bessel function of interest (or its derivative).

The wavelength in any guide filled with a homogeneous dielectric is

$$\lambda_g = \lambda_0 / \sqrt{1 - (\lambda_0/\lambda_c)^2}$$

Where λ_0 is the wavelength in free space, and λ_c is the free-space cutoff wavelength.

Circular wave guides   *continued*

The following tables are useful in determining the values of k. For TE waves the cutoff wavelengths are given in the following table.

Values of λ_c/a (where a = radius of guide)

m\n	0	1	2
1	1.640	3.414	2.057
2	0.896	1.178	0.937
3	0.618	0.736	0.631

For Tm waves the cutoff wavelengths are given in the following table.

Values of λ_c/a

m\n	0	1	2
1	2.619	1.640	1.224
2	1.139	0.896	0.747
3	0.726	0.618	0.541

where n is the order of the bessel function and m is the order of the root. Fig. 8 shows λ_0/λ_g as a function of λ_0/λ_c. From this, λ_g may be determined when λ_0 and λ_c are known.

The pattern of magnetic force of TM waves in a circular wave guide is shown in Fig. 9. Only the maximum lines are indicated. In order to excite this type of pattern, it is necessary to insert a probe along the length of the wave guide and concentric with the H lines. For instance, in the $TM_{0,1}$ type of wave, a probe extending down the length of the wave guide at the very

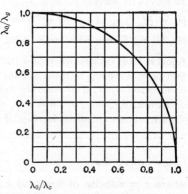

Fig. 8—Chart for determining guide wavelength.

center of the guide would provide the proper excitation. This method of excitation is shown in Fig. 10. Corresponding methods of excitation may be used for the other types of TM waves shown in Fig. 9.

Fig. 11 shows the patterns of electric force for TE waves. Again only the maximum lines are indicated. This type of wave may be excited by an antenna that is parallel to the electric lines of force. The $TE_{1,1}$ wave may be excited by means of an antenna extending across the wave guide. This is illustrated in Fig. 12.

Circular wave guides *continued*

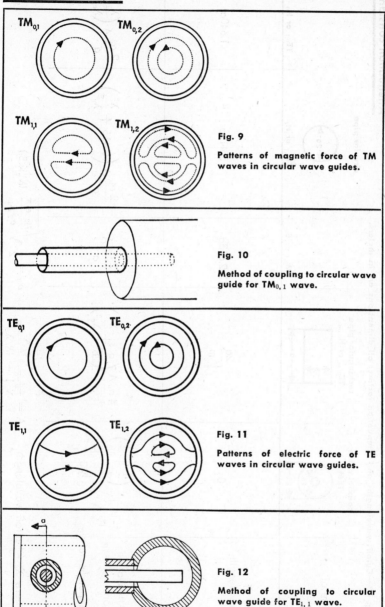

TM$_{0,1}$ TM$_{0,2}$

TM$_{1,1}$ TM$_{1,2}$

Fig. 9

Patterns of magnetic force of TM waves in circular wave guides.

Fig. 10

Method of coupling to circular wave guide for TM$_{0,1}$ wave.

TE$_{0,1}$ TE$_{0,2}$

TE$_{1,1}$ TE$_{1,2}$

Fig. 11

Patterns of electric force of TE waves in circular wave guides.

a

a

section a-a'

Fig. 12

Method of coupling to circular wave guide for TE$_{1,1}$ wave.

Attenuation constants

Fig. 13—Cutoff wavelengths and attenuation factors; all dimensions are in meters.

Type of guide	coaxial cable TEM 	rectangular pipe $TE_{0,m}$ or $H_{0,m}$ 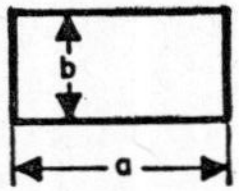	circular pipe  $TM_{0,1}$ or E_0	circular pipe $TE_{1,1}$ or H_1	circular pipe $TE_{0,1}$ or H_0
Cutoff wavelength λ_c	0	$\dfrac{2a}{m}$	$2.613a$	$3.412a$	$1.640a$
Attenuation constant = α (nepers/meter)	$\alpha_0 \sqrt{\dfrac{c}{\lambda}}\ \dfrac{\left(\dfrac{1}{a}+\dfrac{1}{b}\right)}{\log_e \dfrac{b}{a}}$	$\dfrac{4\alpha_0 A}{a}\left(\dfrac{a}{2b}+\dfrac{\lambda^2}{\lambda_c^2}\right)$	$\dfrac{2\alpha_0 A}{a}$	$\dfrac{2\alpha_0 A}{a}\left(0.415+\dfrac{\lambda^2}{\lambda_c^2}\right)$	$\dfrac{2\alpha_0}{a} A\left(\dfrac{\lambda}{\lambda_c}\right)^2$

$$\alpha_0 = \frac{1}{2}\sqrt{\frac{\mu_2\, \epsilon_1\, \pi}{\sigma_2\, \mu_1}} \quad \text{(M.K.S.)}$$

$$A = \frac{\sqrt{c/\lambda}}{\sqrt{1-(\lambda/\lambda_c)^2}}$$

where λ_c = cutoff wavelength

Attenuation constants   *continued*

All of the attenuation constants contain a common coefficient

$$\alpha_\theta = \tfrac{1}{2} \sqrt{\mu_2 \epsilon_1 \pi / \sigma_2 \mu_1}$$

ϵ_1 and μ_1 are the dielectric constant and the magnetic permeability of the insulator, respectively; and σ_2 and μ_2 are the electric conductivity and magnetic permeability of the metal, respectively.

For air and copper,

$$\alpha_0 = 0.35 \times 10^{-9} \text{ nepers/meter} = 0.3 \times 10^{-5} \text{ decibels/kilometer}$$

To convert from nepers/meter to decibels/100 feet, multiply by 264. Fig. 13 summarizes some of the most important formulas. Dimensions a and b are measured in meters.

Attenuation in a wave guide beyond cutoff

When a wave guide is used at a wavelength greater than the cutoff wavelength, there is no real propagation and the fields are attenuated exponentially. The attenuation L in a length d is given by

$$L = 54.5 \frac{d}{\lambda_c} \sqrt{1 - \left(\frac{\lambda_c}{\lambda}\right)^2} \text{ decibels}$$

where λ_c = cutoff wavelength and λ = operating wavelength

Standard wave guides and connectors

The following presents a list of rectangular wave guides that have been adopted as standard, their wavelength range, attenuation factors, and standard connectors.

dimensions inches	Army-Navy type number	cutoff wavelength λ_c (centimeters)	usable wavelength range for $TE_{0,1}$ mode (centimeters)	connectors choke	flange	attenuation in brass wave guide decibels/foot
1½ × 3 × 0.081 wall	RG–48/U	14.4	7.6–11.8	UG–54/U	UG–53/U	0.012 @ 10 cm
1 × 2 × 0.064 wall	RG–49/U	9.5	5.15–7.6	UG–148/U	UG–149/U	0.021 @ 6 cm
¾ × 1½ × 0.064 wall	RG–50/U	6.97	3.66–5.15	UG–150/U	contact type	0.036 @ 5 cm
⅝ × 1¼ × 0.064 wall	RG–51/U	5.7	3.0–4.26	UG–52/U	UG–51/U	0.050 @ 3.6 cm
½ × 1 × 0.050 wall	RG–52/U	4.57	2.4–3.66	UG–40/U	UG–39/U	0.076 @ 3.2 cm

Wave-guide circuit elements

Just as at low frequencies, it is possible to shape metallic or dielectric pieces to produce local concentrations of magnetic or electric energy within a wave guide, and thus produce what are, essentially, lumped inductances or capacitances.

The most convenient form of variable capacitance is a screw projecting into the guide from one side along an electric-field line. In lines handling high levels of pulsed power, such tuners are undesirable because of their tendency to cause breakdown of the air dielectric.

Because of the variation of impedance along a transmission line, it is often possible to replace a lumped capacitance by a lumped inductance at some other point in the line. The most common form of shunted lumped inductance is the diaphragm. Figs. 14 and 15 show the relative susceptance B/Y_0 for symmetrical and asymmetrical diaphragms in rectangular wave guides. These are computed for infinitely thin diaphragms. Finite thicknesses result in an increase in B/Y_0.

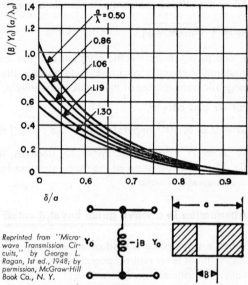

Reprinted from "Microwave Transmission Circuits," by George L. Ragan, 1st ed., 1948; by permission, McGraw-Hill Book Co., N. Y.

Fig. 14—Normalized susceptance of a symmetrical inductive diaphragm.

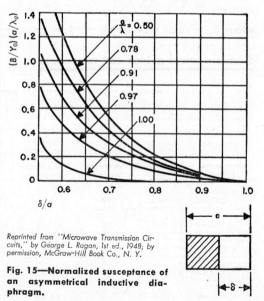

Reprinted from "Microwave Transmission Circuits," by George L. Ragan, 1st ed., 1948; by permission, McGraw-Hill Book Co., N. Y.

Fig. 15—Normalized susceptance of an asymmetrical inductive diaphragm.

Wave-guide circuit elements   *continued*

Another form of shunt inductance that is useful because of mechanical simplicity is a round post completely across the narrow dimension of a rectangular guide (for $TE_{0,1}$ mode). Figs. 16 and 17 give the normalized values of the elements of the equivalent 4-terminal network for several post diameters.

Frequency dependence of wave-guide susceptances may be given approximately as follows:

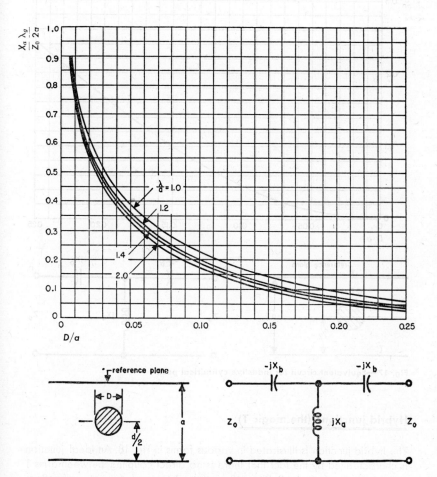

Fig. 16—Equivalent circuit for inductive cylindrical post.

Wave-guide circuit elements   *continued*

Inductive $= B/Y_0 \propto \lambda_g$

Capacitative $= B/Y_0 \propto 1/\lambda_g$ (distributed)

$\qquad\qquad\quad = B/Y_0 \propto \lambda_g/\lambda^2$ (lumped)

Distributed capacitances are found in junctions and slits, whereas tuning screws act as lumped capacitances.

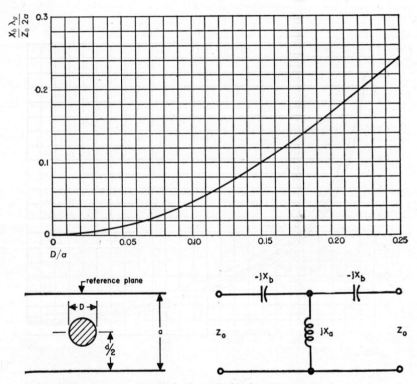

Fig. 17—Equivalent circuit for inductive cylindrical post.

Hybrid junctions (the magic T)

The hybrid junction is illustrated in various forms in Fig. 18. An ideal junction is characterized by the fact that there is no direct coupling between arms 1 and 4 or between 2 and 3. Power flows from 1 to 4 only by virtue of reflec-

Hybrid junctions (the magic T) *continued*

tions in arms 2 and 3. Thus, if arm 1 is excited, the voltage arriving at arm 4 is

$$E_4 = \frac{\sqrt{2}}{2} E_1 \left(\Gamma_2 e^{j2\theta_2} - \Gamma_3 e^{j2\theta_3} \right)$$

and the reflected voltage in arm 1 is

$$E_{r1} = \frac{\sqrt{2}}{2} E_1 \left(\Gamma_2 e^{j2\theta_2} + \Gamma_3 e^{j2\theta_3} \right)$$

where E_1 is the amplitude of the incident wave, Γ_2 and Γ_3 are the reflection coefficients of the terminations of arms 2 and 3, and θ_2 and θ_3 are the respective distances of the terminations from the junctions. In the case of the rings, θ is the distance between the arm-and-ring junction and the termination.

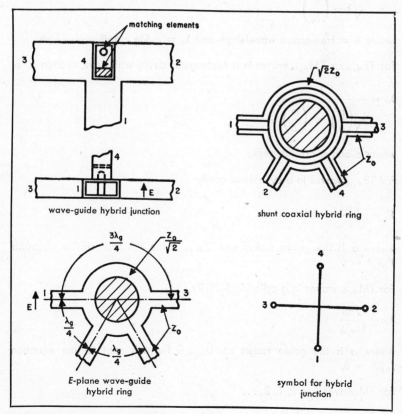

wave-guide hybrid junction

shunt coaxial hybrid ring

E-plane wave-guide hybrid ring

symbol for hybrid junction

Fig. 18—Hybrid junctions (magic T).

Resonant cavities

A cavity enclosed by metal walls will have an infinite number of natural frequencies at which resonance will occur. One of the more common types of cavity resonators is a length of transmission line (coaxial or wave guide) short circuited at both ends.

Resonance occurs when

$$2h = l \frac{\lambda_g}{2} \text{ where } l \text{ is an integer}$$

$2h$ = length of the resonator
λ_g = guide wavelength in resonator

$$= \frac{\lambda}{\sqrt{1 - \left(\frac{\lambda}{\lambda_c}\right)^2}}$$

where λ = free-space wavelength and λ_c = guide cutoff wavelength

For $TE_{n,m}$ or $TM_{n,m}$ waves in a rectangular cavity with cross section a, b,

$$\lambda_c = \frac{2}{\sqrt{\left(\frac{n}{a}\right)^2 + \left(\frac{m}{b}\right)^2}}$$

where n and m are integers.

For $TE_{n,m}$ waves in a cylindrical cavity

$$\lambda_c = \frac{2\pi a}{U'_{n,m}}$$

where a is the guide radius and $U'_{n,m}$ is the mth root of the equation $J'_n(U) = 0$.

For $TM_{n,m}$ waves in a cylindrical cavity

$$\lambda_c = \frac{2\pi a}{U_{n,m}}$$

where a is the guide radius and $U_{n,m}$ is the mth root of the equation $J_n(U) = 0$.

For TM waves $l = 0, 1, 2. \ldots$

For TE waves $l = 1, 2. \ldots$, but not 0

Resonant cavities   *continued*

Rectangular cavity of dimensions a, b, 2h

$$\lambda = \frac{2}{\sqrt{\left(\dfrac{l}{2h}\right)^2 + \left(\dfrac{n}{a}\right)^2 + \left(\dfrac{m}{b}\right)^2}} \quad \text{(where only one of } l, n, m \text{ may be zero).}$$

Cylindrical cavities of radius a and length 2h

$$\lambda = \frac{1}{\sqrt{\left(\dfrac{l}{4h}\right)^2 + \left(\dfrac{1}{\lambda_c}\right)^2}}$$

where λ_c is the guide cutoff wavelength.

Spherical resonators of radius a

$$\lambda = \frac{2\pi a}{U_{n,m}} \text{ for a TE wave} \qquad \lambda = \frac{2\pi a}{U'_{n,m}} \text{ for a TM wave}$$

Values of $U_{n,m}$:

$U_{1,1} = 4.5$, $U_{2,1} = 5.8$, $U_{1,2} = 7.64$

Values of $U'_{n,m}$:

$U'_{1,1} = 2.75 =$ lowest-order root

Additional cavity formulas

type of cavity	mode	λ_0 resonant wavelength	Q (all dimensions in same units)
Right circular cylinder	$TM_{0,1,1}$ (E_0)	$\dfrac{4}{\sqrt{\left(\dfrac{1}{h}\right)^2 + \dfrac{2.35}{a^2}}}$	$\dfrac{\lambda_0}{\delta}\dfrac{a}{\lambda_0}\dfrac{1}{1+\dfrac{a}{2h}}$
	$TE_{0,1,1}$ (H_0)	$\dfrac{4}{\sqrt{\left(\dfrac{1}{h}\right)^2 + \dfrac{5.93}{a^2}}}$	$\dfrac{\lambda_0}{\delta}\dfrac{a}{\lambda_0}\left[\dfrac{1+0.168\left(\dfrac{a}{h}\right)^2}{1+0.168\left(\dfrac{a}{h}\right)^3}\right]$
	$TE_{1,1,1}$ (H_1)	$\dfrac{4}{\sqrt{\left(\dfrac{1}{h}\right)^2 + \dfrac{1.37}{a^2}}}$	$\dfrac{\lambda_0}{\delta}\dfrac{h}{\lambda_0}\left[\dfrac{2.39h^2 + 1.73a^2}{3.39\dfrac{h^3}{a} + 0.73ah + 1.73a^2}\right]$

WAVE GUIDES AND RESONATORS

Resonant cavities *continued*

Characteristics of various types of resonators

type resonator	wavelength, λ	Q
Square prism $TE_{0,1,1}$	$2\sqrt{2}a$	$\dfrac{0.353\lambda}{\delta}\dfrac{1}{1+\dfrac{0.177\lambda}{h}}$
Circular cylinder $TM_{0,1,0}$	$2.61a$	$\dfrac{0.383\lambda}{\delta}\dfrac{1}{1+\dfrac{0.192\lambda}{h}}$
Sphere	$2.28a$	$0.318\dfrac{\lambda}{\delta}$
Sphere with cones	$4a$	Optimum Q for $\theta = 34°$ $0.1095\dfrac{\lambda}{\delta}$
Coaxial TEM	$4h$	Optimum Q for $\dfrac{b}{a} = 3.6$ $(Z_0 = 77$ ohms$)$ $\dfrac{\lambda}{4\delta + 7.2\dfrac{h\delta}{b}}$

Skin depth in meters $= \delta = \sqrt{10^7/2\pi\omega\sigma}$
where $\sigma =$ conductivity of wall in mhos/meter and $\omega = 2\pi \times$ frequency

Resonant cavities   *continued*

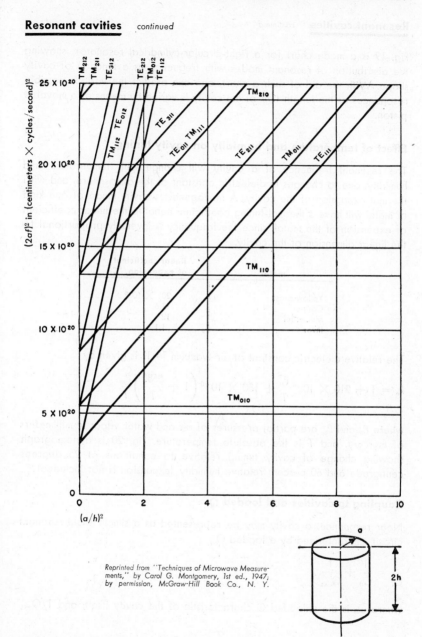

Reprinted from "Techniques of Microwave Measurements," by Carol G. Montgomery, 1st ed., 1947; by permission, McGraw-Hill Book Co., N. Y.

Fig. 19—Mode chart for right-circular-cylinder cavity.

Resonant cavities   *continued*

Fig. 19 is a mode chart for a right-circular-cylindrical resonator, showing the distribution of resonant modes with frequency as a function of cavity shape. With the aid of such a chart, one can predict the various possible resonances as the length (2h) of the cavity is varied by means of a movable piston.

Effect of temperature and humidity on cavity tuning

The resonant frequency of a cavity will change with temperature and humidity, due to changes in dielectric constant of the atmosphere, and with thermal expansion of the cavity. A homogeneous cavity made of one kind of metal will have a thermal-tuning coefficient equal to the linear coefficient of expansion of the metal, since the frequency is inversely proportional to the linear dimension of the cavity.

metal	linear coefficient of expansion/°C
Yellow brass	20×10^{-6}
Copper	17.6
Mild steel	12
Invar	1.1

The relative dielectric constant of air (vacuum = 1) is given by

$$k_e = 1 + 210 \times 10^{-6} \frac{P_a}{T} + 180 \times 10^{-6} \left(1 + \frac{5580}{T}\right)\frac{P_w}{T}$$

where P_a and P_w are partial pressures of air and water vapor in millimeters of mercury, and T is the absolute temperature. Fig. 20 is a nomograph showing change of cavity tuning relative to conditions at 25 degrees centigrade and 60 percent relative humidity (expansion is not included).

Coupling to cavities and loaded Q

Near resonance, a cavity may be represented as a simple shunt-resonant circuit, characterized by a loaded Q

$$\frac{1}{Q_l} = \frac{1}{Q_0} + \frac{1}{Q_{ext}}.$$

where Q_0 is the unloaded Q characteristic of the cavity itself, and $1/Q_{ext}$

Resonant cavities   *continued*

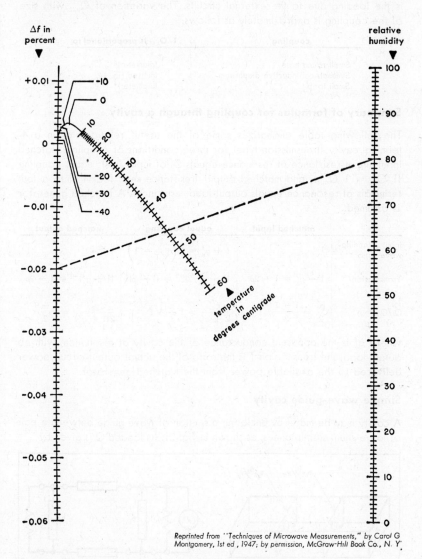

Reprinted from "Techniques of Microwave Measurements," by Carol G
Montgomery, 1st ed , 1947; by permission, McGraw-Hill Book Co., N. Y.

Fig. 20—Effect of temperature and humidity on cavity tuning.

Resonant cavities   *continued*

is the loading due to the external circuits. The variation of Q_{ext} with size of the coupling is approximately as follows:

coupling	$1/Q_{ext}$ is proportional to
Small round hole	(diameter)^6
Symmetrical inductive diaphragm	$(\delta)^4$ see Fig. 14
Small loop	(diameter)^4

Summary of formulas for coupling through a cavity

The following table summarizes some of the useful relationships in a 4-terminal cavity (transmission type) for three conditions of coupling: matched input (input resistance at resonance equals Z_0 of input line), equal coupling $(1/Q_{in} = 1/Q_{out})$, and matched output (resistance seen looking into output terminals at resonance equals output-load resistance). A matched generator is assumed.

	matched input	equal coupling	matched output
Input standing-wave ratio	1	$1 + g_c' = 2\left(\dfrac{1}{\sqrt{T}} - 1\right)$	$1 + 2g_c'$
Transmission	$1 - g_c' = 1 - 2\rho$	$(1 + g_c'/2)^{-2} = (1 - \rho)^2$	$(1 + g_c')^{-1} = 1 - 2\rho$
$Q_l/Q_0 = \rho$	$\dfrac{g_c'}{2} = \dfrac{1 - T}{2}$	$\dfrac{g_c'}{2 + g_c'} = 1 - \sqrt{T}$	$\dfrac{g_c'}{2(1 + g_c')} = \dfrac{1 - T}{2}$

where g_c' is the apparent conductance of the cavity at resonance, with no output load; the transmission T is the ratio of the actual output-circuit power delivered to the available power from the matched generator.

Simple wave-guide cavity

A cavity may be made by enclosing a section of wave guide between a pair of large shunt susceptances, as shown in Fig. 21. Its loaded Q is given by

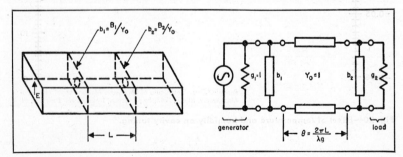

Fig. 21—Wave-guide cavity and equivalent circuit.

Resonant cavities *continued*

$$\frac{1}{Q_l} = \frac{1}{Q_0} + \frac{1}{Q_{in}} + \frac{1}{Q_{out}} = \frac{2}{n\pi} \left(\frac{\lambda}{\lambda_g}\right)^2 \left(\alpha L^r + \frac{1}{b_1^2} + \frac{g_2}{b_2^2}\right)$$

for b_1 and $b_2 \gg 1$, where b_1 and b_2 are the input and output normalized susceptances, g_2 is the conductance seen looking from the output terminals, α is the attenuation constant, and L is given by

$$L = \frac{\lambda_g}{2} \left(1 + \frac{b_1 + b_2}{2\pi b_1 b_2}\right)$$

Resonant irises

Resonant irises may be used to obtain low values of loaded Q (<100). The simplest type is shown in Fig. 22. It consists of an inductive diaphragm and a capacitive screw located in the same plane across the wave guide. For $Q_l < 50$, the losses in the resonant circuit may be ignored, and

$$1/Q_l \approx 1/Q_{ext}$$

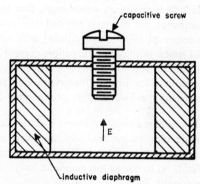

Fig. 22—Resonant iris in wave guide.

To a good approximation, the loaded Q (matched load and matched generator) is given by

$$Q_l = \frac{B_l}{2Y_0}$$

where B_l is the susceptance of the inductive diaphragm. This value may be taken from charts such as Figs. 14 and 15.

■ Antennas

The elementary dipole

Field intensity*

The elementary dipole forms the basis for many antenna computations. Since dipole theory assumes an antenna with current of constant magnitude and phase throughout its length, approximations to the elementary dipole are realized in practice only for antennas shorter than one-tenth wavelength. The theory can be applied directly to a loop whose circumference is less than one-tenth wavelength, thus forming a magnetic dipole. For larger antennas, the theory is applied by assuming the antenna to consist of a large number of infinitesimal dipoles with differences between individual dipoles of space position, polarization, current magnitude, and phase corresponding to the distribution of these parameters in the actual antenna. Field-intensity equations for large antennas are then developed by integrating or otherwise summing the field vectors of the many elementary dipoles.

The outline below concerns electric dipoles. It also can be applied to magnetic dipoles by installing the loop perpendicular to the *PO* line at the center of the sphere in Fig. 1. In this case, vector *h* becomes ϵ, the electric field; ϵ_t becomes the magnetic tangential field; and ϵ_r becomes the radial magnetic field.

Fig. 1

Electric and magnetic components in spherical coordinates for electric dipoles.

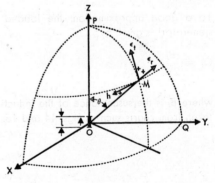

In the case of a magnetic dipole, the table, Fig. 2, showing variations of the field in the vicinity of the dipole, can also be used.

For electric dipoles, Fig. 1 indicates the electric and magnetic field components in spherical coordinates with positive values shown by the arrows.

* Based on R. Mesny, "Radio-Electricité Générale," Etienne Chiron, Paris, France; 1935.

The elementary dipole   *continued*

r = distance OM

θ = angle POM measured
      from P toward M

I = current in dipole

λ = wavelength

f = frequency

$\omega = 2\pi f$

$\alpha = \dfrac{2\pi}{\lambda}$

c = velocity of light (see page 25)

$v = \omega t - \alpha r$

l = length of dipole

The following equations expressed in electromagnetic units* (in vacuum)
result:

$$\epsilon_r = -\frac{c l \lambda I}{\pi}\frac{\cos\theta}{r^3}(\cos v - \alpha r \sin v)$$

$$\epsilon_t = +\frac{c l \lambda I}{2\pi}\frac{\sin\theta}{r^3}(\cos v - \alpha r \sin v - \alpha^2 r^2 \cos v)$$

$$h = - II \frac{\sin\theta}{r^2}(\sin v - \alpha r \cos v)$$

(1)

*See pages 26 and 27.

Fig. 2—Variations of field in the vicinity of a dipole.

r/λ	$1/\alpha r$	A_r	ϕ_r	A_t	ϕ_t	A_h	ϕ_h
0.01	15.9	4,028	3°.6	4,012	3°.6	253	93°.6
0.02	7.96	508	7°.2	500	7°.3	64.2	97°.2
0.04	3.98	65	14°.1	61	15°.0	16.4	104°.1
0.06	2.65	19.9	20°.7	17.5	23°.8	7.67	110°.7
0.08	1.99	8.86	26°.7	7.12	33°.9	4.45	116°.7
0.10	1.59	4.76	32°.1	3.52	45°.1	2.99	122°.1
0.15	1.06	1.66	42°.3	1.14	83°.1	1.56	132°.3
0.20	0.80	0.81	51°.5	0.70	114°.0	1.02	141°.5
0.25	0.64	0.47	57°.5	0.55	133°.1	0.75	147°.5
0.30	0.56	0.32	62°.0	0.48	143°.0	0.60	152°.0
0.35	0.45	0.23	65°.3	0.42	150°.1	0.50	155°.3
0.40	0.40	0.17	68°.3	0.37	154°.7	0.43	158°.3
0.45	0.35	0.134	70°.5	0.34	158°.0	0.38	160°.5
0.50	0.33	0.106	72°.3	0.30	160°.4	0.334	162°.3
0.60	0.265	0.073	75°.1	0.26	164°.1	0.275	165°.1
0.70	0.228	0.053	77°.1	0.22	166°.5	0.234	167°.1
0.80	0.199	0.041	78°.7	0.196	168°.3	0.203	168°.7
0.90	0.177	0.032	80°.0	0.175	169°.7	0.180	170°.0
1.00	0.159	0.026	80°.9	0.157	170°.7	0.161	170°.9
1.20	0.133	0.018	82°.4	0.132	172°.3	0.134	172°.4
1.40	0.114	0.013	83°.5	0.114	173°.5	0.114	173°.5
1.60	0.100	0.010	84°.3	0.100	174°.3	0.100	174°.3
1.80	0.088	0.008	84°.9	0.088	174°.9	0.088	174°.9
2.00	0.080	0.006	85°.4	0.080	175°.4	0.080	175°.4
2.50	0.064	0.004	86°.4	0.064	176°.4	0.064	176°.4
5.00	0.032	0.001	88°.2	0.032	178°.2	0.032	178°.2

A_r = coefficient for radial magnetic field
A_t = coefficient for tangential magnetic field

A_h = coefficient for electric field
ϕ_r, ϕ_t, ϕ_h = phase angles corresponding to coefficients

The elementary dipole   *continued*

These formulas are valid for the elementary dipole at distances that are large compared with the dimensions of the dipole. Length of the dipole must be small with respect to the wavelength, say $l/\lambda < 0.1$. The formulas are for a dipole in free space. If the dipole is placed vertically on a plane of infinite conductivity, its image should be taken into account, thus doubling the above values.

Field at great distance

When distance r exceeds five wavelengths, as is generally the case in radio applications, the radial electric field ϵ_r becomes negligible with respect to the tangential field and

$$\left.\begin{array}{l} \epsilon_r = 0 \\[2mm] \epsilon_t = -\dfrac{2\pi clI}{\lambda r}\sin\theta\cos(\omega t - \alpha r) \\[2mm] h = -\dfrac{\epsilon_t}{c} \end{array}\right\} \qquad (2)$$

Field at short distance

In the vicinity of the dipole $(r/\lambda < 0.01)$, αr is very small and only the first terms between parentheses in (1) remain. The ratio of the radial and tangential field is then

$$\frac{\epsilon_r}{\epsilon_t} = -2\cot\theta$$

Hence, the radial field at short distance has a magnitude of the same order as the tangential field. These two fields are in opposition. Further, the ratio of the magnetic and electric tangential field is

$$\frac{h}{\epsilon_t} = -\frac{\alpha r}{c}\frac{\sin v}{\cos v}$$

The magnitude of the magnetic field at short distances is, therefore, extremely small with respect to that of the tangential electric field, relative to their relationship at great distances. The two fields are in quadrature. Thus, at short distances, the effect of the dipole on an open circuit is much greater than on a closed circuit as compared with the effect at remote points.

The elementary dipole   *continued*

Field at intermediate distance

At intermediate distance, say between 0.01 and 5.0 wavelengths, one should take into account all the terms of the equations (1). This case occurs, for instance, when studying reactions between adjacent antennas. To calculate the fields, it is convenient to transform the equations as follows:

$$\left.\begin{array}{l} \epsilon_r = -\ 2\alpha^2 cII \cos \theta\ A_r \cos (v + \phi_r) \\ \epsilon_t = \alpha^2 cII \sin \theta\ A_t \cos (v + \phi_t) \\ h = \alpha^2 II \sin \theta\ A_h \cos (v + \phi_h) \end{array}\right\} \tag{3}$$

where

$$\left.\begin{array}{ll} A_r = \dfrac{\sqrt{1 + (\alpha r)^2}}{(\alpha r)^3} & \tan \phi_r = \alpha r \\[2ex] A_t = \dfrac{\sqrt{1 - (\alpha r)^2 + (\alpha r)^4}}{(\alpha r)^3} & \cot \phi_t = \dfrac{1}{\alpha r} - \alpha r \\[2ex] A_h = \dfrac{\sqrt{1 + (\alpha r)^2}}{(\alpha r)^2} & \cot \phi_h = -\ \alpha r \end{array}\right\} \tag{4}$$

Values of A's and ϕ's are given in Fig. 2 as a function of the ratio between the distance r and the wavelength λ. The second column contains values of $1/\alpha r$ that would apply if the fields ϵ_t and h behaved as at great distances.

Linear polarization

An electromagnetic wave is linearly polarized when the electric field lies wholly in one plane containing the direction of propagation.

Horizontal polarization: Is the case where the electric field lies in a plane parallel to the earth's surface.

Vertical polarization: Is the case where the electric field lies in a plane perpendicular to the earth's surface.

E plane: Of an antenna is the plane in which the electric field lies. The principal E plane of an antenna is the E plane that also contains the direction of maximum radiation.

H plane: Of an antenna is the plane in which the magnetic field lies. The H plane is normal to the E plane. The principal H plane of an antenna is the H plane that also contains the direction of maximum radiation.

Elliptical and circular polarization

An electromagnetic wave is elliptically polarized when the electric field does not lie wholly in one plane containing the direction of propagation. In a plane normal to the direction of propagation, the electric field rotates around the direction of propagation, making one complete revolution in a time equal to the period of the wave. If x and y are two orthogonal co-ordinate axes in the plane perpendicular to the direction of propagation, the field components along these axes are

$$E_x = A \sin \omega t$$

$$E_y = B \sin (\omega t + \phi)$$

where

A, B = constants

$\omega = 2\pi f$

f = frequency in cycles/second

t = time in seconds

ϕ = phase difference between x and y components in radians

If $\phi = 0$, the field is linearly polarized. If $\phi = \pm \pi/2$ and $A = B$, the field is circularly polarized. If $\phi = +\pi/2$, the field is right-handed-circularly polarized. If $\phi = -\pi/2$, the field is left-handed-circularly polarized. At a fixed instant of time a right-handed-circularly polarized field rotates clockwise around the direction of propagation when viewed in the direction of propagation. In a plane normal to the direction of propagation a right-handed-circularly polarized field rotates counter-clockwise as a function of time. To avoid confusion, the sense of rotation should be specified with respect to the direction of propagation.

The locus of the instantaneous values of the electric field in an elliptically polarized wave is an ellipse in the plane normal to the direction of propagation. The ratio of the minor diameter to the major diameter is called the axial ratio. The axial ratio is unity for circular polarization and zero for linear polarization.

The relative power received by an elliptically polarized receiving antenna as it is rotated in a plane normal to the direction of propagation of an elliptically polarized wave is given by

$$P_r = K \frac{(1 \pm r_1 r_2)^2 + (r_1 \pm r_2)^2 + (1 - r_1^2)(1 - r_2^2) \cos 2\theta}{(1 + r_1^2)(1 + r_2^2)} \tag{5}$$

Elliptical and circular polarization *continued*

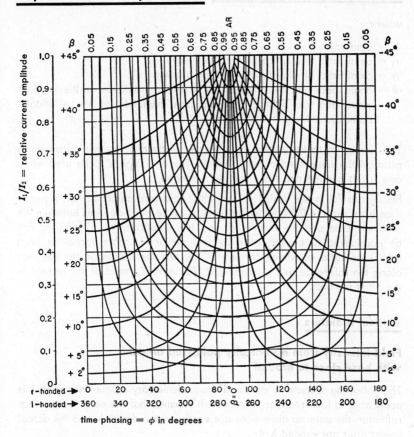

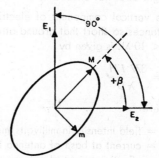

M = ellipse major axis

m = ellipse minor axis

β = inclination of ellipse major axis

$(AR) = m/M$ = axial ratio

$E_1 = k\,I_1 \cos \omega t$

$E_2 = k\,I_2 \cos (\omega t - \phi)$

Fig. 3—Elliptically polarized field as a function of relative current amplitude and phase ϕ. Axial-ratio (AR) lines and β lines are plotted.

Elliptical and circular polarization   continued

where

K = constant
r_1 = axial ratio of elliptically polarized wave
r_2 = axial ratio of elliptically polarized antenna
θ = angle between the direction of maximum amplitude in the incident
wave and the direction of maximum amplitude of the elliptically
polarized antenna

The $+$ sign is to be used if both the receiving and transmitting antennas produce the same hand of polarization. The $(-)$ sign is to be used when one is left handed and the other right handed.

Fig. 3 is useful in the design of circularly polarized antennas. For example if an axial ratio of 0.5 is measured with an angle of 15 degrees between the maximum field and the reference axis, this elliptically polarized field can be considered to be produced by two similar radiators normal to each other, the ratio of whose currents is 1.8, and the current in the radiator along the reference axis is larger and 70 degrees ahead of the current in the other radiator.

Vertical radiators

Field intensity from a vertically polarized antenna with base close to ground

The following formula is obtained from elementary-dipole theory and is applicable to low-frequency antennas. It assumes that the earth is a perfect reflector, the antenna dimensions are small compared with λ, and the actual height does not exceed $\lambda/4 \cdot$

The vertical component of electric field radiated in the ground plane, at distances so short that ground attenuation may be neglected (usually when $D < 10 \lambda$), is given by

$$E = \frac{377\, I\, H_e}{\lambda\, D} \tag{6}$$

where

E = field intensity in millivolts/meter
I = current at base of antenna in amperes
H_e = effective height of antenna
λ = wavelength in same units as H
D = distance in kilometers

Vertical radiators   *continued*

The effective height of a grounded vertical antenna is equivalent to the height of a vertical wire producing the same field along the horizontal as the actual antenna, provided the vertical wire carries a current that is constant along its entire length and of the same value as at the base of the actual antenna. Effective height depends upon the geometry of the antenna and varies slowly with λ. For types of antennas normally used at low and medium frequencies, it is roughly one-half to two-thirds the actual height of the antenna.

For certain antenna configurations effective height can be calculated by the following formulas

Straight vertical antenna: $h \leqslant \lambda/4$

$$H_e = \frac{\lambda}{\pi \sin \dfrac{2\pi h}{\lambda}} \sin^2 \left(\frac{\pi h}{\lambda}\right)$$

where $h =$ actual height

Loop antenna: $A < 0.001 \, \lambda^2$

$$H_e = \frac{2\pi n A}{\lambda}$$

where

$A =$ mean area per turn of loop

$n =$ number of turns

Adcock antenna

$$H_e = \frac{2\pi ab}{\lambda}$$

where

$a =$ height of antenna

$b =$ spacing between antennas

In the above formulas, if H_e is desired in meters or feet, all dimensions h, A, a, b, and λ must be in meters or feet, respectively.

Practical vertical-tower antennas

The field intensity from a single vertical tower insulated from ground and either of self-supporting or guyed construction, such as is commonly used for medium-frequency broadcasting, may be calculated by the following

Vertical radiators   *continued*

formula. This is more accurate than formula (6). Near ground level the formula is valid within the range $2\lambda < D < 10\lambda$.

$$E = \frac{60 I}{D \sin 2\pi\frac{h}{\lambda}} \left[\frac{\cos \left(2\pi\frac{h}{\lambda} \cos \theta\right) - \cos 2\pi\frac{h}{\lambda}}{\sin \theta} \right] \qquad (7)$$

where

E = field intensity in millivolts/meter
I = current at base of antenna in amperes
h = height of antenna
λ = wavelengths in same units as h
D = distance in kilometers
θ = angle from the vertical

Radiation patterns in the vertical plane for antennas of various heights are shown in Fig. 4. Field intensity along the horizontal as a function of antenna height for one kilowatt radiated is shown in Fig. 5.

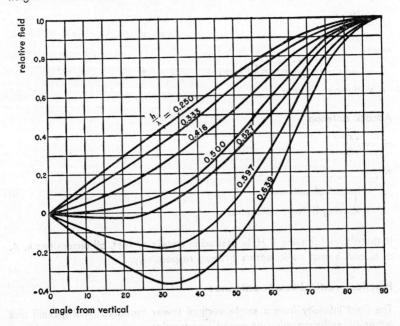

Fig. 4—Field strength as a function of angle of elevation for vertical radiators of different heights.

Vertical radiators   *continued*

Both Figs. 4 and 5 assume sinusoidal distribution of current along the antenna and perfect ground conductivity. Current magnitudes for one-kilowatt power used in calculating Fig. 5 are also based on the assumption that the only resistance is the theoretical radiation resistance of a vertical wire with sinusoidal current.

Since inductance and capacitance are not uniformly distributed along the tower and since current is attenuated in traversing the tower, it is impossible to obtain sinusoidal current distribution in practice. Consequently actual radiation patterns and field intensities differ from Figs. 4 and 5.* The closest approximation to sinusoidal current is found on constant-cross-section towers.

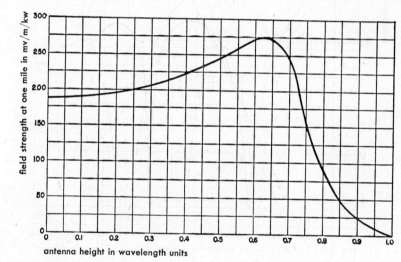

Fig. 5—Field strength along the horizontal as a function of antenna height for a vertical grounded radiator with one kilowatt radiated power.

In addition, antenna efficiencies vary from about 70 percent for 0.15 wavelength physical height to over 95 percent for 0.6 wavelength height. The input power must be multiplied by the efficiency to obtain the power radiated.

Average results of measurements of impedance at the base of several actual vertical radiators, as given by Chamberlain and Lodge†, are shown in Fig. 6.

* For information on the effect of some practical current distributions on field intensities see H. E. Gihring and G. H. Brown, "General Considerations of Tower Antennas for Broadcast Use," *Proceedings of the I.R.E.*, vol. 23, pp. 311–356; April, 1935.

† A. B. Chamberlain and W. B. Lodge, "The Broadcast Antenna," *Proceedings of the I.R.E.*, vol. 24, pp. 11–35; January, 1936.

Vertical radiators   *continued*

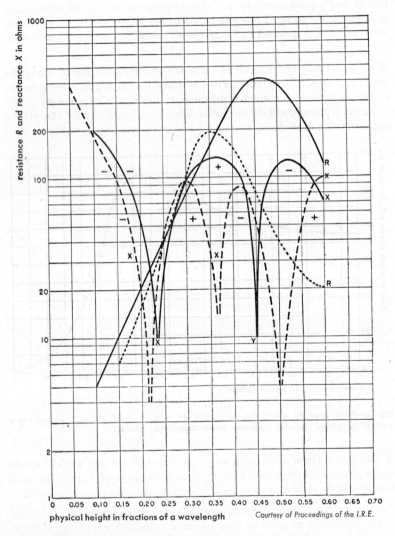

Fig. 6—Resistance and reactance components of impedance between tower base and ground of vertical radiators as given by Chamberlain and Lodge. Solid lines show average results for 5 guyed towers; dashed lines show average results for 3 self-supporting towers.

Vertical radiators   *continued*

For design purposes when actual resistance and current of the projected radiator are unknown, resistance values may be selected from Fig. 6 and the resulting effective current obtained from

$$I_e = \sqrt{\frac{W\eta}{R}} \tag{8}$$

where

I_e = current effective in producing radiation in amperes

W = watts input

η = antenna efficiency, varying from 0.70 at $h/\lambda = 0.15$ to 0.95 at $h/\lambda = 0.6$

R = resistance at base of antenna in ohms

If I_e from (8) is substituted in (7), reasonable approximations to the field intensity at unit distances, such as one kilometer or one mile, will be obtained.

The practical equivalent of a higher tower may be secured by adding a capacitance "hat" with or without tuning inductance at the top of a lower tower.*

A good ground system is important with vertical-radiator antennas. It should consist of at least 120 radial wires, each one-half wavelength or longer, buried 6 to 12 inches below the surface of the soil. A ground screen of high-conductivity metal mesh, bonded to the ground system, should be used on or above the surface of the ground adjacent to the tower.

Field intensity and radiated power from antennas in free space

Isotropic radiator

The power density P at a point due to the power P_t radiated by an isotropic radiator is

$$P = P_t/4\pi R^2 \text{ watts/meter}^2 \tag{9}$$

* For additional information see G. H. Brown, "A Critical Study of the Characteristics of Broadcast Antennas as Affected by Antenna Current Distribution," *Proceedings of the I.R.E.*, vol. 24, pp. 48–81; January, 1936: and G. H. Brown and J. G. Leitch, "The Fading Characteristics of the Top-Loaded WCAU Antenna," *Proceedings of the I.R.E.*, vol. 25, pp. 583–611; May, 1937.

Field intensity and radiated power   *continued*

where

R = distance in meters

P_t = transmitted power in watts

The electric-field intensity E in volts/meter and power density P in watts/meter^2 at any point are related by

$$P = E^2/120\pi$$

where 120π is known as the resistance of free space. From this

$$E = \sqrt{120\pi P} = \sqrt{30P_t}/R \text{ volts/meter} \tag{10}$$

Half-wave dipole

For a half-wave dipole, in the direction of maximum radiation

$$P = 1.64\, P_t/4\pi R^2 \tag{11}$$

$$E = \sqrt{49.2\, P_t}/R \tag{12}$$

These relations are shown in Fig. 7.

Received power

To determine the power intercepted by a receiving antenna, multiply the power density from Fig. 7 by the receiving area. The receiving area is

$$\text{Area} = G\, \lambda^2/4\pi$$

where

G = gain of receiving antenna

λ = wavelength in meters

The receiving areas and gains of common antennas are given in Fig. 25.

Equation (13) can be used to determine the power received by an antenna of gain G_r when the transmitted power P_t is radiated by an antenna of gain G_t.

$$P_r = \frac{P_t G_r G_t \lambda^2}{(4\pi R)^2} \tag{13}$$

G_t and G_r are the gains over an isotropic radiator. If the gains over a dipole are known, instead of gain over isotropic radiator, multiply each gain by 1.64 before inserting in (13).

Field intensity and radiated power *continued*

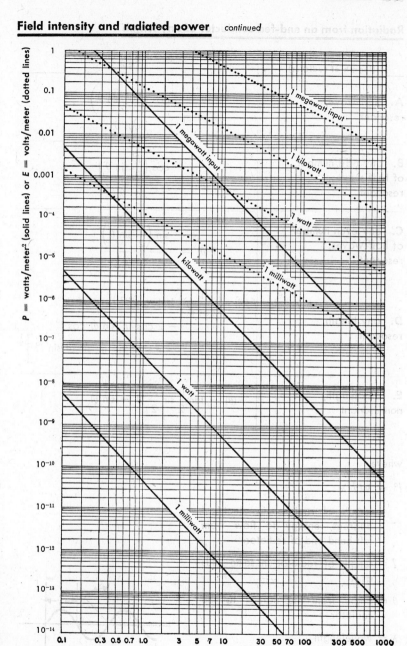

Fig. 7—Power density at various distances from a half-wave dipole.

Radiation from an end-fed conductor of any length

configuration (length of radiator)	expression for intensity $F(\theta)$
A. half-wave, resonant	$F(\theta) = \dfrac{\cos\left(90° \sin\theta\right)}{\cos\theta}$
B. any odd number of half waves, resonant	$F(\theta) = \dfrac{\cos\left(\dfrac{l°}{2}\sin\theta\right)}{\cos\theta}$
C. any even number of half waves, resonant	$F(\theta) = \dfrac{\sin\left(\dfrac{l°}{2}\sin\theta\right)}{\cos\theta}$
D. any length, resonant	$F(\theta) = \dfrac{1}{\cos\theta}\left[1 + \cos^2 l° + \sin^2\theta\,\sin^2 l° \\ - 2\cos(l°\sin\theta)\cos l° \\ - 2\sin\theta\,\sin(l°\sin\theta)\sin l°\right]^{\frac{1}{2}}$
E. any length, nonresonant	$F(\theta) = \tan\dfrac{\theta}{2}\sin\dfrac{l°}{2}(1 - \sin\theta)$

where

$l° = 360l/\lambda$

= length of radiator in electrical degrees, energy to flow from left-hand end of radiator.

l = length of radiator in same units as λ

θ = angle from the normal to the radiator

λ = wavelength

See also Fig. 8.

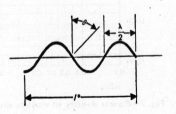

Radiation from an end-fed conductor of any length *continued*

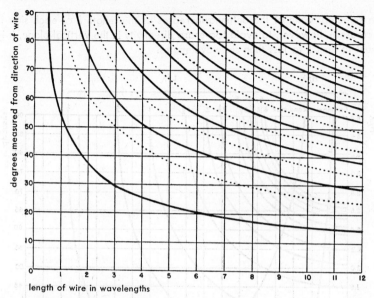

length of wire in wavelengths

Fig. 8—Directions of maximum (solid lines) and minimum (dotted lines) radiation from a single-wire radiator. Direction given here is $(90° − \theta)$.

Rhombic antennas

Linear radiators may be combined in various ways to form antennas such as the horizontal vee, inverted vee, etc. The type most commonly used at high frequencies is the horizontal terminated rhombic shown in Fig. 9.

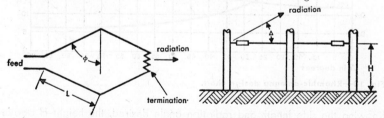

Fig. 9—Dimensions and radiation angles for rhombic antenna.

In designing rhombic antennas* for high-frequency radio circuits, the desired vertical angle Δ of radiation above the horizon must be known or assumed. When the antenna is to operate over a wide range of radiation angles or is to operate on several frequencies, compromise values of *H, L,* and *ϕ* must

* For more complete information see A. E. Harper, "Rhombic Antenna Design," D. Van Nostrand Company, New York, New York; 1941.

Rhombic antennas *continued*

be selected. Gain of the antenna increases as the length L of each side is increased; however, to avoid too-sharp directivity in the vertical plane, it is usual to limit L to less than six wavelengths.

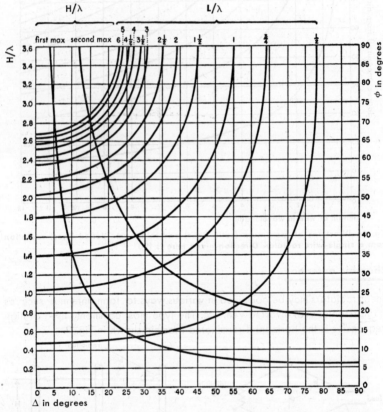

Fig. 10—Rhombic-antenna design chart.

Knowing the side length and radiation angle desired, the height H above ground and the tilt angle ϕ can be obtained from Fig. 10 as in the following example:

Problem: Find H and ϕ if $\Delta = 20$ degrees and $L = 4\lambda$.

Solution: On Fig. 10 draw a vertical line from $\Delta = 20$ degrees to meet $L/\lambda = 4$ curve and H/λ curves. From intersection at $L/\lambda = 4$, read on the right-hand scale $\phi = 71.5$ degrees. From intersection on H/λ curves, there are two possible values on the left-hand scale

a. $H/\lambda = 0.74$ or $H = 0.74\lambda$ **b.** $H/\lambda = 2.19$ or $H = 2.19\lambda$

Rhombic antennas   *continued*

Similarly, with an antenna 4λ on the side and a tilt angle $\phi = 71.5°$, working backwards, it is found that the angle of maximum radiation Δ is 20°, if the antenna is 0.74λ or 2.19λ above ground.

Figs. 11 and 12 give useful information for the calculation of the terminating resistance of rhombic antennas.

A—No. 14
B—No. 12 United States Steel Type
C—No. 10 "12" or American Iron and
D—No. 8   Steel Institute No. 410
E—No. 6   Stainless Steel.
F—No. 6 Iron wire
All sizes are American wire gauge

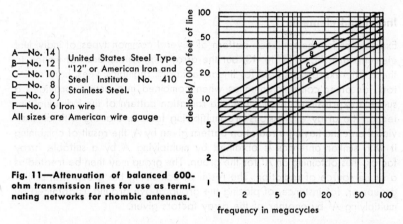

Fig. 11—Attenuation of balanced 600-ohm transmission lines for use as terminating networks for rhombic antennas.

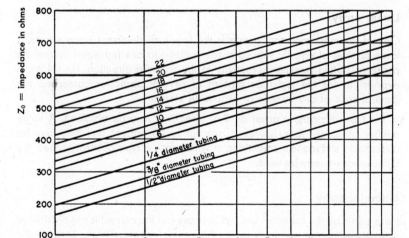

S = center-to-center spacing in inches

Courtesy of Radio Corporation of America

$$Z_0 = 276 \log_{10} \frac{2S}{d} \text{ ohms}$$

S = center-to-center spacing
d = conductor diameter

Fig. 12—Parallel-line spacing and wire size to give 600-ohm terminating impedance for rhombic antennas. Attenuation of 600-ohm lines is given in Fig. 11. All wire sizes are American wire gauge.

Antenna arrays*

The basis for all directivity control in antenna arrays is wave interference. By providing a large number of sources of radiation, it is possible with a fixed amount of power greatly to reinforce radiation in a desired direction while suppressing the radiation in undesired directions. The individual sources may be any type of antenna.

Individual elements

Expressions for the radiation pattern of several common types of individual elements are shown in Fig. 13, but the array expressions are not limited to these. The expressions hold for linear radiators, rhombics, vees, horn radiators, or other complex antennas when combined into arrays, provided a suitable expression is used for A, the radiation pattern of the individual antenna. The array expressions are multiplying factors. Starting with an individual antenna having a radiation pattern given by A, the result of combining it with similar antennas is obtained by multiplying A by a suitable array factor, thus obtaining an A' for the group. The group may then be treated as a single source of radiation. The result of combining the group with similar groups or, for instance, of placing the group above ground, is obtained by multiplying A' by another of the array factors given.

Linear array

One of the most important arrays is the linear multielement array where a large number of equally spaced antenna elements are fed equal currents in phase to obtain maximum directivity in the forward direction. Fig. 14 gives expressions for the radiation pattern of several particular cases and the general case of any number of broadside elements.

In this type of array, a great deal of directivity may be obtained. A large number of minor lobes, however, are apt to be present and they may be undesirable under some conditions, in which case a type of array, called the Binomial array, may be used.

Binomial array

Here again all the radiators are fed in phase but the current is not distributed equally among the array elements, the center radiators in the array being fed more current than the outer ones. Fig. 15 shows the configuration and general expression for such an array. In this case the configuration is made for a vertical stack of loop antennas in order to obtain single-lobe directivity

---

* Examples of problems involving the use of the antenna-array information presented here are given on pp. 394–396.

Antenna arrays   *continued*

Fig. 13—Radiation patterns of several common types of antennas.

type of radiator	current distribution	directivity	
		horizontal E plane $A(\theta)$	vertical H plane $A(\beta)$
A half-wave dipole	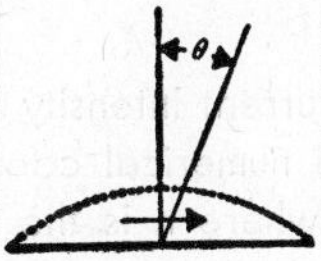	$A(\theta) = K \dfrac{\cos\left(\dfrac{\pi}{2}\sin\theta\right)}{\cos\theta}$ $\approx K\cos\theta$	$A(\beta) = K(1)$
B shortened dipole	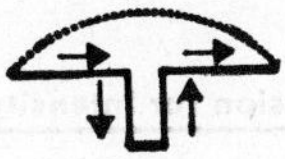	$A(\theta) \approx K\cos\theta$	$A(\beta) = K(1)$
C lengthened dipole	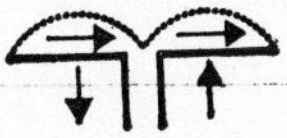	$A(\theta) =$ $K\left[\dfrac{\cos\left(\dfrac{\pi l}{\lambda}\sin\theta\right) - \cos\dfrac{\pi l}{\lambda}}{\cos\theta}\right]$	$A(\beta) = K(1)$
D horizontal loop	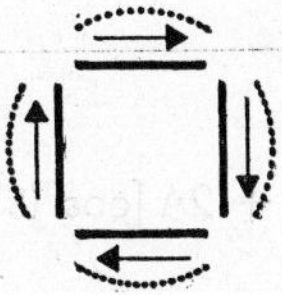	$A(\theta) \approx K(1)$	$A(\beta) = K\cos\beta$
E horizontal turnstile	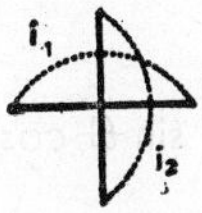 i_1 and i_2 phased 90°	$A(\theta) \approx K'(1)$	$A(\beta) \approx K'(1)$

θ = horizontal angle measured from perpendicular bisecting plane
β = vertical angle measured from horizon
K and K' are constants and $K' \approx 0.7K$

382

in the vertical plane. If such an array were desired in the horizontal plane, say n dipoles end to end, with the specified current distribution the expression would be

$$F(\theta) = 2^{n-1} \left[\frac{\cos\left(\frac{\pi}{2}\sin\theta\right)}{\cos\theta} \right] \cos^{n-1}\left(\tfrac{1}{2} S° \sin\theta\right)$$

The term binomial results from the fact that the current intensity in the successive array elements is in accordance with the numerical coefficients of the terms in the binomial expansion $(a + b)^{n-1}$ where n is the number of elements in the array. This is shown in Fig. 15.

Fig. 14—Linear-multielement-array broadside directivity. See Fig. 13 to compare A for common antenna types.

	configuration of array	expression for intensity F(θ)
A	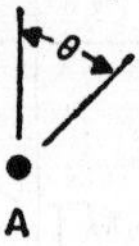	$F(\theta) = A[1]$
B	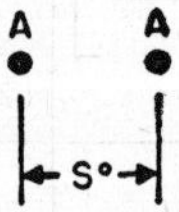	$F(\theta) = 2A\left[\cos\left(\frac{S°}{2}\sin\theta\right)\right]$
C	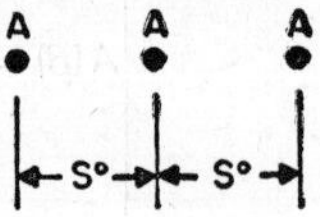	$F(\theta) = A + 2A\left[\cos\left(S° \sin\theta\right)\right]$
D	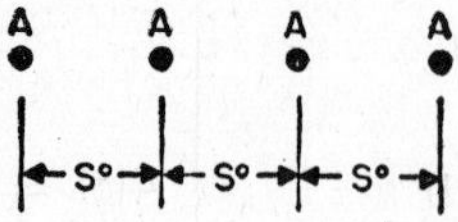	$F(\theta) = 4A\left[\cos\left(S° \sin\theta\right)\cos\left(\frac{S°}{2}\sin\theta\right)\right]$
E	*m* radiators (general case)	$F(\theta) = A\,\dfrac{\sin\left(m\,\dfrac{S°}{2}\sin\theta\right)}{\sin\left(\dfrac{S°}{2}\sin\theta\right)}$

Antenna arrays   *continued*

Fig. 15—Development of the binomial array. The expression for the general case is given in E.

configuration of array	expression for intensity $F(\beta)$
A $F(\beta) = \cos\beta[1]$	

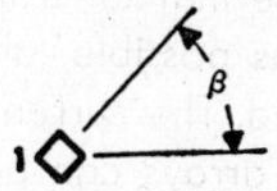

A

$$F(\beta) = \cos\beta[1]$$

B

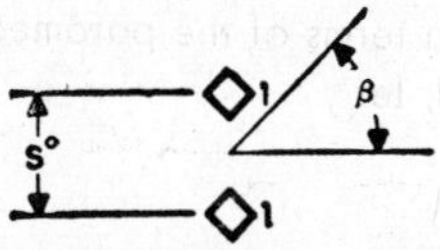

$$F(\beta) = 2\cos\beta\left[\cos\left(\frac{S^\circ}{2}\sin\beta\right)\right]$$

C

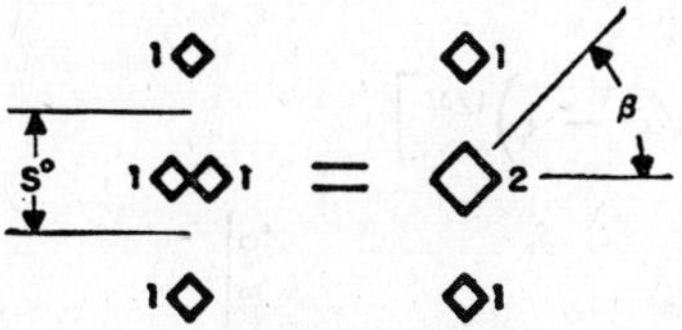

$$F(\beta) = 2^2\cos\beta\left[\cos^2\left(\frac{S^\circ}{2}\sin\beta\right)\right]$$

D

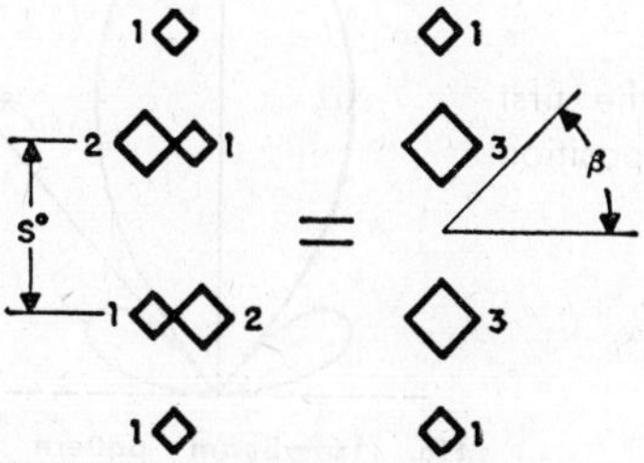

$$F(\beta) = 2^3\cos\beta\left[\cos^3\left(\frac{S^\circ}{2}\sin\beta\right)\right]$$

E

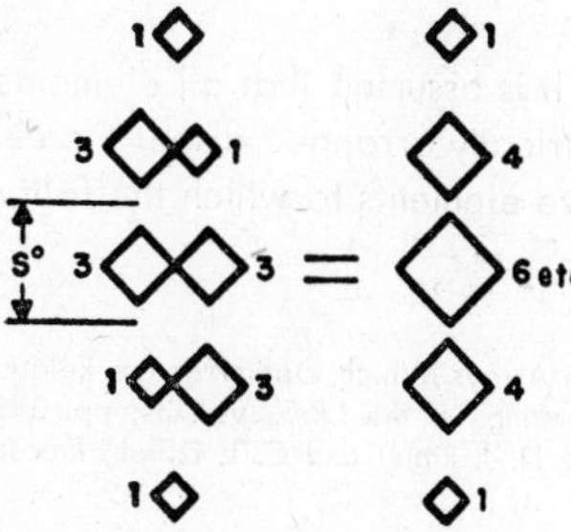

$$F(\beta) = 2^4\cos\beta\left[\cos^4\left(\frac{S^\circ}{2}\sin\beta\right)\right]$$

and in general:

$$F(\beta) =$$
$$2^{n-1}\cos\beta\left[\cos^{n-1}\left(\frac{S^\circ}{2}\sin\beta\right)\right]$$

where n = number of loops in the array

Optimum current distribution for broadside arrays*

It is the purpose here to give design equations and to illustrate a method of calculating the optimum current distribution in broadside arrays. The resulting current distribution is optimum in the sense that (a) if the side-lobe level is specified, the beam width is as narrow as possible, and (b) if the first null is specified, the side-lobe level is minimized. The current distribution for 4- through 12-; and 16-, 20-, and 24-element arrays can be calculated after either the side-lobe level or the position of the first null is specified.

Parameter Z: All design equations are given in terms of the parameter Z. To determine Z if the side-lobe level is specified, let

$$r = \frac{\text{(maximum amplitude of main lobe)}}{\text{(maximum amplitude of side lobe)}}$$

then

$$Z = \tfrac{1}{2}\left[\left(r + \sqrt{r^2 - 1}\right)^{1/M} + \left(r - \sqrt{r^2 - 1}\right)^{1/M}\right]$$

where

$M = 2N - 1$ for an array of $2N$ elements

$\quad = 2N$ for an array of $2N + 1$ elements

To determine Z if the position of the first null is specified (Fig. 16), let $\theta_0 =$ position of first null. Then

$$Z = \frac{\cos\left(\pi/2M\right)}{\cos\left(\dfrac{\pi S}{\lambda}\sin\theta_0\right)}$$

where $S =$ spacing between elements.

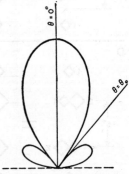

Fig. 16—Beam pattern for broadside array, showing first null at θ_0.

Design equations: The following are in Z. It is assumed that all elements are isotropic, are fed in phase, and are symmetrically arranged about the center. See Fig. 17 for designation of the respective elements to which the following currents I apply.

---

* C. L. Dolph, "A Current Distribution for Broadside Arrays Which Optimizes the Relationship Between Beam Width and Side-Lobe Level," *Proceedings of the I.R.E.*, vol. 34, pp. 335–348; June, 1946. See also discussion on subject paper by H. J. Riblet and C. L. Dolph, *Proceedings of the I.R.E.*, vol. 35, pp. 489–492; May, 1947.

Antenna arrays *continued*

4-element array

$$I_2 = Z^3$$
$$I_1 = 3(I_2 - Z)$$

8-element array

$$I_4 = Z^7$$
$$I_3 = 7(I_4 - Z^5)$$
$$I_2 = 5I_3 - 14I_4 + 14Z^3$$
$$I_1 = 3I_2 - 5I_3 + 7I_4 - 7Z$$

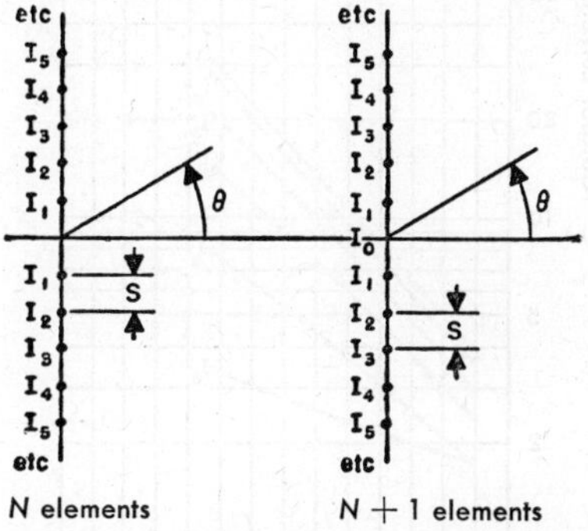

12-element array

$$I_6 = Z^{11}$$
$$I_5 = 11(I_6 - Z^9)$$
$$I_4 = 9I_5 - 44I_6 + 44Z^7$$
$$I_3 = 7I_4 - 27I_5 + 77I_6 - 77Z^5$$
$$I_2 = 5I_3 - 14I_4 + 30I_5 - 55I_6 + 55Z^3$$
$$I_1 = 3I_2 - 5I_3 + 7I_4 - 9I_5 + 11I_6 - 11Z$$

16-element array

$$I_8 = Z^{15}$$
$$I_7 = 15I_8 - 15Z^{13}$$
$$I_6 = 13I_7 - 90I_8 + 90Z^{11}$$
$$I_5 = 11I_6 - 65I_7 + 275I_8 - 275Z^9$$
$$I_4 = 9I_5 - 44I_6 + 156I_7 - 450I_8 + 450Z^7$$
$$I_3 = 7I_4 - 27I_5 + 77I_6 - 182I_7 + 378I_8 - 378Z^5$$
$$I_2 = 5I_3 - 14I_4 + 30I_5 - 55I_6 + 91I_6 - 140I_8 + 140Z^3$$
$$I_1 = 3I_2 - 5I_3 + 7I_4 - 9I_5 + 11I_6 - 13I_7 + 15I_8 - 15Z$$

The relative current values necessary for optimum current distribution are plotted as a function of side-lobe level in decibels for 8-, 12-, and 16-element arrays (Figs. 18–20).

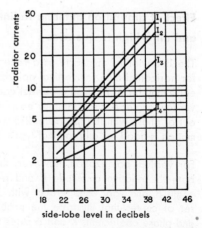

Fig. 17—**Broadside array of N and N + 1 elements showing nomenclature of radiators, spacing S, and beam-angular measurement θ.**

Courtesy of Proceedings of the I.R.E.

Courtesy of Proceedings of the I.R.E.

Fig. 18—**The relative current values for an 8-element array necessary for "the optimum current distribution" as a function of side-lobe level in decibels.**

Antenna arrays *continued*

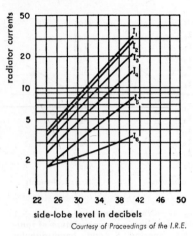

side-lobe level in decibels

Courtesy of Proceedings of the I.R.E.

side-lobe level in decibels

Courtesy of Proceedings of the I.R.E.

Fig. 19—The relative current values for a 12-element array necessary for "the optimum current distribution" as a function of side-lobe level in decibels.

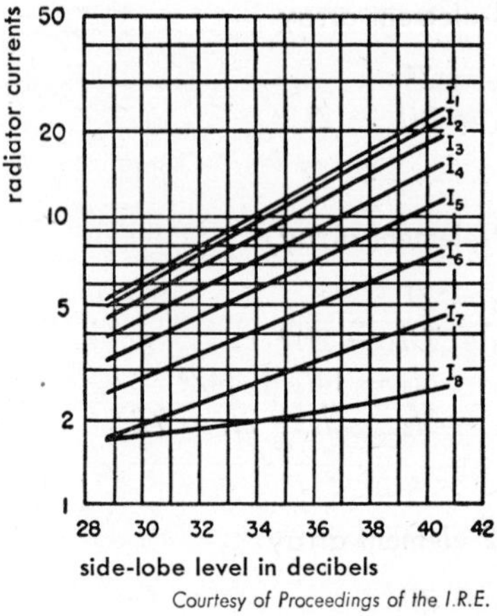

Fig. 20—The relative current values for a 16-element array necessary for "the optimum current distribution" as a function of side-lobe level in decibels.

Effect of ground on antenna radiation at very-high and ultra-high frequencies

The behavior of the earth as a reflecting surface is considerably different for horizontal than for vertical polarization. For horizontal polarization the earth may be considered a perfect conductor, i.e., the reflected wave at all vertical angles β is substantially equal to the incident wave and 180 degrees out of phase with it. $F(\beta)$ in Fig. 21B was derived on this basis. The approximation is good for all practical types of ground.

For vertical polarization, however, the problem is much more complex as both the relative amplitude K and relative phase ϕ change with vertical angle β, and vary considerably with different types of ground. Fig. 22 is a set of curves that illustrate the problem. The subscripts to the amplitude and phase coefficients K and ϕ refer to the type of polarization.

It is to be noted particularly that at grazing incidence ($\beta = 0$) the reflection coefficient is the same for vertical and horizontal polarization. This is substantially true for all practical ground conditions.

Antenna arrays   *continued*

Directivity of several miscellaneous arrays

Fig. 21—Directivity of several array problems that do not fall into any of the preceding classes.

configuration of array	expression for intensity
A. two radiators any phase ϕ 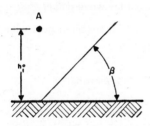	$F(\theta) =$ $$[A_1^2 + A_2^2 + 2A_1A_2 \cos{(S° \sin \theta + \phi)}]^{\frac{1}{2}}$$ When $A_1 = A_2$, $$F(\theta) = 2A \cos \left(\frac{S°}{2} \sin \theta + \frac{\phi}{2} \right)$$
B. radiator above ground (horizontal polarization) 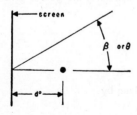	$$F(\beta) = 2A \sin{(h_1° \sin \beta)}$$
C. radiator parallel to screen 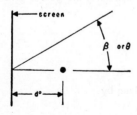	$$F(\beta) = 2A \sin{(d° \cos \beta)}$$ or $$F(\theta) = 2A \sin{(d° \cos \theta)}$$

$S°$ = spacing in electrical degrees

$h_1°$ = height of radiator in electrical degrees

$d°$ = spacing of radiator from screen in electrical degrees

Antenna arrays   *continued*

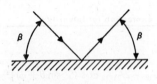

Fig. 22—Typical ground-reflection coefficients for horizontal and vertical polarizations.

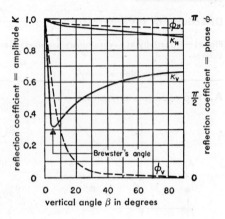

Electromagnetic horns and parabolic reflectors

Radiation from a wave guide may be obtained by placing an electromagnetic horn of a particular size at the end of the wave guide.

Fig. 23 gives data for designing a horn to have a specified gain with the shortest length possible. The length L_1 is given by

$$L_1 = L\left(1 - \frac{a}{2A} - \frac{b}{2B}\right)$$

where

a = wide dimension of wave guide in the H plane

b = narrow dimension of wave guide in E plane

If $L \geqslant a^2/\lambda$, where a = longer dimension of aperture, the gain is given by
$G = 10ab/\lambda^2$

The half-power width in the E plane is given by
51 λ/b degrees
and the half-power width in the H plane is given by
70 λ/a degrees
where

E = electric vector

H = magnetic vector

Fig. 24 shows how the angle between 10-decibel points varies with aperture.

Electromagnetic horns and parabolic reflectors   *continued*

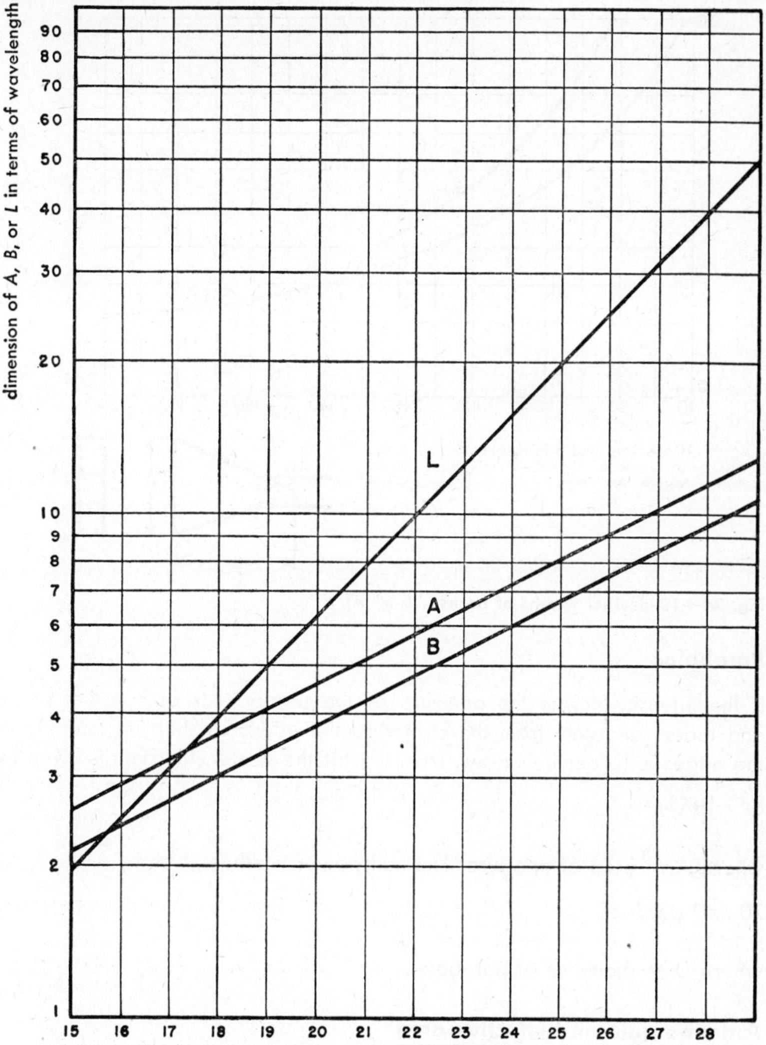

dimension of A, B, or L in terms of wavelength

gain in decibels above isotropic radiator

L = axial length to apex

A = width of aperture in H plane

B = width of aperture in E plane

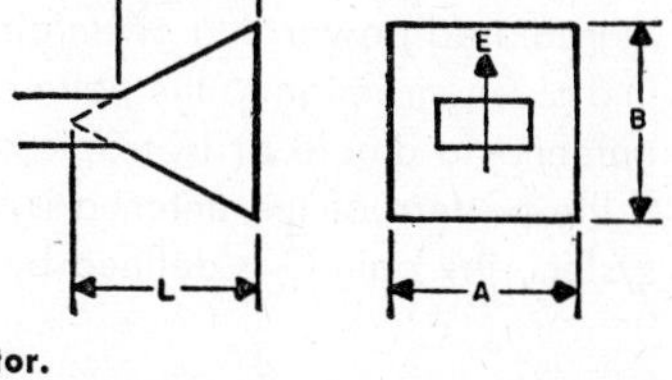

Fig. 23—Design of electromagnetic-horn radiator.

Electromagnetic horns and parabolic reflectors *continued*

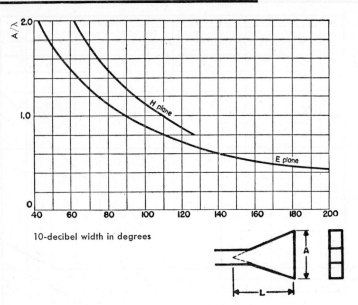

10-decibel width in degrees

Fig. 24—10-decibel widths of horns. $L \geqslant A^2/\lambda$

Parabolas

If the intensity across the aperture of the parabola is of constant phase and tapers smoothly from the center to the edges so that the intensity at the edges is 10 decibels down from that at the center, the gain is given by

$$G = 8A/\lambda^2$$

where A = area of aperture. The half-power width is given by

$70 \lambda/D$ degrees

where D = diameter of parabola.

Antenna gain and effective area

The gain of an antenna is a measure of how well the antenna concentrates its radiated power in a given direction. It is the ratio of the power radiated in a given direction to the power radiated in the same direction by a standard antenna (a dipole or isotropic radiator), keeping the input power constant. If the pattern of the antenna is known and there are no ohmic losses in the system, the gain G is defined by

Antenna gain and effective area *continued*

$$G = \left(\frac{\text{maximum power intensity}}{\text{average power intensity}}\right) = \frac{|E_0|^2}{\underset{\substack{\text{all} \\ \text{angles}}}{\int\int} |E|^2 \, d\Omega} \tag{14}$$

where

$|E_0|$ = magnitude of the field at the maximum of the radiation pattern

$|E|$ = magnitude of the field in any direction

The effective area A_r of an antenna is defined by

$$A_r = \frac{G\lambda^2}{4\pi} \tag{15}$$

where

G = gain of the antenna
λ = wavelength

The power delivered by a matched antenna to a matched load connected to its terminals is PA_r, where P is the power density in watts/meter^2 at the antenna and A_r is the effective area in meters^2.

The gains and receiving areas of some typical antennas are given in Fig. 25.

Fig. 25—Power gain G and effective area A of several common antennas.

radiator	gain above isotropic radiator	effective area
Isotropic radiator	1	$\lambda^2/4\pi$
Infinitesimal dipole or loop	1.5	$1.5 \ \lambda^2/4\pi$
Half-wave dipole	1.64	$1.64 \ \lambda^2/4\pi$
Optimum horn (mouth area = A)	$10 \ A/\lambda^2$	$0.81 \ A$
Horn (maximum gain for fixed length—see Fig. 24, mouth area = A)	$5.6 \ A/\lambda^2$	$0.45 \ A$
Parabola or metal lens	6.3 to $7.5 \ A/\lambda^2$	0.5 to $0.6 \ A$
Broadside array (area = A)	$4\pi \ A/\lambda^2$ (max)	A (max)
Omnidirectional stacked array (length = L, stack interval $\leqslant \lambda$)	$\approx 2L/\lambda$	$\approx L \ \lambda/2\pi$
Turnstile	1.15	$1.15 \ \lambda^2/4\pi$

Antenna gain and effective area   *continued*

The gains and effective areas given in Fig. 25 apply in the receiving case only; when the polarizations are not the same, the gain is given by

$$G_\theta = G \cos^2\theta \qquad (16)$$

where

G = gain of the antenna
θ = angle between plane of polarization of the antenna and the incident field

Equation (16) applies only to linear polarization. Equation (5) gives the variation for circular or elliptical polarization. If a circularly polarized antenna is used to receive power from an incident wave of the same screw sense, the gains and receiving areas in Fig. 25 are correct. If a circularly polarized antenna is used to receive power from a linearly polarized wave (or vice versa) the gain or receiving area will be one-half those of Fig. 25.

If the half-power widths of a narrow-beam antenna are known, the approximate gain above an isotropic radiator may be computed from

$$G = \frac{30,000}{W_E W_H} \qquad (17)$$

where

W_E = E-plane half-power width in degrees
W_H = H-plane half-power width in degrees

Equation (17) is not accurate if the half-power widths are greater than about 20 degrees, or if there are many large side lobes.

Vertically stacked horizontal loops

Radiation pattern for array at right is

$$F(\beta) = \frac{\sin\left(\dfrac{nS°}{2} \sin\beta\right)}{\sin\left(\dfrac{S°}{2} \sin\beta\right)} \cos\beta$$

where

n = number of loops
$S°$ = spacing in electrical degrees
S = spacing in radians

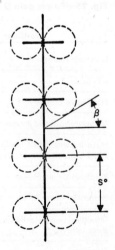

Vertically stacked horizontal loops   *continued*

The gain is

$$\text{gain} = \left\{ \frac{1}{n} + \frac{6}{n^2} \sum_{k=1}^{n-1} (n - k) \left[\frac{\sin kS^\circ}{(kS)^3} - \frac{\cos kS^\circ}{(kS)^2} \right] \right\}^{-1}$$

The gain as a function of the number of loops and the electrical spacing is given in Fig. 26.

The data are also directly applicable to stacked dipoles, discones, tripoles, etc., and all other antenna systems that have vertical directivity but are omnidirectional in the horizontal plane. Such antennas are widely used for frequency-modulation, television, and radio-beacon applications.

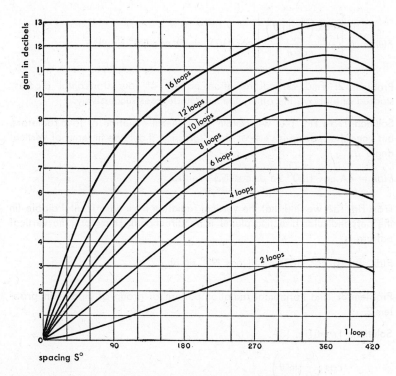

Fig. 26—Gain of linear array of horizontal loops vertically stacked.

Examples in the solution of antenna-array problems

Problem 1: Find horizontal radiation pattern of four colinear horizontal dipoles, spaced successively $\lambda/2$, or 180 degrees.

Solution: From Fig. 14D, radiation from four radiators spaced 180 degrees is given by

$$F(\theta) = 4A \cos (180^\circ \sin \theta) \cos (90^\circ \sin \theta)$$

From Fig. 13A, the horizontal radiation of a half-wave dipole is given by

$$A = K \frac{\cos \left(\dfrac{\pi}{2} \sin \theta \right)}{\cos \theta}$$

therefore, the total radiation

$$F(\theta) = K \left[\frac{\cos \left(\dfrac{\pi}{2} \sin \theta \right)}{\cos \theta} \right] \cos (180^\circ \sin \theta) \cos (90^\circ \sin \theta)$$

Problem 2: Find vertical radiation pattern of four horizontal dipoles, stacked one above the other, spaced 180 degrees successively.

Solution: From Fig. 14D we obtain the general equation of four radiators, but since the spacing is vertical, the expression should be in terms of vertical angle β.

$$F(\beta) = 4A \cos (180^\circ \sin \beta) \cos (90^\circ \sin \beta).$$

From Fig. 13A we find that the vertical radiation from a horizontal dipole (in the perpendicular bisecting plane) is nondirectional. Therefore the vertical pattern is

$$F(\beta) = K(1) \cos (180^\circ \sin \beta) \cos (90^\circ \sin \beta)$$

Problem 3: Find horizontal radiation pattern of group of dipoles in problem 2.

Solution: From Fig. 13A.

$$F(\theta) = K \frac{\cos \left(\dfrac{\pi}{2} \sin \theta \right)}{\cos \theta} \approx K \cos \theta$$

Examples in the solution of antenna-array problems   *continued*

Problem 4: Find the vertical radiation pattern of stack of five loops spaced $2\lambda/3$, or 240 degrees, one above the other, all currents equal in phase and amplitude.

Solution: From Fig. 14E, using vertical angle because of vertical stacking,

$$F(\beta) = A \frac{\sin \left[5(120°) \sin \beta\right]}{\sin (120° \sin \beta)}$$

From Fig. 13D, we find A for a horizontal loop in the vertical plane

$$A = F(\beta) = K \cos \beta$$

Total radiation pattern

$$F(\beta) = K \cos \beta \frac{\sin \left[5(120°) \sin \beta\right]}{\sin (120° \sin \beta)}$$

Problem 5: Find radiation pattern (vertical directivity) of the five loops in problem 4, if they are used in binomial array. Find also current intensities in the various loops.

Solution: From Fig. 15E

$$F(\beta) = K \cos \beta \left[\cos^4(120° \sin \beta)\right]$$

(all terms not functions of vertical angle β are combined in constant K)

Current distribution $(1 + 1)^4 = 1 + 4 + 6 + 4 + 1$, which represent the current intensities of successive loops in the array.

Problem 6: Find horizontal radiation pattern from two vertical dipoles spaced one-quarter wavelength apart when their currents differ in phase by 90 degrees.

Solution: From Fig. 21A

$$s° = \lambda/4 = 90° = \text{spacing}$$
$$\phi = 90° = \text{phase difference}$$

Then,

$$F(\theta) = 2A \cos (45 \sin \theta + 45°)$$

Problem 7: Find the vertical radiation pattern and the number of nulls in the vertical pattern $(0 \leqslant \beta \leqslant 90)$ from a horizontal loop placed three wavelengths above ground.

Solution

$$h_1° = 3(360) = 1080°$$

Examples in the solution of antenna-array problems   *continued*

From Fig. 21B

$F(\beta) = 2A \sin (1080 \sin \beta)$

From Fig. 13D for loop antennas

$A = K \cos \beta$

Total vertical radiation pattern

$F(\beta) = K \cos \beta \sin (1080 \sin \beta)$

A null occurs wherever $F(\beta) = 0$.

The first term, $\cos \beta$, becomes 0 when $\beta = 90$ degrees.

The second term, $\sin (1080 \sin \beta)$, becomes 0 whenever the value inside the parenthesis becomes a multiple of 180 degrees. Therefore, number of nulls equals

$$1 + \frac{h_1^\circ}{180} = 1 + \frac{1080}{180} = 7$$

Problem 8: Find the vertical and horizontal patterns from a horizontal half-wave dipole spaced $\lambda/8$ in front of a vertical screen.

Solution:

$$d^\circ = \frac{\lambda}{8} = 45^\circ$$

From Fig. 21C

$F(\beta) = 2A \sin (45^\circ \cos \beta)$

$F(\theta) = 2A \sin (45^\circ \cos \theta)$

From Fig. 13A for horizontal half-wave dipole

Vertical pattern $A = K(1)$

Horizontal pattern $A = K \dfrac{\cos \left(\dfrac{\pi}{2} \sin \theta \right)}{\cos \theta}$

Total radiation patterns are

Vertical: $F(\beta) = K \sin (45^\circ \cos \beta)$

Horizontal: $F(\theta) = K \dfrac{\cos \left(\dfrac{\pi}{2} \sin \theta \right)}{\cos \theta} \sin (45^\circ \cos \theta)$

■ Radio-wave propagation

Very-long waves—up to 60 kc/s

The received field intensity in microvolts/meter has been experimentally found to follow the Austin-Cohen equation,

$$E = \frac{298 \times 10^3 \sqrt{P}}{D} \cdot \sqrt{\frac{\theta}{\sin \theta}} \cdot \epsilon^{-\alpha D/\sqrt{\lambda}} \tag{1}$$

where

E = received field intensity in microvolts/meter

P = radiated power from the transmitter antenna in kilowatts

D = kilometers between transmitter and receiver

θ = transmission distance in radians

ϵ = 2.718

λ = wavelength of radiation in kilometers

α = attenuation constant

The two nomograms, Figs. 1 and 2,* give solutions for the most important problems related to very-long-wave propagation. The first nomogram solves the following equations

$$\sqrt{P} = \frac{H I}{\lambda} \cdot \frac{377}{298} \tag{2}$$

$$M = \frac{E}{298 \times 10^3 \sqrt{P}} \tag{3}$$

where

H = radiation height (effective height) in meters

I = antenna current in amperes

M = quantity used in Fig. 2

Example

To effect a solution of the above equations:

a. On Fig. 1, draw two straight lines, the first connecting a value of H with a value of I, the second connecting a value of λ with a value of P; if both

* The nomograms, Figs. 1 and 2 are due to Mrs. M. Lindeman Phillips of the Central Radio Propagation Laboratory, National Bureau of Standards, Washington, D. C.

Very-long waves   *continued*

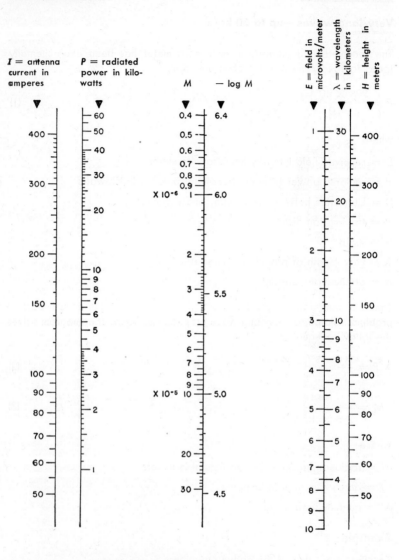

Fig. 1—First nomogram for the solution of very-long-wave field strength. For the solution of P and M, equations (2) and (3).

Very-long waves *continued*

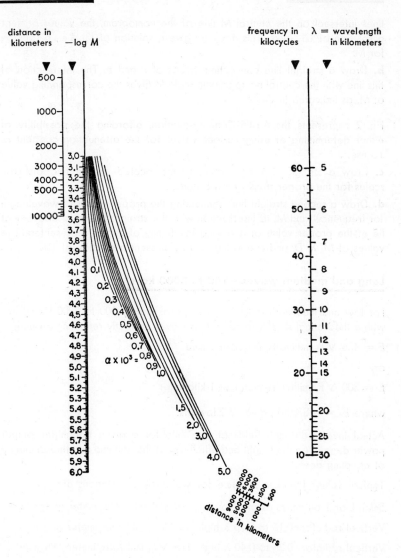

distance in kilometers —log M

frequency in kilocycles   λ = wavelength in kilometers

Fig. 2—Second nomogram for the determination of very-long-wave field strength by the Austin-Cohen equation (1). Value *M* is first determined from Fig. 1.

Very-long waves *continued*

lines intersect on the central M line of the nomogram, the values present a solution of (2). *Note:* This does *not* give a solution of (3), i.e., a solution for M.

b. Draw a straight line connecting values of P and E. The intersection of this line with the central nomographic scale M gives the corresponding value of M, as indicated in (3).

Fig. 2 represents the Austin-Cohen equation, affording the possibility of either determining or using various values for the attenuation constant α. To use,

c. Draw a straight line connecting points located on the two distance scales for the proper transmission distance.

d. Draw a second straight line connecting the proper values of wavelength (or frequency) and M; its intersection with the straight line in (c) above must lie at the proper value of α among the family of curves represented. The values of M, λ, D, and α thus indicated represent a solution of (1).

Long and medium waves—100 to 3000 kc/s*

For low and medium frequencies, of approximately 100 to 3000 kilocycles, with a theoretical short vertical antenna over perfectly reflecting ground:

$E = 186 \sqrt{P_r}$ millivolts/meter at 1 mile

or,

$E = 300 \sqrt{P_r}$ millivolts/meter at 1 kilometer

where $P_r =$ radiated power in kilowatts.

Actual inverse-distance fields at one mile for a given transmitter output power depend on the height and efficiency of the antenna and the efficiency of coupling devices.

Typical values found in practice for well-designed stations are:

Small L or T antennas as on ships: $\quad$ 25 $\sqrt{P_t}$ millivolts/meter at 1 mile

Vertical radiators 0.15 to 0.25 λ high: 150 $\sqrt{P_t}$ millivolts/meter at 1 mile

Vertical radiators 0.25 to 0.40 λ high: 175 $\sqrt{P_t}$ millivolts/meter at 1 mile

Vertical radiators 0.40 to 0.60 λ high
$\quad$ or top-loaded vertical radiators: $\quad$ 220 $\sqrt{P_t}$ millivolts/meter at 1 mile

* For more exact methods of computation see F. E. Terman, "Radio Engineers' Handbook," 1st edition, McGraw-Hill Book Company, New York, New York, 1943; Section 10. Also, K. A. Norton, "The Calculation of Ground-Wave Field Intensities Over a Finitely Conducting Spherical Earth," *Proceedings of the I.R.E.*, vol. 29, pp. 623–639; December, 1941.

Long and medium waves *continued*

where P_t = transmitter output power in kilowatts. These values can be increased by directive arrangements.

The surface-wave field (commonly called *ground wave*) at greater distances can be found from Figs. 3–6. Figs. 4–6 are based on a field strength of 186 millivolts/meter at one mile. The ordinates should be multiplied by the ratio of the actual field at 1 mile to 186 millivolts/meter.

Fig. 3—Ground conductivity and dielectric constant for medium- and long-wave propagation to be used with Norton's, van der Pol's, Eckersley's, or other developments of Sommerfeld propagation formulas.

terrain	conductivity σ in emu	dielectric constant ϵ in esu
Sea water	4×10^{-11}	80
Fresh water	5×10^{-14}	80
Dry, sandy flat coastal land	2×10^{-14}	10
Marshy, forested flat land	8×10^{-14}	12
Rich agricultural land, low hills	1×10^{-13}	15
Pastoral land, medium hills and forestation	5×10^{-14}	13
Rocky land, steep hills	2×10^{-14}	10
Mountainous (hills up to 3000 feet)	1×10^{-14}	5
Cities, residential areas	2×10^{-14}	5
Cities, industrial areas	1×10^{-15}	3

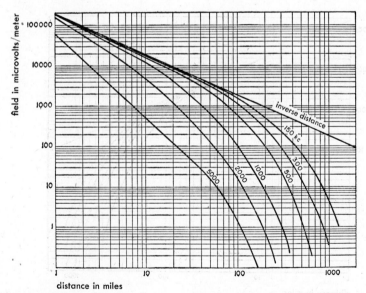

Fig. 4—Strength of surface waves as a function of distance with a vertical antenna for good earth ($\sigma = 10^{-13}$ emu and $\epsilon = 15$ esu).

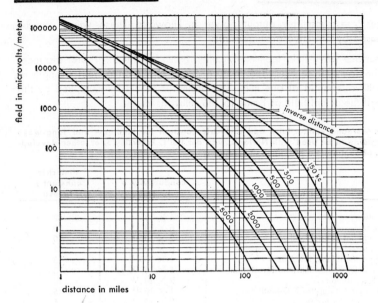

Fig. 5—As Fig. 4, for poor earth ($\sigma = 2 \times 10^{-14}$ emu and $\epsilon = 5$ esu).

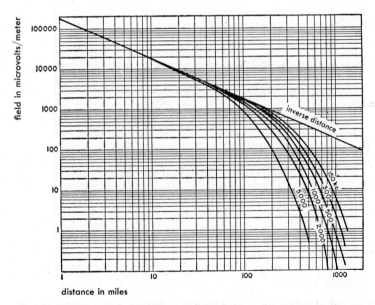

Fig. 6—As Fig. 4, for sea water ($\sigma = 4 \times 10^{-11}$ emu and $\epsilon = 80$ esu).

Long and medium waves   *continued*

Figs. 4, 5, and 6 do not include the effect of *sky waves* reflected from the ionosphere. Sky waves cause fading at medium distances and produce higher field intensities than the surface wave at longer distances, particularly at night and on the lower frequencies during the day. Sky-wave field intensity is subject to diurnal, seasonal, and irregular variations due to changing properties of the ionosphere.

The annual median field strengths are functions of the latitude, the frequency on which the transmission takes place, and the phase of the solar sunspot cycle at a given time.

The dependence of the annual median field for transmissions on frequencies around the middle of the United States standard broadcast band is shown on Fig. 7 for a period of sunspot maximum (1939) and on Fig. 8, for a period of sunspot minimum (1944).

The curves are given for 35, 40, and 45 degrees latitude. The latitude used to characterize a path is that of a control point on the path. The control point is taken to be the midpoint of a path less than 1000 miles long; and for a longer path, the reflection point (for two-reflection transmission) that is at the higher latitude.

The curves are extracted from a report of the Federal Communications Commission in 1946.*

Short waves—3 to 25 mc/s

At frequencies between about 3 and 25 megacycles and distances greater than about 100 miles, transmission depends entirely on sky waves reflected from the ionosphere. This is a region high above the earth's surface where the rarefied air is sufficiently ionized (primarily by ultraviolet sunlight) to reflect or absorb radio waves, such effects being controlled almost exclusively by the free-electron density. The ionosphere is usually considered as consisting of the following *layers*.

D layer: At heights from about 50 to 90 kilometers,† it exists only during daylight hours, and ionization density corresponds with the altitude of the sun.

This layer reflects very-low- and low-frequency waves, absorbs medium-frequency waves, and weakens high-frequency waves through partial absorption.

* Committee III—Docket 6,741, "Skywave Signal Range at Medium Frequencies," Federal Communications Commission, Washington, D. C.; 1946.
† 1 kilometer = 0.621 mile.

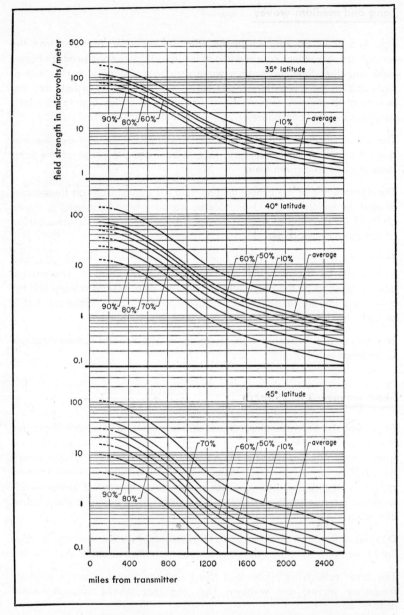

Fig. 7—Sky-wave signal range at medium frequencies for 1939 (sunspot maximum). Shown are the values exceeded by field intensities (hourly median values) for various percentages of the nights per year per 100 millivolts/meter radiated at 1 mile. Annual average is also shown. Values are given for latitudes of 35, 40, and 45 degrees.

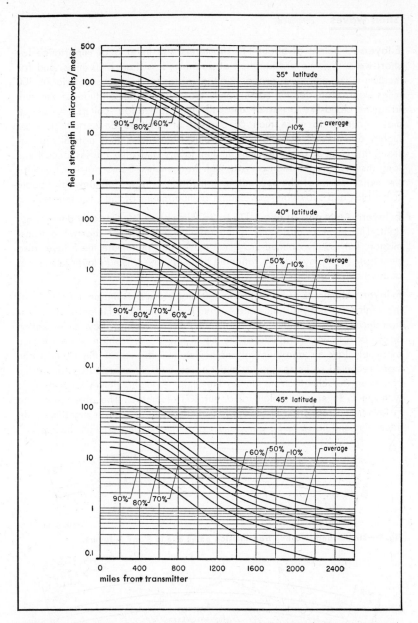

Fig. 8—Sky-wave signal range at medium frequencies for 1944 (sunspot minimum). Shown are the values exceeded by field intensities (hourly median values) for various percentages of the nights per year per 100 millivolts/meter radiated at 1 mile. Annual average is also shown. Values are given for latitudes of 35, 40, and 45 degrees.

Short waves *continued*

E layer: At height of about 110 kilometers, this layer is of importance for short-wave daytime propagation at distances less than 1000 miles, and for medium-wave nighttime propagation at distances in excess of about 100 miles. Ionization density corresponds closely with the altitude of the sun. Irregular cloud-like areas of unusually high ionization, called *sporadic E* may occur up to more than 50 percent of the time on certain days or nights. *Sporadic E* occasionally prevents frequencies that normally penetrate the E layer from reaching higher layers and also causes occasional long-distance transmission at very high frequencies. Some portion (perhaps the major part) of the sporadic-E ionization is now definitely ascribable to visible- and subvisible-wavelength bombardment of the atmosphere.

F_1 layer: At heights of about 175 to 250 kilometers, it exists only during daylight. This layer occasionally is the reflecting region for shortwave transmission, but usually oblique-incidence waves that penetrate the E layer also penetrate the F_1 layer to be reflected by the F_2 layer. The F_1 layer introduces additional absorption of such waves.

F_2 layer: At heights of about 250 to 400 kilometers, F_2 is the principal reflecting region for long-distance short-wave communication. Height and ionization density vary diurnally, seasonally, and over the sunspot cycle. Ionization does not follow the altitude of the sun in any simple fashion, since (at such extremely low air densities and molecular-collision rates) the medium can store received solar energy for many hours, and, by energy transformation, can even detach electrons during the night. At night, the F_1 layer merges with the F_2 layer at a height of about 300 kilometers. The absence of the F_1 layer, and reduction in absorption of the E layer, causes nighttime field intensities and noise to be generally higher than during daylight hours.

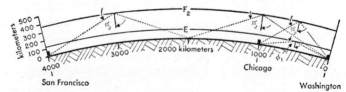

Fig. 9—Single- and two-hop transmission paths due to E and F_2 layers.

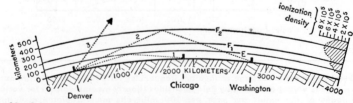

Fig. 10—Schematic explanation of skip-signal zones.

Short waves   *continued*

As indicated to the right on Fig. 10, these *layers* are contained in a thick region throughout which ionization generally increases with height. The layers are said to exist where the ionization gradient is capable of refracting waves back to earth. Obliquely incident waves follow a curved path through the ionosphere due to gradual refraction or bending of the wave front. When attention need be given only to the end result, the process can be assimilated to a reflection.

Depending on the ionization density at each layer, there is a *critical* or highest frequency f_c at which the layer reflects a vertically incident wave. Frequencies higher than f_c pass through the layer at vertical incidence. At oblique incidence, and distances such that the curvature of the earth and ionosphere can be neglected, the maximum usable frequency is given by

$$(muf) = f_c \sec \phi$$

where

(muf) = maximum usable frequency for the particular layer and distance

ϕ = angle of incidence at reflecting layer

At greater distances, curvature is taken into account by the modification

$$(muf) = kf_c \sec \phi$$

where k is a correction factor that is a function of distance and vertical distribution of ionization.

f_c and height, and hence ϕ for a given distance, vary for each layer with local time of day, season, latitude, and throughout the eleven-year sunspot cycle. The various layers change in different ways with these parameters. In addition, ionization is subject to frequent abnormal variations.

The loss at reflection for each layer is a minimum at the maximum usable frequency and increases rapidly for frequencies lower than maximum usable frequency.

Short waves travel from the transmitter to the receiver by reflections from the ionosphere and earth in one or more *hops* as indicated in Figs. 9 and 10. Additional reflections may occur along the path between the bottom edge of a higher layer and the top edge of a lower layer, the wave finally returning to earth near the receiver.

Fig. 9 illustrates single-hop transmission, Washington to Chicago, via the *E* layer (ϕ_1). At higher frequencies over the same distance, single-hop transmission would be obtained via the F_2 layer (ϕ_2). Fig. 9 also shows two-hop

Short waves   *continued*

transmission, Washington to San Francisco, via the F_2 layer (ϕ_3). Fig. 10 indicates transmission on a common frequency, (1) single-hop via E layer, Denver to Chicago, and, (2) single-hop via F_2, Denver to Washington, with, (3) the wave failing to reflect at higher angles, thus producing a *skip* region of no signal between Denver and Chicago.

Actual transmission over long distances is more complex than indicated by Figs. 9 and 10, because the layer heights and critical frequencies differ with time (and hence longitude) and with latitude. Further, scattered reflections occur at the various surfaces.

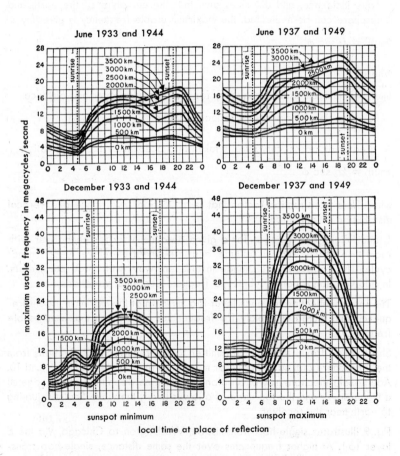

Fig. 11—Single-hop transmission at various frequencies.

Short waves *continued*

Maximum usable frequencies (muf) for single-hop transmission at various distances throughout the day are given in Fig. 11. These approximate values apply to latitude 39° N for the approximate minimum years (1944 and 1955) and approximate maximum years (1949 and 1960) of the sunspot cycle. Since the maximum usable frequency and layer heights change from month to month, the latest predictions should be obtained whenever available.

This information is published (in the form of contour diagrams, similar to Fig. 14, supplemented by nomograms) by the National Bureau of Standards in the U. S. A., and equivalent predictions are supplied by similar organizations in other countries.

Preferably, operating frequencies should be selected from a specific frequency band that is bounded above and below by limits that are systematically determinable for the transmission path under consideration. The recommended upper limit is called the *optimum working frequency* (owf) and is defined as 85 percent of the *maximum usable frequency* (muf). The 85-percent limit provides some margin for ionospheric irregularities and turbulence, as well as statistical deviation of day-to-day ionospheric characteristics from the predicted monthly median value. So far as may be consistent with available frequency assignments, operation in reasonable proximity to the upper frequency limit is preferable, in order to reduce absorption loss.

The lower limit of the normally available band of frequencies is called the *lowest useful high frequency* (luhf). Below this limit ionospheric absorption is likely to be excessive, and radiated-power requirements quite uneconomical. [For lack of better information the (luhf) was formerly arbitrarily designated at 50 percent of the (muf). Even for single-hop transmission, the 50-percent factor is now considered unreliable, and it will usually be very misleading when applied to multiple-hop paths.] For a given path, season, and time, the (luhf) may now be predicted by a systematic graphical procedure, roughly similar to that illustrated below for the determination of (muf). Unlike the (muf), the predicted (luhf) has to be corrected by a series of factors dependent on radiated power, directivity of transmitting and receiving antennas in azimuth and elevation, class of service, and presence of local noise sources. Available data include atmospheric-noise maps, field-intensity charts, contour diagrams for absorption factors, and nomograms facilitating the computation. The procedure is formidable but worth while. The current technique includes some approximations and estimates that are gradually being replaced by an influx of new information derived from measured data.

Short waves   *continued*

The upper and lower frequency limits change continuously throughout the day, whereas it is ordinarily impractical to change operating frequencies correspondingly. Each operating frequency, therefore, should be selected to fall within the above limits for a substantial portion of the daily operating period.

If the operating frequency already has been dictated by outside considerations, and if this frequency has been found to be safely below the maximum usable frequency, then the same noise maps, absorption contours, nomograms, and correction factors (mentioned above) may be applied to the systematic statistical determination of a *lowest required radiated power* (lrrp), which will just suffice to maintain the specified grade of service.

For single-hop transmission, frequencies should be selected on the basis of local time and other conditions existing at the mid-point of the path. In view of the layer heights and the fact that practical antennas do not operate effectively below angles of about three degrees, single-hop transmission cannot be achieved for distances in excess of about 2500 miles (4000 kilometers) via F_2 layer, or in excess of about 1250 miles (2000 kilometers) via the E layer. Multiple-hop transmission must occur for longer distances and, even at distances of less than 2500 miles, the major part of the received signal frequently arrives over a two- or more-hop path. In analyzing two-hop paths, each hop is treated separately and the lowest frequency required on either hop becomes the maximum usable frequency for the circuit.

It is usually impossible to predict accurately the course of radio waves on circuits involving more than two hops because of the large number of possible paths and the scattering that occurs at each reflection. When investigating F_2-layer transmission for such long-distance circuits, it is customary to consider the conditions existing at points 2000 miles along the path from each end as the points at which the maximum usable frequencies should be calculated.

When investigating E-layer transmission, the corresponding control points are 1000 kilometers (620 miles) from each end. For practical purposes, F_1-layer transmission (usually of minor importance) is lumped with E-layer transmission and evaluated at the same control points.

Forecasts of short-wave propagation

In addition to forecasts for ionospheric disturbances, the Central Radio Propagation Laboratories of the National Bureau of Standards issues monthly *Basic Radio Propagation Predictions* 3 months in advance used to

Forecasts of short-wave propagation   *continued*

determine the optimum working frequencies for shortwave communication. Indication of the general nature of the CRPL data and a much abbreviated example of their use follows:

Example

To determine working frequencies for use between San Francisco and Wellington, N. Z.

Method

a. Place a transparent sheet over Fig. 12 and mark thereon the equator, a line across the equator showing the meridian of time desired (viz., GCT or PST), and locations of San Francisco and Wellington.

b. Transfer sheet to Fig. 13, keeping equator lines of chart and transparency aligned. Slide from left to right until terminal points marked fall along a Great Circle line. Sketch in this Great Circle between terminals and mark "control points" 2000 kilometers along this line from each end.

c. Transfer sheet to Fig. 14, showing muf for transmission via the F_2 layer. Align equator as before. Slide sheet from left to right placing meridian line on time desired and record frequency contours at control points. This illustration assumes that radio waves are propagated over this path via the F_2 layer. Eliminating all other considerations, 2 sets of frequencies, corresponding to the control points, are found as listed below, the lower of which is the (muf). The (muf), decreased by 15 percent, gives the optimum working frequency.

Maximum usable frequency

GCT	at San Francisco control point (2000 km from San Francisco)	at Wellington, N. Z. control point (2000 km from Wellington)	optimum working frequency = lower of (muf) $\times$ 0.85
0000	32.0	31.5	26.8
0400	34.2	25.0	21.0
0800	23.2	13.7	11.7
1200	18.0	14.8	12.6
1600	23.4	12.2	10.4
2000	24.6	2.88	20.9

Transmission may also take place via other layers. For the purpose of illustration only and without reference to the problem above, Figs. 15 and 16 have been reproduced to show characteristics of the E and sporadic-E layers. The complete detailed step-by-step procedure, including special considerations in the use of this method, are contained in the complete CRPL forecasts.

Forecasts of short-wave propagation *continued*

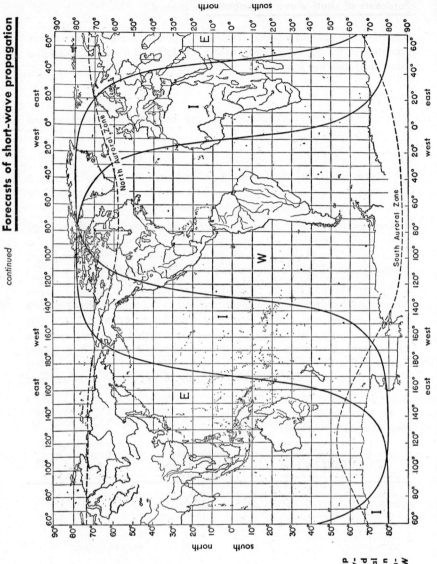

Fig. 12—World map showing zones covered by predicted charts and auroral zones. Zones shown are *E* = east, *I* = intermediate, and *W* = west.

Forecasts of short-wave propagation

continued

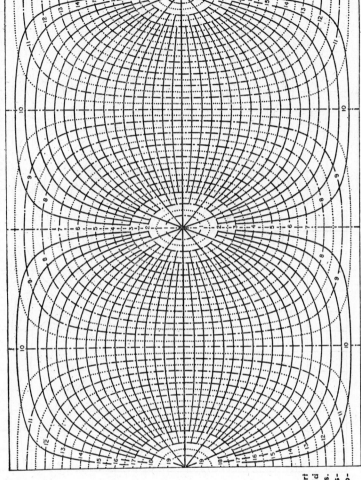

Fig. 13—Great circle chart centered on equator. Solid lines represent great circles. Dot-dash lines indicate distances in thousands of kilometers.

Forecasts of short-wave propagation

continued

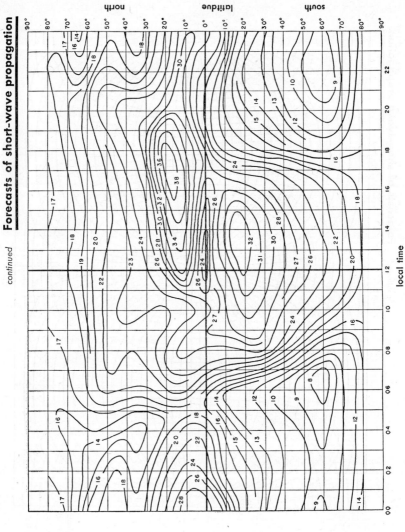

Fig. 14—F₂ 4000-kilometer maximum usable frequency in megacycles. Zone *I* (see Fig. 12) predicted for July, 1946.

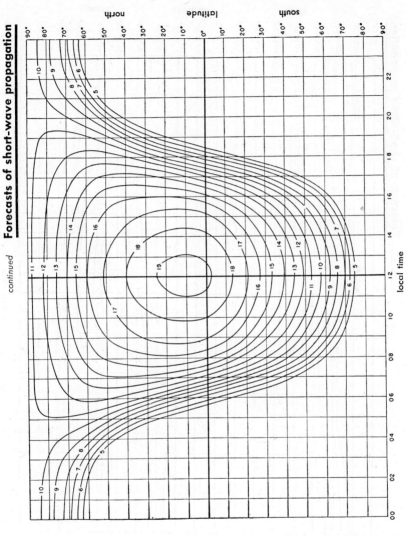

Fig. 15—E-layer 2000-kilometer maximum usable frequency in megacycles predicted for July, 1946.

Forecasts of short-wave propagation

continued

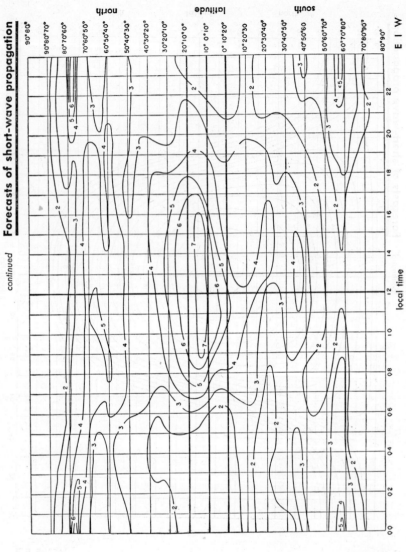

Fig. 16—Median fE_s in megacycles (sporadic-E layer) predicted for July, 1946.

Forecasts of short-wave propagation   *continued*

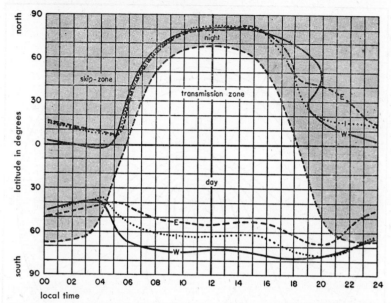

Fig. 17—F-layer transmission for a 2000-kilometer guard band for control points on the 4000-kilometer (muf) contour. Frequency is 15 percent below 30 megacycles. For December, 1946. Zones are E = east, W = west, and I = intermediate. Map is a modified cylindrical projection.

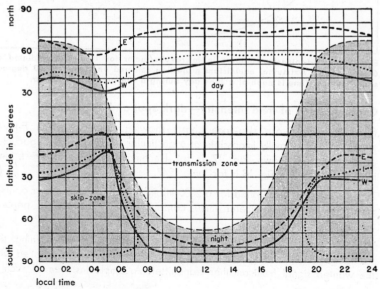

Fig. 18—As Fig. 17, for June, 1947.

Forecasts of short-wave propagation *continued*

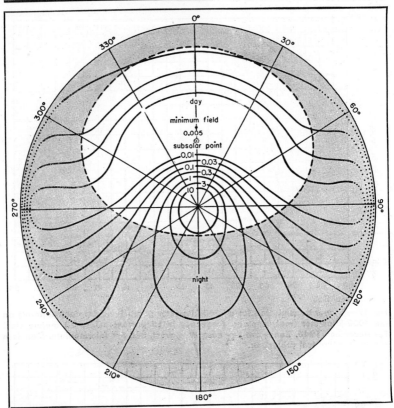

Fig. 19A—Field-intensity contours in microvolts/meter for 1 kilowatt radiated at 6 megacycles. Azimuthal equidistant projection centered on station at 40 degrees south latitude. Time is noon of a June day during a sunspot-minimum year.

Contour charts of field intensity—dark spot and skip zones

Figs. 17 and 18 are *skip-zone* charts showing areas in which F-layer transmission is normally impossible at a particular frequency, 30 megacycles on the example shown. Fig. 17 is for December, 1946, east, west, and intermediate zones. Fig. 18 is for June, 1947.

These charts are established for a 2000-kilometer guard-distance for control points on the 4000-kilometer (muf) contour for a frequency 15 percent below 30 megacycles.

World-coverage field-intensity contours are useful for determining the strength of an interfering signal from a given transmitter, as compared with the wanted signal from another transmitter. A sample instance of such a

Forecasts of short-wave propagation   *continued*

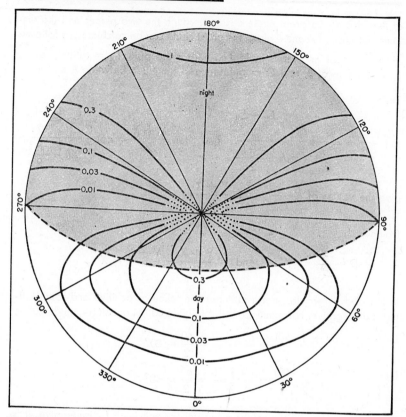

Fig. 19B—Field intensity at antipodes, drawn to twice the scale of Fig. 19A.

field-intensity-contour chart is shown in Figs. 19A and B. The field is given in microvolts/meter for a 1-kilowatt station at 6 megacycles. Fig. 19A is an azimuthal equidistant projection centered on the transmitter (periphery of figure represents antipodes). Fig. 19B, at twice the scale, is centered on antipodes, but for a half-sphere only. These diagrams are useful in determining the point on the surface of the earth where the field intensity is a minimum, the so-called *dark spot*.

Great-circle calculations

Mathematical method

Referring to Figs. 20, 21, and 22, A and B are two places on the earth's surface the latitudes and longitudes of which are known. The angles X and Y

Great-circle calculations   *continued*

at A and B of the great circle passing through the two places and the distance Z between A and B along the great circle can be calculated as follows:

B = place of greater latitude, i.e., nearer the pole, L_A = latitude of A, L_B = latitude of B, and C = difference of longitude between A and B,

Then,

$$\tan \frac{Y-X}{2} = \cot \frac{C}{2} \frac{\sin \dfrac{L_B - L_A}{2}}{\cos \dfrac{L_B + L_A}{2}} \qquad \text{and} \qquad \tan \frac{Y+X}{2} = \cot \frac{C}{2} \frac{\cos \dfrac{L_B - L_A}{2}}{\sin \dfrac{L_B + L_A}{2}}$$

give the values of $\dfrac{Y-X}{2}$ and $\dfrac{Y+X}{2}$,

from which

$$\frac{Y+X}{2} + \frac{Y-X}{2} = Y \qquad \text{and} \qquad \frac{Y+X}{2} - \frac{Y-X}{2} = X$$

In the above formulas, north latitudes are taken as positive and south latitudes as negative. For example, if B is latitude $60°$ N and A is latitude $20°$ S,

$$\frac{L_B + L_A}{2} = \frac{60 + (-20)}{2} = \frac{60 - 20}{2} = \frac{40}{2} = 20°$$

$$\frac{L_B - L_A}{2} = \frac{60 - (-20)}{2} = \frac{60 + 20}{2} = \frac{80}{2} = 40°$$

If both places are in the southern hemisphere and $L_B + L_A$ is negative, it is simpler to call the place of greater south latitude B and to use the above method for calculating bearings from true south and to convert the results afterwards to bearings east of north.

The distance Z (in degrees) along the great circle between A and B is given by the following:

$$\tan \frac{Z}{2} = \tan \frac{L_B - L_A}{2} \left(\sin \frac{Y+X}{2} \right) \Big/ \left(\sin \frac{Y-X}{2} \right)$$

The angular distance Z (in degrees) between A and B may be converted to linear distance as follows:

Z (in degrees) $\times$ 111.195 = kilometers
Z (in degrees) $\times$ 69.093 = statute miles
Z (in degrees) $\times$ 60.000 = nautical miles

Great-circle calculations   *continued*

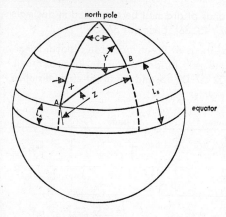

Fig. 20

L_A = latitude of A
L_B = latitude of B
C = difference of longitude

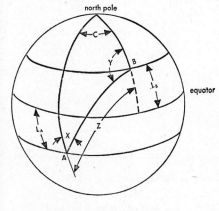

Fig. 21

L_A = latitude of A
L_B = latitude of B
C = difference of longitude

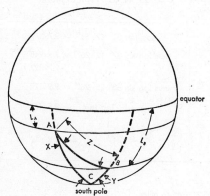

Fig. 22

L_A = latitude of A
L_B = latitude of B
C = difference of longitude

Great-circle calculations   *continued*

In multiplying, the minutes and seconds of arc must be expressed in decimals of a degree. For example, $Z = 37° 45' 36''$ becomes $37.755°$.

Example: Find the great-circle bearings at Brentwood, Long Island, Longitude 73° 15' 10'' W, Latitude 40° 48' 40'' N, and at Rio de Janeiro, Brazil, Longitude 43° 22' 07'' W, Latitude 22° 57' 09'' S; and the great-circle distance in statute miles between the two points.

	longitude	latitude	
Brentwood	73° 15' 10'' W	40° 48' 40'' N	L_B
Rio de Janeiro	43° 22' 07'' W	(−)22° 57' 09'' S	L_A
C	29° 53' 03''	17° 51' 31''	$L_B + L_A$
		63° 45' 49''	$L_B - L_A$

$$\frac{C}{2} = 14° 56' 31'' \qquad \frac{L_B + L_A}{2} = 8° 55' 45'' \qquad \frac{L_B - L_A}{2} = 31° 52' 54''$$

log cot 14° 56' 31'' = 10.57371	log cot 14° 56' 31'' = 10.57371
plus log cos 31° 52' 54'' = 9.92898	plus log sin 31° 52' 54'' = 9.72277
0.50269	0.29648
minus log sin 8° 55' 45'' = 9.19093	minus log cos 8° 55' 45'' = 9.99471
$\log \tan \frac{Y+X}{2}$ = 1.31176	$\log \tan \frac{Y-X}{2}$ = 0.30177
$\frac{Y+X}{2}$ = 87° 12' 26''	$\frac{Y-X}{2}$ = 63° 28' 26''

Bearing at Brentwood $= \dfrac{Y+X}{2} + \dfrac{Y-X}{2} = Y = 150° 40' 52''$ East of North

Bearing at Rio de Janeiro $= \dfrac{Y+X}{2} - \dfrac{Y-X}{2} = X = 23° 44' 00''$ West of North

$\dfrac{L_B - L_A}{2} = 31° 52' 54''$	log tan 31° 52' 54'' = 9.79379
	plus log sin 87° 12' 26'' = 9.99948
$\dfrac{Y+X}{2} = 87° 12' 26''$	9.79327
	minus log sin 63° 28' 26'' = 9.95170
$\dfrac{Y-X}{2} = 63° 28' 26''$	$\log \tan \dfrac{Z}{2}$ = 9.84157
	$\dfrac{Z}{2} = 34° 46' 24'' \qquad Z = 69° 32' 48''$

$69° 32' 48'' = 69.547°$

Linear distance $= 69.547 \times 69.093 = 4805.21$ statute miles

Great-circle calculations   continued

Use of the nomogram of Fig. 24*

Note: Values near the ends of the nomogram scales of Fig. 24 are subject to error because the scales are compressed. If exact values are required in those regions, they should be calculated by means of the trigonometric formulas of the preceding section.

Method: In Fig. 23, Z and S are the locations of the transmitting and receiving stations, where Z is the west and S the east end of the path. *If a point lies in the southern hemisphere, its angle of latitude is always taken as negative. Northern-hemisphere latitudes are taken as positive.*

a. To obtain the great-circle distance ZS (short route):

1. Draw a slant line from (lat Z — lat S) measured up from the bottom on the left-hand scale to (lat Z + lat S) measured down from the top on the right-hand scale. If (lat Z — lat S) or (lat Z + lat S) is negative, regard it as positive.

2. Determine the separation in longitude of the stations. Regard as positive. If the angle so obtained is greater than 180 degrees, then subtract from 360 degrees. Measure this angle along the bottom scale, and erect a vertical line to the slant line obtained in (1).

3. From the intersection of the lines draw a horizontal line to the left-hand scale. This gives ZS in degrees.

4. Convert the distance ZS to kilometers, miles, or nautical miles, by using the scale at the bottom of Fig. 24.

Note: The *long great-circle route* in degrees is simply $360 - ZS$. The value will always be greater than 180 degrees. Therefore, in order to obtain the dis-

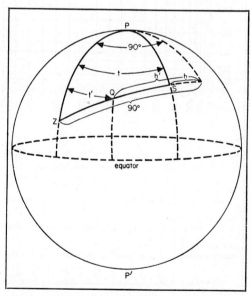

Fig. 23—Diagram of transmission between points Z and S. For use with Fig. 24.

* Taken from Bureau of Standards Radio Propagation Prediction Charts.

Great-circle calculations   *continued*

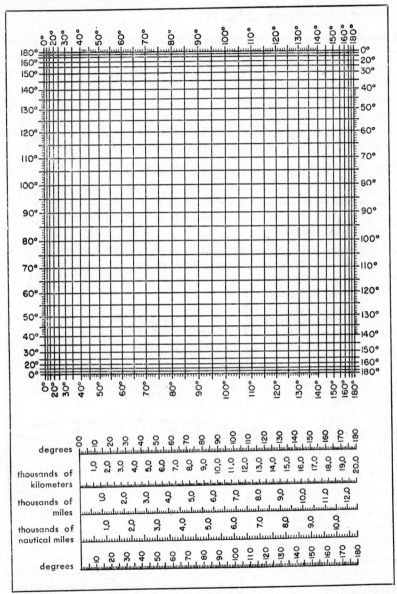

Fig. 24—Nomogram (after D'Ocagne) for obtaining great-circle distances, bearings, solar zenith angles, and latitude and longitude of transmission-control points. With conversion scale for various units.

Great-circle calculations   *continued*

tance in miles from the conversion scale, the value for the degrees in excess of 180 degrees is added to the value for 180 degrees.

b. To obtain the bearing angle *PZS* (short route):

1. Subtract the short-route distance *ZS* in degrees obtained in (a) above from 90 degrees to get *h*. The value of *h* may be negative, but should always be regarded as positive.

2. Draw a slant line from (lat $Z - h$) measured up from the bottom on the left-hand scale to (lat $Z + h$) measured down from the top on the right-hand scale. If (lat $Z - h$) or (lat $Z + h$) is negative, regard it as positive.

3. From (90° — lat *S*) measured up from the bottom on the left-hand scale, draw a horizontal line until it intersects the previous slant line.

4. From the point of intersection draw a vertical line to the bottom scale. This gives the bearing angle *PZS*. The angle may be either east or west of north, and must be determined by inspection of a map.

c. To obtain the bearing angle *PSZ*:

1. Repeat steps (1), (2), (3), and (4) in (b) above, interchanging *Z* and *S* in all computations. The result obtained is the interior angle *PSZ*, in degrees.

2. The bearing angle *PSZ* is 360 degrees minus the result obtained in (1) (as bearings are customarily given clockwise from due north).

Note: The *long-route bearing angle* is simply obtained by adding 180 degrees to the short-route value as determined in (b) or (c) above.

d. To obtain the latitude of Q, the mid- or other point of the path (this calculation is in principle the converse of (b) above):

1. Obtain *ZQ* in degrees. If Q is the midpoint of the path, *ZQ* will be equal to one-half *ZS*. If Q is one of the 2000-kilometer control points, *ZQ* will be approximately 18 degrees, or $ZS - 18°$.

2. Subtract *ZQ* from 90 degrees to get h'. If h' is negative, regard it as positive.

3. Draw a slant line from (lat $Z - h'$) measured up from the bottom on the left-hand scale, to (lat $Z + h'$) measured down from the top on the right-hand scale. If (lat $Z - h'$) or (lat $Z + h'$) is negative, regard it as positive.

4. From the bearing angle *PZS* (taken always as less than 180 degrees) measured to the right on the bottom scale, draw a vertical line to meet the above slant line.

5. From this intersection draw a horizontal line to the left-hand scale.

Great-circle calculations   *continued*

6. Subtract the reading given from 90 degrees to give the latitude of Q. (If the answer is negative, then Q is in the southern hemisphere.)

e. To obtain the longitude difference *t'* between Z and Q (this calculation is in principle the converse of (a) above):

1. Draw a straight line from (lat Z − lat Q) measured up from the bottom on the left-hand scale to (lat Z + lat Q) measured down from the top on the right-hand scale. If (lat Z − lat Q) or (lat Z + lat Q) is negative, regard it as positive.

2. From the left-hand side, at ZQ, in degrees, draw a horizontal line to the above slant line.

3. At the intersection drop a vertical line to the bottom scale, which gives *t'* in degrees.

Available maps and tables

Great-circle initial courses and distances are conveniently determined by means of navigation tables such as

a. Navigation Tables for Navigators and Aviators—HO No. 206.

b. Large Great-Circle Charts:

HO Chart No. 1280—North Atlantic
     1281—South Atlantic
     1202—North Pacific
     1203—South Pacific
     1204—Indian Ocean

The above tables and charts may be obtained at a nominal charge from United States Navy Department Hydrographic Office, Washington, D. C.

Ultra-high-frequency line-of-sight conditions

Straight-line diagrams

The index of refraction of the normal lower atmosphere (troposphere) decreases with height so that radio rays above approximately 200 megacycles follow a curved path, slightly bent downward toward the earth. If the real earth is replaced by a fictitious earth having an enlarged radius 4/3 times the earth's true radius (3963 × 4/3 = 5284 miles), the radio rays may be drawn on profiles as straight lines.

The radio distance to effective horizon is given with a good approximation by

Ultra-high-frequency line-of-sight conditions   *continued*

$$d = \sqrt{2h}$$

where

h = height in feet above sea level
d = radio distance to effective horizon in miles
when the height is very small compared to the earth's radius.

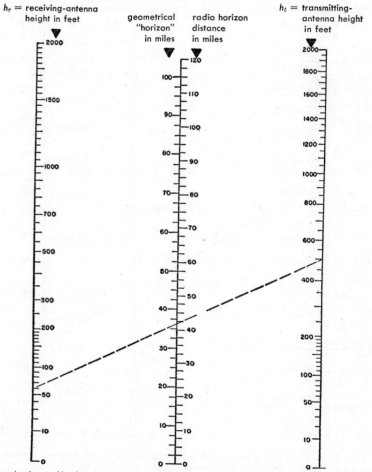

Example shown: Height of receiving antenna 60 feet, height of transmitting antenna 500 feet, and maximum radio-path length = 41.5 miles.

Fig. 25—Nomogram giving radio-horizon distance in miles when h_r and h_t are known.

Ultra-high-frequency line-of-sight conditions   *continued*

Over a smooth earth, a transmitter antenna at height h_t (feet) and a receiving antenna at height h_r (feet) are in radio line-of-sight provided the spacing in miles is less than $\sqrt{2h_t} + \sqrt{2h_r}$.

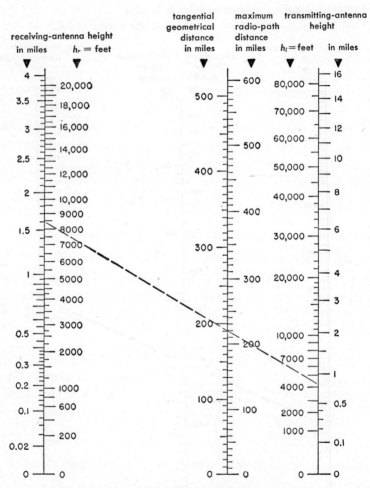

Example shown: Height of receiving-antenna airplane 8500 feet (1.6 miles), height of transmitting-antenna airplane 4250 feet (0.8 mile); maximum radio-path distance = 220 miles.

Fig. 26—Nomogram giving radio-path length and tangential distance for transmission between two airplanes at heights h_r and h_t.

Ultra-high-frequency line-of-sight conditions   *continued*

The nomogram in Fig. 25 gives the radio-horizon distance between a transmitter at height h_t and a receiver at height h_r. Fig. 26 extends the first nomogram to give the radio-path maximum length between two airplanes whose altitudes are known.

Alternative "flat-earth" method

Instead of drawing the rays as straight lines and the earth's surface with a circular cross-section, an alternative approximate method of using a "flat" earth and curved rays is frequently convenient. The arc $H_1H_0H_2$ of the effective earth cross-section is replaced by the line $H_1T_0H_2$, and the straight ray P_1QP_2 becomes a fictitious curved ray P_1PP_2 (Fig. 27).

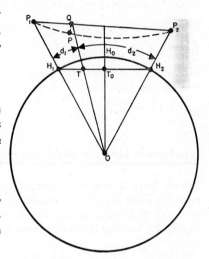

The approximate value of the deviation QP in feet of this curved ray from the straight-line path is

$$QP \approx d_1d_2/2$$

where d_1 and d_2 are expressed in miles. This is called the dip, and its maximum value occurs for $d_1 = d_2$ and is equal to

$$(d_1 + d_2)^2/8$$

The apparent lack of homogeneity in these formulas is due to the inclusion of the radius of the earth in the numerical constant.

Fig. 27—Flat-earth method of determining line of sight.

Where there are one or more obstacles to be investigated for line-of-sight clearance (Fig. 28), a convenient method is to draw a flat profile, draw a straight line between transmitter and receiver antennas, and a parallel line below it at a vertical distance equal to the maximum dip. Anything below the lower line is not an obstacle. For anything above it, the corresponding dip must be checked to determine if there is actual obstruction.

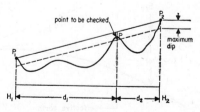

Fig. 28—Determination of possible obstructions in a radio path.

Fresnel-zone clearance at UHF

A criterion to determine whether the earth is sufficiently removed from the radio line-of-sight ray to allow mean free-space propagation conditions to apply is to have the first Fresnel zone clear all obstacles in the path of the rays. This first zone is bounded by points for which the transmission path from transmitter to receiver is greater by one-half wavelength than the direct path. Let d be the length of the direct path and d_1 and d_2 be the distances to transmitter and receiver. The radius of the first Fresnel zone corresponding to d_2 is approximately given by

$$R_1{}^2 = \lambda \frac{d_1 d_2}{d}$$

where all quantities are expressed in the same units.

The maximum occurs when $d_1 = d_2$ and is equal to

$$R_{1m} = \tfrac{1}{2}\sqrt{\lambda d}$$

Expressing d in miles and frequency F in megacycles/second, the first Fresnel-zone radius at half distance is given in feet by

$$R_{1m} = 1{,}140\sqrt{d/F}$$

Interference between direct and reflected U-H-F rays

Where there is one reflected ray combining with the direct ray at the receiving point (Fig. 29), the resulting field strength (neglecting the difference in angles of arrival, and assuming perfect reflection at T) is related to the free-space intensity by the following equation, irrespective of the polarization:

$$E = 2E_d \sin 2\pi \frac{\delta}{2\lambda}$$

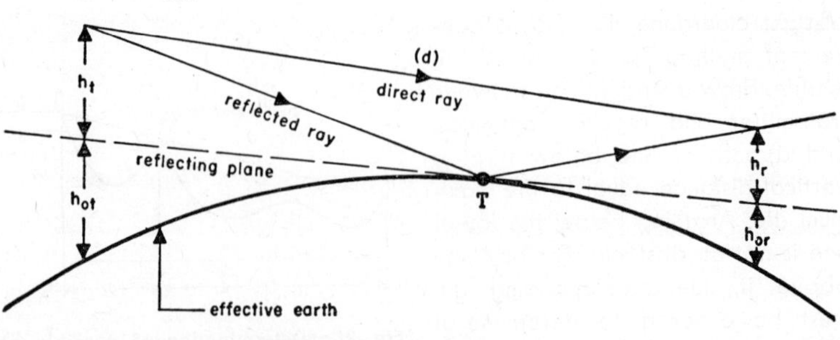

Fig. 29—Interference between direct and reflected rays.

Interference between direct and reflected U-H-F rays   *continued*

where

E = resulting field strength
E_d = direct-ray field strength $\Big\}$ same units

δ = geometrical length difference between direct and reflected paths, which is given to a close approximation by

$$\delta = 2h_t h_r/d$$

if h_t and h_r are the heights of transmitter and receiver points above reflecting plane on effective earth.

The following cases are of interest:

$E = 2E_d$ for $h_t h_r = d\lambda/4$.

$E = E_d$ for $h_t h_r = d\lambda/12$

In case $h_t = h_r = h$,

$$E = 2E_d \text{ for } h = \sqrt{d\lambda/4}$$

$$E = E_d \text{ for } h = \sqrt{d\lambda/12}$$

All of these formulas are written with the same units for all quantities.

Space-diversity reception

When h_r is varied, the field strength at the receiver varies approximately according to the preceding formula. The use of two antennas at different heights provides a means of compensating to a certain extent for changes in electrical-path differences between direct and reflected rays by selection of the stronger signal (space-diversity reception).

The spacing should be approximately such as to give a $\lambda/2$ variation between geometrical-path differences in the two cases. An approximate value of the spacing is given by $\lambda d/4h_t$ when all quantities are in the same units.

The spacing in feet for d in miles, h_t in feet, and λ in centimeters is given by

$$\text{spacing} = 43.4 \frac{\lambda d}{h_t}$$

Example: $\lambda = 3$ centimeters, $d = 20$ miles, and $h_t = 50$ feet; therefore

$$\text{spacing} = 52 \text{ feet}$$

Assuming $h_r = h_t$, the total height of the receiving point in this case would be 70 (minimum for line-of-sight) $+ 50 + 52 = 172$ feet

Interference between direct and reflected U-H-F rays *continued*

Variation of field strength with distance

Fig. 30 shows the variation of resulting field strength with distance and frequency; this effect is due to interference between the free-space wave and the ground-reflected wave as these two components arrive in or out of phase.

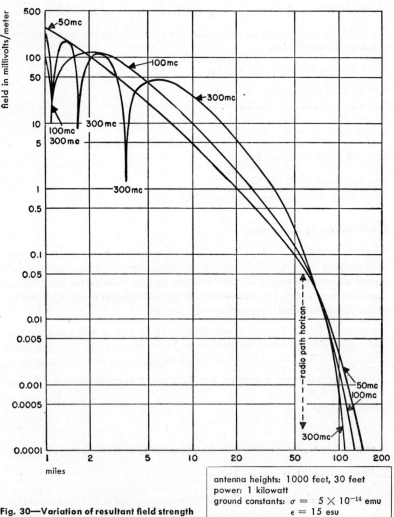

Fig. 30—Variation of resultant field strength with distance and frequency.

antenna heights: 1000 feet, 30 feet
power: 1 kilowatt
ground constants: $\sigma = 5 \times 10^{-14}$ emu
$\epsilon = 15$ esu
polarization: horizontal

Interference between direct and reflected U-H-F rays   continued

To compute the field accurately under these conditions, it is necessary to calculate the two components separately and to add them in correct phase relationship. The phase and amplitude of the reflected ray is determined by the geometry of the path and the change in magnitude and phase at ground reflection. For horizontally polarized waves, the reflection coefficient can be taken as approximately one, and the phase shift at reflection as 180 degrees, for nearly all types of ground and angles of incidence. For vertically polarized waves, the reflection coefficient and phase shift vary appreciably with the ground constants and angle of incidence.

For methods of computing field intensities at and beyond the radio-path horizon, or when the antenna height is not negligible compared to distance, see reference below.*

Measured field intensities usually show large deviations from point to point due to reflections from irregularities in the ground, buildings, trees, etc.

Fading at ultra-high frequencies

Apart from signal-strength variations due to multipath transmission, line-of-sight propagation is affected by other causes, such as abnormal variation of refractive index with height in the lower atmosphere. This was observed ever since microwaves were used for telecommunication, starting with the Calais-Dover experimental link in 1930 and following years on wavelengths of 17 centimeters.†

As previously noted, average atmospheric refraction results in a moderate extension of the radio transmission path beyond the geometric horizon. It should be noted, however, that relatively stable and widespread departures from average refraction occur frequently, and may be predicted with fair accuracy from a sufficiently detailed knowledge of local meteorological data. The atmospheric water-vapor gradient is of primary importance, with the vertical temperature gradient exerting a significant supplementary effect. The results occasionally include the formation of radio shadows or "dead spots" even within the geometric horizon. However, greater interest and importance attaches to the production of "mirage" effects that may extend radar and communication channels very far beyond the normally expected range. On such occasions the water-vapor density ordinarily decreases with height, while the temperature may

* "The Propagation of Radio Waves Through the Standard Atmosphere," Summary Technical Report of the Committee on Propagation, vol. 3, National Defense Research Council, Washington, D. C.; 1946.

† See for instance, A. G. Clavier, "Propagation Tests with Micro-Rays," *Electrical Communication*, vol. 15, pp. 211–219; January, 1937.

Fading at ultra-high frequencies   *continued*

increase over a limited range of heights. The radio wave is then *trapped* and efficiently transmitted within a *duct* that may have the earth's surface as a lower boundary, or may lie completely above the surface. In either case it may act as would a wave guide, with a definite low-frequency cut-off dependent upon its vertical dimension. Boundary heights vary widely (from a fraction of a meter to a few kilometers). Very low boundaries ordinarily occur only over the sea, and then require relatively smooth water. For best results under such conditions, antennas must be placed within the duct (and sometimes very close to the water). This is a noteworthy exception to the general trend toward maximum elevation of microwave equipment. Additional data will be found in the literature.*

There is also some absorption due to water vapor in the atmosphere and to rainfalls. Water vapor has an absorption band at a wavelength of 1.33 centimeters and oxygen at 0.5 and 0.25 centimeters.

For transmission paths of the order of 30 miles, it is considered good engineering practice to allow for possible variations of signal strength between -20 and $+10$ decibels with respect to free-space propagation.

Free-space transmission formulas for U-H-F links

Free-space attenuation

Let the incoming wave be assimilated to a plane wave with a power flow per unit area equal to P_0. The available power at the output terminals of a receiving antenna may be expressed as

$$P_r = A_r P_0$$

where A_r is the effective area of the receiving antenna.

The free-space path attenuation is given by

$$\text{Attenuation} = 10 \log \frac{P_t}{P_r}$$

where P_t is the power radiated from the transmitting antenna (same units as for P_r). Then

$$\frac{P_r}{P_t} = \frac{A_r A_t}{d^2 \lambda^2}$$

---

* See "Tropospheric Propagation and Radio Meteorology," Central Radio Propagation Laboratory Report CRPL—T3, National Bureau of Standards, Washington, D. C.; October, 1946. Also, "Meteorological Factors in Radio-Wave Propagation"; report of 1946 conference with The Royal Meteorological Society, published by The Physical Society, London.

Free-space transmission formulas for U-H-F links   *continued*

where

A_r = effective area of receiving antenna
A_t = effective area of transmitting antenna
λ = wavelength
d = distance between antennas

The length and surface units in the formula should be consistent. This is valid provided $d \gg 2a^2/\lambda$, where a is the largest linear dimension of either of the antennas.

Effective areas of typical antennas

Hypothetical isotropic antenna (no heat loss)

$$A = \frac{1}{4\pi} \lambda^2 \approx 0.08 \lambda^2$$

Small uniform-current dipole, short compared to wavelength (no heat loss)

$$A = \frac{3}{8\pi} \lambda^2 \approx 0.12 \lambda^2$$

Half-wavelength dipole (no heat loss)
$A \approx 0.13 \lambda^2$

Parabolic reflector of aperture area S (here, the factor 0.54 is due to non-uniform illumination of the reflector)
$A \approx 0.54 S$

Very long horn with small aperture dimensions compared to length
$A = 0.81 S$

Horn producing maximum field for given horn length
$A = 0.45 S$

The aperture sides of the horn are assumed to be large compared to the wavelength.

Path attenuation between isotropic antennas

This is

$$\frac{P_t}{P_r} = 4.56 \times 10^3 \ f^2 d^2$$

where

f = megacycles/second
d = miles

Free-space transmission formulas for U-H-F links   *continued*

Path attenuation α (in decibels) is

$$\alpha = 37 + 20 \log f + 20 \log d$$

A nomogram for the solution of α is given in Fig. 31.

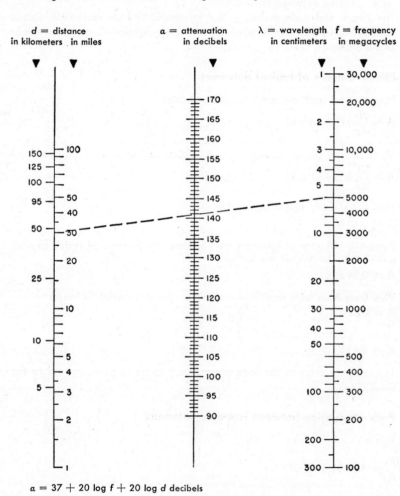

$\alpha = 37 + 20 \log f + 20 \log d$ decibels

Example shown: distance 30 miles, frequency 5000 megacycles;
attenuation = 141 decibels

Fig. 31—Nomogram for solution of path attenuation α between isotropic antennas.

Free-space transmission formulas for U-H-F links continued

Gain with respect to hypothetical isotropic antennas

Where directive antennas are used in place of isotropic antennas, the transmission formula becomes

$$\frac{P_r}{P_t} = G_t \, G_r \left[\frac{P_r}{P_t}\right]_{\text{isotropic}}$$

where G_t and G_r are the power gains due to the directivity of the transmitting and receiving antennas, respectively.

The apparent power gain is equal to the ratio of the effective area of the antenna to the effective area of the isotropic antenna (which is equal to $\lambda^2/4\pi \approx 0.08 \, \lambda^2$).

The apparent power gain due to a parabolic reflector is thus

$$G = 0.54 \left(\frac{\pi D}{\lambda}\right)^2$$

where D is the aperture diameter, and an illumination factor of 0.54 is assumed. In decibels, this becomes

$$10 \log G = 20 \log f + 20 \log D - 52.6$$

where

f = megacycles/second
D = aperture diameter in feet

The solution for G may be found in the nomogram, Fig. 32.

Beam angle

The beam angle θ in degrees is related to the apparent power gain G of a parabolic reflector with respect to isotropic antennas approximately by

$$\theta^2 \approx \frac{27,000}{G}$$

Since $G = 5.6 \times 10^{-6} \, D^2 f^2$, the beam angle becomes

$$\theta \approx \frac{7 \times 10^4}{fD}$$

Free-space transmission formulas for U-H-F links   *continued*

where

θ = beam angle between 3-decibel points in degrees
f = frequency in megacycles
D = diameter of parabola in feet

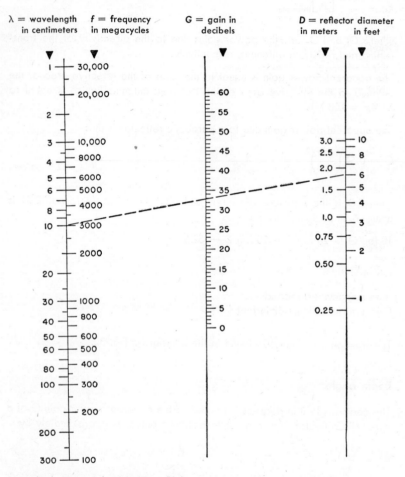

10 log G = 20 log f + 20 log D — 52.6

Example shown: Frequency 3000 megacycles, diameter 6 feet; gain = 33 decibels

Fig. 32—Nomogram for determination of apparent power gain G (in decibels) of a parabolic reflector.

Free-space transmission formulas for U-H-F links   *continued*

Transmitter power for a required output signal/noise ratio

Using the above expressions for path attenuation and reflector gain, the ratio of transmitted power to theoretical receiver noise, in decibels, is given by

$$10 \log \frac{P_t}{P_n} = A_p + \frac{S}{N} + (NF) - G_t - G_r - \overline{(NIF)}$$

where

S/N = required signal/noise ratio at receiver in decibels

(NF) = noise figure of receiver in decibels (see chapter "Radio noise and interference" for definition)

$\overline{(NIF)}$ = noise improvement factor in decibels due to modulation methods where extra bandwidth is used to gain noise reduction (see chapter "Modulation" for definition)

P_n = theoretical noise power in receiver (see chapter "Radio noise and interference")

P_t = radiated transmitter power

G_t = gain of transmitting antenna in decibels

G_r = gain of receiving antenna in decibels

A_p = path attenuation in decibels

An equivalent way to compute the transmitter power for a required output signal/noise ratio is given below directly in terms of reflector dimensions and system parameters:

a. Normal free-space propagation,

$$P_t = \frac{\beta_1 \beta_2}{40} \frac{BL^2}{f^2 r^4} \frac{E}{K} \frac{S}{N}$$

b. With allowance for fading,

$$P_t = \frac{\beta_1 \beta_2}{40} \frac{BL^2}{f^2 r^4} \frac{F}{K} \sigma \left(\frac{S}{N}\right)_m$$

c. For multirelay transmission in n equal hops,

$$P_t = \frac{\beta_1 \beta_2}{40} \frac{BL^2 n}{f^2 r^4} \frac{F}{K} \sigma \left(\frac{S}{N}\right)_{nm}$$

Free-space transmission formulas for U-H-F links   *continued*

d. Signal/noise ratio for nonsimultaneous fading is

$$10 \log (S/N)_n = 10 \log \sigma (S/N)_{1m} - 10 \log \bar{n}$$

where

P_t = power in watts available at transmitter output terminals (kept constant at each repeater point)   •

β_1 = loss power ratio (numerical) due to transmission line at transmitter

β_2 = same as β_1 at receiver

B = root-mean-square bandwidth (generally approximated to bandwidth between 3-decibel attenuation points) in megacycles

L = total length of transmission in miles

f = carrier frequency in megacycles/second

r = radius of parabolic reflectors in feet

F = power-ratio noise figure of receiver (a numerical factor; see chapter "Radio noise and interference")

K = improvement in signal/noise ratio due to the modulation utilized (numerical). For instance, $K = 3m^2$ for frequency modulation, where m is the ratio of maximum frequency deviation to maximum modulating frequency

σ = numerical ratio between available signal power in case of normal propagation to available signal power in case of maximum expected fading

S/N = required signal/noise power ratio at receiver

$(S/N)_m$ = minimum required signal/noise power ratio in case of maximum expected fading

$(S/N)_{nm}$ = same as above in case of n hops, at repeater number n

$(S/N)_{1m}$ = same as above at first repeater

n = number of equal hops

m = number of hops where fading occurs

$\bar{n} = n - m + \sum_{1}^{m} \sigma_k$

σ_k = ratio of available signal power for normal conditions to available signal power in case of actual fading in hop number k (equation holds in case signal power is increased instead of decreased by abnormal propagation or reduced hop distance)

■ Radio noise and interference

Noise and its sources

Noise and interference from other communication systems are two factors limiting the useful operating range of all radio equipment.

The values of the main different sources of radio noise versus frequency are plotted in Fig. 1.

Atmospheric noise is shown in Fig. 1 as the average peaks would be read on the indicating instrument of an ordinary field-intensity meter. This is lower than the true peaks of atmospheric noise. Man-made noise is shown as the peak values that would be read on the EEI—NEMA—RMA standard noise meter. Receiver and antenna noise is shown with the peak values 13 decibels higher than the values obtained with an energy averaging device such as a thermoammeter.

Atmospheric noise

This noise is produced mostly by lightning discharges in thunderstorms. The noise level is thus dependent on frequency, time of day, weather, season of the year, and geographical location.

Subject to variations due to local stormy areas, noise generally decreases with increasing latitude on the surface of the globe. Noise is particularly severe during the rainy seasons in certain areas such as Caribbean, East Indies, equatorial Africa, northern India, etc. Fig. 1 shows median values of atmospheric noise for the U. S. A. and these values may be assumed to apply approximately to other regions lying between 30 and 50 degrees latitude north or south.

Rough approximations for atmospheric noise in other regions may be obtained by multiplying the values of Fig. 1 by the following factors:

degrees of latitude	nighttime		daytime	
	100 kc/s	10 mc/s	100 kc/s	10 mc/s
90–50	0.1	0.3	0.05	0.1
50–30	1	1	1	1
30–10	2	2	3	2
10– 0	5	4	6	3

Atmospheric noise is the principal limitation of radio service on the lower frequencies. At frequencies above about 30 megacycles, the noise falls to levels generally lower than receiver noise.

The peak amplitude of atmospheric noise usually may be assumed to be proportional to the square root of receiver bandwidth.

Noise and its sources *continued*

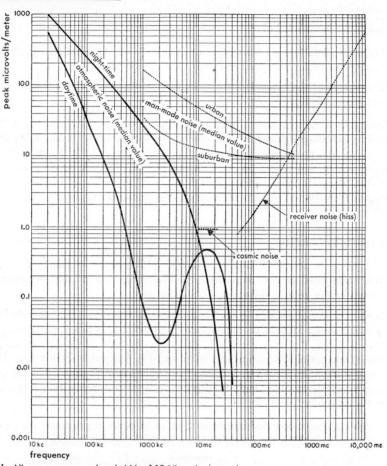

1. All curves assume a bandwidth of 10 kilocycles/second.
2. Refer to Fig. 2 for converting man-made-noise curves to bandwidths greater than 10 kilocycles. For all other curves, noise amplitude varies as the square root of bandwidth.
3. The chart shows the field intensities required to equal the peak receiver noise values assuming
   a. The use of a half-wave-dipole antenna.
   b. A receiver noise level greater than the ideal receiver level by a factor varying from 10 decibels at 50 megacycles to 15 decibels at 1000 megacycles.
4. Transmission-line loss is not considered in the calculations.
5. For antennas having a gain with respect to a half-wave dipole, equivalent noise-field intensities are less than indicated above in proportion to the net gain of the antenna–transmission-line combination.

Fig. 1—Major sources of radio-frequency noise, showing amplitudes at various frequencies. For the U.S.A. and regions of similar latitude.

Noise and its sources *continued*

Cosmic noise

The intensity of cosmic noise is generally lower than the perturbations due to other sources. In the absence of atmospheric and man-made noise, however, it may become the limiting factor in reception between 10 and 300 megacycles. Three types of cosmic noises have so far been detected in radio receivers.

Galaxy noise: Was first found by Jansky on 200 megacycles (1933), and later by Grote Reber on 150 megacycles. It has the same character as thermal-electronic noise, but shows a spatial distribution with a maximum originating in the general region of the Milky Way.

Thermal noise: Due to celestial bodies, observed by Southworth in 1945 on 3000 to 30,000 megacycles for solar radiation, and utilized at Massachusetts Institute of Technology to determine the apparent temperature of the sun and moon, the measurements being made on millimetric waves.

Anomalous solar radiation: Observed by English radio amateurs on 30 megacycles (1936), and dependent on the sunspot cycle (Appleton).

Man-made noise

This includes interference produced by sources such as motorcar ignition, electric motors, electric switching gear, high-tension line leakage, diathermy, industrial-heating generators. The field intensity from these sources is greatest in densely populated and industrial areas.

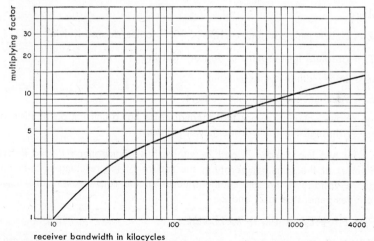

Fig. 2—Bandwidth factor. **Multiply value of man-made noise from Fig. 1 by the factor above for receiver bandwidths greater than 10 kilocycles.**

Noise and its sources *continued*

The nature of man-made noise is so variable that it is difficult to formulate a simple rule for converting 10-kilocycle-bandwidth receiver measurements to other bandwidth values. For instance, the amplitude of the field strength radiated by a diathermy device will be the same in a 100- as in a 10-kilocycle bandwidth receiver. Conversely, peak-noise field strength due to automobile ignition will be considerably greater with a 100- than with a 10-kilocycle bandwidth. According to the best available information, the peak field strengths of man-made noise (except diathermy and other narrow-band noise) increases as the receiver bandwidth is increased, substantially as shown in Fig. 2.

The man-made noise curves in Fig. 1 show typical median values for the U.S.A. In accordance with statistical practice, median values are interpreted to mean that 50 percent of all sites will have lower noise levels than the values of Fig. 1; 70 percent of all sites will have noise levels less than 1.9 times these values; and 90 percent of all sites, less than seven times these values.

Thermal noise

Thermal noise is caused by the thermal agitation of electrons in resistances. Let R = resistive component in ohms of an impedance Z. The root-mean-square value of thermal-noise voltage is given by

$$E^2 = 4 R kT \cdot \Delta f$$

where

k = Boltzmann's constant = 1.38×10^{-23} joules/degree Kelvin[*]

T = absolute temperature in degrees Kelvin

Δf = bandwidth in cycles/second

E = root-mean-square noise voltage

The above equation means that thermal noise has a uniform distribution of power through the radio-frequency spectrum.

In case two impedances Z_1 and Z_2 with resistive components R_1 and R_2 are in series at the same temperature, the square of the resulting root-mean-square voltage is the sum of the squares of the root-mean-square noise voltages generated in Z_1 and Z_2;

$$E^2 = E_1{}^2 + E_2{}^2 = 4(R_1 + R_2) kT \cdot \Delta f$$

[*] J. W. M. DuMond and E. R. Cohen, "Our Knowledge of the Atomic Constants F, N, m, and k in 1947, and of Other Constants Derivable Therefrom," *Reviews of Modern Physics*, vol. 20, pp. 82–108; January, 1948: p. 107.

Noise and its sources   *continued*

In case the same impedances are in parallel at the same temperature, the resulting impedance Z is calculated as is usually done for alternating-current circuits, and the resistive component R of Z is then determined. The root-mean-square noise voltage is the same as it would be for a pure resistance R.

It is customary in temperate climates to assign to T a value such that $1.38T = 400$, corresponding to about 17 degrees centigrade or 63 degrees Fahrenheit. Then

$$E^2 = 1.6 \times 10^{-20} R \cdot \Delta f$$

Tube noise

The electric current emitted from a cathode consists of a large number of electrons and consequently exhibits fluctuations that produce tube noise and set a limitation to the minimum signal voltage that can be amplified. This is also called *shot* or *Schottky* effect.

Shot effect in temperature-limited case: The root-mean-square value I_n of the fluctuating (noise) component of the plate current is given in amperes by

$$I_n{}^2 = 2\epsilon I \cdot \Delta f$$

where

$I =$ plate direct current in amperes

$\epsilon =$ electronic charge $= 1.6 \times 10^{-19}$ coulombs

$\Delta f =$ bandwidth in cycles/second

Shot effect in space-charge-controlled region: The space charge tends to eliminate a certain amount of the fluctuations in the plate current. The following equations are generally found to give good approximations of the plate-current root-mean-square noise component in amperes.

For diodes:

$$I_n{}^2 = 4 k \times 0.64 \, T_c \, g \cdot \Delta f$$

For negative-grid triodes:

$$I_n{}^2 = 4 k \times \frac{0.64}{\sigma} \, T_c \, g_m \cdot \Delta f$$

where

$k =$ Boltzmann's constant $= 1.38 \times 10^{-23}$ joules/degree Kelvin

Noise and its sources   *continued*

T_c = cathode temperature in degrees Kelvin

g = diode plate conductance

g_m = triode transconductance

σ = tube parameter varying between 0.5 and 1.0

Δf = bandwidth in cycles/second

Multicollector tubes: Excess noise appears in multicollector tubes due to fluctuations in the division of the current between the different electrodes. Let a pentode be considered, for instance, and let e_g be the root-mean-square noise voltage that, if applied on the grid, would produce the same noise component in the plate current. Let e_t be the same quantity when the tube is operated as a triode. North has given

$$e_g{}^2 = \left(1 + 8.7\, \sigma\, \frac{I_{c2}}{g_m} \frac{1000}{T_c} \right) e_t{}^2$$

where

I_{c2} = screen current in amperes

g_m = pentode transconductance

σ, T_c = as above

Equivalent noise input-resistance values: The most practical way of expressing the properties of vacuum tubes with respect to noise is to determine the *equivalent noise input resistance*; that is to say, the value of a resistance that, if considered as a source of thermal noise applied to the driving grid, would produce the same noise component in the anode circuit.

The information below has been given by Harris,[*] and is found to give practical approximations.

For triode amplifiers:

$$R_{eg} = 2.5/g_m$$

For pentode amplifiers:

$$R_{eg} = \frac{I_b}{I_b + I_{c2}} \left(\frac{2.5}{g_m} + \frac{20\, I_{c2}}{g_m{}^2} \right)$$

[*] W. A. Harris, "Fluctuations in Space-Charge-Limited Currents at Moderately High Frequencies, Part V—Fluctuations in Vacuum-Tube Amplifiers and Input Systems," *RCA Review* vol. 5, pp. 505–524; April, 1941: and vol. 6, pp. 114–124, July, 1941.

Noise and its sources   *continued*

For triode mixers:

$$R_{eg} = 4/g_c$$

For pentode mixers:

$$R_{eg} = \frac{I_b}{I_b + I_{c2}} \left(\frac{4}{g_c} + \frac{20\,I_{c2}}{g_c{}^2} \right)$$

For multigrid converters and mixers:

$$R_{eg} = \frac{19\,I_b(I_a - I_b)}{g_c{}^2\,I_a}$$

where

R_{eg} = equivalent grid noise resistance in ohms

g_m = transconductance in mhos

I_b = average plate current in amperes

I_{c2} = average screen-grid current in amperes

g_c = conversion conductance in mhos

I_a = sum of currents from cathode to all other electrodes in amperes

The cathode temperature is assumed to be 1000 degrees Kelvin in the foregoing formulas, and the equivalent-noise-resistance temperature is assumed to be 293 degrees Kelvin.

Low-noise triode amplifiers have noise resistances of the order of 200 ohms; low-noise pentode amplifiers, 700 ohms; pentode mixers, 3000 ohms. Frequency converters have much higher noise resistances, of the order of 200,000 ohms.

Noise measurements — noise figure

Measurement for broadcast receivers*

For standard broadcast receivers, the noise properties are determined by means of the equivalent noise sideband input (ENSI). The receiver is connected as shown in Fig. 3.

* "Standards on Radio Receivers: Methods of Testing Broadcast Radio Receivers, 1938," published by The Institute of Radio Engineers; 1942.

448

Noise measurements — noise figure   *continued*

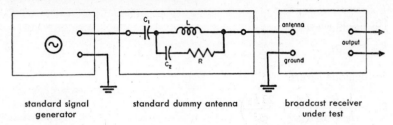

Fig. 3—Measurement of equivalent noise sideband input of a broadcast receiver.

Components of the standard dummy antenna are

C_1 = 200 micromicrofarads

C_2 = 400 micromicrofarads

L = 20 microhenries

R = 400 ohms

The equivalent noise sideband input

$$(ENSI) = m\, E_s \sqrt{P'_n/P'_s}$$

where

E_s = root-mean-square unmodulated carrier-input voltage

m = degree of modulation of signal carrier at 400 cycles/second

P'_s = root-mean-square signal-power output when signal is applied

P'_n = root-mean-square noise-power output when signal input is reduced to zero

It is assumed that no appreciable noise is transferred from the signal generator to the receiver, and that m is small enough for the receiver to operate without distortion.

Noise figure of a receiver

A more precise evaluation of the quality of a receiver as far as noise is concerned is obtained by means of its *noise figure.*[*]

It should be clearly realized that the noise figure evaluates only the linear part of the receiver, i.e., up to the demodulator.

[*] The definition of the noise figure was first given by H. T. Friis, "Noise Figures of Radio Receivers," *Proceedings of the I.R.E.*, vol. 32, pp. 419–422; July, 1944.

Noise measurements — noise figure   *continued*

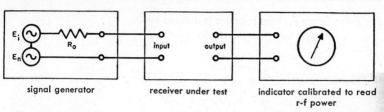

signal generator   receiver under test   indicator calibrated to read
                                                                        r-f power

Fig. 4—Measurement of the noise figure of a receiver. The receiver is considered as a 4-terminal network. (Output refers to last i-f stage.)

The equipment used for measuring noise figure is shown in Fig. 4. The incoming signal (applied to the receiver) is replaced by an unmodulated signal generator with

R_0 = internal resistive component

E_i = root-mean-square carrier voltage

E_n = root-mean-square noise voltage produced in signal generator

Then

$$E_n{}^2 = 4 \, k \, T_0 \, R_0 \, \Delta f'$$

where

k = Boltzmann's constant = 1.38×10^{-23} joules/degree Kelvin

T_0 = temperature in degrees Kelvin

$\Delta f'$ = effective bandwidth of receiver (determined as on p. 450)

If the receiver does not include any other source of noise, the ratio $E_i{}^2/E_n{}^2$ is equal to the power carrier/noise ratio measured by the indicator.

$$\frac{E_i{}^2}{E_n{}^2} = \frac{E_i{}^2/4R_0}{k \, T_0 \, \Delta f'} = \frac{P_i}{N_i}$$

The quantities $E_i{}^2/4R_0$ and $k \, T_0 \, \Delta f'$ are called the *available* carrier- and noise-input powers, respectively.

The output carrier/noise power ratio measured in a resistance R may be considered as the ratio of an available carrier-output power P_o to an available noise-output power N_o.

Noise measurements — noise figure   *continued*

The noise figure F of the receiver is defined by

$$\frac{P_o}{N_o} = \frac{1}{F} \times \frac{P_i}{N_i}$$

$$F = \frac{N_o}{N_i} \times \frac{1}{P_o/P_i} = \frac{E^2_{i1:1}}{4k\,T_0\,R_0\,\Delta f'} = \frac{P_{i1:1}}{k\,T_0\,\Delta f'}$$

The ratio P_o/P_i is the available gain G of the receiver.

Noise figure is often expressed in decibels:

$$F_{db} = 10\log_{10} F$$

Effective bandwidth: $\Delta f'$ of the receiver is

$$\Delta f' = \frac{1}{G}\int G_f\,df$$

where G_f is the differential available gain. $\Delta f'$ is generally approximated to the bandwidth of the receiver between those points of the response showing a 3-decibel attenuation with respect to the center frequency.

Noise figure of cascaded networks

The overall noise figure of two networks a and b in cascade (Fig. 5) is

$$F_{ab} = F_a + \frac{F_b - 1}{G_a}$$

provided $\Delta f_b' \leqslant \Delta f_a'$

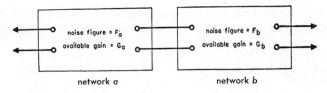

Fig. 5—Overall noise figure F_{ab} of two networks, a and b, in cascade.

The value of F is a measure of the quality of the input tubes of the circuits. Up to some 300 megacycles, noise figures of 2 to 4 have been obtained. From 3000 to 6000 megacycles, the noise figure varies between 10 and 40

Noise measurements — noise figure   *continued*

for the tubes at present available. It goes up to about 50 for 10,000-mega-cycle receivers.

The additional noise due to external sources influencing real antennas (such as cosmic noise), may be accounted for by an apparent antenna temperature, bringing the available noise-power input to $k\,T_a\,\Delta f'$ instead of $N_i = k\,T_0\,\Delta f'$ (the physical antenna resistance at temperature T_0 is generally negligible in high-frequency systems). The internal noise sources contribute $(F-1)\,N_i$ as before, so that the new noise figure is given by

$$F'N_i = (F-1)N_i + k\,T_0\,\Delta f'$$
$$F' = F - 1 + T_a/T_0$$

The average temperature of the antenna for a 6-megacycle equipment is found to be 3000 degrees Kelvin, approximately. The contribution of external sources is thus of the order of 10, compared with a value of $(F-1)$ equal to 1 or 2, and becomes the limiting factor of reception. At 3000 megacycles, however, values of T_a may fall below T_0, while noise figures are of the order of 20.

Noise improvement factor*

In case the receiver includes demodulation processes that produce a carrier/noise ratio improvement (NIF), this improvement ratio must, of course, be considered when evaluating the carrier required to produce a desired output carrier/noise ratio.

Measurement of external radio noise

External noise fields, such as atmospheric, cosmic, and man-made, are measured in the same way as radio-wave field strengths†, with the exception that peak, rather than average, values of noise are usually of interest, and that the overall bandpass action of the measuring apparatus must be accurately known in measuring noise. When measuring noise varying over wide limits with time, such as atmospheric noise, it is generally best to employ automatic recorders.

* For a discussion of noise improvement factor (NIF) in such systems as frequency modulation and pulse demodulation, see the chapter "Modulation."

† For methods of measuring field strengths and, hence, noise, see "Standards on Radio Wave Propagation: Measuring Methods, 1942," published by The Institute of Radio Engineers. For information on suitable circuits to obtain peak values, particularly with respect to man-made noise, see C. V. Agger, D. E. Foster, and C. S. Young, "Instruments and Methods of Measuring Radio Noise," *Electrical Engineering*, vol. 59, pp. 178–192; March, 1940.

Interference effects in various systems

Besides noise, the efficiency of radio-communication systems can be limited by the interference produced by other radio-communication systems. The amount of tolerable signal/interference ratio, and the determination of conditions for entirely satisfactory service, are necessary for the specification of the amount of harmonic and spurious frequencies that can be allowed in transmitter equipments, as well as for the correct spacing of adjacent channels.

The following information has been extracted from "Final Acts of the International Telecommunication and Radio Conferences (Appendix 1)," Atlantic City, 1947.

Fig. 6—Curves giving the envelopes for Fourier spectra of the emission resulting from several shapes of a single telegraph dot. For the upper curve the dot is taken to be rectangular and its length is ½ of the period T corresponding to the fundamental dotting frequency. The dotting speed in bauds is $B = 1/t = 2/T$. The bottom curve would result from the insertion of a filter with a passband equal to 5 units on the f/B scale, and having a slope of 30 decibels/octave outside of the passband.

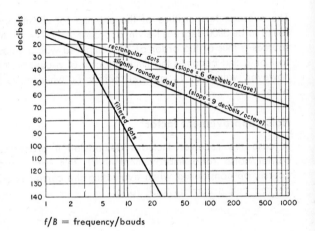

f/B = frequency/bauds

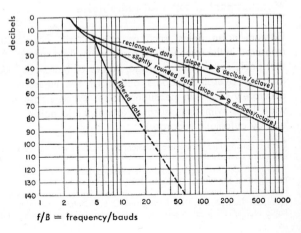

f/B = frequency/bauds

Fig. 7—Received power as a function of frequency separation between transmitter frequency and midband frequency of the receiver.

Interference effects in various systems   *continued*

Available information is not sufficient to give reliable rules in the cases of frequency modulation, pulse emission, and television transmission.

Simple telegraphy

It is considered that satisfactory radiotelegraph service is provided when the radio-frequency interference power available in the receiver, averaged over a cycle when the amplitude of the interfering wave is at a maximum, is at least 10 decibels below the available power of the desired signal averaged in the same manner, at the time when the desired signal is a minimum.

In order to determine the amount of interference produced by one telegraph channel on another, Figs. 6 and 7 will be found useful.

Frequency-shift telegraphy—facsimile

It is estimated that the interference level of — 10 decibels as recommended in the previous case will also be suitable for frequency-shift telegraphy and facsimile.

Double-sideband telephony

The multiplying factor for frequency separation between carriers as required for various ratios of signal/interference is given in the following table. This factor should be multiplied by the highest modulation frequency.

ratio of desired to interfering carriers in decibels	mutliplying factor for various ratios of signal/interference			
	20 db	30 db	40 db	50 db
60	0	0	0	0
50	0	0	0	0.60
40	0	0	0.60	1.55
30	0	0.60	1.55	1.85
20	0.60	1.55	1.85	1.96
10	1.55	1.85	1.96	2.00
0	1.85	1.96	2.00	2.55
— 10	1.96	2.00	2.55	2.85
— 20	2.00	2.55	2.85	3.2
— 30	2.55	2.85	3.2	3.6
— 40	2.85	3.2	3.6	4.0
— 50	3.2	3.6	4.0	4.5
— 60	3.6	4.0	4.5	5.1
— 70	4.0	4.5	5.1	5.7
— 80	4.5	5.1	5.7	6.4
— 90	5.1	5.7	6.4	7.2
— 100	5.7	6.4	7.2	8.0

Interference effects in various systems   *continued*

The acceptance band of the receiving filters in cycles/second is assumed to be 2 × (highest modulation frequency), and the cutoff characteristic is assumed to have a slope of 30 decibels/octave.

Broadcasting

As a result of a number of experiments, it is possible to set down the following results for carrier frequencies between 150 and 285 kilocycles/second and between 525 and 1560 kilocycles.

frequency separation between carriers in kilocycles	minimum ratio of desired and interfering carriers in decibels
11	0*
10	6†
9	14†
8	26‡
5 (or less)	60†

* extrapolated   † experimental   ‡ interpolated

These experimental results agree reasonably well with the theoretical results of the preceding table with a highest modulation frequency of about 4500 cycles/second, and with a signal/interference ratio of 50 decibels.

Single-sideband telephony

Experience shows that the separation between adjacent channels need be only great enough to insure that the nearest frequency of the interfering signal is 40 decibels down on the receiver filter characteristic when due allowance has been made for the frequency instability of the carrier wave.

Spurious responses

In superheterodyne receivers, where a nonlinear element is used to get a desired intermediate-frequency signal from the mixing of the incoming signal and a local-oscillator signal, interference from spurious external signals results in a number of undesired frequencies that may fall within the intermediate-frequency band. Likewise, when two local oscillators are mixed in a transmitter or receiver to produce a desired output frequency, several unwanted components are produced at the same time due to the imperfections of the mixer characteristic. The following tables show how the location of the spurious frequencies can be determined.

Spurious responses *continued*

Symbols

f_1 = signal frequency (or first source)

f_1' = spurious signal ($f_1' = f_1$ for mixing local sources, but when dealing with a receiver, usually $f_1' \neq f_1$)

f_2 = local-injection frequency (or second source)

f_x = desired mixer-output frequency

f_x' = spurious mixer-output frequency

$k = m + n$ = order of response, where m and n are positive integers

Coincidence: Is where $f_1' = f_1$ and $f_x' = f_x$

Defining and coincidence equations

type	defining equations (mixing for difference frequency)	coincidence	type	defining equations (mixing for sum frequency)	coincidence
I	$f_x = \pm(f_1 - f_2)$ $f_x' = \pm(nf_2 - mf_1')$	$\left[\dfrac{f_2}{f_1}\right]_{co} = \dfrac{m+1}{n+1}$	IV	$f_x = f_1 + f_2$ $f_x' = mf_1' - nf_2$	$\left[\dfrac{f_2}{f_1}\right]_{co} = \dfrac{m-1}{n+1}$
II	$f_x = \pm(f_1 - f_2)$ $f_x' = \pm(mf_1' - nf_2)$	$\left[\dfrac{f_2}{f_1}\right]_{co} = \dfrac{m-1}{n-1}$	V	$f_x = f_1 + f_2$ $f_x' = nf_2 - mf_1'$	$\left[\dfrac{f_2}{f_1}\right]_{co} = \dfrac{m+1}{n-1}$
III	$f_x = f_1 - f_2$ $f_x' = mf_1' + nf_2$	$\left[\dfrac{f_2}{f_1}\right]_{co} = \dfrac{1-m}{n+1}$	VI	$f_x = f_1 + f_2$ $f_x' = mf_1' + nf_2$	$\left[\dfrac{f_2}{f_1}\right]_{co} = \dfrac{1-m}{n-1}$

In types I and II, both f_x and f_x' must use the same sign throughout.

Types III and VI are relatively unimportant except when $m = n = 1$.

Image ($m = n = 1$)

kind of mixing	receiver ($f_x' = f_x$)		two local sources ($f_1' = f_1$)
Difference	$f_1' = \pm(2f_2 - f_1)$ $= \pm(f_1 - 2f_x)$ $= f_1 + 2f_x$	$f_2 < f_1$ $f_2 > f_1$	$f_x' = f_1 + f_2$
Sum	$f_1' = f_1 + 2f_2$ $= 2f_x - f_1$		$f_x' = \pm(f_1 - f_2)$

Intermediate-frequency rejection: Must be provided for spurious signal $f_1' = f_x$ where $m = 1$, $n = 0$.

Spurious responses *continued*

Selectivity equations

For types I, II, IV, and V only.

When $f_x' = f_x$

$$\frac{f_1' - f_1}{f_1} = \frac{A}{m} \left\{ \frac{f_2}{f_1} - \left[\frac{f_2}{f_1} \right]_{co} \right\}$$

When $f_1' = f_1$

$$\frac{f_x' - f_x}{f_1} = B \left\{ \frac{f_2}{f_1} - \left[\frac{f_2}{f_1} \right]_{co} \right\}$$

$$\frac{f_x' - f_x}{f_x} = C \frac{(f_2/f_1) - [f_2/f_1]_{co}}{1 \mp f_2/f_1}$$

Where the coefficients and the $\mp$ signs are

type	A	B $f_2 < f_1$	B $f_2 > f_1$	C	$\mp$ sign
I	$n + 1$	A	$-A$	A	$-$
II	$n - 1$	$-A$	A	$-A$	$-$
IV	$n + 1$	$-A$	$-A$	$-A$	$+$
V	$n - 1$	A	A	A	$+$

Variation of output frequency vs input-signal deviation

For any type

$$\Delta f_x' = \pm m \, \Delta f_1'$$

Use the $+$ or the $-$ sign according to defining equation for type in question.

Table of spurious responses

Type I coincidences: $\left[\dfrac{f_2}{f_1} \right]_{co} = \dfrac{m + 1}{n + 1}$, where $f_x' = f_x$ and $f_1' = f_1$

Spurious responses _continued_

frequency ratio = $[f_2/f_1]_{co}$			lowest order			higher orders
fraction	decimal	reciprocal	k_I	m_I	n_I	
1/1	1.000	1.000	2	1	1	All even orders $m = n$ (See note b)
8/9	0.889	1.125	15	7	8	
7/8	0.875	1.143	13	6	7	
6/7	0.857	1.167	11	5	6	
5/6	0.833	1.200	9	4	5	
4/5	0.800	1.250	7	3	4	
7/9	0.778	1.286	14	6	8	$\begin{cases} m_I = 5 \\ n_I = 7 \end{cases}$
3/4	0.750	1.333	5	2	3	
5/7	0.714	1.400	10	4	6	
7/10	0.700	1.429	15	6	9	$\begin{cases} m_I = 3 \\ n_I = 5 \end{cases} \begin{cases} = 5 \\ = 8 \end{cases}$
2/3	0.667	1.500	3	1	2	
5/8	0.625	1.600	11	4	7	
3/5	0.600	1.667	6	2	4	$\begin{cases} m_I = 5 \\ n_I = 9 \end{cases}$
4/7	0.571	1.750	9	3	6	
5/9	0.556	1.800	12	4	8	
6/11	0.545	1.833	15	5	10	$\begin{cases} m_I = 1 \\ n_I = 3 \end{cases} \begin{cases} = 2 \\ = 5 \end{cases} \begin{cases} = 3 \\ = 7 \end{cases} \begin{cases} = 4 \\ = 9 \end{cases}$
1/2	0.500	2.000	1	0	1	

Types II, IV, and V coincidences: For each ratio $[f_2/f_1]_{co}$ there are also the following responses

type	k	m	n
II	$k_{II} = k_I + 4$	$m_{II} = m_I + 2$	$n_{II} = n_I + 2$
IV	$k_{IV} = k_I + 2$	$m_{IV} = m_I + 2$	$n_{IV} = n_I$
V	$k_V = k_I + 2$	$m_V = m_I$	$n_V = n_I + 2$

Notes:

a. When $f_2 > f_1$ use reciprocal column and interchange the values of m and n.

b. At $[f_2/f_1]_{co} = 1/1$, additional important responses are

type II: $m = n = 2$

type IV: $m = 2, n = 0$

type V: $m = 0, n = 2$

Spurious responses   *continued*

Chart of spurious responses

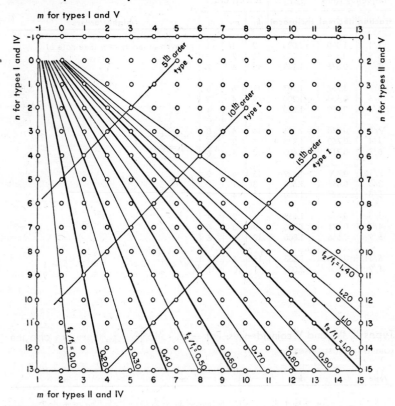

m for types I and V

n for types I and IV

n for types II and V

m for types II and IV

Each circle represents a spurious response coincidence, where $f_1' = f_1$ and $f_x' = f_x$.

Example: Suppose two frequencies whose ratio is $f_2/f_1 = 0.12$ are mixed to obtain the sum frequency. The spurious responses are found by laying a transparent straightedge on the chart, passing through the circle $-1, -1$ and lying a little to the right of the line marked $f_2/f_1 = 0.10$. It is observed that the straightedge passes near circles indicating the responses

Type IV $\begin{cases} m = 1 \\ n = 0 \end{cases}$ $\begin{cases} = 2 \\ = 7 \end{cases}$ $\begin{cases} = 2 \\ = 8 \end{cases}$

Type V $\begin{cases} m = 0 \\ n = 9 \end{cases}$ $\begin{cases} = 0 \\ = 10 \end{cases}$

The actual frequencies of the responses f_x' or f_1' can be determined by substituting these coefficients m and n in the defining equations.

■ Radar fundamentals

General

A simplified diagram of a set for *RA*dio *D*irection *A*nd *R*ange finding is shown in Fig. 1. A pulsed high-power transmitter emits centimeter waves for approximately a microsecond through a highly directive antenna to illuminate the target. The returned echo is picked up by the same antenna,

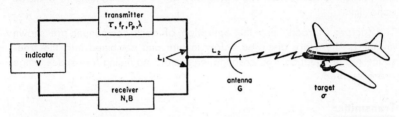

Fig. 1—Simplified diagram of a radar set.

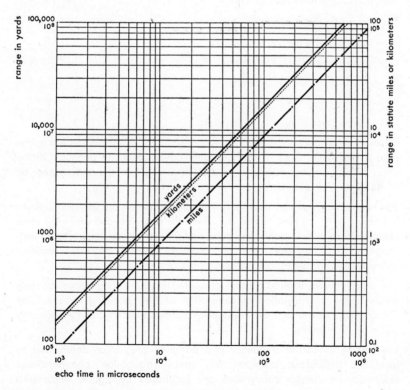

Fig. 2—Time between transmission and reception of a reflected signal.

General *continued*

amplified by a high-gain wideband receiver, and displayed on an indicator. Direction of a target is usually indicated by noting the direction of the narrow-beam antenna at the time the echo is received. The range is measured in terms of time because the radar pulse travels with the speed of light, 300 meters one way per microsecond, or approximately 10 microseconds per round-trip radar mile. Fig. 2 gives the range corresponding to a known echo time.

The factors characterizing the operation of each component are shown in Fig. 1. These are discussed below in turn and combined into the free-space range equation. The propagation factors modifying free-space range are presented.

Transmitter

Important transmitter factors are:

τ = pulse length in microseconds

f_r = pulse rate in cycles/second

d = duty cycle = $\tau f_r \times 10^{-6}$ = P_a/P_p

P_a = average power in kilowatts

P_p = peak power in kilowatts

λ = carrier wavelength in centimeters

Pulse length is generally about one microsecond. A longer pulse may be used for greater range, if the oscillator power capacity permits. On the other hand, if a range resolution of $\triangle R$ feet is required, the pulse cannot be longer than $\triangle R/500$ microseconds.

The repetition frequency must be low enough to permit the desired maximum unambiguous range ($f_r < 90,000/R_u$). This is the range beyond which the echo returns after the next transmitter pulse and thus may be mistaken for a short-range echo of the next cycle. If this range is small, oscillator maximum average power may impose an upper limit.

The peak power required may be computed from the range equation (see below) after determination or assumption of the remaining factors. Peak and average power may be interconverted by use of Fig. 3. Pulse energy is $P_p\tau \times 10^{-3}$ joules.

The choice of carrier frequency is a complex one, often determined by available oscillators, antenna size, and propagation considerations. Frequency-wavelength conversions are facilitated by Fig. 4, which also defines the band nomenclature.

Transmitter *continued*

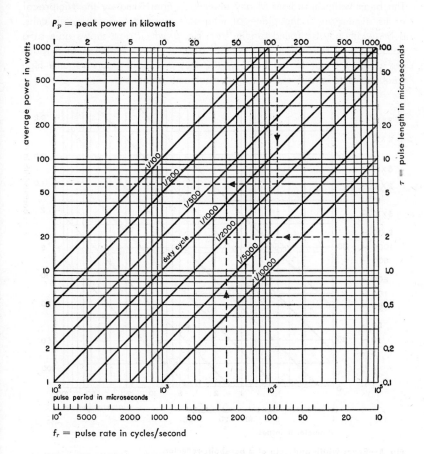

P_p = peak power in kilowatts

average power in watts

τ = pulse length in microseconds

pulse period in microseconds

f_r = pulse rate in cycles/second

Fig. 3—Power-time relationships.

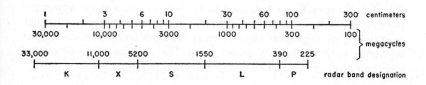

centimeters

megacycles

radar band designation

Fig. 4—Correlation between frequency, wavelength, and band nomenclature for radar.

Antenna

The beam width in radians of any antenna is approximately the reciprocal of its dimension in the plane of interest expressed in wavelength units. Beam width may be found readily from Fig. 5, which also shows gain of a paraboloid of revolution. The angular accuracy and resolution of a radar are roughly equal to the beam width; thus precision radars require high frequencies to avoid excessively cumbersome antennas.

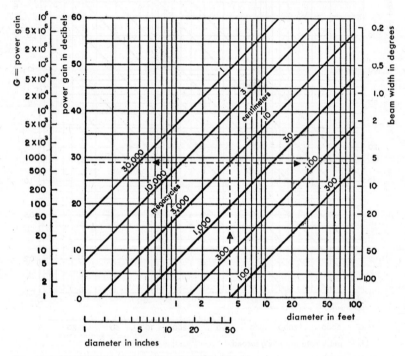

Fig. 5—Beam width and gain of a parabolic reflector.

Target echoing area

The radar cross section σ is defined as 4π times the ratio of the power per unit solid angle scattered back toward the transmitter, to the power per unit area striking the target. For large complex structures and short wavelengths, the values vary rapidly with aspect angle. The effective areas of several important configurations are listed in the following table.*

*L. N. Ridenour, "Radar System Engineering," v. 1, Radiation Laboratory Series, McGraw-Hill Book Company, New York, New York; 1947. See pp. 64–68, 78, 80.

Target echoing area *continued*

reflector	σ
Tuned $\lambda/2$ dipole	$0.22\lambda^2$
Small sphere with radius $= a$, where $a/\lambda < 0.15$	$9\pi a^2 (2\pi a/\lambda)^4$
Large sphere with radius $= a$, where $a/\lambda > 1$	πa^2
Corner reflector with one edge $= a$ (maximum)	$4\pi a^4/3\lambda^2$
Flat plate with area $= A$ (normal incidence)	$4\pi A^2/\lambda^2$
Cylinder with radius $= a$, length $= L$ (normal incidence)	$2\pi L^2 a/\lambda$
Small airplane (AT–11)	200 feet^2
Large airplane (B–17)	800 feet^2
Small cargo ship	1,500 feet^2
Large cargo ship	160,000 feet^2

Receiver

The receiver is characterized by an overall noise figure N, defined as the ratio of carrier power available from the antenna to theoretical noise

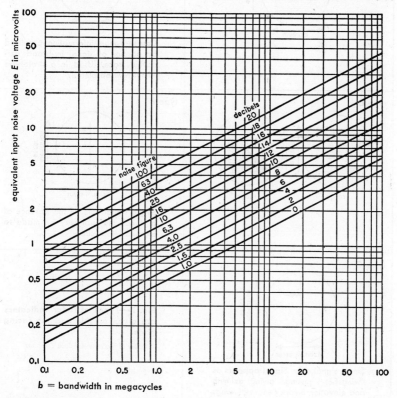

Fig. 6—Noise figure of a receiver of given bandwidth.

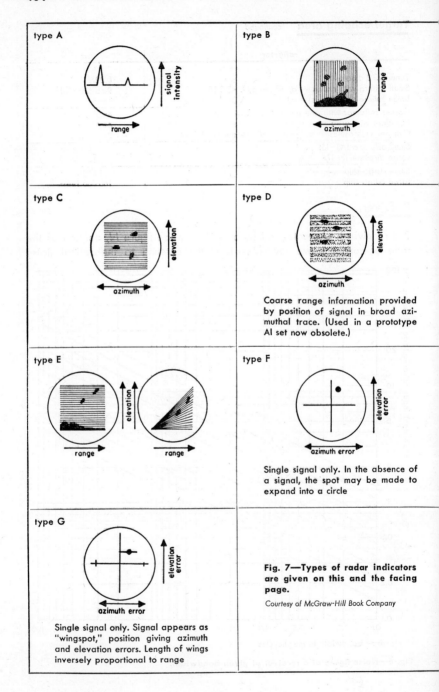

type A

signal intensity

range

type B

range

azimuth

type C

elevation

azimuth

type D

elevation

azimuth

Coarse range information provided by position of signal in broad azimuthal trace. (Used in a prototype AI set now obsolete.)

type E

elevation

range

range

type F

elevation error

azimuth error

Single signal only. In the absence of a signal, the spot may be made to expand into a circle

type G

elevation error

azimuth error

Single signal only. Signal appears as "wingspot," position giving azimuth and elevation errors. Length of wings inversely proportional to range

Fig. 7—Types of radar indicators are given on this and the facing page.

Courtesy of McGraw-Hill Book Company

type H

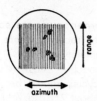

Signal appears as two dots. Left dot gives range and azimuth of target. Relative position of right dot gives rough indication of elevation

type I

Antenna scan is conical. Signal is a circle, the radius proportional to range. Brightest part indicates direction from axis of cone to target

type J

Same as type A, except time base is circular, and signals appear as radial pips

type K

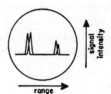

Type A with lobe-switching antenna. Spread voltage splits signals from two lobes. When pips are of equal size, antenna is on target

type L

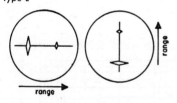

Same as type K, but signals from two lobes are placed back to back

type M

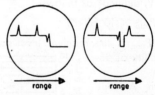

Type A with range step or range notch. When pip is aligned with step or notch, range can be read from dial or counter

type N

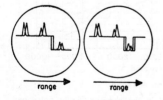

A combination of type K and type M

type P (PPI)

Range is measured radially from center

Receiver   *continued*

power KTb, when the mean noise power and the carrier power are equal.* This equality must be observed at some stage in the receiver where both have been amplified so highly as to override completely any noise introduced by succeeding stages. $KT = 4.1 \times 10^{-21}$, and b = receiver bandwidth in cycles/second. The bandwidth in megacycles should be $1.2/\tau$, plus an allowance for frequency drift, thus usually about $2/\tau$. Fig. 6 enables the determination of the noise figure of a receiver operating from any source impedance, Z_g ohms. E is one-half the open-circuit voltage of a fifty-ohm source, adjusted for receiver output carrier-plus-noise 3 decibels above noise alone.

Thus, if the generator is calibrated for microvolts into Z_g ohms, use $\sqrt{50/Z_g}$ times the indicated voltage. If it is calibrated for voltage into an open circuit, multiply by $\frac{1}{2}\sqrt{50/Z_g}$, but add series resistance to make source = Z_g ohms, for which the receiver input is designed.

Indicator

The many types of radar indicators are shown in Fig. 7. Type A is the first type used, and the best example of a deflection-modulated display. The PPI is the most common intensity-modulated type. For the purpose of determining maximum radar range, an indicator is characterized by a visibility factor V, defined† as follows:

$$V = \tau P_{min} \times 10^{-6}/NKT$$

where P_{min} is the receiver input-signal power in watts for a 50-percent probability of detection. For an A-scope presentation, V may be found from Fig. 8, where τ is in microseconds, and B is in megacycles. The values are conservative, but the effects of changing τB and f_r are shown correctly.

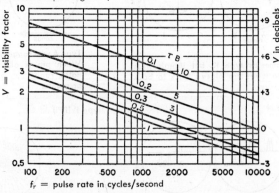

f_r = pulse rate in cycles/second

Fig. 8—Visibility factor for an A scope.

*Receiver noise figures are more completely discussed in the chapter "Radio noise and interference," p. 448–451.

† K. A. Norton, and A. C. Omberg, "The Maximum Range of a Radar Set," *Proceedings of the I.R.E.*, v. 35, pp. 4–24; January, 1947: p. 6.

Range equation

The theoretical maximum free-space range of a radar using an isotropic common receiving and transmitting antenna, lossless transmission line, and a perfect receiver, may be found as follows:

Transmitted pulse energy $= P'$ (in peak watts) $\times \tau'$ (in seconds)

Energy incident on target $= P'\tau'/4\pi R^2$ per unit area

Energy returned to antenna $= P'\tau'\sigma/(4\pi R^2)^2$ per unit area

Energy at receiver input $= P'\tau'\sigma\lambda^2/(4\pi)^3R^4$

where σ, λ, and R are in the same units.

Receiver input-noise energy $= KT = 4.11 \times 10^{-21}$ joules. Assuming that the receiver adds no noise, and that the signal is visible on the indicator when signal and noise energies are equal, the maximum range is found to be

$$R^4 = \frac{P'\tau'\sigma\lambda^2}{(4\pi)^3KT}$$

The free-space range of an actual radar will be modified by several dimensionless factors, primarily antenna gain G, receiver noise figure N, and indicator visibility factor V, as discussed above.

Additional minor losses may be lumped under factors L_1 and L_2, one-way and two-way loss factors, respectively. L_1 includes losses in transmission lines running from the TR switch to both transmitter and receiver, as well as TR loss, usually about 1 decibel. L_2 includes loss of the transmission line between TR box and antenna, and atmospheric absorption.

The range equation, including these factors, and using convenient units, is

$$R_m = 0.1146 \sqrt[4]{P_p\tau\sigma\lambda^2G^2L_1L_2^2/VN}$$

where

$R_m =$ maximum free-space range in miles

$P_p =$ peak power in kilowatts

$\tau =$ pulse width in microseconds

$\sigma =$ effective target area in square feet

$\lambda =$ wavelength in centimeters

The use of this equation is facilitated by use of decibels throughout, since many of the factors are readily found in this form. Thus, to find maximum radar range,

Range equation   *continued*

a. From Fig. 9, find $(P_p + \tau + \sigma + \lambda^2)$ in decibels.

b. Add $2 \times$ (gain in decibels of common antenna).

c. Subtract $(L_1 + 2L_2 + V + N)$ in decibels. Note V may be negative.

d. From the net result and Fig. 9, find R_m in miles.

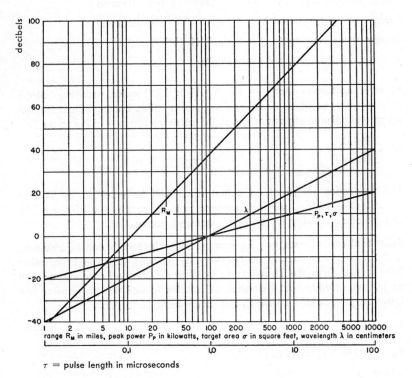

range R_M in miles, peak power P_p in kilowatts, target area σ in square feet, wavelength λ in centimeters

τ = pulse length in microseconds

Fig. 9—The radar range equation.

Reflection lobes

The maximum theoretical free-space range of a radar is often appreciably modified, especially for low-frequency sets, by reflections from the earth's surface. For low angles and a flat earth, the modifying factor is

$$F = 2 \sin \frac{(2\pi h_1 h_2)}{\lambda R}$$

where h_1, h_2, and R are defined in Fig. 10, all in the same units as λ. The result-

Reflection lobes *continued*

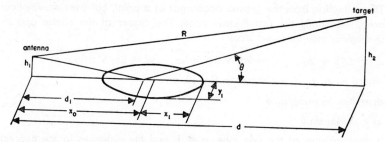

Fig. 10—Radar geometry, showing reflection from flat earth.

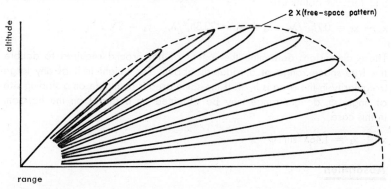

Fig. 11—Vertical-lobe pattern resulting from reflections from earth.

ing vertical pattern is shown in Fig. 11 for a typical case. The angles of the maxima of the lobes and the minima, or nulls, may be found from

$$\theta_m = \frac{h_2}{R} = \frac{n\lambda}{4h_1}$$

where

θ_m = angle of maximum in radians, when $n = 1, 3, 5 \ldots$.

= angle of minimum in radians, when $n = 0, 2, 4 \ldots$.

This expression may be applied to the problem of finding the height of a maximum or null over the curved earth with the following approximate result:

$$H_2 = 44 \, n \, \lambda \, D / H_1 + D^2/2$$

where

H = feet

λ = centimeters

D = miles

Reflection zone

The reflection from the ground occurs not at a point, but over an elliptical area, essentially the first Fresnel zone. The center of the ellipse and its dimensions may be found from

$$x_0 = d_1(1 + 2a), \quad x_1 = 2d_1 \sqrt{a(1 + a)}, \quad y_1 = 2h_1 \sqrt{a(1 + a)}$$

where x_0, x_1, y_1, d, are shown in Fig. 10, and

$$d_1 = h_1 d/h_2 = h_1/\sin \theta$$

$$a = \lambda/4h_1 \sin \theta$$

In the maximum of the first lobe, $a = 1$, and the distances to the nearest and farthest points are

$$x_0 - x_1 = 0.7h_1^2/\lambda, \quad x_0 + x_1 = 23.3h_1^2/\lambda, \quad y_1 = 2\sqrt{2}\, h_1$$

These dimensions determine the extent of flat ground required to double the free-space range of a radar as above. The height limit of any large irregularity in the area is $h_1/4$. If the same area is available on a sloping site of angle ϕ, double range may be obtained on a target on the horizon. In this case

$$x_0 + x_1 = 1.46\lambda/\sin^2 \phi$$

Absorption

When passing through atmospheric moisture, microwaves suffer an attenuation at an approximate rate of

$$L \approx 10Q/\lambda^2$$

where

L = attenuation in decibels/mile

λ = wavelength in centimeters

Q = rate of rainfall in inches/hour

Refraction

The moisture content of the air is also responsible for refraction of radar waves. In the so-called "standard" atmosphere, the moisture content decreases with height so that there is a tendency for the waves to curve toward the earth. This may be taken into account by assuming straight-line propagation over an earth of 4/3 the actual radius, or 5280 miles, for convenience. This value has been assumed in the equation for lobe height given above.

Refraction   *continued*

When the decrease in moisture content with height is abnormally rapid, a condition of super-refraction or anomalous propagation is said to exist. This effect is common over large bodies of water, and is strongest for the shortest wavelengths. Thus, S-band radars often show targets far beyond the normal horizon.

Terminology

A brief glossary is presented below of various terms that have fallen into most common use in the field of radar. In view of the fact that these terms, being widely familiar, may not be defined in the technical literature, they are presented here. Complete glossaries may be found in many of the more widely used radar texts.

AI: Aircraft interception. Short-range airborne radar sets that guide night-fighters in their interception of enemy aircraft.

ATR switch: Anti-TR switch to prevent received power from entering transmitter.

Blister: The housing for radar antenna (see Radome).

BTO: Bombing through overcast.

Chaff: Foil-and-paper strips dropped from airplanes to create false signals on enemy radar sets (see Window).

Clutter: Echoes from fixed or relatively slow-moving objects, e.g., hills, towers, clouds, sea surface.

Coherent: Refers to correspondence in phase at some time between two oscillations.

Coho: Coherent oscillator used with MTI.

Duct: Atmospheric phenomenon causing radar waves to bend toward earth, increasing radar range.

Duplexer: Navy term for TR switch.

GCA: Ground-controlled approach. The technique and/or apparatus for "talking down" an aircraft into approach for landing in poor visibility.

GCI: Ground (or ship) controlled interception. GCI stations vector (i.e., supply bearings) to within visual or radar range of enemy aircraft.

GL: Gun laying. Range, bearing, and elevation are provided by GL equipment to direct guns and control their fire.

IFF: Identification of friend or foe. Method of automatically challenging and receiving positive response from aircraft or ship.

Terminology *continued*

Jamming: Introduction of false radiation into enemy radio and radar devices.

LO: Local oscillator.

MTI: Moving-target indicator.

PPI: Plan-position indicator.

PPPI or P³I: Precision PPI.

P⁴I: Photographic-projection PPI.

Racon: Radar beacon used as a navigational aid, blind landing of planes, etc

Radome: Antenna housing.

RCM: Radio or radar counter measures.

RDF: Radio direction finding, also Radiolocation. British terms for Radar.

SLC: Search-light-control radar.

Sralo: Stable local oscillator, used with MTI.

TR switch: Transmit-receive device to prevent application of full transmitter power to receiver input.

Window: Mechanical reflecting devices dropped by planes to confuse enemy radar.

▨ Broadcasting

Introduction

Radio broadcasting for public entertainment in the U.S.A. is at present of three general types.

Standard broadcasting: Utilizing amplitude modulation in the 550–1600-kilocycle/second band.

Frequency-modulation: Broadcasting in the 88–108-megacycle/second band.

Television broadcasting: Utilizing amplitude-modulated video and frequency-modulated aural transmission in the (low) 54–88-megacycle band and the (high) 174–216-megacycle band.

There is also

International broadcasting: On assigned frequencies in the region between 6000 and 21,700 kilocycles in accordance with international agreement*.

Operation in these bands in the U.S.A. is subject to licensing and technical regulations of the Federal Communications Commission.

Selected administrative and technical information and rules from F.C.C. publications applicable to each of these broadcast applications, are given in this chapter.

General reference: "Rules Governing Radio Broadcast Service of June 25, 1940, revised to June 16, 1948," Federal Communications Commission, Washington, D.C.

Standard broadcasting†

Standard-broadcast stations are licensed for operation on 10-kilocycle-spaced channels occupying the band 550–1600 kilocycles, inclusive, and are classified as follows.

---

* A more detailed explanation of international-broadcasting frequency assignments and requirements is given in the chapter "Frequency data," pp. 9-11.

† See "Standards of Good Engineering Practice Concerning Standard Broadcast Stations August 1, 1939, revised to Oct. 30, 1947," Federal Communications Commission, Washington, D.C.

Standard broadcasting   *continued*

class of station	class of channel	normal service	permissible power in kilowatts	signal-intensity contour in microvolts/meter of area protected from objectionable interference	
				day (ground-wave)	night
Ia	Clear	Primary and secondary	50	SC = 100 AC = 500	Not duplicated
Ib	Clear	Primary and secondary	10 to 50	SC = 100 AC = 500	500 (50% sky wave)
II	Clear	Primary	0.25 to 50	500	2500 (Ground wave)
III–A	Regional	Primary	1 to 5	500	2500 (Ground wave)
III–B	Regional	Primary	Night = 0.5 to 1 Day = 5	500	4000 (Ground wave)
IV	Local	Primary	0.1 to 0.25	500	4000 (Ground wave)

SC = same channel   AC = adjacent channel
Taken from "Standards of Good Engineering Practice Concerning Standard Broadcasting, August 1, 1939, revised October 30, 1947," Federal Communications Commission, Washington, D.C.

Field-intensity requirements

Primary service

City areas: 2 to 50 millivolts/meter, ground wave
Rural areas: 0.1 to 1.0 millivolt/meter, ground wave

Secondary service

All areas having sky-wave field intensity greater than 500 microvolts/meter for 50 percent or more of the time.

Coverage data

The charts of Figs. 1–3 show computed values of ground-wave field intensity as a function of the distances from the transmitting antenna. These are used for the determination of coverage and interference. They were computed for the frequencies indicated, a dielectric constant equal to 15 for ground and 80 for sea water (referred to air as unity), and for the surface conductivities noted. The curves are for radiation from a short vertical antenna at the surface of a uniformly conductive spherical earth, with an antenna power and efficiency such that the inverse-distance field is 100 millivolts/meter at one mile.

Standard broadcasting   *continued*

The following table gives data on ground inductivity and conductivity in the U.S.A.

type of terrain	inductivity referred to air = 1	conductivity in emu	absorption factor at 50 miles, 1000 kilocycles*
Sea water, minimum attenuation	81	4.64×10^{-11}	1.0
Pastoral, low hills, rich soil, typical of Dallas, Texas; Lincoln, Nebraska; and Wolf Point, Montana, areas	20	3×10^{-13}	0.50
Pastoral, low hills, rich soil, typical of Ohio and Illinois	14	10^{-13}	0.17
Flat country, marshy, densely wooded, typical of Louisiana near Mississippi River	12	7.5×10^{-14}	0.13
Pastoral, medium hills, and forestation, typical of Maryland, Pennsylvania, New York, exclusive of mountainous territory and sea coasts	13	6×10^{-14}	0.09
Pastoral, medium hills, and forestation, heavy clay soil, typical of central Virginia	13	4×10^{-14}	0.05
Rocky soil, steep hills, typical of New England	14	2×10^{-14}	0.025
Sandy, dry, flat, typical of coastal country	10	2×10^{-14}	0.024
City, industrial areas, average attenuation	5	10^{-14}	0.011
City, industrial areas, maximum attenuation	3	10^{-15}	0.003

* This figure is stated for comparison purposes in order to indicate at a glance which values of conductivity and inductivity represent the higher absorption. It is the ratio between field intensity obtained with the soil constants given and with no absorption. From "Standards of Good Engineering Practice Concerning Standard Broadcasting, August 1, 1939, revised October 30, 1947," Federal Communications Commission, Washington, D.C.

Station performance requirements

Operation is maintained in accordance with the following specifications.

Modulation: Amplitude modulation of at least 85 to 95 percent.

Audio-frequency distortion: Harmonics less than 5 percent arithmetical sum or root-mean-square amplitude up to 85 percent modulation; less than 7.5 percent for 85 to 95 percent modulation.

Audio-frequency response: Transmission characteristic flat between 100 and 5000 cycles to within 2 decibels, referred to 1000 cycles.

Standard broadcasting   *continued*

Noise: At least 50 decibels, unweighted, below 100 percent modulation for the frequency band 150 to 5000 cycles, and at least 40 decibels down outside this range.

Carrier-frequency stability: Within 20 cycles of assigned frequency.

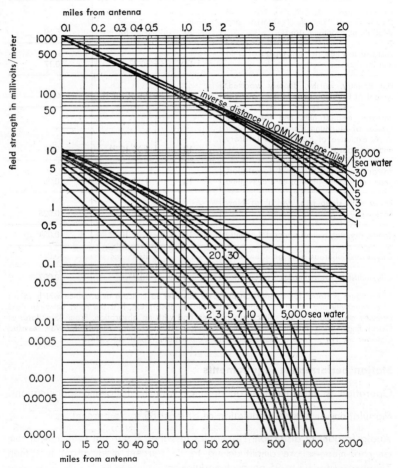

Fig. 1—Ground-wave field intensity plotted against distance. Computed for 550 kilocycles. Dielectric constant = 15. Ground-conductivity values above are emu $\times$ 10^{14}.

Frequency modulation*

Frequency-modulation broadcasting stations are authorized for operation on 100 allocated channels each 200 kilocycles wide extending consecutively from channel No. 201 on 88.1 megacycles to No. 300 on 107.9 megacycles.

* See "Federal Communications Commission Rules and Regulations Governing FM Broadcast Services September 20, 1945, revised to January 9, 1946," Federal Communications Commission, Washington, D.C.

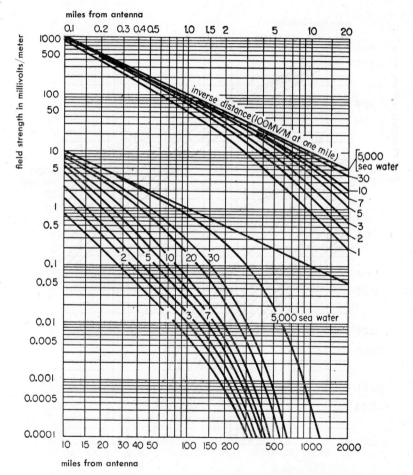

Fig. 2—Ground-wave field intensity plotted against distance. Computed for 1000 kilocycles. Dielectric constant = 15. Ground-conductivity values above are emu $\times 10^{14}$.

Frequency modulation   *continued*

Commercial broadcasting is authorized on channels No. 221 (92.1 megacycles) through No. 300. Noncommercial educational broadcasting is
licensed on channels No. 201 through 220 (89.9 megacycles).

Station service classification

Licenses are issued to stations of two main classifications.

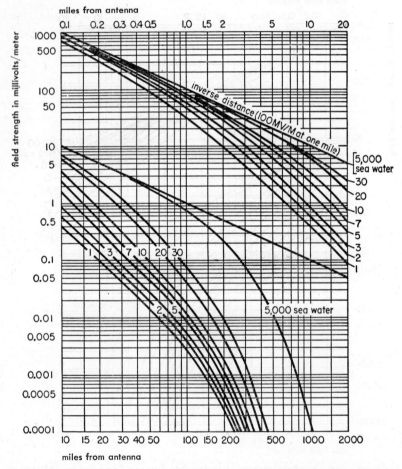

Fig. 3—Ground-wave field intensity plotted against distance. Computed for 1600 kilocycles. Dielectric constant = 15. Ground-conductivity values above are emu $\times\ 10^{14}$.

Frequency modulation   *continued*

Class-A stations: Render service primarily to communities other than the principal city of an area. A maximum effective rated power of 1 kilowatt and an antenna height of 250 feet are permitted.

Class-B stations: Render service primarily to a metropolitan district or principal city and its surrounding rural area, or to primarily rural areas. In *FM Area I*, which includes New England and the North- and Middle-Atlantic-states areas, they are licensed to operate with 10 kilowatts minimum, 20 kilowatts maximum, effective rated power and 300 feet minimum, 500 feet maximum, effective antenna height. In *FM Area II* (balance of U.S.A. outside of Area *I*), class-B stations are licensed to operate with 2 kilowatts minimum, 20 kilowatts maximum, effective rated power and 300 feet minimum, 500 feet maximum, effective antenna height.

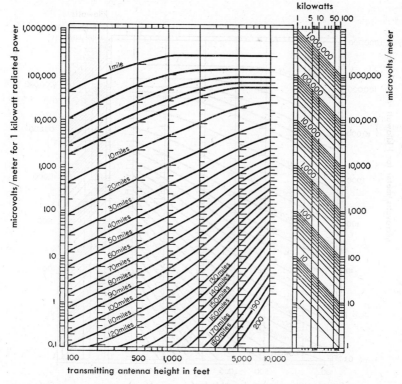

Fig. 4—Ground-wave signal range for television band 46 megacycles. Conductivity = 5 × 10⁻¹⁴ emu, and dielectric constant = 15. Receiving-antenna height = 30 feet. For horizontal (and approximately for vertical) polarization.

Frequency modulation   *continued*

Coverage data

The frequency-modulation broadcasting service area is considered to be only that served by the ground wave. The median field intensity considered necessary for adequate service in city, business, or factory areas is 100 microvolts/meter; in rural areas, 50 microvolts/meter is specified. A median field intensity of 3000 to 5000 microvolts/meter is specified for the principal city to be served. The curves of Fig. 7 give data for determination of F-M broadcast-station coverage as a function of rated power and antenna height.

Objectionable interference from other stations may limit the service area. Such interference is considered by the F.C.C. to exist when the ratio of desired to undesired signal values is as follows:

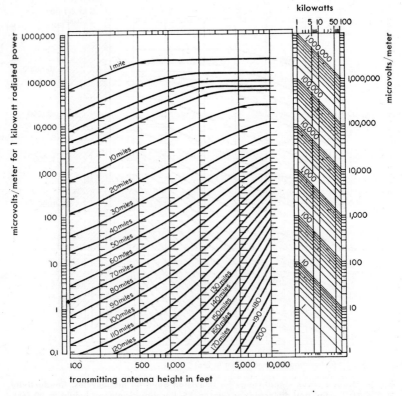

Fig. 5—Ground-wave signal range for television band 63 megacycles. Conductivity = 5 × 10⁻¹⁴ emu, and dielectric constant = 15. Receiving-antenna height = 30 feet. For horizontal (and approximately for vertical) polarization.

Frequency modulation *continued*

Same channel: 10/1

Adjacent channel (200-kc/s separation): 2/1

Values are ground-wave median field for the desired signal, and the tropospheric-signal intensity exceeded for 1 percent of the time for the undesired signal. It is considered that stations having alternate-channel spacing (400-kilocycle separation) may be operated in the same coverage area without objectionable mutual interference.

Station performance requirements

Operation is maintained in accordance with the following specifications.

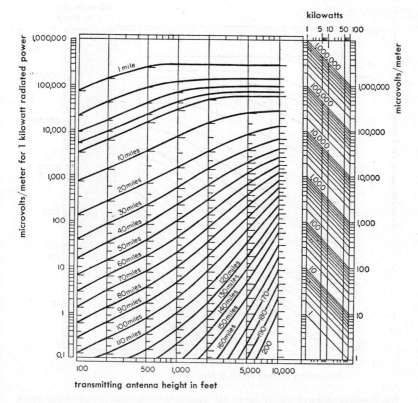

Fig. 6—**Ground-wave signal range for television band 82 megacycles. Conductivity = 5 × 10⁻¹⁴ emu, and dielectric constant = 15. Receiving-antenna height = 30 feet. For horizontal (and approximately for vertical) polarization.**

Frequency modulation   continued

Audio-frequency response: Transmitting system capable of transmitting the band of frequencies 50 to 15,000 cycles. Preemphasis employed and response maintained within limits shown by curves of Fig. 9.

Audio-frequency distortion: Maximum combined audio-frequency harmonic root-mean-square voltage in system output less than

modulating frequency in cycles/second	percent harmonic
50–100	3.5
100–7500	2.5
7500–15000	3.0

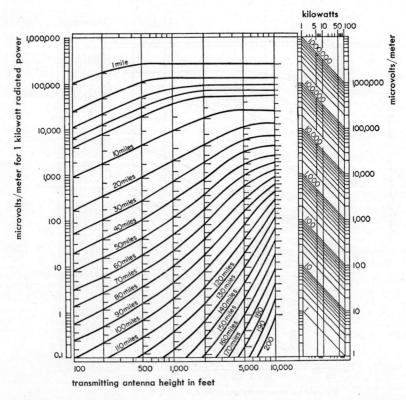

Fig. 7—Ground-wave signal range for frequency-modulation broadcasting band, 98 megacycles. Conductivity = 5 × 10⁻¹⁴ emu, and dielectric constant = 15. Receiving-antenna height = 30 feet. For horizontal (and approximately for vertical) polarization.

Frequency modulation continued

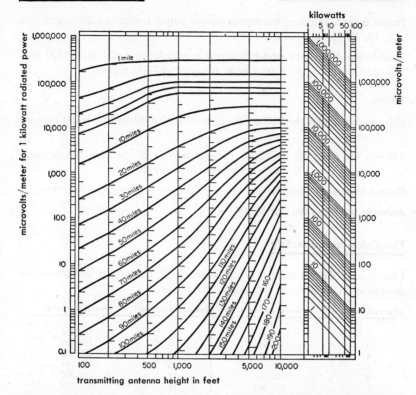

Fig. 8—Ground-wave signal range for television band 195 megacycles. Conductivity = 5 × 10⁻¹⁴ emu, and dielectric constant = 15. Receiving-antenna height = 30 feet. For horizontal (and approximately for vertical) polarization.

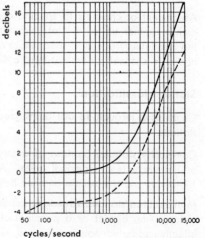

Fig. 9—Standard pre-emphasis curve for frequency-modulation and television aural broadcasting. Time constant = 75 micro-seconds (solid line). Frequency-response limits are set by the two lines.

Frequency modulation   *continued*

Power output: Standard transmitter power output ratings are 250 watts, and 1, 3, 10, 25, 50, and 100 kilowatts.

Modulation: Frequency modulation with a modulating capability of 100 percent corresponding to a frequency swing of ± 75 kilocycles.

Noise:

FM—In the band 50 to 15,000 cycles, at least 60 decibels below 100-percent swing.

AM—In the band 50 to 15,000 cycles, at least 50 decibels below level representing 100-percent amplitude modulation.

Center-frequency stability: Within ± 2000 cycles of assigned frequency.

Antenna polarization: Horizontal.

Television broadcasting

Television-broadcast stations are (January, 1949) authorized for commercial operation on 12 channels designated as follows:

channel number	band in mc/s	channel number	band in mc/s
2	54–60	8	180–186
3	60–66	9	186–192
4	66–72	10	192–198
5	76–82	11	198–204
6	82–88	12	204–210
7	174–180	13	210–216

Assignment of channels to specific areas has been made by the F.C.C. in such a manner as to facilitate maximum interference-free coverage within the available frequency spectrum. Within a given area, operation is on alternate channels or with at least a 4-megacycle channel guard band.

Station classification

Channels 2 through 13 are authorized for three basic types of television stations.

Community stations: Stations of this type render service to smaller metropolitan districts or principal cities. An effective radiated peak power of 1 kilowatt and a maximum antenna height of 500 feet are permitted.

Metropolitan stations: Are designed primarily to render service to a single metropolitan district or a principal city and surrounding rural area. Peak effective radiated power is limited to 50 kilowatts at a maximum antenna

Television broadcasting *continued*

height of 500 feet above average terrain. Greater heights with equal or less power may be permitted.

Rural stations: Are proposed to serve an area predominantly rural in character. Technical conditions of operation of such stations, as well as their licensing, are determined upon special action of the F.C.C.

Broadcast coverage

The television-broadcast service area, like that of frequency modulation, is considered to be that region receiving a satisfactory ground-wave signal intensity. Median field intensities (at synchronizing-pulse peaks) considered necessary for service are

City, business, or factory areas: 5000 microvolts/meter
Residential and rural areas: 500 microvolts/meter

The curves of Figs. 4–8 give coverage distance through the allocated television-frequency bands as a function of radiated power and antenna height.

Objectionable visual interference, limiting the satisfactory signal values indicated above, is considered to exist when the ratio of desired/undesired signals is

Same channel: 100/1
Adjacent channel (6-mc/s separation):   2/1

The desired-signal intensity is that of the ground-wave median field, while the undesired-signal value is the tropospheric signal intensity exceeded for 10 percent of the time. It is considered that stations having an alternate-channel (12-megacycle) or a 10-megacycle separation may be operated in the same coverage area without objectionable interference.

Overall station performance requirements

F.C.C. television standards (December 19, 1945) are

Channel width: 6 megacycles/second.

Picture carrier location: 4.5 megacycles below aural center frequency.

Aural center frequency: 0.25 megacycles below upper-frequency limit of channel.

Polarization of radiation: Horizontal.

Modulation: Amplitude-modulated composite picture and synchronizing signal on visual carrier, together with frequency-modulated audio signal on aural carrier shall be included in a single television channel (Figs. 10 and 11).

Television broadcasting *continued*

Visual transmission requirements

Modulation: Amplitude modulation.

Radio-frequency-amplitude characteristic: As per Fig. 10.

Scanning lines: 525 lines/frame, interlaced two to one.

Frame frequency: 30/second.

Field frequency: 60/second.

Aspect ratio: 4 units horizontal to 3 units vertical.

Scanning sequence:
Horizontal—left to right
Vertical—top to bottom

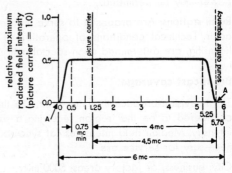

channel frequency spectrum in megacycles
referred to lower frequency limit of channel

Fig. 10—Radio-frequency amplitude characteristic of television picture transmission. Field intensity at points A shall not exceed 20 decibels below picture carrier. Drawing not to scale.

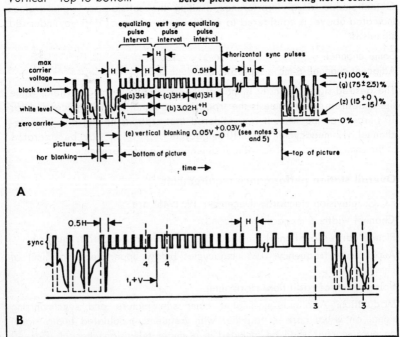

Fig. 11—(Above and at right) Television composite-signal waveform data.

Television broadcasting *continued*

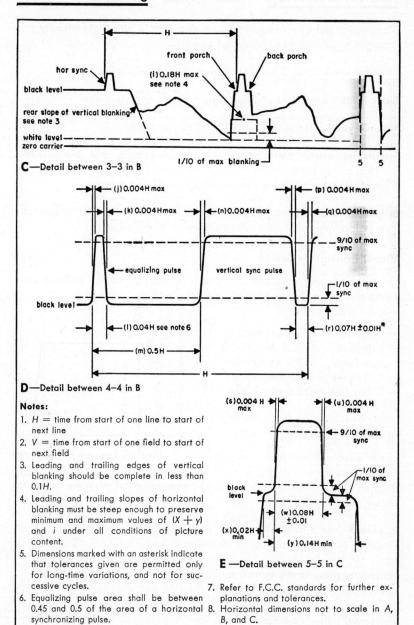

C—Detail between 3–3 in B

D—Detail between 4–4 in B

E—Detail between 5–5 in C

Notes:

1. H = time from start of one line to start of next line
2. V = time from start of one field to start of next field
3. Leading and trailing edges of vertical blanking should be complete in less than 0.1H.
4. Leading and trailing slopes of horizontal blanking must be steep enough to preserve minimum and maximum values of $(X + y)$ and i under all conditions of picture content.
5. Dimensions marked with an asterisk indicate that tolerances given are permitted only for long-time variations, and not for successive cycles.
6. Equalizing pulse area shall be between 0.45 and 0.5 of the area of a horizontal synchronizing pulse.
7. Refer to F.C.C. standards for further explanations and tolerances.
8. Horizontal dimensions not to scale in A, B, and C.

Fig. 11 — *continued*

Television broadcasting *continued*

Transmission polarity: Negative (i.e., a decrease in initial light intensity corresponds to an increase in radiated power).

Pedestal level: 75 ± 2 percent of peak carrier amplitude.

Black level: Constant at or closely approaching pedestal level.

White level: 15 percent or less of peak carrier amplitude.

Transmitter output variation: At synchronizing peak and black levels, the total output variation due to noise, hum, response, etc., shall not exceed 5 percent of synchronizing-peak amplitude within each frame.

Brightness characteristic: Transmitter output shall vary in substantially inverse logarithmic relation to the brightness of the subject.

Visual transmitter design

Overall frequency response: The output measured into the antenna after vestigial-sideband filters shall be within limits of +0 and

— 2 decibels   at 0.5 megacycles
— 2 decibels   at 1.25 megacycles
— 3 decibels   at 2.0 megacycles
— 6 decibels   at 3.0 megacycles
— 12 decibels at 3.5 megacycles

with respect to video amplitude characteristic of Fig. 12.

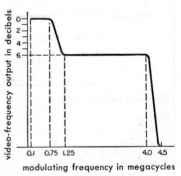

Fig. 12—Ideal demodulated amplitude characteristic of television transmitter

Lower-sideband radiation: For modulating frequency of 1.25 megacycles or greater, radiation must be 20 decibels below carrier level.

Radiated radio-frequency-signal envelope: Specified by Fig. 11 as modified by vestigial operation characteristic of Fig. 10.

Horizontal pulse-timing variations: Variation of time interval between successive pulse leading edges to be less than 0.5 percent of average interval.

Horizontal pulse-repetition stability: Rate of change of leading-edge recurrence frequency shall not exceed 0.15 percent/second.

Television broadcasting   *continued*

Aural transmitter

Effective radiation: Greater than 50 percent and less than 150 percent of visual-transmitter peak radiated power.

Modulation: Frequency modulation with 100-percent swing of ± 25 kilocycles. Required maximum swing = ± 40 kilocycles.

Audio-frequency response: 50 to 15,000 cycles within limits and utilizing preemphasis as shown in Fig. 10.

Audio-frequency distortion: Maximum combined harmonic root-mean-square output voltage shall be less than

modulating frequency in cycles/second	percent harmonic
50– 100	3.5
100– 7500	2.5
7500–15000	3.0

Noise

FM—55 decibels below 100-percent swing.
AM—50 decibels below level corresponding to 100-percent modulation.

■ Wire transmission

Telephone transmission-line data

Line constants of copper open-wire pairs

8- and 12-inch spacing

Insulators:
40 pairs toll and double-petticoat (DP) per mile
53 pairs Pyrex glass (CS) per mile

Temperature 68° fahrenheit

| freq in kc/s | resistance in ohms/loop mile | | | | | | inductance in millihenries/loop mile | | | | | |
| | 165 mil | | 128 mil | | 104 mil | | 165 mil | | 128 mil | | 104 mil | |
	12" DP	8" CS	12" DP	8" CS	12" DP	8" CS	12" DP	8" CS	12" DP	8" CS	12" DP	8" CS
0.1	4.10	4.10	6.82	6.82	10.33	10.33	3.37	3.11	3.53	3.27	3.66	3.40
0.5	4.13	4.13	6.83	6.83	10.34	10.34	3.37	3.10	3.53	3.27	3.66	3.40
1.0	4.19	4.19	6.87	6.87	10.36	10.36	3.37	3.10	3.53	3.27	3.66	3.40
1.5	4.29	4.29	6.94	6.94	10.41	10.41	3.37	3.10	3.53	3.26	3.66	3.40
2.0	4.42	4.42	7.02	7.02	10.47	10.47	3.36	3.10	3.53	3.26	3.66	3.40
3.0	4.76	4.76	7.24	7.24	10.62	10.62	3.35	3.09	3.52	3.26	3.66	3.40
5.0	5.61	5.61	7.92	7.92	11.11	11.11	3.34	3.08	3.52	3.25	3.66	3.40
10	7.56	7.56	10.05	10.05	12.98	12.98	3.31	3.04	3.49	3.23	3.64	3.38
20	10.23	10.23	13.63	13.63	17.14	17.14	3.28	3.02	3.46	3.20	3.61	3.35
30	12.26	12.26	16.26	16.26	20.55	20.55	3.26	3.00	3.44	3.17	3.58	3.33
50	15.50	15.50	20.41	20.41	25.67	25.67	3.25	2.99	3.43	3.16	3.57	3.31
100	21.45	21.45	28.09	28.09	35.10	35.10	3.24	2.98	3.42	3.15	3.55	3.29
150	26.03	26.03	33.96	33.96	42.42	42.42	3.23	2.97	3.41	3.14	3.54	3.28
200	29.89	29.89	38.93	38.93	48.43	48.43	3.23	2.97	3.40	3.14	3.54	3.28
500	46.62	46.62	60.53	60.53	74.98	74.98	3.22	2.96	3.39	3.13	3.53	3.27
1000	65.54	65.54	84.84	84.84	104.9	104.9	3.22	2.96	3.38	3.12	3.52	3.26

| freq in kc/s | leakage conductance in micromhos/loop mile | | | |
| | dry—all gauges | | wet—all gauges | |
	12"—DP	8"—CS	12"—DP	8"—CS
0.1	0.04	0.04	2.5	2.0
0.5	0.15	0.06	3.0	2.3
1.0	0.29	0.11	3.5	2.6
1.5	0.43	0.15	4.0	2.9
2.0	0.57	0.20	4.5	3.2
3.0	0.85	0.30	5.5	3.7
5.0	1.4	0.49	7.5	4.6
10	2.8	0.97	12.1	6.6
20	5.6	1.9	20.5	9.6
30	8.4	2.9	28.0	12.1
50	14.0	4.8	41.1	15.7

| wire size | capacitance in microfarads/loop mile | |
	12"	8"
in space		
165 mil	0.00898	0.00978
128 mil	0.00855	0.00928
104 mil	0.00822	0.00888
on 40-wire line, dry		
165 mil	0.00915	0.01000
128 mil	0.00871	0.00948
104 mil	0.00857	0.00908
on 40-wire line, wet		
165 mil	0.0093	0.0102
128 mil	0.0089	0.0097
104 mil	0.0085	0.0093

Telephone transmission-line data *continued*

Line constants of 40% Copperweld open-wire pairs

8- and 12-inch spacing

Insulators:
  40 pairs toll and double-petticoat (DP) per mile
  53 pairs Pyrex glass (CS) per mile

Temperature 68° fahrenheit

freq in kc/s	resistance in ohms/loop mile						inductance in millihenries/loop mile					
	165 mil		128 mil		104 mil		165 mil		128 mil		104 mil	
	12″ DP	8″ CS	12″ DP	8″ CS	12″ DP	8″ CS	12″ DP	8″ CS	12″ DP	8″ CS	12″ DP	8″ CS
0.0	9.8	9.8	16.2	16.2	24.6	24.6	—	—	—	—	—	—
0.1	10.0	10.0	16.3	16.3	24.6	24.6	3.37	3.11	3.53	3.27	3.66	3.40
0.5	10.0	10.0	16.4	16.4	24.7	24.7	3.37	3.10	3.53	3.27	3.66	3.40
1.0	10.1	10.1	16.6	16.6	24.8	24.8	3.37	3.10	3.53	3.27	3.66	3.40
1.5	10.1	10.1	16.7	16.7	24.9	24.9	3.37	3.10	3.53	3.26	3.66	3.40
2.0	10.2	10.2	16.8	16.8	25.2	25.2	3.36	3.10	3.53	3.26	3.66	3.40
3.0	10.4	10.4	17.1	17.1	25.4	25.4	3.35	3.09	3.52	3.26	3.66	3.40
5.0	10.6	10.6	17.4	17.4	26.0	26.0	3.34	3.08	3.52	3.25	3.66	3.40
10	10.8	10.8	17.7	17.7	26.5	26.5	3.31	3.04	3.49	3.23	3.64	3.38
20	11.4	11.4	18.2	18.2	27.1	27.1	3.28	3.02	3.46	3.20	3.61	3.35
30	12.3	12.3	18.8	18.8	27.5	27.5	3.26	3.00	3.44	3.17	3.58	3.33
50	14.5	14.5	20.4	20.4	28.7	28.7	3.25	2.99	3.43	3.16	3.57	3.31
100	20.8	20.8	26.5	26.5	33.3	33.3	3.24	2.98	3.42	3.15	3.55	3.29
150	25.9	25.9	32.5	32.5	39.6	39.6	3.23	2.97	3.41	3.14	3.54	3.28

freq in kc/s	leakage conductance in micromhos/loop mile			
	dry—all gauges		wet—all gauges	
	12″—DP	8″—CS	12″—DP	8″—CS
0.1	0.04	0.04	2.5	2.0
0.5	0.15	0.06	3.0	2.3
1.0	0.29	0.11	3.5	2.6
1.5	0.43	0.15	4.0	2.9
2.0	0.57	0.20	4.5	3.2
3.0	0.85	0.30	5.5	3.7
5.0	1.4	0.49	7.5	4.6
10	2.8	0.97	12.1	6.6
20	5.6	1.9	20.5	9.6
30	8.4	2.9	28.0	12.1
50	14.0	4.8	41.1	15.7

wire size	capacitance in microfarads/loop mile	
	12″	8″
in space		
165 mil	0.00898	0.00978
128 mil	0.00855	0.00928
104 mil	0.00822	0.00888
on 40-wire line, dry		
165 mil	0.00915	0.01000
128 mil	0.00871	0.00948
104 mil	0.00857	0.00908
on 40-wire line, wet		
165 mil	0.0093	0.0102
128 mil	0.0089	0.0097
104 mil	0.0085	0.0093

Telephone transmission-line data   continued

Attenuation of copper open-wire pairs

8- and 12-inch spacing

Insulators:
40 pairs toll and double-petticoat (DP) per mile
53 pairs Pyrex glass (CS) per mile

Temperature 68° fahrenheit

dry weather

| freq in kc/s | 165 mil | | | 128 mil | | | 104 mil | | |
	12″ DP	12″ CS	8″ CS	12″ DP	12″ CS	8″ CS	12″ DP	12″ CS	8″ CS
0.1	0.023	0.023	0.025	0.032	0.032	0.034	0.041	0.041	0.0425
0.5	0.029	0.029	0.0315	0.045	0.045	0.048	0.063	0.063	0.067
1.0	0.030	0.030	0.0325	0.047	0.047	0.0505	0.067	0.067	0.072
1.5	0.031	0.031	0.0335	0.048	0.048	0.051	0.068	0.068	0.073
2.0	0.0325	0.032	0.035	0.0485	0.048	0.052	0.069	0.069	0.074
3.0	0.036	0.034	0.038	0.051	0.050	0.054	0.071	0.070	0.076
5.0	0.044	0.041	0.0445	0.057	0.055	0.0595	0.076	0.074	0.080
10	0.061	0.056	0.0605	0.076	0.070	0.076	0.093	0.087	0.094
20	0.088	0.076	0.083	0.108	0.096	0.104	0.129	0.116	0.125
30	0.110	0.092	0.100	0.135	0.116	0.125	0.159	0.140	0.151
50	0.148	0.118	0.127	0.179	0.147	0.158	0.209	0.176	0.189
100	—	0.165	0.178	—	0.204	0.220	—	0.244	0.262
150	—	0.203	0.218	—	0.249	0.268	—	0.296	0.317
200	—	0.235	0.25	—	—	—	—	—	—
500	—	—	0.42±	—	—	—	—	—	—
1000	—	—	0.7±	—	—	—	—	—	—

wet weather

| freq in kc/s | 165 mil | | | 128 mil | | | 104 mil | | |
	12″ DP	12″ CS	8″ CS	12″ DP	12″ CS	8″ CS	12″ DP	12″ CS	8″ CS
0.1	0.032	0.029	0.030	0.043	0.039	0.040	0.054	0.049	0.0505
0.5	0.037	0.034	0.036	0.053	0.050	0.053	0.072	0.069	0.0705
1.0	0.039	0.035	0.037	0.056	0.052	0.055	0.076	0.073	0.0775
1.5	0.041	0.037	0.0385	0.058	0.0535	0.0565	0.078	0.0745	0.0795
2.0	0.043	0.038	0.040	0.060	0.0545	0.058	0.0805	0.076	0.0805
3.0	0.0485	0.041	0.044	0.064	0.0575	0.061	0.0845	0.078	0.083
5.0	0.060	0.050	0.0525	0.075	0.0645	0.068	0.094	0.084	0.089
10	0.085	0.068	0.072	0.102	0.083	0.0885	0.120	0.101	0.106
20	0.127	0.095	0.101	0.150	0.116	0.123	0.173	0.137	0.144
30	0.161	0.118	0.124	0.188	0.142	0.150	0.216	0.168	0.176
50	0.220	0.154	0.162	0.253	0.185	0.195	0.287	0.217	0.227
100	—	0.228	0.237	—	0.271	0.283	—	0.313	0.326
150	—	0.288	0.299	—	0.339	0.353	—	0.390	0.405

Telephone transmission-line data *continued*

Attenuation of 40% Copperweld open-wire pairs

8- and 12-inch spacing

Insulators:
40 pairs toll and double-petticoat (DP) per mile
53 pairs Pyrex glass (CS) per mile

Temperature 68° fahrenheit

dry weather

freq in kc/s	attenuation in decibels per mile								
	165 mil			128 mil			104 mil		
	12″ DP	12″ CS	8″ CS	12″ DP	12″ CS	8″ CS	12″ DP	12″ CS	8″ CS
0.2	0.054	0.054	0.057	0.073	0.073	0.077	0.091	0.091	0.096
0.5	0.067	0.067	0.071	0.097	0.097	0.103	0.127	0.127	0.134
1.0	0.073	0.073	0.078	0.112	0.112	0.120	0.152	0.152	0.162
1.5	0.076	0.076	0.082	0.118	0.118	0.127	0.162	0.162	0.174
2.0	0.077	0.077	0.083	0.120	0.120	0.130	0.168	0.168	0.180
3.0	0.079	0.079	0.085	0.124	0.124	0.134	0.174	0.174	0.188
5.0	0.082	0.082	0.088	0.127	0.127	0.138	0.179	0.179	0.195
10	0.085	0.085	0.092	0.131	0.131	0.142	0.186	0.186	0.201
20	0.088	0.088	0.096	0.135	0.135	0.147	0.191	0.191	0.207
30	0.095	0.095	0.103	0.139	0.139	0.152	0.195	0.195	0.211
50	0.110	0.110	0.119	0.150	0.150	0.163	0.206	0.206	0.221
100	0.156	0.156	0.168	0.188	0.188	0.203	0.234	0.234	0.252
150	0.199	0.199	0.214	0.233	0.233	0.251	0.273	0.273	0.293

wet weather

freq in kc/s	12″ DP	12″ CS	8″ CS	12″ DP	12″ CS	8″ CS	12″ DP	12″ CS	8″ CS
0.2	0.066	0.060	0.063	0.089	0.081	0.084	0.111	0.101	0.105
0.5	0.077	0.072	0.076	0.111	0.104	0.110	0.145	0.136	0.142
1.0	0.083	0.078	0.084	0.126	0.119	0.126	0.168	0.160	0.169
1.5	0.088	0.082	0.087	0.130	0.124	0.133	0.178	0.170	0.181
2.0	0.089	0.083	0.089	0.136	0.128	0.137	0.184	0.176	0.188
3.0	0.093	0.086	0.092	0.140	0.132	0.142	0.192	0.183	0.196
5.0	0.100	0.091	0.097	0.147	0.137	0.148	0.201	0.190	0.205
10	0.111	0.098	0.104	0.159	0.145	0.155	0.214	0.200	0.215
20	0.126	0.107	0.115	0.175	0.155	0.166	0.233	0.212	0.228
30	0.145	0.120	0.127	0.197	0.168	0.177	0.253	0.224	0.238
50	0.184	0.147	0.153	0.230	0.190	0.199	0.288	0.247	0.261
100	0.282	0.219	0.227	0.314	0.254	0.265	0.372	0.303	0.317
150	0.370	0.285	0.295	0.415	0.324	0.336	0.461	0.367	0.382

continued **Telephone transmission-line data**

Characteristics of standard types of aerial copper-wire telephone circuits

1000 cycles per second

DP (double petticoat) insulators for all 12- and 18-inch spaced wires.
CS (special glass with steel pin) insulators for all 8-inch spaced wires.

type of circuit	gauge of wires mils	spacing of wires inches	primary constants per loop mile				propagation constant				line impedance				wave-length miles	velocity miles per second	attenuation db per mile
			R ohms	L henries	C μf	G μmho	polar		rectangular		polar		rectangular				
							magnitude	angle deg +	α	β	magnitude	angle deg	R ohms	X ohms			
Non-pole pair phys	165	8	4.11	.00311	.01000	.11	.0353	83.99	.00370	.0351	565	5.88	562	58	179.0	179,000	.0325
Non-pole pair side	165	12	4.11	.00337	.00915	.29	.0352	84.36	.00346	.0350	612	5.35	610	57	179.5	179,500	.030
Pole pair side	165	18	4.11	.00364	.00863	.29	.0355	84.75	.00325	.0353	653	5.00	651	57	178.0	178,000	.028
Non-pole pair phan	165	12	2.06	.00208	.01514	.58	.0355	85.34	.00288	.0354	373	4.30	372	28	177.5	177,500	.025
Non-pole pair phys	128	8	6.74	.00327	.00948	.11	.0358	80.85	.00569	.0353	603	8.97	596	94	178.0	178,000	.0505
Non-pole patr side	128	12	6.74	.00353	.00871	.29	.0356	81.39	.00533	.0352	650	8.32	643	94	178.5	178,500	.047
Pole pair side	128	18	6.74	.00380	.00825	.29	.0358	81.95	.00502	.0355	693	7.72	686	93	177.0	177,000	.044
Non-pole pair phan	128	12	3.37	.00216	.01454	.58	.0357	82.84	.00445	.0355	401	6.73	398	47	177.0	177,000	.039
Non-pole pair phys	104	8	10.15	.00340	.00908	.11	.0367	77.22	.00811	.0358	644	12.63	629	141	175.5	175,500	.072
Non-pole pair side	104	12	10.15	.00366	.00837	.29	.0363	77.93	.00760	.0355	692	11.75	677	141	177.0	177,000	.067
Pole pair side	104	18	10.15	.00393	.00797	.29	.0365	78.66	.00718	.0358	730	10.97	717	139	175.5	175,500	.063
Non-pole pair phan	104	12	5.08	.00223	.01409	.58	.0363	79.84	.00640	.0357	421	9.70	415	71	176.0	176,000	.056

Notes: 1. All values are for dry-weather conditions.
2. All capacitance values assume a line carrying 40 wires.
3. Resistance values are for temperature of 20° C (68° F).

continued

Telephone transmission-line data

Representative values of toll-cable line and propagation constants

13, 16, and 19 AWG quadded toll cable
Nonloaded
All figures for loop-mile basis
Temperature 55° fahrenheit

freq in kc/s	resistance ohms/mile 13	16	19	inductance millihenries/mile 13	16	19	conductance micromhos/mile 13	16	19	capacitance µf/mile 13, 16, or 19	characteristic impedance ohms 13	16	19	phase shift radians/mile 13	16	19	attenuation decibels/mile 13	16	19
0	20.7	41.8	83.8	1.070	1.100	1.112	—	—	—	0.0610	—	—	—						
0.1	20.7	41.8	83.8	1.069	1.100	1.112	0.40	0.25	0.10	0.0610	530−j505	745−j730	1050−j1040	0.020	0.027	0.040	0.17	0.24	0.35
0.5	20.7	41.9	83.9	1.065	1.099	1.112	1.4	0.75	0.40	0.0609	250−j210	345−j315	480−j460	0.050	0.064	0.092	0.36	0.51	0.77
1.0	20.8	42.0	84.0	1.060	1.098	1.111	2.5	1.5	1.0	0.0609	195−j140	255−j215	345−j319	0.075	0.092	0.133	0.47	0.69	1.06
1.5	20.9	42.1	84.1	1.057	1.097	1.111	3.5	2.0	1.6	0.0608	170−j105	225−j175	290−j255	0.100	0.116	0.17	0.53	0.79	1.27
2.0	21.0	42.2	84.2	1.053	1.096	1.110	4.5	2.65	2.35	0.0608	160−j85	205−j150	255−j215	0.120	0.140	0.20	0.58	0.87	1.44
3.0	21.3	42.4	84.3	1.046	1.095	1.110	6.5	4.15	4.05	0.0607	145−j63	180−j115	217−j170	0.170	0.189	0.25	0.63	1.00	1.68
5.0	22.0	43.0	84.5	1.035	1.093	1.109	10.5	7.6	8.0	0.0606	135−j42	155−j72	182−j120	0.26	0.28	0.35	0.70	1.16	2.03
10	24.0	44.5	85.3	1.007	1.085	1.105	21.0	18.5	20.0	0.0605	131−j23	142−j40	155−j73	0.50	0.52	0.59	0.80	1.32	2.43
20	29.1	49.5	89.0	0.968	1.066	1.095	47.0	46.2	50.0	0.0604	128−j15	137−j25	141−j41	0.97	1.00	1.07	1.04	1.55	2.77
30	35.5	55.4	94.0	0.945	1.047	1.085	78.0	80.5	87.5	0.0602	126−j12	135−j18	137−j30	1.43	1.48	1.57	1.27	1.78	3.02
50	47.5	67.0	105.5	0.910	1.015	1.065	150.	160.	180.	0.0600	124−j10	133−j13	134−j20	2.34	2.42	2.60	1.75	2.24	3.53
100	71.3	91.7	137.0	0.870	0.963	1.017	350.	400.	450.	0.0598	121−j7.3	130−j9	131−j13	4.54	4.71	5.00	2.72	3.31	4.80
150	90.0	111.2	165.0	0.850	0.935	0.980	600.	700.	800.	0.0595	119−j6.0	127−j7	129−j11	6.73	6.94	7.25	3.60	4.27	6.00
200	—	—	—	—	—	—	—	—	—	—	—	—	—	—	—	—	—	—	7.00
500	—	—	—	—	—	—	—	—	—	—	—	—	—	—	—	—	—	—	12 ‡
1000	—	—	—	—	—	—	—	—	—	—	—	—	—	—	—	—	—	—	18 ‡
For 0° F: Increase by	—	—	—	—	—	—	50%	50%	50%	—	—	—	—	—	—	—	—	—	—
Decrease by	9%	9%	9%	0.5%	0.5%	0.5%	—	—	—	2%	—	—	—	2%	2%	2%	9%	9%	9%
For 110° F: Increase by	8%	8%	8%	—	—	—	—	—	—	2%	—	—	—	2%	2%	2%	9%	9%	9%
Decrease by	—	—	—	0.4%	0.4%	0.4%	50%	50%	50%	—	—	—	—	—	—	—	—	—	—

continued **Telephone transmission-line data**

Approximate characteristics of standard types of paper-insulated toll telephone cable circuits
1000 cycles per second

wire gauge AWG	type of loading*	spacing of load coils miles	constants assumed to be distributed per loop mile R ohms	L henries	C µf	G µmho	propagation constant polar magnitude	angle deg +	rectangular α	β	line impedance polar magnitude	angle deg	rectangular R ohms	X ohms	wavelength miles	velocity miles per second	cut-off frequency fc	attenuation decibels per mile
side circuit																		
19	N.L.S.	—	84.0	0.001	0.061	1.0	0.183	47.0	0.1249	0.134	470	42.8	345	319.4	46.9	46900	—	1.06
19	H-31-S	1.135	87.2	0.028	0.061	1.0	0.277	76.6	0.0643	0.269	710	13.2	691	162.2	23.3	23300	6700	0.56
19	H-44-S	1.135	88.4	0.039	0.061	1.0	0.319	79.9	0.0561	0.314	818	9.2	806	140.8	20.0	20000	5700	0.49
19	H-88-S	1.135	91.2	0.078	0.061	1.0	0.441	84.6	0.0418	0.439	1131	5.2	1126	102.8	14.3	14300	4000	0.36
19	H-172-S	1.135	96.3	0.151	0.061	1.0	0.610	87.0	0.0323	0.609	1565	2.8	1563	76.9	10.3	10300	2900	0.28
19	B-88-S	0.568	97.7	0.156	0.061	1.0	0.620	87.0	0.0322	0.619	1590	2.8	1588	76.7	10.2	10200	5700	0.28
16	N.L.S.	—	42.1	0.001	0.061	1.5	0.129	49.1	0.0842	0.097	331	40.7	255	215.4	64.5	64500	—	0.69
16	H-31-S	1.135	44.5	0.028	0.061	1.5	0.266	82.8	0.0334	0.264	683	7.0	677	83.0	23.8	23800	6700	0.29
16	H-44-S	1.135	45.7	0.039	0.061	1.5	0.315	84.6	0.0296	0.313	808	5.2	805	72.8	20.1	20000	5700	0.26
16	H-88-S	1.135	48.5	0.078	0.061	1.5	0.438	87.6	0.0224	0.437	1124	2.7	1123	53.1	14.4	14400	4000	0.19
16	H-172-S	1.135	53.6	0.151	0.061	1.5	0.608	88.3	0.0183	0.608	1562	1.5	1562	41.1	10.3	10300	2900	0.16
16	B-88-S	0.568	54.9	0.156	0.061	1.5	0.618	88.3	0.0185	0.618	1587	1.5	1587	41.4	10.2	10200	5700	0.16
13	N.L.S.	—	20.8	0.001	0.061	2.5	0.094	52.9	0.0568	0.075	242	36.9	195	140.0	83.6	83600	—	0.47
phantom circuit																		
19	N.L.P.	—	42.0	0.0007	0.100	1.5	0.165	47.8	0.1106	0.122	262	42.0	195	175.2	51.5	51500	—	0.96
19	H-18-P	1.135	43.5	0.017	0.100	1.5	0.270	78.7	0.0529	0.264	429	11.1	421	82.6	23.8	23800	7000	0.46
19	H-25-P	1.135	44.2	0.023	0.100	1.5	0.308	81.3	0.0466	0.305	491	8.5	485	72.4	20.6	20600	5900	0.40
19	H-50-P	1.135	45.7	0.045	0.100	1.5	0.424	85.3	0.0351	0.423	675	4.5	673	53.3	14.9	14900	4200	0.30
19	H-63-P	1.135	47.8	0.056	0.100	1.5	0.472	86.0	0.0331	0.471	752	3.8	750	49.8	13.3	13300	3700	0.29
19	B-50-P	0.568	49.0	0.089	0.100	1.5	0.594	87.4	0.0273	0.593	945	2.4	944	39.8	10.6	10600	3900	0.24
16	N.L.P.	—	21.0	0.0007	0.100	2.4	0.116	50.0	0.0746	0.089	185	39.0	144	116.3	70.6	70600	—	0.65
16	H-18-P	1.135	22.2	0.017	0.100	2.4	0.262	84.0	0.0273	0.260	417	5.8	415	41.8	24.1	24100	7000	0.24
16	H-25-P	1.135	22.8	0.023	0.100	2.4	0.303	85.4	0.0243	0.302	483	4.4	481	36.8	20.8	20800	5900	0.21
16	H-50-P	1.135	24.3	0.045	0.100	2.4	0.422	87.4	0.0189	0.422	672	2.4	672	27.5	14.9	14900	4200	0.16
16	H-63-P	1.135	26.4	0.056	0.100	2.4	0.471	87.7	0.0185	0.471	749	2.0	749	26.6	13.4	13400	3700	0.16
16	B-50-P	0.568	27.5	0.089	0.100	2.4	0.593	88.5	0.0157	0.593	944	1.3	944	21.4	10.6	10600	5900	0.14
13	N.L.P.	—	10.4	0.0007	0.100	2.4	0.086	55.1	0.0442	0.071	137	33.9	114	76.3	89.1	89100	—	0.43
physical circuit																		
16	B-22	0.568	43.1	0.040	0.061	1.5	0.315	85.0	0.0273	0.314	809	4.8	806	67.1	20.0	20000	11300	0.24

* The letters H and B indicate loading-coil spacings of 6000 and 3000 feet, respectively.

continued **Telephone transmission-line data**

Approximate characteristics of standard types of paper-insulated exchange telephone cable circuits

1000 cycles per second

wire gauge AWG	code no	type of loading	loop mile constants		propagation constant				mid-section characteristic impedance				wave length miles	velocity miles per second	cut-off freq	atten db per mile
			C μf	G μmho	polar mag	polar angle deg	rect. α	rect. β	polar mag	polar angle deg	rect. Z_{01}	rect. Z_{02}				
26	BST	NL	.083	1.6	—	—	—	—	910	—	—	—	—	—	—	2.9
	ST	NL	.069	1.6	.439	45.30	.307	.310	1007	44.5	719	706	20.4	20,400	—	2.67
24	DSM	NL	.085	1.9	—	—	—	—	725	—	—	—	—	—	—	2.3
	ASM	NL	.075	1.9	.355	45.53	.247	.251	778	44.2	558	543	25.0	25,000	—	2.15
		M88	.075	1.9	.448	70.25	.151	.421	987	23.7	904	396	14.9	14,900	3100	1.31
		H88	.075	1.9	.512	75.28	.130	.495	1122	14.6	1122	292	12.7	12,700	3700	1.13
		B88	.075	1.9	.684	81.70	.099	.677	1532	8.1	1515	215	9.3	9,270	5300	0.86
22	CSA	NL	.083	2.1	.297	45.92	.207	.213	576	43.8	416	399	29.4	29,400	—	1.80
		M88	.083	2.1	.447	76.27	.106	.434	905	13.7	880	214	14.5	14,500	2900	0.92
		H88	.083	2.1	.526	80.11	.0904	.519	1051	9.7	1040	177	12.1	12,100	3500	0.79
		H135	.083	2.1	.644	83.50	.0729	.640	1306	6.3	1300	144	9.8	9,800	2800	0.63
		B88	.083	2.1	.718	84.50	.0689	.718	1420	5.3	1410	130	8.75	8,750	5000	0.60
		B135	.083	2.1	.890	86.50	.0549	.890	1765	3.3	1770	102	7.05	7,050	4000	0.48
19	CNB	NL	.085	1.6	—	—	—	—	400	—	—	—	—	—	—	1.23
	DNB	NL	.066	1.6	.188	47.00	.128	.138	453	42.8	333	308	45.7	45,700	—	1.12
		M88	.066	1.6	.383	82.42	.0505	.380	950	8.9	939	146	16.6	16,600	3200	0.44
		H88	.066	1.6	.459	84.60	.0432	.459	1137	5.2	1130	103	13.7	13,700	3900	0.38
		H135	.066	1.6	.569	86.53	.0345	.570	1413	4.0	1410	99	11.0	11,000	3200	0.30
		H175	.066	1.6	.651	87.23	.0315	.651	1643	3.3	1640	95	9.7	9,700	2800	0.27
		B88	.066	1.6	.641	86.94	.0342	.641	1565	2.8	1560	77	9.8	9,800	5500	0.30
16	NH	NL	.064	1.5	.133	49.10	.0868	.1004	320	40.6	243	208	62.6	62,600	—	0.76
		M88	.064	1.5	.377	85.88	.0271	.377	937	4.6	934	76	16.7	16,700	3200	0.24
		H88	.064	1.5	.458	87.14	.0238	.458	1130	2.8	1130	55	13.7	13,700	3900	0.21

In the third column of the above table the letters M, H, and B indicate loading-coil spacings of 9000 feet, 6000 feet, and 3000 feet, respectively, and the figures show the inductance of the loading coils used.

Representative values of line and propagation constants of miscellaneous cables

All figures for loop-mile basis

Nonloaded

Temperature 55° fahrenheit

16-gauge spiral-four (disc-insulated) toll-entrance cable

freq in kc/s	resistance ohms/mile	inductance mh/mile	conductance μmhos/mile	capacitance μf/mile	characteristic impedance ohms	phase shift radians/ mile	attenuation db/mile
0.1	42.4	2.00	0.042	0.02491	—	0.024	0.18
0.5	42.9	1.98	0.053	0.02491	540−j460	0.045	0.32
1.0	43.4	1.94	0.074	0.02491	428−j324	0.067	0.44
1.5	43.9	1.89	0.102	0.02491	380−j275	0.085	0.49
2.0	44.4	1.82	0.127	0.02491	350−j230	0.101	0.55
3.0	45.5	1.74	0.186	0.02490	307−j157	0.145	0.64
5.0	47.5	1.64	0.320	0.02490	279−j107	0.218	0.74
10	50.8	1.56	0.72	0.02489	258−j63	0.405	0.85
20	56.9	1.53	1.95	0.02488	226−j36	0.78	0.99
30	63.0	1.52	3.54	0.02488	248−j26	1.15	1.10
50	73.0	1.51	7.1	0.02488	245−j19	1.90	1.31
100	94.8	1.46	16.9	0.02488	243−j13	3.80	1.71
150	113.5	1.44	27.1	0.02488	240−j10	5.65	2.08
200	130.0	1.43	38.0	0.02487	—	—	2.35

22 AWG emergency cable

side:							
0	166	1.00	—	—	—	—	—
1	—	—	1.3	0.063	468−j449	—	1.53
phant:							
0	83	0.69	—	—	—	—	—
1	—	—	2.1	0.100	265−j250	—	1.37

19 AWG CL emergency cable

side:							
dry 0	92	1.39	negligible	—	—	—	—
wet 0	92	1.39	negligible	—	—	—	—
dry 1	—	—	negligible	0.110	272−j244	—	1.48
wet 1	—	—	negligible	0.14	239−j214	—	1.69
phant:							
dry 0	46	0.5	negligible	—	—	—	—
wet 0	46	0.5	negligible	—	—	—	—
dry 1	—	—	negligible	0.25	124−j116	—	1.58
wet 1	—	—	negligible	0.28	117−j109	—	1.69

Telephone transmission-line data   *continued*

Coaxial cable 0.27-inch diam (New York—Philadelphia 1936 type)

Temperature 68° fahrenheit

freq in kc/s	resistance ohms/mile	inductance mh/mile	conductance μmhos/mile	capacitance μf/mile	characteristic impedance ohms	phase shift radians/ mile	attenuation db/mile
50	24	0.48	23	0.0773	78.5	—	1.3
100	32	0.47	46	0.0773	78	—	1.9
300	56	0.445	156	0.0772	76	—	3.2
1000	100±	0.43	570	0.0771	74.5	—	6.1

Coaxial cable 0.27-inch diam (Stevens Point—Minneapolis type)

Temperature 68° fahrenheit

10	—	—	—	—	—	—	0.75
20	—	—	—	—	—	—	0.92
30	—	—	—	—	—	—	1.10
50	—	—	—	—	79 −j6	—	1.38
100	—	—	—	—	77.8−j4	—	1.70
300	—	—	—	—	76.1−j2	—	3.00
1000	—	—	—	—	75 −j1.3	—	5.6
3000	—	—	—	—	74.5−j1.1	—	10
10000	—	—	—	—	—	—	18

Coaxial cable 0.375-inch diam (Polyethylene discs)

10	—	—	—	—	—	—	0.53
20	—	—	—	—	—	—	0.65
30	—	—	—	—	—	—	0.72
50	—	—	—	—	50±	—	0.90
100	—	—	—	—	—	—	1.18
300	—	—	—	—	—	—	2.1
1000	—	—	—	—	—	—	4.0
3000	—	—	—	—	—	—	7
10000	—	—	—	—	—	—	13

Carrier systems

Frequency allocations for open-wire carrier systems

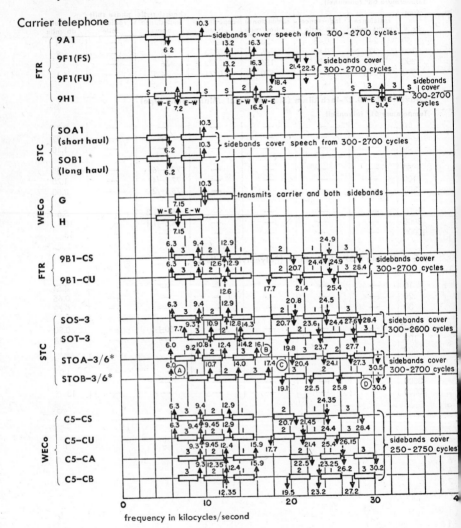

frequency in kilocycles/second

* See p. 501 for telegraph-band A, B, C, D, frequency allocations.

Carrier systems *continued*

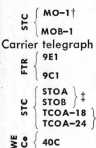

Program carrier

STC { MO-1† / MOB-1 }

Carrier telegraph

FTR { 9E1 / 9C1 }

STC { STOA / STOB } ‡ / TCOA-18 / TCOA-24 }

WECo { 40C }

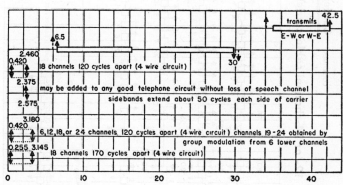

frequency in kilocycles/second

Notes:

Solid arrows = carrier frequencies
Dotted arrows = pilot frequencies

↑ = east–west or A–B direction
↓ = west–east or B–A direction

⌐‾1‾⌐ = channel No. 1

S = signalling frequency

FTR = Federal Telephone and Radio Corporation
STC = Standard Telephones and Cables, Limited
WECo = Western Electric Company

* Carrier frequencies of the 6 channels in each of the 4 telegraph bands represented by A, B, C, and D for STOA–3/6 and STOB–3/6 on p. 500 are as follows:

A	B	C	D
6.54 kc	16.63 kc	19.27 kc	29.36 kc
6.66	16.75	19.39	29.48
6.78	16.87	19.51	29.60
6.90	16.99	19.63	29.72
7.02	17.11	19.75	29.84
7.14	17.23	19.87	29.96

† Manufacture discontinued.
‡ See p. 500 under "Carrier telephone."

continued **Carrier systems**

Frequency allocations for 12-channel open-wire and 12- or 24-channel cable-carrier systems

Notes:

Carriers spaced 4 kilocycles apart.
Sidebands include speech from 200 to 3300 cycles.
Frequencies shown are line frequencies obtained by two or more stages of modulation.
Solid arrows = carrier frequencies
Dotted arrows = pilot frequencies

↑ = east–west or A–B direction
↓ = west–east or B–A direction
Channel numbers are shown at the base of each arrow.
STC = Standard Telephones and Cables, Limited
WECo = Western Electric Company

continued

Frequency allocations and modulation steps for coaxial-cable carrier systems

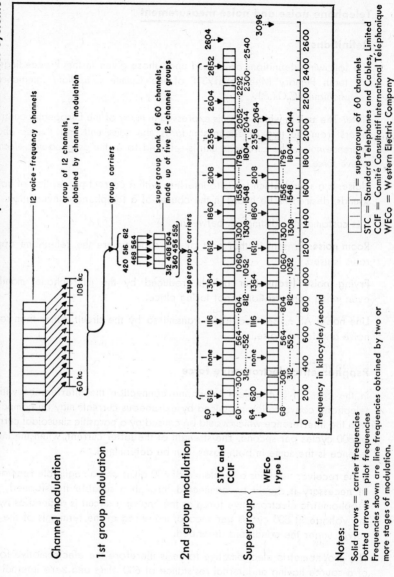

Notes:

Solid arrows = carrier frequencies
Dotted arrows = pilot frequencies
Frequencies shown are line frequencies obtained by two or more stages of modulation.

= supergroup of 60 channels

STC = Standard Telephones and Cables, Limited
CCIF = Comité Consultatif International Téléphonique
WECo = Western Electric Company

Telephone noise and noise measurement

Definitions

The following definitions are based upon those given in the Proceedings of the tenth Plenary Meeting (1934) of the *Comité Consultatif International Téléphonique* (C.C.I.F.).

Note: The unit in which noise is expressed in many of the European countries differs from the two American standards, the *noise unit* and the *db above reference noise.* The European unit is referred to as the *psophometric electromotive force.*

Noise: Is a sound which tends to interfere with a correct perception of vocal sounds, desired to be heard in the course of a telephone conversation.

It is customary to distinguish between:

Room noise: Present in that part of the room where the telephone apparatus is used.

Frying noise (transmitter noise): Produced by the microphone, manifest even when conversation is not taking place.

Line noise: All noise electrically transmitted by the circuit, other than room noise and frying noise.

Psophometric electromotive force

In the case of a complete telephone connection the interference with a telephone conversation produced by extraneous currents may be compared with the interference which would be caused by a parasitic sinusoidal current of 800 cycles per second. The strength of the latter current, when the interference is the same in both cases, can be determined.

If the receiver used has a resistance of 600 ohms and a negligible reactance (if necessary it should be connected through a suitable transformer), the psophometric electromotive force at the end of a circuit is defined as twice the voltage at 800 cycles per second, measured at the terminals of the receiver under the conditions described.

The psophometric electromotive force is therefore the electromotive force of a source having an internal resistance of 600 ohms and zero internal reactance which, when connected directly to a standard receiver of 600 ohms resistance and zero reactance, produces the same sinusoidal current at 800 cycles per second as in the case with the arrangements indicated above.

An instrument known as the *psophometer* has been designed. When connected directly across the terminals of the 600-ohm receiver, it gives a reading of

Telephone noise and noise measurement   *continued*

half of the psophometric electromotive force for the particular case considered.

In a general way, the term *psophometric voltage* between any two points refers to the reading on the instrument when connected to these two points.

If, instead of a complete connection, only a section thereof is under consideration, the psophometric electromotive force with respect to the end of that section is defined as twice the psophometric voltage measured at the terminals of a pure resistance of 600 ohms, connected at the end of the section, if necessary through a suitable transformer.

The C. C. I. F. has published a specification for a psophometer which is included in Volume II of the Proceedings of the Tenth Plenary Meeting in 1934. An important part of this psophometer is a filter network associated with the measuring circuit whose function is to *weight* each frequency in accordance with its interference value relative to a frequency of 800 cycles.

Noise levels

The amount of noise found on different circuits, and even on the same circuit at different times, varies through quite wide limits. Further, there is no definite agreement as to what constitutes a *quiet* circuit, a *noisy* circuit, etc. The following values should therefore be regarded merely as a rough indication of the general levels that may be encountered under the different conditions

Open-wire circuit	db above ref noise
Quiet	20
Average	35
Noisy	50

Cable circuit	
Quiet	15
Average	25
Noisy	40

Relationship of European and American noise units

The psophometric emf can be related to the American units: the *noise unit* and the *decibel above reference noise*.

The following chart shows this relationship together with correction factors for psophometric measurements on circuits of impedance other than 600 ohms.

Telephone noise and noise measurement   *continued*

Relationship of European and American units

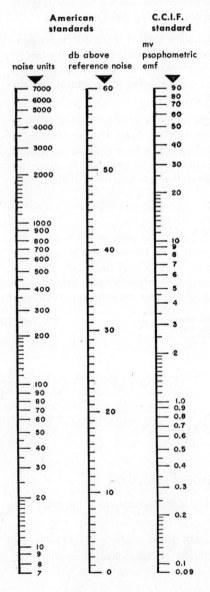

American standards		C.C.I.F. standard
noise units	db above reference noise	mv psophometric emf

a. The relationship of noise units to decibels above reference noise is obtained from technical report No. 1B–5 of the joint subcommittee on development and research of the Bell Telephone System and the Edison Electric Institute.

b. The relationship of db above reference noise to psophometric emf is obtained from the Proceedings of Comité Consultatif International Téléphonique, 1934.

c. The C.C.I.F. expresses noise limits in terms of the psophometric emf for a circuit of 600 ohms resistance and zero reactance, terminated in a resistance of 600 ohms. Measurements made in terms of the potential difference across the terminations, or on circuits of impedance other than 600 ohms, should be corrected as follows:

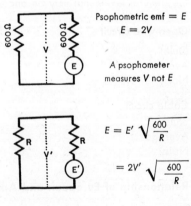

Psophometric emf $= E$

$$E = 2V$$

A psophometer measures V not E

$$E = E' \sqrt{\frac{600}{R}}$$

$$= 2V' \sqrt{\frac{600}{R}}$$

d. Reference noise—with respect to which the American noise measuring set is calibrated—is a 1000-cycle/second tone 90 decibels below 1 milliwatt.

Telegraph facilities

Signaling speeds and pulse lengths

The graph below shows the speeds of various telegraph systems. The American Morse curve is based on an average character of 8.5 units determined from actual count of representative traffic. The Continental Morse curve similarly on 9 units, and the Cable Morse on 3.7 units.

system	speed of usual types	
	frequency in cycles	bauds
Grounded wire	75	150
Simplex (telephone)	50	100
Composite	15	30
Metallic telegraph	85	170
Carrier channel		
Narrow band	40	80
Wide band	75	150

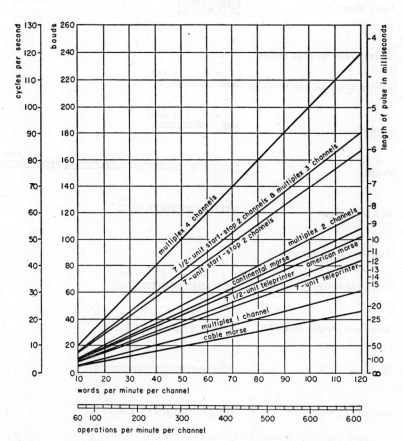

Feed holes: For Morse, (number feed holes/second) = (number cycles/second) For multiplex and teleprinter, (number feed holes/second) = (words/minute)/10

Telegraph facilities *continued*

Comparison of telegraph codes in current and recent use

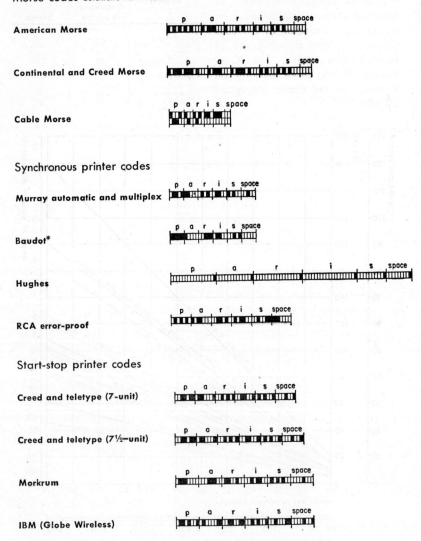

Morse codes *automatic transmission*

American Morse

Continental and Creed Morse

Cable Morse

Synchronous printer codes

Murray automatic and multiplex

Baudot*

Hughes

RCA error-proof

Start-stop printer codes

Creed and teletype (7-unit)

Creed and teletype (7½-unit)

Morkrum

IBM (Globe Wireless)

* Add two units to each character for 2-channel, and one unit to each character for 4-channel operation. These allow for synchronization and retardation.

■ Electroacoustics

Theory of sound waves*

Sound (or a sound wave) is an alteration in pressure, stress, particle displacement, or particle velocity that is propagated in an elastic material; or the superposition of such propagated alterations. Sound (or sound sensation) is also the sensation produced through the ear by the above alterations.

Wave equation

The behavior of sound waves is given by the wave equation

$$\nabla^2 p = \frac{1}{c^2} \frac{\partial^2 p}{\partial t^2} \qquad (1)$$

where p is the instantaneous pressure increment above and below a steady pressure (dynes/centimeter^2); p is a function of time and of the three coordinates of space. Also,

$t =$ time in seconds

$c =$ velocity of propagation in centimeters/second

$\nabla^2 =$ the Laplacian, which for the particular case of rectangular coordinates x, y, and z (in centimeters), is given by

$$\nabla^2 \equiv \frac{\partial^2}{\partial x^2} + \frac{\partial^2}{\partial y^2} + \frac{\partial^2}{\partial z^2} \qquad (2)$$

For a plane wave of sound, where variations with respect to y and z are zero, $\nabla^2 p = \partial^2 p/\partial x^2 = d^2 p/dx^2$; the latter is approximately equal to the curvature of the curve showing p versus x at some instant. Equation (1) states simply that, for variations in x only, the acceleration in pressure p (the second time derivative of p) is proportional to the curvature in p (the second space derivative of p).

For a gas (as air), the velocity of propagation c is related to other parameters of the medium by the equation

$$c = \sqrt{\gamma p_0/\rho_0} \qquad (3)$$

* Lord Rayleigh, "Theory of Sound," vols. I and II, Dover Publications, New York, New York; 1945. P. M. Morse, "Vibration and Sound," 2nd edition, McGraw-Hill Book Company, New York, New York; 1948.

Theory of sound waves *continued*

where

γ = ratio of the specific heat at constant pressure to that at constant volume

p_0 = the steady pressure of the gas in dynes/centimeter^2

ρ_0 = the steady or average density of the gas in grams/centimeter^3

The range of variation of these parameters is given in Fig. 1 for typical substances at standard conditions (20 degrees centigrade, 760 millimeters of mercury).

Fig. 1—Table of sound-propagation parameters in various substances.

substance	density ρ_0 grams/centimeter^3	velocity of propagation c centimeters/second	characteristic acoustic resistance $\rho_0 c$ grams/centimeter^2 /second
Air	0.00121	34,400	41.6
Hydrogen	0.00009	127,000	11.4
Carbon dioxide	0.0020	25,800	51.3
Salt water	1.03	150,400	155,000
Mercury	13.5	140,000	1,900,000
Hard rubber	1.1	140,000	150,000
Hard glass	2.4	600,000	1,440,000

Sinusoidal variations in time are usually of interest. For this case the usual procedure is to put p = (real part of $\bar{p}\epsilon^{j\omega t}$), where $\bar{p}$ now satisfies the equation

$$\nabla^2 \bar{p} + (\omega/c)^2 \bar{p} = 0 \qquad (4)$$

The vector complex velocity $\bar{v}$ of the sound wave in the medium is related to the complex pressure $\bar{p}$ by the formula

$$\bar{v} = -(1/j\omega\rho_0)\ \text{grad}\ \bar{p} \qquad (5)$$

The specific acoustical impedance $\bar{Z}$ at any point in the medium is the ratio of the complex pressure to the complex velocity, or

$$\bar{Z} = \bar{p}/\bar{v} \qquad (6)$$

The solutions of (1) and (4) take particularly simple and instructive forms for the case of one dimensional plane and spherical waves in one direction. Fig. 2 gives a summary of the pertinent information.

For example, the acoustical impedance for spherical waves has an equivalent electrical circuit comprising a resistance shunted by an inductance. In this

Theory of sound waves   *continued*

Fig. 2—Table of solutions for various parameters.

factor	type of sound wave	
	plane wave	spherical wave
Equation for p	$\dfrac{\partial^2 p}{\partial x^2} = \dfrac{1}{c^2}\dfrac{\partial^2 p}{\partial t^2}$	$\dfrac{\partial^2 p}{\partial x^2} + \dfrac{2}{r}\dfrac{\partial p}{\partial r} = \dfrac{1}{c^2}\dfrac{\partial^2 p}{\partial t^2}$
Equation for $\bar{p}$	$\dfrac{d^2\bar{p}}{dx^2} + \left(\dfrac{\omega}{c}\right)^2 \bar{p} = 0$	$\dfrac{d^2\bar{p}}{dx^2} + \dfrac{2}{r}\dfrac{d\bar{p}}{dt} + \left(\dfrac{\omega}{c}\right)^2 \bar{p} = 0$
Solution for p	$p = F\left(t - \dfrac{x}{c}\right)$	$p = \dfrac{1}{r} F\left(t - \dfrac{x}{c}\right)$
Solution for $\bar{p}$	$\bar{p} = \bar{A}\epsilon^{-i\omega x/c}$	$\bar{p} = \dfrac{1}{r}\bar{A}\epsilon^{-i\omega r/c}$
Solution for $\bar{v}$	$\bar{v} = \dfrac{\bar{A}}{\rho_0 c}\epsilon^{-i\omega x/c}$	$\bar{v} = \dfrac{\bar{A}}{\rho_0 c r}\left(1 + \dfrac{c}{j\omega r}\right)\epsilon^{-i\omega r/c}$
$\bar{Z}$	$\bar{Z} = \rho_0 c$	$\bar{Z} = \rho_0 c \Big/ \left(1 + \dfrac{c}{j\omega r}\right)$
Equivalent electrical circuit for $\bar{Z}$	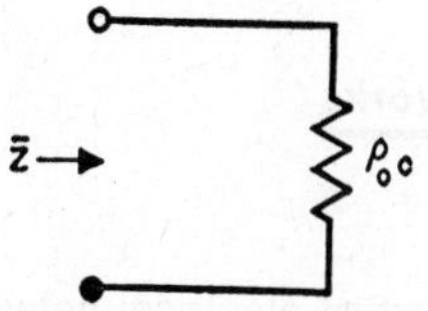	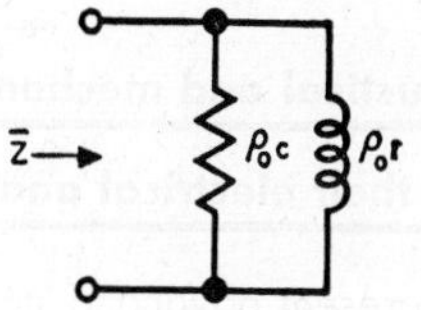

where

p = excess pressure in dynes/centimeter^2

$\bar{p}$ = complex excess pressure in dynes/centimeter^2

t = time in seconds

x = space coordinate for plane wave in centimeters

r = space coordinate for spherical wave in centimeters

$\bar{v}$ = complex velocity in centimeters/second

$\bar{Z}$ = specific acoustic impedance in dyne-seconds/centimeter^3

c = velocity of propagation in centimeters/second

$\omega = 2\pi f$; f = frequency in cycles/second

F = an arbitrary function

$\bar{A}$ = complex constant

ρ_0 = density of medium in grams/centimeter^3

Theory of sound waves   *continued*

form, it is obvious that a small spherical source (r is small) cannot radiate efficiently since the radiation resistance $\rho_0 c$ is shunted by a small inductance $\rho_0 r$. Efficient radiation begins approximately at the frequency where the resistance $\rho_0 r$ equals the inductive (mass) reactance $\rho_0 c$. This is the frequency at which the period ($= 1/f$) equals the time required for the sound wave to travel the peripheral distance $2\pi r$.

Sound intensity

The sound intensity is the average rate of sound energy transmitted in a specified direction through a unit area normal to this direction at the point considered. In the case of a plane or spherical wave, the intensity in the direction of propagation is given by

$$I = p^2/\rho c \quad \text{ergs/second/centimeter}^2$$

where

p = pressure (dynes/centimeter^2)
ρ = density of the medium (grams/centimeter^3) and
c = velocity of propagation (centimeters/second)

The sound intensity is usually measured in decibels, in which case it is known as the intensity level and is equal to 10 times the logarithm (to the base 10) of the ratio of the sound intensity (expressed in watts/centimeter^2) to the reference level of 10^{-16} watts/centimeter^2. Fig. 3 shows the intensity levels of some familiar sounds.

Acoustical and mechanical networks

and their electrical analogs*

The present advanced state of the art of electrical network theory suggests its advantageous application, by analogy, to equivalent acoustical and mechanical networks. Actually, Maxwell's initial work on electrical networks was based upon the previous work of LaGrange in dynamical systems. The following is a brief summary showing some of the network parameters available in acoustical and mechanical systems and their analysis using LaGrange's equations.

Fig. 4 shows the analogous behavior of electrical, acoustical, and mechanical systems. These are analogous in the sense that the equations (usually differential equations) formulating the various physical laws are alike.

* E. G. Keller, "Mathematics of Modern Engineering," vol. 2, 1st ed., John Wiley, New York, New York; 1942. Also, H. F. Olson, "Dynamical Analogies," 1st ed., D. Van Nostrand, New York, New York; 1943.

Acoustical and mechanical networks

and their electrical analogs   *continued*

Fig. 3—Table of intensity levels.

type of sound	intensity level in decibels above 10^{-16} watts/centimeter^2	intensity in microwatts/ centimeter^2	root-mean-square sound pressure in dynes/ centimeter^2	root-mean-square particle velocity in centimeters/ second	peak-to-peak particle displacement for sinsuoidal tone at 1000 cycles in centimeters
Threshold of painful sound	130	1000	645	15.5	6.98×10^{-3}
Airplane, 1600 rpm, 18 feet	121	126	228	5.5	2.47×10^{-3}
Subway, local station, express passing	102	1.58	40.7	0.98	4.40×10^{-4}
Noisest spot at Niagara Falls	92	0.158	12.9	0.31	1.39×10^{-4}
Average automobile, 15 feet	70	10^{-3}	0.645	15.5×10^{-3}	6.98×10^{-6}
Average conversational speech $3\frac{1}{4}$ feet	70	10^{-3}	0.645	15.5×10^{-3}	6.98×10^{-6}
Average office	55	3.16×10^{-5}	0.114	2.75×10^{-3}	1.24×10^{-6}
Average residence	40	10^{-6}	20.4×10^{-3}	4.9×10^{-4}	2.21×10^{-7}
Quiet whisper, 5 feet	18	6.3×10^{-9}	1.62×10^{-3}	3.9×10^{-5}	1.75×10^{-8}
Reference level	0	10^{-10}	2.04×10^{-4}	4.9×10^{-6}	2.21×10^{-9}

Acoustical and mechanical networks

and their electrical analogs   *continued*

Fig. 4A—Table of analogous behavior of systems—parameter of energy dissipation (or radiation).

electrical	mechanical	acoustical
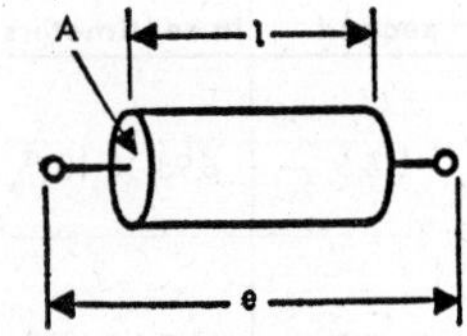	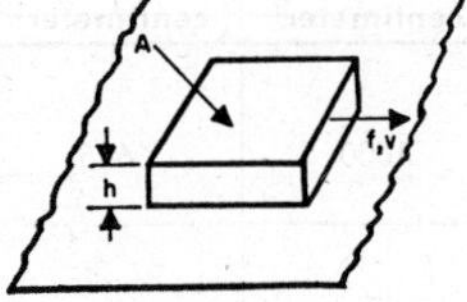	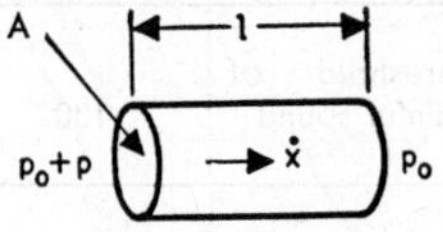
current in wire	viscous damping vane	gas flow in small pipe

$P = Ri^2$	$P = R_m v^2$	$P = R_a \dot{X}^2$
$i = \dfrac{e}{R} = \dfrac{dq}{dt} = \dot{q}$	$v = \dfrac{f}{R_m} = \dfrac{dx}{dt} = \dot{x}$	$\dot{X} = \dfrac{p}{R_a} = \dfrac{dX}{dt}$
$R = \dfrac{\rho l}{A}$	$R_m = \dfrac{\mu A}{h}$	$R_a = \dfrac{8\mu\pi l}{A^2}$

where

i = current in amperes

e = voltage in volts

q = charge in coulombs

t = time in seconds

R = resistance in ohms

ρ = resistivity in ohm-centimeters

l = length in centimeters

A = cross-sectional area of wire in centimeters[2]

P = power in watts

where

v = velocity in centimeters/second

f = force in dynes

x = displacement in centimeters

t = time in seconds

R_m = mechanical resistance in dyne-seconds/centimeter

μ = coefficient of viscosity in poise

h = height of damping vane in centimeters

A = area of vane in centimeters[2]

P = power in ergs/second

where

$\dot{X}$ = volume velocity in centimeters[3]/second

p = excess pressure in dynes/centimeter[2]

X = volume displacement in centimeters[3]

t = time in seconds

R_a = acoustic resistance in dyne-seconds/centimeter[5]

μ = coefficient of viscosity in poise

l = length of tube in centimeters

A = area of circular tube in centimeters[2]

P = power in ergs/second

Acoustical and mechanical networks

and their electrical analogs   continued

Fig. 4B—Table of analogous behavior of systems—parameter of energy storage (electrostatic or potential energy).

electrical	mechanical	acoustical
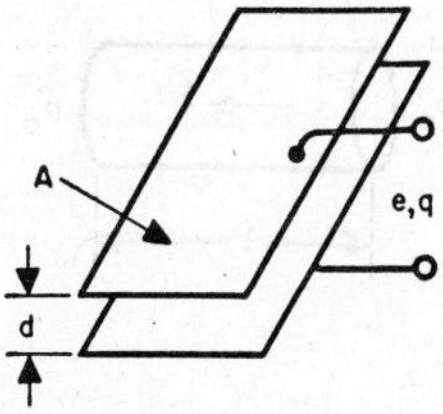	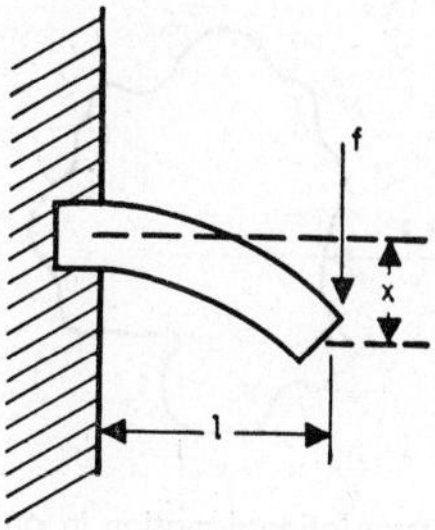	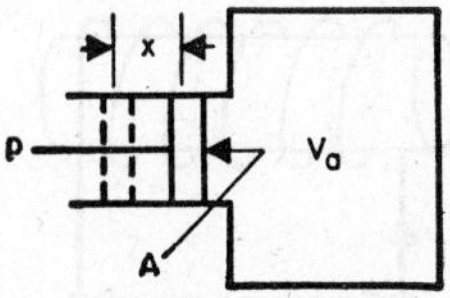

capacitor with closely spaced plates	clamped-free (cantilever beam)	piston acoustic compliance (at audio frequencies, adiabatic expansion)
$W_e = \dfrac{q^2}{2C} = \dfrac{Sq^2}{2}$	$V = \dfrac{x^2}{2C_m} = \dfrac{S_m x^2}{2}$	$V = \dfrac{X^2}{2C_a} = \dfrac{S_a X^2}{2}$
$q = Ce = \dfrac{e}{S}$	$x = C_m f = \dfrac{f}{S_m}$	$X = C_a p = \dfrac{p}{S_a} = xA$
$C = \dfrac{kA}{36\pi d} \times 10^{-11}$	$C_m = \dfrac{l^3}{3EI}$	$C_a = \dfrac{V_o}{c^2 \rho}$

where

C = capacitance in farads

S = stiffness = $1/C$

W_e = energy in watt-seconds

k = relative dielectric constant ($= 1$ for air, numeric)

A = area of plates in centimeters[2]

d = separation of plates in centimeters

where

C_m = mechanical compliance in centimeters/dyne

S_m = mechanical stiffness = $1/C_m$

V = potential energy in ergs

E = Young's modulus of elasticity in dynes/centimeter[2]

I = moment of inertia of cross-section in centimeters[4]

l = length of beam in centimeters

where

C_a = acoustical compliance in centimeters[5]/dyne

S_a = acoustical stiffness = $1/C_a$

V = potential energy in ergs

c = velocity of sound in enclosed gas in centimeters/second

ρ = density of enclosed gas in grams/centimeter[3]

V_o = enclosed volume in centimeters[3]

A = area of piston in centimeters[2]

Acoustical and mechanical networks

and their electrical analogs   continued

Fig. 4C—Table of analogous behavior of systems—parameter of energy storage (magnetostatic or kinetic energy).

electrical	mechanical	acoustical

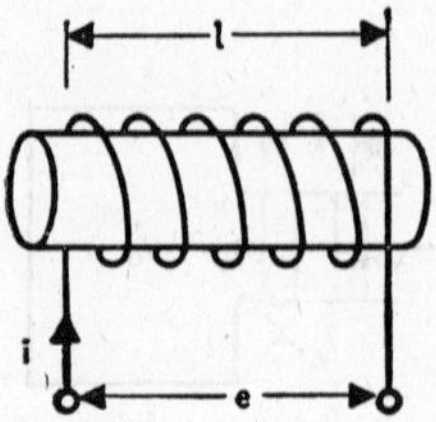

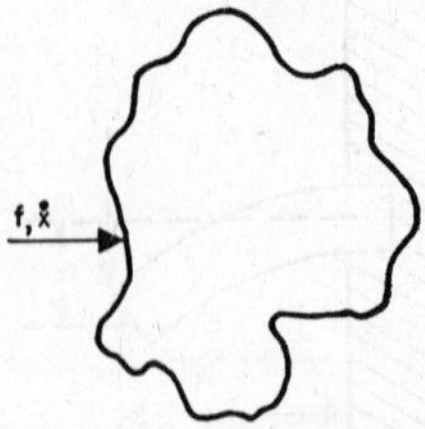

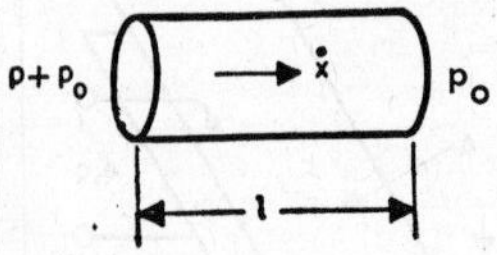

for a very long solenoid	for translational motion in one direction m is the actual weight in grams	gas flow in a pipe

$$W_m = \frac{Li^2}{2}$$

$$T = \frac{mv^2}{2}$$

$$T = \frac{M\dot{X}^2}{2}$$

$$e = L\frac{di}{dt} = L\frac{d^2q}{dt^2} = L\ddot{q}$$

$$f = m\frac{dv}{dt} = m\frac{d^2x}{dt^2} = m\ddot{x}$$

$$p = M\frac{d\dot{X}}{dt} = M\frac{d^2X}{dt^2} = M\ddot{X}$$

$$L = 4\pi \, ln^2 \, Ak \times 10^{-9}$$

$$M = \frac{\rho l}{A}$$

where

L = inductance in henries

W_m = energy in watt-seconds

l = length of solenoid in centimeters

A = area of solenoid in centimeters^2

n = number of turns of wire/centimeter

k = relative permeability of core (= 1 for air, numeric)

where

m = mass in grams

T = kinetic energy in ergs

where

M = inertance in grams/centimeter^4

T = kinetic energy in ergs

l = length of pipe in centimeters

A = area of pipe in centimeters^2

ρ = density of gas in grams/centimeter^3

Acoustical and mechanical networks

and their electrical analogs   *continued*

LaGrange's equations

The LaGrangian equations are partial differential equations describing the stored and dissipated energy and the generalized coordinates of the system. They are

$$\frac{d}{dt}\left(\frac{\partial T}{\partial \dot{q}_v}\right) + \frac{\partial F}{\partial \dot{q}_v} + \frac{\partial V}{\partial q_v} = Q_v, \quad v = 1, 2, \ldots, n, \tag{7}$$

where T and V are, as in Fig. 4, the system's total kinetic and potential energy (in ergs), F is $\frac{1}{2}$ the rate of energy dissipation (in ergs/second, Rayleigh's dissipation function), Q_v the generalized forces (dynes), and q_v the generalized coordinates (which may be angles in radians, or displacements in centimeters). For most systems (and those considered herein) the generalized coordinates are equal in number to the number of degrees of freedom in the systems required to determine uniquely the values of T, V, and F.

Example

As an example of the application of these equations toward the design of electroacoustical transducers, consider the idealized crystal microphone in Fig. 5.

This system has 2 degrees of freedom since only 2 motions, namely the diaphragm displacement x_d and the crystal displacement x_c, are needed to specify the system's total energy and dissipation.

A sound wave impinging upon the microphone's diaphragm creates an excess pressure p (dynes/centimeter[2]). The force on the diaphragm is then pA (dynes), where A is the effective area of the diaphragm. The diaphragm has

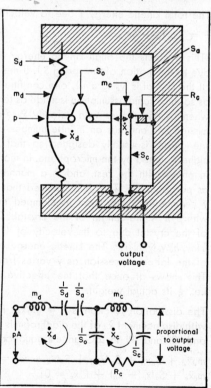

Fig. 5—Crystal microphone analyzed by use of LaGrange's equations.

Acoustical and mechanical networks

and their electrical analogs   *continued*

an effective mass m_d, in the sense that the kinetic energy of all the parts associated with the diaphragm velocity $\dot{x}_d$ $(= dx_d/dt)$ is given by $m_d\dot{x}_d^2/2$. The diaphragm is supported in place by the stiffness S_d. It is coupled to the crystal via the stiffness S_o. The crystal has a stiffness S_c, an effective mass of m_c (to be computed below), and is damped by the mechanical resistance R_c. The only other remaining parameter is the acoustical stiffness S_a introduced by compression of the air-tight pocket enclosed by the diaphragm and the case of the microphone.

The total potential energy V stored in the system for displacements x_d and x_c from equilibrium position, is

$$V = \tfrac{1}{2}S_d x_d^2 + \tfrac{1}{2}S_a (x_d A)^2 + \tfrac{1}{2}S_c x_c^2 + \tfrac{1}{2}S_o (x_d - x_c)^2 \tag{8}$$

The total kinetic energy T due to velocities $\dot{x}_d$ and x_c is

$$T = \tfrac{1}{2}m_c \dot{x}_c^2 + \tfrac{1}{2}m_d \dot{x}_d^2 \tag{9}$$

(This neglects the small kinetic energy due to motion of the air and that due to the motion of the spring S_o). If the total weight of the unclamped part of the crystal is w_c (grams), one can find the effective mass m_c of the crystal as soon as some assumption is made as to movement of the rest of the crystal when its end moves with velocity $\dot{x}_c$. Actually, the crystal is like a transmission line and has an infinite number of degrees of freedom. Practically, the crystal is usually designed so that its first resonant frequency is the highest passed by the microphone. In that case, the end of the crystal moves in phase with the rest, and in a manner that, for simplicity, is here taken as parabolically. Thus it is assumed that an element of the crystal located y centimeters away from its clamped end moves by the amount $(y/h)^2 x_c$, where h is the length of the crystal. The kinetic energy of a length dy of the crystal due to its velocity of $(y/h)^2\dot{x}_c$ and its mass of $(dy/h)w_c$ is $\tfrac{1}{2}(dy/h)w_c(y/h)^4\dot{x}_c^2$. The kinetic energy of the whole crystal is the integral of the latter expression as y varies from 0 to h. The result is $\tfrac{1}{2}(w_c/5)\dot{x}_c^2$. This shows at once that the effective mass of the crystal is $m_c = w_c/5$, i.e., $\tfrac{1}{5}$ its actual weight.

The dissipation function is $F = \tfrac{1}{2}R_c\dot{x}_c^2$. Finally, the driving force associated with displacement x_d of the diaphragm is pA. Substitution of these expressions and (8) and (9) in LaGrange's equations (7) results in the force equations

$$\left.\begin{array}{l} m_d\ddot{x}_d + S_d x_d + S_o A^2 x_d + S_o(x_d - x_c) = pA \\ m_c\ddot{x}_c + S_o(x_c - x_d) + R_c\dot{x}_c = 0 \end{array}\right\} \tag{10}$$

These are the mechanical version of Kirchhoff's law that the sum of all the resisting forces (rather than voltages) are equal to the applied force. The

Acoustical and mechanical networks

and their electrical analogs   *continued*

equivalent electrical circuit giving these same differential equations is shown in Fig. 5. The crystal produces, by its piezoelectric effect, an open-circuit voltage proportional to the displacement x_c. By means of this equivalent circuit, it is now easy, by using the usual electrical-circuit techniques, to find the voltage generated by this microphone per unit of sound-pressure input, and also its amplitude- and phase-response characteristic as a function of frequency.

It is important to note that this process of analysis not only results in the equivalent electrical circuit, but also determines the effective values of the parameters in that circuit.

Sound in enclosed rooms*

Good acoustics—governing factors

Reverberation time or amount of reverberation: Varies with frequency and is measured by the time required for a sound, when suddenly interrupted, to die away or decay to a level 60 decibels (db) below the original sound.

The reverberation time and the shape of the reverberation-time/frequency curve can be controlled by selecting the proper amounts and varieties of sound-absorbent materials and by the methods of application. Room occupants must be considered inasmuch as each person present contributes a fairly definite amount of sound absorption.

Standing sound waves: Resonant conditions in sound studios cause standing waves by reflections from opposing parallel surfaces, such as ceiling-floor and parallel walls, resulting in serious peaks in the reverberation-time/frequency curve. Standing sound waves in a room can be considered comparable to standing electrical waves in an improperly terminated transmission line where the transmitted power is not fully absorbed by the load.

Room sizes and proportions for good acoustics

The frequency of standing waves is dependent on room sizes: frequency decreases with increase of distances between walls and between floor and ceiling. In rooms with two equal dimensions, the two sets of standing waves occur at the same frequency with resultant increase of reverberation time at resonant frequency. In a room with walls and ceilings of cubical contour this effect is tripled and elimination of standing waves is practically impossible.

* F. R. Watson, "Acoustics of Buildings," 3rd ed., John Wiley and Sons, New York, New York; 1941.

Sound in enclosed rooms   *continued*

The most advantageous ratio for height:width:length is in the proportion of $1:2^{1/3}:2^{2/3}$ or separated by $\frac{1}{3}$ or $\frac{2}{3}$ of an octave.

In properly proportioned rooms, resonant conditions can be effectively reduced and standing waves practically eliminated by introducing numerous surfaces disposed obliquely. Thus, large-order reflections can be avoided by breaking them up into numerous smaller reflections. The object is to prevent sound reflection back to the point of origin until after several re-reflections.

Most desirable ratios of dimensions for broadcast studios are given in Fig. 6.

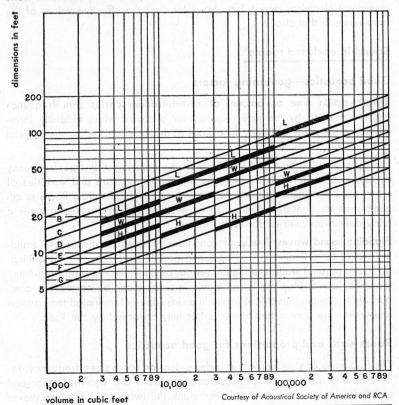

Courtesy of Acoustical Society of America and RCA

Fig. 6—Preferred room dimensions based on $2^{1/3}$ ratio. Permissible deviation ±5 percent.

type room	H:W:L	chart designation
Small	1:1.25:1.6	E:D:C:
Average shape	1:1.60:2.5	F:D:B:
Low ceiling	1:2.50:3.2	G:C:B:
Long	1:1.25:3.2	F:E:A:

Sound in enclosed rooms   *continued*

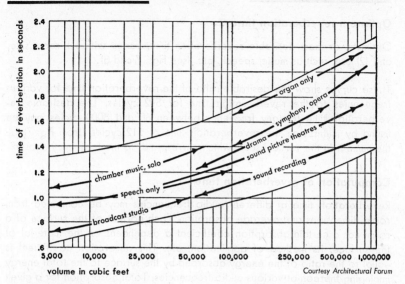

Fig. 7—Optimum reverberation time in seconds for various room volumes at 512 cycles per second.

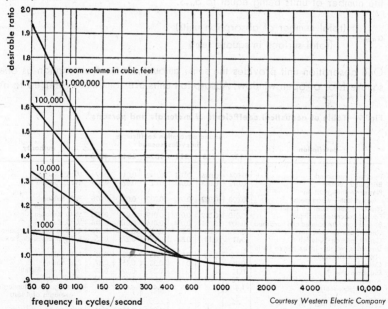

Fig. 8—Desirable relative reverberation time versus frequency for various structures and auditoriums.

Sound in enclosed rooms   *continued*

Optimum reverberation time

Optimum, or most desirable reverberation time, varies with (1) room size, and (2) use, such as music, speech, etc. (see Figs. 7 and 8).

These curves show the desirable ratio of the reverberation time for various frequencies to the reverberation time for 512 cycles. The desirable reverberation time for any frequency between 60 and 8000 cycles may be found by multiplying the reverberation time at 512 cycles (from Fig. 7) by the number in the vertical scale which corresponds to the frequency chosen.

Computation of reverberation time

Reverberation time at different audio frequencies may be computed from room dimensions and average absorption. Each portion of the surface of a room has a certain absorption coefficient a dependent on the material of the surface, its method of application, etc. This absorption coefficient is equal to the ratio of the energy absorbed by the surface to the total energy impinging thereon at various audio frequencies. Total absorption for a given surface area in square feet S is expressed in terms of absorption units, the number of units being equal to $a_{av}S$.

$$a_{av} = \frac{\text{(total number of absorption units)}}{\text{(total surface in square feet)}}$$

One absorption unit provides the same amount of sound absorption as one square foot of open window. Absorption units are sometimes referred to as

Fig. 9—Table of acoustical coefficients of materials and persons*

description	sound absorption coefficients in cycles/second						authority
	128	256	512	1024	2048	4096	
Brick wall unpainted	0.024	0.025	0.031	0.042	0.049	0.07	W. C. Sabine
Brick wall painted	0.012	0.013	0.017	0.02	0.023	0.025	W. C. Sabine
Plaster + finish coat on wood lath—wood studs	0.020	0.022	0.032	0.039	0.039	0.028	P. E. Sabine
Plaster + finish coat on metal lath	0.038	0.049	0.060	0.085	0.043	0.056	V. O. Knudsen
Poured concrete unpainted	0.010	0.012	0.016	0.019	0.023	0.035	V. O. Knudsen
Poured concrete painted and varnished	0.009	0.011	0.014	0.016	0.017	0.018	V. O. Knudsen
Carpet, pile on concrete	0.09	0.08	0.21	0.26	0.27	0.37	Building Research Station
Carpet, pile on ⅛ in felt	0.11	0.14	0.37	0.43	0.27	0.25	Building Research Station
Draperies, velour, 18 oz per sq yd in contact with wall	0.05	0.12	0.35	0.45	0.38	0.36	P. E. Sabine
Ozite ⅜ in	0.051	0.12	0.17	0.33	0.45	0.47	P. E. Sabine
Rug, axminster	0.11	0.14	0.20	0.33	0.52	0.82	Wente and Bedell
Audience, seated per sq ft of area	0.72	0.89	0.95	0.99	1.00	1.00	W. C. Sabine
Each person, seated	1.4	2.25	3.8	5.4	6.6	—	Bureau of Standards, averages of 4 tests
Each person, seated	—	—	—	—	—	7.0	Estimated
Glass surfaces	0.05	0.04	0.03	0.025	0.022	0.02	Estimated

* Reprinted by permission from Architectural Acoustics by V. O. Knudsen, published by John Wiley and Sons, Inc.

Sound in enclosed rooms *continued*

"open window" or "OW" units.

$$T = \frac{0.05V}{-S \log_e(1 - a_{av})}$$

where T = reverberation time in seconds, V = room volume in cubic feet, S = total surface of room in square feet, a_{av} = average absorption coefficient of room at frequency under consideration.

For absorption coefficients a of some typical building materials, see Fig. 9. Fig. 10 shows absorption coefficients for some of the more commonly used materials for acoustical correction.

Fig. 10—Table of acoustical coefficients of materials used for acoustical correction

material	cycles/second						noise-red coef *	manufactured by
	128	256	512	1024	2048	4096		
Corkoustic—B4	0.08	0.13	0.51	0.75	0.47	0.46	0.45	Armstrong Cork Co.
Corkoustic—B6	0.15	0.28	0.82	0.60	0.58	0.38	0.55	Armstrong Cork Co.
Cushiontone A-3	0.17	0.58	0.70	0.90	0.76	0.71	0.75	Armstrong Cork Co.
Koustex	0.10	0.24	0.64	0.92	0.77	0.75	0.65	David E. Kennedy, Inc.
Sanacoustic (metal) tiles	0.25	0.56	0.99	0.99	0.91	0.82	0.85	Johns-Manville Sales Corp.
Permacoustic tiles ¾ in	0.19	0.34	0.74	0.76	0.75	0.74	0.65	Johns-Manville Sales Corp.
Low-frequency element	0.66	0.60	0.50	0.50	0.35	0.20	0.50	Johns-Manville Sales Corp.
Triple-tuned element	0.66	0.61	0.80	0.74	0.79	0.75	0.75	Johns-Manville Sales Corp.
High-frequency element	0.20	0.46	0.55	0.66	0.79	0.75	0.60	Johns-Manville Sales Corp.
Absorbatone A	0.15	0.28	0.82	0.99	0.87	0.98	0.75	Luse Stevenson Co.
Acoustex 60R	0.14	0.28	0.81	0.94	0.83	0.80	0.70	National Gypsum Co.
Econacoustic 1 in	0.25	0.40	0.78	0.76	0.79	0.68	0.70	National Gypsum Co.
Fiberglas acoustical tiletype TW—PF 9D	0.22	0.46	0.97	0.90	0.68	0.52	0.75	Owens-Corning Fiberglas Corp.
Acoustone D ¹¹⁄₁₆ in	0.13	0.26	0.79	0.88	0.76	0.74	0.65	U. S. Gypsum Company
Acoustone F ¹³⁄₁₆ in	0.16	0.33	0.85	0.89	0.80	0.75	0.70	U. S. Gypsum Company
Acousti-celotex type C-6 1¼ in	0.30	0.56	0.94	0.96	0.69	0.56	0.80	The Celotex Corp.
Absorbex type A 1 in	0.41	0.71	0.96	0.88	0.85	0.96	0.85	The Celotex Corp.
Acousteel B metal facing 1⅝ in	0.29	0.57	0.98	0.99	0.85	0.57	0.85	The Celotex Corp.

Courtesy Acoustics Materials Association

* The noise-reduction coefficient is the average of the coefficients at frequencies from 256 to 2048 cycles inclusive, given to the nearest 5 percent. This average coefficient is recommended for use in comparing materials for noise-quieting purposes as in offices, hospitals, banks, corridors, etc.

Public-address systems*

Electrical power levels for public-address requirements

Indoor: Power-level requirements are shown in Fig. 11.
Outdoor: Power-level requirements are shown in Fig. 12.

Note: Curves are for an exponential trumpet-type horn. Speech levels above reference—average 70 db, peak 80 db. For a loudspeaker of 25-percent efficiency, 4 times the power output would be required or an equivalent of 6 decibels. For one of 10-percent efficiency, 10 times the power output would be required or 10 decibels.

* H. F. Olson, "Elements of Acoustical Engineering," 2nd ed., D. Van Nostrand, New York, New York; 1941.

Public-address systems   *continued*

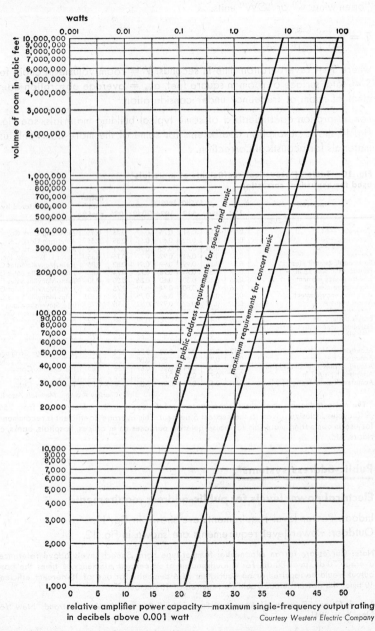

watts

volume of room in cubic feet

normal public address requirements for speech and music

maximum requirements for concert music

relative amplifier power capacity—maximum single-frequency output rating
in decibels above 0.001 watt

Courtesy Western Electric Company

**Fig. 11—Room volume and relative amplifier power capacity. To the indicated power
level depending on loudspeaker efficiency, there must be added a correction factor
which may vary from 4 decibels for the most efficient horn-type reproducers to
20 decibels for less efficient cone loudspeakers.**

Public-address systems   *continued*

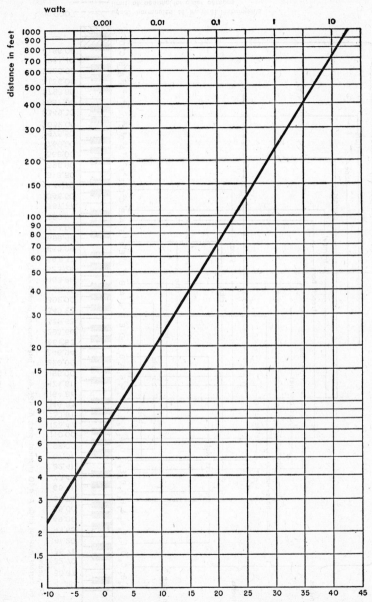

watts

relative amplifier power capacity—maximum single-frequency output rating in decibels above 0.001 watt

Courtesy Western Electric Company

Fig. 12—Distance from loudspeaker and relative amplifier power capacity required for speech, average for 30° angle of coverage. For angles over 30°, more loudspeakers and proportional output power are required. Depending on loudspeaker efficiency, a correction factor must be added to the indicated power level, varying approximately from 4 to 7 decibels for the more-efficient type of horn loudspeakers.

Acoustic spectrum

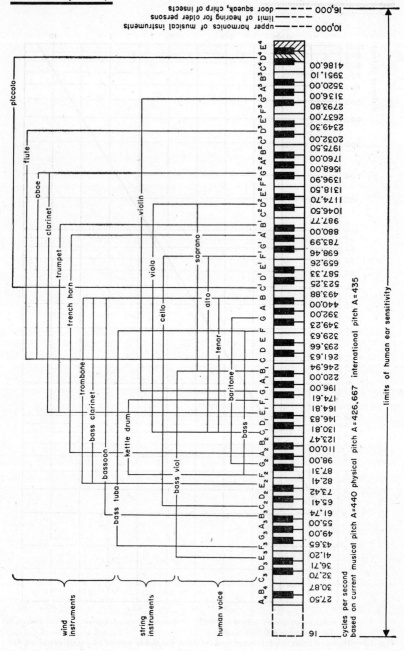

Sounds of speech and music*

A large amount of data are available regarding the wave shapes and statistical properties of the sounds of speech and music. Below are given some of these data that are of importance in the design of transmission systems.

Minimum-discernible-bandwidth changes

Fig. 13 gives the increase in high-frequency bandwidth required to produce a minimum discernible change in the output quality of speech and music.

Fig. 13—Table showing bandwidth increases necessary to give an even chance of quality improvement being noticeable. All figures are in kilocycles.

minus one limen		reference frequency	plus one limen	
speech	music		music	speech
—	—	3	3.0	3.3
3.4	3.3	4	4.8	4.8
4.1	4.1	5	6.0	6.9
4.6	5.0	6	7.4	9.4
5.1	5.8	7	9.3	12.8
5.5	6.4	8	11.0	—
5.8	6.9	9	12.2	—
6.2	7.4	10	13.4	—
6.4	8.0	11	15.0	—
7.0	9.8	13	—	—
7.6	11.0	15	—	—

These bandwidths are known as difference-limen units. For example, a system transmitting music and having an upper cutoff frequency of 6000 cycles would require a cutoff-frequency increase to 7400 cycles before there is a 50-percent chance that the change can be discerned. (Curve B, Fig. 14.)

Fig. 14 is based upon the data of Fig. 13. For any high-frequency cutoff along the abscissa, the ordinates give the next higher and next lower cutoff frequencies for which there is an even chance of discernment. As expected, one ob-

* H. Fletcher, "Speech and Hearing," 1st ed., D. Van Nostrand Company, New York, New York; 1929. S. S. Stevens, and H. Davis, "Hearing," J. Wiley and Sons, New York, New York; 1938.

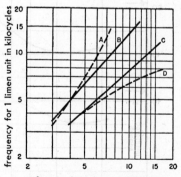

reference frequency in kilocycles
Courtesy of Bell System Technical Journal

Fig. 14 — Minimum-discernible-bandwidth changes. Curves show:

A—Plus 1 limen for speech
B—Plus 1 limen for music
C—Minus 1 limen for music
D—Minus 1 limen for speech

Sounds of speech and music   *continued*

serves that, for frequencies beyond about 4000 cycles, restriction of upper cutoff affects music more appreciably than speech.

Peak factor

One of the important factors in deciding upon the power-handling capacity of amplifiers, loudspeakers, etc., is the fact that in speech very large fluctuations of instantaneous level are present. Fig. 15 shows the peak factor (ratio of peak to root-mean-square pressure) for unfiltered (or wideband) speech, for separate octave bandwidths below 500 cycles, and for separate $\frac{1}{2}$-octave bandwidths above 500 cycles. The peak values for sound pressure of unfiltered speech, for example, rise 10 decibels higher than the averaged root-mean-square value over an interval of $\frac{1}{8}$ second, which corresponds roughly to a syllabic period. However, for a much longer interval of time, say the time duration of one sentence, the peak value reached by the sound pressure for unfiltered speech is about 20 decibels higher than the root-mean-square value averaged for the entire sentence.

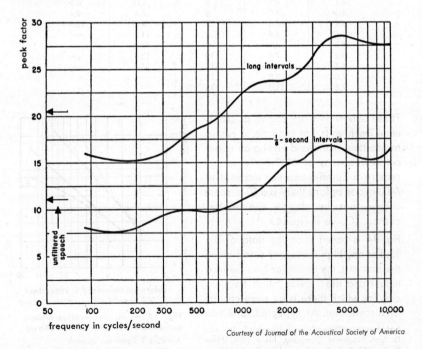

Courtesy of *Journal of the Acoustical Society of America*

Fig. 15—Peak factor (ratio of peak/root-mean-square pressures) in decibels for speech in 1- and 1/2-octave frequency bands, for 1/8- and 75-second time intervals.

Sounds of speech and music   *continued*

Thus, if the required sound-pressure output demands a long-time average of, say, 1 watt of electrical power from an amplifier, then, to take care of the instantaneous peaks in speech, a maximum-peak-handling capacity of 100 watts is needed. If the amplifier is tested for amplitude distortion with a sine wave, 100 watts of peak-instantaneous power exists when the average power of the sine-wave output is 50 watts. This shows that if no amplitude distortion is permitted at the peak pressures in speech sounds, the amplifier should give no distortion when tested by a sine wave of an average power 50 times greater than that required to give the desired long-time-average root-mean-square pressure.

The foregoing puts a very stringent requirement on the amplifier peak power. In relaxing this specification, one of the important questions is what percentage of the time will speech overload an amplifier of lower power than that necessary to take care of all speech peaks. This is answered in Fig. 16; the abscissa gives the probability of the $\dfrac{\text{peak}}{\text{long-time-average}}$ powers exceeding the ordinates for continuous speech and white noise. When multiplied by 100, this probability gives the expected percent of time during which peak distortion occurs. If 1 percent is taken as a suitable criterion,

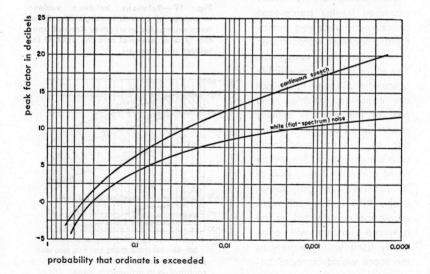

probability that ordinate is exceeded

Fig. 16—Statistical properties of the peak factor in speech. The abscissa gives the probability (ratio of the time) that the peak factor in the uninterrupted speech of one person exceeds the ordinate value. Peak factor = (decibels instantaneous peak value) — (decibels root-mean-square long-time average).

Sounds of speech and music   *continued*

then a 12-decibel ratio of $\dfrac{\text{peak}}{\text{long-time-average}}$ powers is sufficient. Thus, the amplifier should be designed with a power reserve of 16 in order that peak clipping may occur not more than about 1 percent of the time.

Speech-communication

systems

In many applications of the transmission of intelligence by speech sounds, a premium is placed on intelligibility rather than flawless reproduction. Especially important is the reduction of intelligibility as a function of both the background noise and the restriction of transmission-channel bandwidth. Intelligibility is usually measured by the percentage of correctly received monosyllabic nonsense words uttered in an uncorrelated sequence. This score is known as syllable articulation. Because the sounds are nonsense syllables, one part of the word is entirely uncorrelated with the remainder, so it is not consistently possible to guess the whole word correctly if only part of it is received intelligibly. Obviously, if the test speech were a commonly used word, or say a whole sentence with commonly used word sequences, the score would increase because of correct guessing from the context. Fig. 17 shows the inter-relationship between syllable, word, and sentence

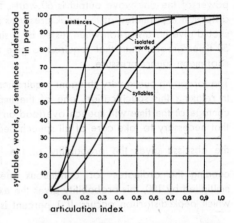

Fig. 17—Relations between various measures of speech intelligibility. Relations are approximate; they depend upon the type of material and the skill of the talkers and listeners.

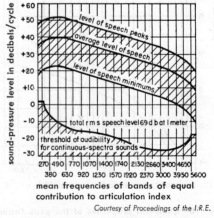

mean frequencies of bands of equal contribution to articulation index

Courtesy of Proceedings of the I.R.E.

Fig. 18—Bands of equal articulation index. 0 decibels = 0.0002 dyne/centimeter.

Speech-communication systems   *continued*

articulation. Also given is a quantity known as articulation index.

The concept and use of articulation index is obtained from Fig. 18. The abscissa is divided into 20 bandwidths of unequal frequency interval. Each of these bands will contribute 5 percent to the articulation index when the speech spectrum is not masked by noise and is sufficiently loud to be above the threshold of audibility. The ordinates give the root-mean-square peaks and minimums (in $\frac{1}{8}$-second intervals), and the average sound pressures created at 1 meter from a speaker's mouth in an anechoic (echo-free) chamber. The units are in decibels pressure per cycle relative to a pressure of 0.0002 dynes/centimeter^2. (For example, for a bandwidth of 100 cycles, rather than 1 cycle, the pressure would be that indicated plus 20 decibels; the latter figure is obtained by taking 10 times logarithm (to the base 10) of the ratio of the 100-cycle band to the indicated band of 1 cycle.)

An articulation index of 5 percent results in any of the 20 bands when a full 30-decibel range of speech-pressure peaks to speech-pressure minimums is obtained in that band. If the speech minimums are masked by noise of a higher pressure, the contribution to articulation is accordingly reduced to a value given by $\frac{1}{6}$ [(decibels level of speech peaks) — (decibels level of average noise)]. Thus, if the average noise is 30 decibels under the speech peaks, this expression gives 5 percent. If the noise is only 10 decibels below the speech peaks, the contribution to articulation index reduces to $\frac{1}{6} \times 10 = 1.67$ percent. If the noise is more than 30 decibels below the speech peaks, a value of 5 percent is used for the articulation index. Such a computation is made for each of the 20 bands of Fig. 18, and the results are added to give the expected articulation index.

A number of important results follow from Fig. 18. For example, in the presence of a large white (thermal-agitation) noise having a flat spectrum, an improvement in articulation results if pre-emphasis is used. A pre-emphasis rate of about 8 decibels/octave is sufficient.

Loudness

Equal loudness contours: Fig. 19 gives average hearing characteristics of the human ear at audible frequencies and at loudness levels of zero to 120 decibels versus intensity levels expressed in decibels above 10^{-16} watt per square centimeter. Ear sensitivity varies considerably over the audible range of sound frequencies at various levels. A loudness level of 120 decibels is heard fairly uniformly throughout the entire audio range but, as indicated in Fig. 19, a frequency of 1000 cycles at a 20-decibel level will be heard at very nearly the same intensity as a frequency of 60 cycles at a 60-decibel level. These curves explain why a loudspeaker operating at lower-than-

Loudness   *continued*

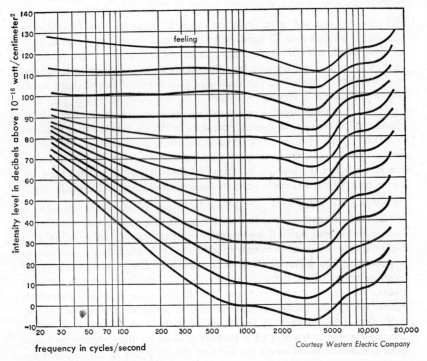

frequency in cycles/second

Courtesy Western Electric Company

Fig. 19—Equal loudness contours.

normal-level sounds as though the higher frequencies were accentuated and the lower tones seriously attenuated or entirely lacking; also, why music, speech, and other sounds, when reproduced, should have very nearly the same intensity as the original rendition. To avoid perceptible deficiency of lower tones, a symphony orchestra, for example, should be reproduced at an acoustical level during the loud passages of 90 to 100 decibels.

■ Servo mechanisms

Definitions

A servo system is a combination of elements for controlling a source of power. The output of the system or some function of the output is fed back for comparison with the input, and the difference between these quantities is used to control the power. Examples of servo systems are: automatic gain controls, automatic-frequency-control systems, positioning systems, etc.

A servo mechanism is a servo system that involves mechanical motion.

Basic system elements

The basic elements of the system (Fig. 1) are:

An input quantity θ_i

An output quantity θ_o

A mixer or comparator that subtracts θ_o from θ_i to yield an error quantity $\epsilon = \theta_i - \theta_o$

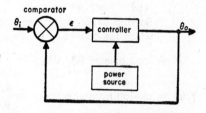

Fig. 1—Example of simple servo system.

A controller which so regulates the flow of power from the power source that ϵ tends toward zero. The controller may include amplifiers, motors, and other devices.

Classification of servo mechanisms

Servo mechanisms may be classified as follows:

Use: Remote control, power amplification, indicating instruments, computers, etc.

Motive characteristics: Hydraulic servos, thyratron servos, Ward-Leonard controls, amplidyne controls, two-phase alternating-current servos, mechanical-torque amplifiers, pneumatic servos, etc.

Control characteristics: Relay-type servo in which the full power of the motor is applied as soon as the error is large enough to operate a relay, definite-correction servo where the power of the motor is controlled in finite steps at definite time intervals, continuous-control servos in which the power of the motor is continuously controlled by some function of the error. Only the continuous type of servo is treated in the following material.

Fundamental quantities for linear-lumped-constant servos

$f(t)$ = function of time $\qquad$ (1)

$F(p)$ = Laplace transform of $f(t)$ $\qquad$ (2)

θ_i = input quantity $\qquad$ (3)

θ_o = output quantity $\qquad$ (4)

ϵ = error quantity = $\theta_i - \theta_o$ $\qquad$ (5)

$Y(p)$ = loop transfer function

$\qquad = \dfrac{\theta_o(p)}{\epsilon(p)} = \dfrac{|K\, Q_m(p)}{p^s P_n(p)}$ where $m < n$ and s is an integer. $|K$ is defined in (7). Q_m and P_n are polynomials of degree m and n, of which the coefficient of zero power of p is taken as unity. $\qquad$ (6)

$|K$ = loop gain = $\lim\limits_{p \to 0} p^s Y(p)$ $\qquad$ (7)

$Y_o(p)$ = overall transfer function = $\dfrac{\theta_o(p)}{\theta_i(p)} = \dfrac{Y(p)}{1 + Y(p)} = |K_o \dfrac{S_m(p)}{R_n(p)}$, $\qquad$ (8)

where S_m, R_n are polynomials similar to Q_m and P_n in (6) above

$Y_i(p)$ = error-input transfer function = $\dfrac{\epsilon(p)}{\theta_i(p)}$ $\qquad$ (9)

$\qquad = \dfrac{1}{1 + Y(p)} = \dfrac{p^s P_n(p)}{1 + |KQ_m(p)}$

f_{ss} = steady-state quantity = $f(t) = \lim\limits_{\substack{t \to \infty \\ p \to 0}} pF(p)$ $\qquad$ (10)

When $s = 1$ in (6), the system is termed a *zero-displacement-error system*, since from equations (9) and (10), $\epsilon_{ss} = 0$ when $\theta_i(t)$ is a step displacement. Similarly, when $s = 2$, the system is termed a *zero-velocity-error system* since $\epsilon_{ss} = 0$ when $\theta_i(t)$ is a step velocity. Obviously a zero-velocity-error system is also a zero-displacement-error system.

Positioning-type servo mechanisms

The fundamental quantities described above are applicable to all classifications of continuous-servo mechanisms. The remaining material in this chapter applies to positioning systems using electronic and electromechanical devices. Other servo mechanisms can be treated in exactly analogous fashions.

Positioning-type servo mechanisms   *continued*

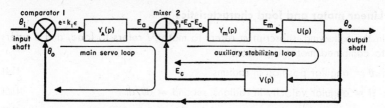

Fig. 2—Positioning-type servo.

A typical positioning servo is shown in Fig. 2. For this system:

$$Y(p) = \frac{\theta_o(p)}{\epsilon(p)} = \frac{k_1 Y_A(p) Y_m(p) \ U(p)}{1 + Y_m(p) U(p) \ V(p)} \tag{11}$$

$$Y_o(p) = \frac{\theta_o(p)}{\theta_i(p)} = \frac{k_1 Y_A(p) Y_m(p) \ U(p)}{1 + k_1 Y_A(p) Y_m(p) U(p) + Y_m(p) U(p) V(p)} \tag{12}$$

$$Y_i(p) = \frac{\epsilon(p)}{\theta_i(p)} = \frac{1 + Y_m(p) U(p) \ V(p)}{1 + k_1 Y_A(p) Y_m(p) U(p) + Y_m(p) U(p) V(p)} \tag{13}$$

Comparator 1: Is an error-measuring system that converts the difference between θ_i and θ_o into error voltage e, where e $= k_1\epsilon$. k_1 is usually a real constant. Examples of error-measuring systems are shown in Fig. 3.

Mixer 2: Is a circuit arrangement that subtracts E_c from E_a to yield a voltage $e_1 = E_a - E_c$.

U(p): Represents the motor and load characteristics. It includes the motor gearing and all inertias and forces imposed by the load. Quantities and relationships making up and describing $U(p)$ are described by (14) to (34).

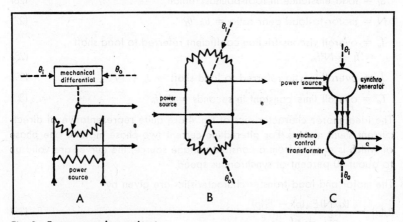

Fig. 3—Error-measuring systems.

Positioning-type servo mechanisms   *continued*

Linear motor and load characteristics

In the following, subscript m refers to motor, l refers to load, and o refers to combined motor and load:

$$\theta = \text{angular position in radians} \tag{14}$$

$$\Omega = \text{angular velocity in radians/second} = d\theta/dt \tag{15}$$

$$M_m = \text{motor-developed torque in foot-pounds} \tag{16}$$

$$J_m = \text{motor inertia in slug-feet}^2 \tag{17}$$

$$E_m = \text{impressed volts} \tag{18}$$

$$k_t = \text{motor stalled-torque constant in foot-pounds/volt}$$
$$= (\Delta M_m / \Delta E_m)_{\Omega_m} \tag{19}$$

$$k_m = \text{velocity constant in radians/second/volt}$$
$$= (\Delta \Omega_m / \Delta E_m)_{M_m} \tag{20}$$

f_m = motor internal-damping characteristic in foot-pound-seconds

$$\text{per radian} = -\frac{k_t}{k_m} = \left(-\frac{\Delta M_m}{\Delta \Omega_m} \right)_{E_m} \tag{21}$$

$$r_m = \text{motor torque-inertia constant in } 1/\text{seconds}^2 = M_m/J_m \tag{22}$$

$$J_l = \text{load inertia in slug-feet}^2 \tag{23}$$

f_l = load viscous-friction coefficient in foot-pound-seconds per radian $\tag{24}$

$$F_l = \text{load coulomb friction in foot-pounds} \tag{25}$$

$$S_l = \text{load elastance in foot-pounds/radian} \tag{26}$$

$$N = \text{motor-to-load gear ratio} = \theta_m/\theta_l \tag{27}$$

f_o = overall viscous-friction coefficient referred to load shaft
$$= f_l + N^2 f_m \tag{28}$$

$$J_o = \text{overall inertia referred to load shaft} = J_l + N^2 J_m \tag{29}$$

$$T_o = \text{overall time constant in seconds} = J_o/f_o \tag{30}$$

The ideal motor characteristics of Fig. 4 are quite representative of direct-current shunt motors. For alternating-current two-phase motors, one phase of which is excited from a constant-voltage source, the curves are valid up to about 40 percent of synchronous speed.

The motor and load-transfer characteristics are given by

$$\theta_o(p) = \frac{(k_t/N) E_m(p) - F_l(p)}{p^2 J_o + p f_o + S} \tag{31}$$

Positioning-type servo mechanisms   *continued*

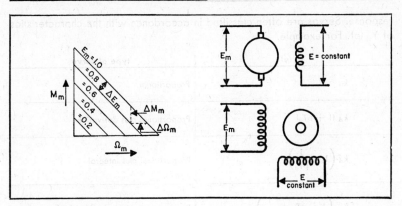

Fig. 4—Ideal motor curves.

When $S = 0$, which is very often the case,

$$\theta_o(p) = \frac{(k_t/N)E_m(p) - F_l(p)}{p(f_o + pJ_o)} \tag{32}$$

and

$$U(p) = \frac{\theta_o(p)}{E_m(p)} = \frac{k_t}{N(f_o + pJ_o)p} - \frac{F_l(p)}{E_m(p)(f_o + pJ_o)p} \tag{33}$$

When F_l can be assumed zero, then

$$U(p) = \frac{k_t}{N(f_o + pJ_o)p} = \frac{k_t}{Nf_op(T_op + 1)} \tag{34}$$

$Y_m(p)$: Represents the power amplifier that energizes the motor system $U(p)$. This amplifier may be of the hard-tube, thyratron, fixed-magnetic, or rotary-magnetic (amplidyne) types. Typical values of $Y_m(p)$ are:

$$Y_m(p) = \frac{K_a}{1 + pT_a} \tag{35}$$

for electronic amplifiers, where T_a is often of negligible magnitude, and

$$Y_m(p) = \frac{K_a}{(1 + pT_a)(1 + pT_b)} \tag{36}$$

for a 2-stage magnetic amplifier.

$Y_A(p)$: Represents the error-voltage amplifier. This amplifier may include various equalizing networks that modify e as required to improve the servo

Positioning-type servo mechanisms   *continued*

response. Servos are often classified in accordance with the characteristics of $Y_A(p)$. For example,

$Y_A(p)$	type of servo
k_A	Proportional
$k_A (1 + pT_a)$	Proportional plus derivative
$k_A \left(1 + \dfrac{1}{pT_a}\right)$	Proportional plus integral
$k_A \left(1 + pT_a + \dfrac{1}{pT_b}\right)$	Proportional plus derivative plus integral

Practical circuits that approximate some of these characteristics are shown in Fig. 5.

The above circuits are for use where the steady-state error voltage e_{ss} has a direct-current value. In those cases where e_{ss} is a sinusoid of frequency ω_0, the bridged-T circuit is useful as a proportional-plus-derivative network (Figs. 6 and 7). For the circuit to possess approximately proportional-plus-derivative characteristics, it is necessary that

$$Y(j\omega) = G[1 + jT_d(\omega - \omega_0)] \tag{37}$$

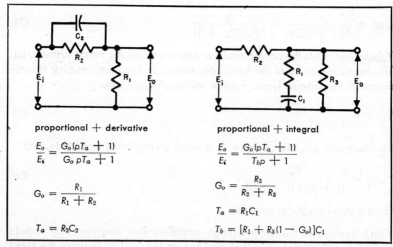

proportional + derivative

$$\frac{E_o}{E_i} = \frac{G_o(pT_a + 1)}{G_o\, pT_a + 1}$$

$$G_o = \frac{R_1}{R_1 + R_2}$$

$$T_a = R_2 C_2$$

proportional + integral

$$\frac{E_o}{E_i} = \frac{G_o(pT_a + 1)}{T_b p + 1}$$

$$G_o = \frac{R_3}{R_2 + R_3}$$

$$T_a = R_1 C_1$$

$$T_b = [R_1 + R_3(1 - G_o)]C_1$$

Fig. 5—Direct-current equalizing networks.

Positioning-type servo mechanisms   *continued*

This is true when

$$R_1 = \frac{1}{T_d\omega_0^2 C}, \quad R_3 = \frac{T_d}{C}, \quad \text{and} \quad G = \frac{2}{T_d^2\omega_0^2 + 2} \tag{38}$$

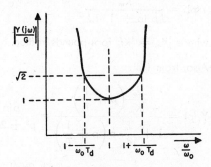

$$\frac{E_o}{E_i} = \frac{T_1T_3p^2 + 2T_1p + 1}{T_1T_3p^2 + (2T_1 + T_3)p + 1}$$

$$T_1 = R_1C$$

$$T_3 = R_3C$$

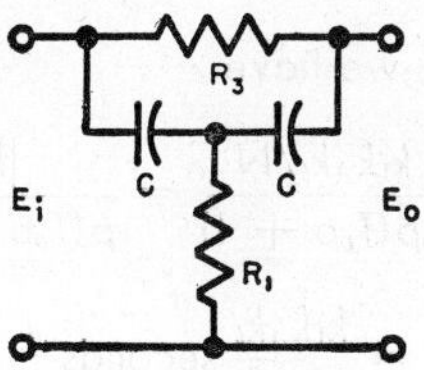

Fig. 6—Alternating-current derivative network.

V(p): Is a feedback and amplifier network that is used effectively to modify the characteristics of the power amplifier and motor elements. Often this takes the form of a tachometer generator coupled to the output shaft, or equivalent, that develops a voltage e_g proportional to the output-shaft speed. This voltage may be further modified by circuits that are usually of the derivative type. Typical circuits are shown in Fig. 8.

Fig. 7—Alternating-current derivative network characteristics.

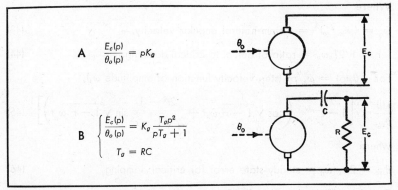

A $\quad \dfrac{E_c(p)}{\theta_o(p)} = pK_g$

B $\quad \begin{cases} \dfrac{E_c(p)}{\theta_o(p)} = K_g \dfrac{T_gp^2}{pT_g + 1} \\ T_g = RC \end{cases}$

Fig. 8—Tachometer feedback network.

Typical positioning-servo mechanisms

Simple viscous-damped system

For this servo, referring to Fig. 2,

$$Y_A(p) = k_A, \quad Y_m(p) = 1, \quad V(p) = 0, \quad \text{and} \quad U(p) = \frac{k_t/N}{f_o p \, (T_o p + 1)} \tag{39}$$

From (11), we have

$$Y(p) = \frac{k_1 k_A k_t/N}{f_o p (T_o p + 1)} = \frac{|K}{p(T_o p + 1)} \tag{40}$$

where $|K = \dfrac{k_1 k_A k_t}{f_o N}$ seconds^{-1}

or

$$Y(p) = \frac{|K_m}{J_o p \, (p + 1/T_o)} \tag{41}$$

where $|K_m = |K f_o$ foot-pounds/radian.

Also, from (13),

$$\left.\begin{aligned}
Y_i(p) &= \frac{\dfrac{J_o}{|K_m}\left(p + \dfrac{1}{T_o}\right)}{1 + \dfrac{J_o}{|K_m} p \left(p + \dfrac{1}{T_o}\right)} = \frac{p(p + 2r\omega_n)}{p^2 + 2r\omega_n p + \omega_n^2} \\[2mm]
&= \frac{p(p + 2r\omega_n)}{[p + \omega_n(r + \sqrt{r^2 - 1})][p + \omega_n(r - \sqrt{r^2 - 1})]}
\end{aligned}\right\} \tag{42}$$

Where

$$\omega_n = (|K_m/J_o)^{\frac{1}{2}} = \text{system natural angular velocity}, \tag{43}$$

$$r = 1/2T_o\omega_n = \text{ratio of actual to critical damping}. \tag{44}$$

For $\theta_i(p) = \omega_i/p^2$ (step-velocity function of amplitude ω_i),

$$\frac{\epsilon(t)}{\theta_{ssc}} = r\left[1 - \epsilon^{-r\omega_n t}\left(\cos\sqrt{1 - r^2}\,\omega_n t + \frac{2r^2 - 1}{2r\sqrt{1 - r^2}}\sin\sqrt{1 - r^2}\,\omega_n t\right)\right] \tag{45}$$

where

$$\theta_{ssc} = 2\omega_i/\omega_n = \text{steady-state error for critical damping} \tag{46}$$

Equation (45) is plotted in Fig. 9.

Typical positioning-servo mechanisms *continued*

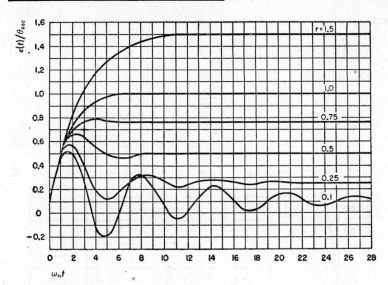

Fig. 9—Proportional viscous-damped system.

Proportional-plus-derivative system

The transfer functions of this system are identical with those of the proportional system, except that

$$Y_A(p) = k_A(1 + pT_A) \tag{47}$$

so that

$$Y(p) = \frac{|K_m}{J_o} \frac{1 + pT_A}{p\,(p + 1/T_o)} \tag{48}$$

and

$$Y_i(p) = \frac{p\,(p + 1/T_o)}{p^2 + p\left(\dfrac{1}{T_o} + \dfrac{|K_m}{J_o}T_A\right) + \dfrac{|K_m}{J_o}} = \frac{p\,(p + 2\omega_n cr)}{p^2 + 2r\omega_n p + \omega_n^2} \tag{49}$$

Where

$$\omega_n = (|K_m/J_o)^{\frac{1}{2}} \tag{50}$$

$$c = \frac{1/T_o}{\dfrac{1}{T_o} + \omega_n^2 T_A} = \text{ratio of viscous to overall damping,} \tag{51}$$

and

$$r = \frac{1}{2\omega_n}\left(\frac{1}{T_o} + \omega_n^2 T_A\right) = \frac{1}{2\omega_n c T_o} \tag{52}$$

For $\theta_i(p) = \omega_i/p^2$,

$$\epsilon(t) = \frac{2rc\omega_i}{\omega_n}\left[1 - \epsilon^{-r\omega_n t}\left(\cos\sqrt{1 - r^2}\ \omega_n t + \frac{2r^2 c - 1}{2rc\sqrt{1 - r^2}}\right.\right.$$

$$\left.\left.\times \sin\sqrt{1 - r^2}\ \omega_n t\right)\right] \tag{53}$$

Equation (53) for $c = 0$ (i.e., $1/T_o = 0$ and $f_o = 0$) is plotted in Fig. 10.

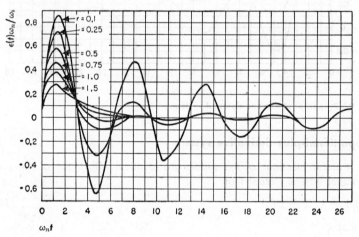

Fig. 10—Proportional-plus-derivative system.

Examples of simple system with auxiliary feedback loop

For this system (Fig. 2), $Y_A(p) = k_A$ and $Y_m(p) = 1$;

$$U(p) = \frac{k_t/N}{f_o p(T_o p + 1)} = \frac{k_t/N}{p^2 J_o + f_o p}$$

$V(p) = k_g p$ for the circuit of Fig. 8A.

$\qquad = k_g T_g p^2$ for the circuit of Fig. 8B, assuming $1 \gg pT_g$, so that

$$Y(p) = \frac{\dfrac{k_A k_t/N}{p^2 J_o + p f_o}}{1 + \dfrac{k_t V(p)}{N(p^2 J_o + p f_o)}} = \frac{k_A k_t/N}{p^2 J_o + f_o p + \dfrac{k_t}{N} V(p)} \tag{54}$$

Typical positioning-servo mechanisms *continued*

It is seen therefore that, if $V(p) = k_g p$, the effect is to increase the motor damping to $f_o + k_t k_g / N$.

Similarly, when $V(p) = k_g T_g p^2$, the overall inertia is effectively increased to $J_o + k_t k_g T_g / N$.

Since k_g can be negative or positive, it follows that $V(p)$ provides a method of effectively decreasing or increasing the damping and inertia.

Servo-mechanism performance criteria

It is very difficult to describe completely or specify the performance of servo mechanisms. However, the following *steady-state* quantities and their typical magnitudes may be used as a guide.

Static error ϵ_s = error when input shaft is at rest   (55)

Velocity figure of merit $K_V = \omega_i/\epsilon_{ss}$ = input velocity/error   (56)

Acceleration figure of merit $K_\alpha = \alpha_i/\epsilon_{ss}$ = input acceleration/error   (57)

Typical performance values are:

quantity	excellent	good	poor
ϵ_s	15 min	1 deg	5 deg
K_V	200 sec^{-1}	100 sec^{-1}	25 sec^{-1}
K_α	150 sec^{-2}	75 sec^{-2}	15 sec^{-2}

Stability criteria

A system is unstable when its amplitude of oscillation theoretically increases without limit. Instability is mathematically determined by taking the denominator of $Y_o(p)$ or $Y_i(p)$, equations (8) and (9),

$$D = \sum_{i=0}^{i=n} a_i p_i \qquad (58)$$

and putting it into the form

$$D = (p + p_0)(p + p_1)(p + p_2) \dots (p + p_n) \qquad (59)$$

If any root p_i has a negative real part, the system is then unstable.

The labor involved in transforming (58) into (59) is considerable, particularly when n exceeds 2. To avoid this labor Routh has specified requirements for

Stability criteria   *continued*

the coefficients a_i. If these requirements are satisfied, no p_i has a negative real part.

The requirements, known as the "Routh stability criteria," are as follows:

a. All coefficients a_i must be positive.

b. A certain relationship, depending upon the degree of D, must exist between the coefficients a_i.

For the lower-degree equations, the relationships in b above are as follows.

a. For the first and quadratic degrees, the coefficient of p must exceed zero:

b. Cubic, $a_3 p^3 + a_2 p^2 + a_1 p + a_0$.
For stability, $a_2 a_1 > a_3 a_0$.

c. Quartic, $a_4 p^4 + a_3 p^3 + a_2 p^2 + a_1 p + a_0$.
For stability, $a_3 a_2 a_1 > a_3{}^2 a_0 + a_1{}^2 a_4$.

d. Quintic, $a_5 p^5 + a_4 p^4 + a_3 p^3 + a_2 p^2 + a_1 p + a_0$.
For stability,
$$a_2(a_4 a_1 - a_5 a_0)(a_4 a_3 - a_5 a_2) > a_4(a_4 a_1 - a_5 a_0)^2 + a_0(a_4 a_3 - a_5 a_2)^2.$$

A second method for determining stability is known as the "Nyquist stability criterion." This method consists of obtaining the locus of the loop-transfer function $Y(p)$, (6) in the Y plane for values of $p = j\omega$, where ω varies from $+\infty$ to $-\infty$. If the locus, described in a positive sense, encloses the point $-1,0$, the system is un-

stable. (By positive sense is meant that the interior of the locus is always on the left as the point describes the locus.) Since the locus is always symmetrical about the real axis, it is necessary to draw only the locus for positive values of ω; the remainder of the locus is then obtained by reflection in the real axis.

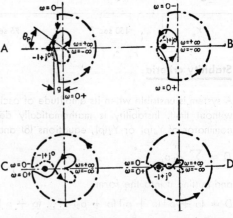

Fig. 11 shows loci for several simple systems. Curves A and C represent stable systems, curve B an unstable system. Curve D is a conditionally stable one; that is, for a

Fig. 11—Typical Nyquist loci. Plotted in $Y(j\omega)$ plane.
solid line = locus for $0 \leqslant \omega \leqslant \infty$
dotted = locus for $-\infty \leqslant \omega \leqslant 0$
dash-dot = locus for $\omega = 0$

Stability criteria *continued*

particular range of values of $|K$ it is unstable, but it is stable for both larger and smaller values. It is unstable as shown.

Curve A illustrates a zero-displacement-error system; curve C a zero-velocity-error system.

Curve A also demonstrates the phase margin θ_p, and gain margin g. The phase margin is the angle between the negative real axis and the Y vector when $|Y| = 1$. The gain margin is the value of $|Y|$ when the phase angle is 180 degrees. The gain margin is often specified in decibels, so that $g = 20 \log |Y|$. Typical satisfactory values are 15 decibels for g and 50 degrees for θ_p.

Linearity considerations

The preceding material applies strictly to linear systems. Actually all systems are nonlinear to some extent. This nonlinearity may cause serious deterioration in performance. Common sources of nonlinearity are:

a. Nonlinear motor characteristics.

b. Overloading of amplifiers by noise.

c. Static friction.

d. Backlash in gears, potentiometers, etc. For good performance it is recommended that the total backlash should not exceed 20 percent of the expected static error.

e. Low-efficiency gear or worm drives that cause locking action.

In spite of all the available types and sources of nonlinearity, it is usually found that when care is taken to minimize it, the linear theory applies quite well.

■ Miscellaneous data

Atmospheric data

Pressure–altitude graph

Design of electrical equipment for aircraft is somewhat complicated by the requirement of additional insulation for high voltages as a result of the decrease in atmospheric pressure. The extent of this effect may be determined from the chart below and the information on the opposite page.

1 inch mercury = 25.4 mm mercury = 0.4912 pounds/inch^2

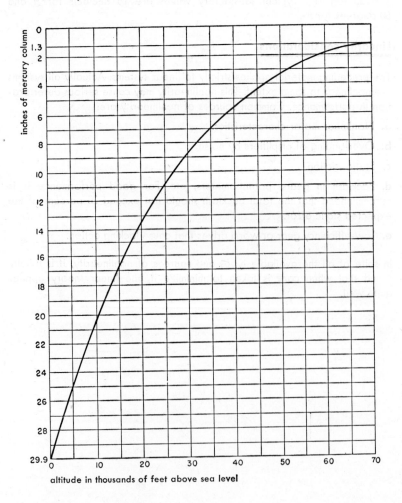

altitude in thousands of feet above sea level

Atmospheric data   *continued*

Spark-gap breakdown voltages

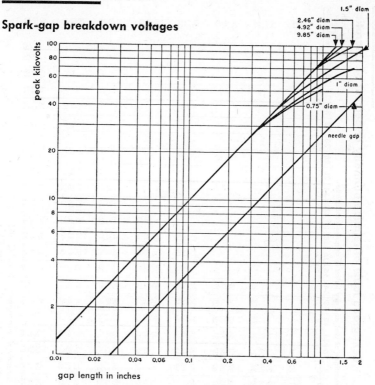

gap length in inches

Data above is for a voltage that is continuous or at a frequency low enough to permit complete deionization between cycles, between needle points, or clean, smooth spherical surfaces (electrodes ungrounded) in dust-free dry air. Temperature is 25 degrees centigrade and pressure is 760 millimeters (29.9 inches) of mercury. The following multiplying factors apply for atmospheric conditions other than those stated above:

pressure		temperature in degrees centigrade					
in Hg	mm Hg	−40	−20	0	20	40	60
5	127	0.26	0.24	0.23	0.21	0.20	0.19
10	254	0.47	0.44	0.42	0.39	0.37	0.34
15	381	0.68	0.64	0.60	0.56	0.53	0.50
20	508	0.87	0.82	0.77	0.72	0.68	0.64
25	635	1.07	0.99	0.93	0.87	0.82	0.77
30	762	1.25	1.17	1.10	1.03	0.97	0.91
35	889	1.43	1.34	1.26	1.19	1.12	1.05
40	1016	1.61	1.51	1.42	1.33	1.25	1.17
45	1143	1.79	1.68	1.58	1.49	1.40	1.31
50	1270	1.96	1.84	1.73	1.63	1.53	1.44
55	1397	2.13	2.01	1.89	1.78	1.67	1.57
60	1524	2.30	2.17	2.04	1.92	1.80	1.69

Centigrade table of relative humidity or percent of saturation

dry bulb degrees centigrade	0.5	1.0	1.5	2.0	2.5	3.0	3.5	4.0	4.5	5	6	7	8	9	10	11	12	13	14	15	16	18	20	22	24	26	28	30	32	34	36	38	40
4	93	85	77	70	63	56	48	41	34	28	15																						
8	94	87	81	74	68	62	56	50	45	39	28	17																					
12	94	89	84	78	73	68	63	58	53	48	38	30	21	12																			
16	95	90	85	81	76	71	67	62	58	54	45	37	29	21	14	7																	
20	96	91	87	82	78	74	70	66	62	58	51	44	36	30	23	17	11																
22	96	92	87	83	79	75	72	68	64	60	53	46	40	34	27	21	16	11															
24	96	92	88	85	81	77	74	70	66	63	56	49	43	37	31	26	21	14	10														
26	96	92	88	85	81	77	74	71	67	64	57	51	45	39	34	28	23	18	13														
28	96	92	89	85	82	78	75	72	68	65	59	53	47	42	37	31	26	21	17	13													
30	96	93	89	86	82	79	76	73	70	67	61	55	50	44	39	35	30	24	20	16	12												
32	96	93	90	86	83	80	77	74	71	68	62	56	51	46	41	36	32	27	23	19	15	10											
34	97	93	90	87	84	81	77	74	71	69	63	58	53	48	43	38	34	30	26	22	18	13	10										
36	97	93	90	87	84	81	78	75	72	70	64	59	54	50	45	41	36	32	28	24	21	15	10										
38	97	93	90	87	84	81	79	76	73	70	65	60	56	51	46	42	38	34	30	27	23	18	13										
40	97	94	91	88	85	82	79	76	74	71	66	61	57	52	48	44	40	36	32	29	25	21	16	11									
44	97	94	91	88	86	83	80	77	75	73	68	63	59	54	50	47	43	39	36	32	29	23	17	12									
48	97	94	92	88	86	84	81	78	76	74	69	65	61	56	53	49	45	42	39	35	33	27	21	16	12								
52	97	94	92	89	87	84	82	79	77	75	70	66	62	58	55	51	48	44	41	38	35	30	25	20	16	11							
56	97	95	92	90	87	85	83	80	78	76	72	68	64	60	57	53	50	46	43	40	38	32	27	23	19	15	11						
60	98	95	93	90	88	86	83	81	79	77	73	69	65	62	58	55	52	48	45	43	40	35	30	26	21	18	14	11					
70	98	96	93	91	90	87	85	83	81	79	75	71	68	65	61	58	55	52	50	47	44	40	35	31	27	23	20	17	14				
80	98	96	94	92	90	88	86	84	83	81	77	74	71	67	64	61	58	56	53	50	48	43	39	35	31	28	24	22	19	16	14	11	
90	98	96	95	93	91	89	87	85	84	82	79	76	73	69	67	64	61	58	56	53	51	47	42	39	35	32	28	26	23	20	18	16	14
100	99	97	95	93	92	90	88	86	85	83	80	77	74	71	68	66	63	60	58	56	54	49	45	42	38	35	32	29	26	24	22	19	17

difference between readings of wet and dry bulbs in degrees centigrade

Example: Assume dry-bulb reading (thermometer exposed directly to atmosphere) is 20° C and wet-bulb reading is 17° C, or a difference of 3° C. The relative humidity at 20° C is then 74%.

Atmospheric data *continued*

Combined psychrometric and volume chart

Shows pounds of water per pound of dry air, and volume in feet³ per pound of dry air

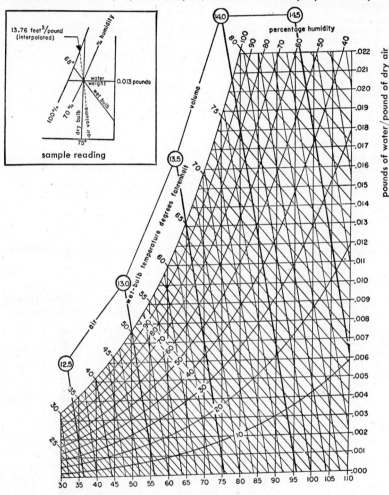

dry-bulb temperature **in** degrees fahrenheit

For sample reading:

Dry-bulb thermometer reads 75 degrees
Wet-bulb thermometer reads 68 degrees

Then,
Humidity = 70 percent
Pounds of water/pound of dry air = 0.013
Air volume = 13.76 feet³/pound dry air
Weight of water/foot³ air = 0.013/13.76
　　　　　　　　= 0.00094 pounds

Weather data

Compiled from "Climate and Man," Yearbook of Agriculture, U. S. Dept. of Agriculture 1941. Obtainable from Superintendent of Documents, Government Printing Office, Washington 25, D.C.

Temperature extremes

United States

Lowest temperature	−66° F	Riverside Range Station, Wyoming (Feb. 9, 1933)
Highest temperature	134° F	Greenland Ranch, Death Valley, California (July 10, 1933)

Alaska

Lowest temperature	−78° F	Fort Yukon (Jan. 14, 1934)
Highest temperature	100° F	Fort Yukon

World

Lowest temperature	−90° F	Verkhoyansk, Siberia (Feb. 5 and 7, 1892)
Highest temperature	136° F	Azizia, Libya, North Africa (Sept. 13, 1922)
Lowest mean temperature (annual)	−14° F	Framheim, Antarctica
Highest mean temperature (annual)	86° F	Massawa, Eritrea, Africa

Precipitation extremes

United States

Wettest state	Louisiana—average annual rainfall 55.11 inches
Dryest state	Nevada—average annual rainfall 8.81 inches
Maximum recorded	New Smyrna, Fla., Oct. 10, 1924—23.22 inches in 24 hours
Minimums recorded	Bagdad, Calif., 1909–1913—3.93 inches in 5 years
	Greenland Ranch, Calif.—1.35 inches annual average

World

Maximums recorded	Cherrapunji, India, Aug. 1841—241 inches in 1 month
	(Average annual rainfall of Cherrapunji is 426 inches)
	Bagui, Luzon, Philippines, July 14–15, 1911—46 inches in 24 hours
Minimums recorded	Wadi Halfa, Anglo-Egyptian Sudan and Awan, Egypt are in the "rainless' area; average annual rainfall is too small to be measured

World temperatures

territory	maximum ° F	minimum ° F	territory	maximum ° F	minimum ° F
NORTH AMERICA			ASIA *continued*		
Alaska	100	−78	India	120	−19
Canada	103	−70	Iraq	123	19
Canal Zone	97	63	Japan	101	−7
Greenland	86	−46	Malay States	97	66
Mexico	118	11	Philippine Islands	101	58
U. S. A.	134	−66	Siam	106	52
West Indies	102	45	Tibet	85	−20
			Turkey	111	−22
SOUTH AMERICA			U. S. S. R.	109	−90
Argentina	115	−27			
Bolivia	82	25	**AFRICA**		
Brazil	108	21	Algeria	133	1
Chile	99	19	Anglo-Egyptian Sudan	126	28
Venezuela	102	45	Angola	91	33
			Belgian Congo	97	34
EUROPE			Egypt	124	31
British Isles	100	4	Ethiopia	111	32
France	107	−14	French Equatorial Africa	118	46
Germany	100	−16	French West Africa	122	41
Iceland	71	−6	Italian Somaliland	93	61
Italy	114	4	Libya	136	35
Norway	95	−26	Morocco	119	5
Spain	124	10	Rhodesia	103	25
Sweden	92	−49	Tunisia	122	28
Turkey	100	17	Union of South Africa	111	21
U. S. S. R.	110	−61			
			AUSTRALASIA		
ASIA			Australia	127	19
Arabia	114	53	Hawaii	91	51
China	111	−10	New Zealand	94	23
East Indies	101	60	Samoan Islands	96	61
French Indo-China	113	33	Solomon Islands	97	70

Weather data *continued*

World precipitation

territory	highest average				lowest average				yearly average inches
	Jan inches	April inches	July inches	Oct inches	Jan inches	April inches	July inches	Oct inches	
NORTH AMERICA									
Alaska	13.71	10.79	8.51	22.94	.15	.13	.93	.37	43.40
Canada	8.40	4.97	4.07	6.18	.48	.31	1.04	.73	26.85
Canal Zone	3.74	4.30	16.00	15.13	.91	2.72	7.28	10.31	97.54
Greenland	3.46	2.44	3.27	6.28	.35	.47	.91	.94	24.70
Mexico	1.53	1.53	13.44	5.80	.04	.00	.43	.35	29.82
U. S. A.									29.00
West Indies	4.45	6.65	5.80	6.89	.92	1.18	1.53	5.44	49.77
SOUTH AMERICA									
Argentina	6.50	4.72	2.16	3.35	.16	.28	.04	.20	16.05
Bolivia	6.34	1.77	.16	1.42	3.86	1.46	.16	1.30	24.18
Brazil	13.26	12.13	10.47	6.54	2.05	2.63	.01	.05	55.42
Chile	11.78	11.16	16.63	8.88	.00	.00	.03	.00	46.13
Venezuela	2.75	6.90	6.33	10.44	.02	.61	1.87	3.46	40.01
EUROPE									
British Isles	5.49	3.67	3.78	5.57	1.86	1.54	2.38	2.63	36.16
France	3.27	2.64	2.95	4.02	1.46	1.65	.55	2.32	27.48
Germany	1.88	2.79	5.02	2.97	1.16	1.34	2.92	1.82	26.64
Iceland	5.47	3.70	3.07	5.95	5.47	3.70	3.07	5.59	52.91
Italy	4.02	4.41	2.40	5.32	1.44	1.63	.08	2.10	29.74
Norway	8.54	4.13	5.79	8.94	1.06	1.34	1.73	2.48	40.51
Spain	2.83	3.70	2.05	3.58	1.34	1.54	.04	1.77	22.74
Sweden	1.52	1.07	2.67	2.20	.98	.78	1.80	1.60	18.12
Turkey	3.43	1.65	1.06	2.52	3.43	1.65	1.06	2.52	28.86
U. S. S. R.	1.46	1.61	3.50	2.07	.49	.63	.20	.47	18.25
ASIA									
Arabia	1.16	.40	.03	.09	.32	.18	.02	.09	3.05
China	1.97	5.80	13.83	6.92	.15	.61	5.78	.67	50.63
East Indies	18.46	10.67	6.54	10.00	7.48	2.60	.20	.79	78.02
French Indo-China	.79	4.06	12.08	10.61	.52	2.07	9.24	3.67	65.64
India	3.29	33.07	99.52	13.83	.09	.06	.47	.00	75.18
Iraq	1.37	.93	.00	.08	1.17	.48	.00	.05	6.75
Japan	10.79	8.87	9.94	7.48	2.06	2.83	5.02	4.59	70.18
Malay States	9.88	7.64	6.77	8.07	9.88	7.64	6.77	8.07	95.06
Philippine Islands	2.23	1.44	17.28	10.72	.82	1.28	14.98	6.71	83.31
Siam	.33	1.65	6.24	8.32	.33	1.65	6.24	8.32	52.36
Turkey	4.13	2.75	1.73	3.34	2.05	1.73	.21	.93	25.08
U. S. S. R.	1.79	2.05	3.61	4.91	.08	.16	.10	.06	11.85
AFRICA									
Algeria	4.02	2.06	.35	3.41	.52	.11	.00	.05	9.73
Anglo-Egyptian Sudan	.08	4.17	7.87	4.29	.00	.00	.00	.00	18.27
Angola	8.71	5.85	.00	3.80	.09	.63	.00	.09	23.46
Belgian Congo	9.01	6.51	.13	2.77	3.69	1.81	.00	1.88	39.38
Egypt	2.09	.16	.00	.28	.00	.00	.00	.00	3.10
Ethiopia	.59	3.42	10.98	3.39	.28	3.11	8.23	.79	49.17
French Equatorial Africa	9.84	13.42	6.33	13.58	.00	.34	.04	.86	57.55
French West Africa	.10	1.61	8.02	1.87	.00	.00	.18	.00	19.51
Italian Somaliland	.00	3.66	1.67	2.42	.00	3.60	1.67	2.42	17.28
Libya	3.24	.48	.02	1.53	2.74	.18	.00	.67	13.17
Morocco	3.48	2.78	.07	2.47	1.31	.36	.00	.23	15.87
Rhodesia	8.40	.95	.04	1.20	5.81	.65	.00	.88	29.65
Tunisia	2.36	1.30	.08	1.54	2.36	1.30	.08	1.54	15.80
Union of South Africa	6.19	3.79	3.83	5.79	.06	.23	.27	.12	26.07
AUSTRALASIA									
Australia	15.64	5.33	6.57	2.84	.34	.85	.07	.00	28.31
Hawaii	11.77	13.06	9.89	10.97	3.54	2.06	1.04	1.97	82.43
New Zealand	3.34	3.80	5.55	4.19	2.67	2.78	2.99	3.13	43.20
Samoan Islands	18.90	11.26	2.60	7.05	18.90	11.26	2.60	7.05	118.47
Solomon Islands	13.44	8.24	6.26	7.91	13.44	8.24	6.26	7.91	115.37

Weather data *continued*

Wind-velocity and temperature extremes in North America

Maximum corrected wind velocity for a period of 5 minutes in miles/hour.

station	wind miles/hour	temperature degrees fahrenheit	
		maximum	minimum
UNITED STATES, 1871–1947			
Albany, New York	60	104	−24
Amarillo, Texas	70	107	−16
Buffalo, New York	73	97	−20
Charleston, South Carolina	81	104	7
Chicago, Illinois	65	105	−23
Bismarck, North Dakota	74	108	−45
Hatteras, North Carolina	90	95	8
Miami, Florida	123	96	27
Minneapolis, Minnesota	65	108	−34
Mobile, Alabama	87	103	−1
Mt. Washington, New Hampshire	140*	80	−46
Nantucket, Massachusetts	66	92	−6
New York, New York	81	102	−14
North Platte, Nebraska	73	109	−35
Pensacola, Florida	91	103	7
Washington, D.C.	53	106	−15
San Juan, Puerto Rico	135	94	62
CANADA, 1947			
Banff, Alberta	52	97	−45
Kamloops, British Columbia	34	107	−31
Sable Island, Novia Scotia	64	86	−12
Toronto, Ontario	48	105	−46

* Gusts were recorded at 225 miles/hour (corrected).

Wind velocities and pressures

indicated velocities miles per hour* V_i	actual velocities miles per hour V_a	cylindrical surfaces pressure lbs/ft^2 projected areas $P = 0.0025V_a^2$	flat surfaces pressure lbs/ft^2 $P = 0.0042V_a^2$
10	9.6	0.23	0.4
20	17.8	0.8	1.3
30	25.7	1.7	2.8
40	33.3	2.8	4.7
50	40.8	4.2	7.0
60	48.0	5.8	9.7
70	55.2	7.6	12.8
80	62.2	9.7	16.2
90	69.2	12.0	20.1
100	76.2	14.5	24.3
110	83.2	17.3	29.1
120	90.2	20.3	34.2
125	93.7	21.9	36.9
130	97.2	23.6	39.7
140	104.2	27.2	45.6
150	111.2	30.9	51.9
160	118.2	34.9	58.6
170	125.2	39.2	65.7
175	128.7	41.4	69.5
180	132.2	43.7	73.5
190	139.2	48.5	81.5
200	146.2	53.5	89.8

* As measured with a cup anemometer, these being the average maximum for a period of five minutes.

Principal power supplies in foreign countries

territory	d-c volts	a-c volts	frequency
NORTH AMERICA			
Alaska	—	110, 220	60
British Honduras	110	—	—
Canada	110	**110,** 115, 150, 230	60, 25
Costa Rica	110	**110**	60
Cuba	110, 220	**110,** 220	60
Dominican Republic	110	**110,** 120	60
Guatemala	220, 125	**110,** 220	60, 50
Haiti	—	110, 220	60, 50
Hawaii	—	110, 220	60, 25
Honduras	110, 220	**110,** 220	60
Mexico	110, 220	**110, 125,** 115, 220, 230	60, 50
Newfoundland	—	110, 115	60, 50
Nicaragua	110	**110**	60
Panama (Republic)	—	110, 220	60, 50
Panama (Canal Zone)	—	110	25
Puerto Rico	110, 220	**110**	60
Salvador	110, 220	**110**	60
Virgin Islands	110, 220	—	—
WEST INDIES			
Bahamas Is.	—	115	60
Barbados	—	110	50
Bermuda	—	110	60
Curacao	—	127	50
Jamaica	—	110	40, 60
Martinique	—	115, 200	50
Trinidad	—	110, 220	60
SOUTH AMERICA			
Argentina	**220**	**220,** 225	50, 60, 43
Bolivia	110	**110,** 220	50, 60
Brazil	—	127, 120, 220	50, 60
Chile	220, 110	**220**	50, 60
Colombia	—	**110,** 220, 150	60, 50
Ecuador	—	**110**	60
Paraguay	**220**	220	50
Peru	110	**110,** 220	60, 50
Uruguay	220	**220**	50
Venezuela	110, 220	**110,** 220	60, 50
EUROPE			
Albania	220	**220,** 125, 150	50
Austria	220, 110, 150	**220,** 125, 150, 120, 127, 110	50
Azores	220	220	50
Belgium	220, 110, 120	**220,** 127, 110, 115, 135	50, 40
Bulgaria	220, 120	**220,** 120, 150	50
Cyrus (Br.)	**220**	110	50
Czechoslovakia	220, 150, 110, 120, 150	**220,** 110, 115, 127	50, 42
Denmark	220, 110	**220,** 120, 127	50
Estonia	**220,** 110	220, 127	50
Finland	120, 220, 110	**220,** 120, 110, 115	50
France	110, 220, 120, 125	**110, 115,** 120, 125, 220, 230	50, 25
Germany	220, 110, 120, 250	**220,** 127, 120, 110	50, 25
Gibraltar	220	**110,** 220	76
Greece	**220,** 110	**127,** 220	50
Hungary	220, 110, 120	**220,** 110, 115, 120	50, 42
Iceland	**220,** 110	**220,** 110, 120	50
Irish Free State	**220**	**220,** 380, 200	50
Italy	120, 220, 150	**150, 127,** 125, 115, 220, 110	42, 50, 45
Latvia	220, 110	**220,** 120	50
Lithuania	220, 110	**220**	50
Malta	—	105, 210	100
Monaco	—	110	42
Netherlands	220	220, 120, 127	50
Norway	220	**220, 230,** 130, 127, 110, 120, 150	50
Poland	220, 110	**220,** 120, 110	50
Portugal	220, 150, 125	**220,** 110, 125	50, 42
Rumania	**220,** 110, 105, 120	120, 220, 110, 115, 105	50, 42
Russia	220, 110, 120, 115, 250	**120,** 110, 220	50
Spain	**110,** 120, 115, 105	**120,** 125, 150, 110, 115, 220, 130	50
Sweden	220, 110, 120, 115, 250	**220,** 110, 190, 127, 125	50, 25
Switzerland	220, 120, 110, 150	120, **220,** 145, 150, 110, 120	50, 40
Turkey	110, 220	**220,** 110	50
United Kingdom	**230,** 220, 440	**230,** 220, 240, 250	50, 40, 25
Yugoslavia	110. 120	**120,** 220, 150	50, 42

Principal power supplies in foreign countries *continued*

territory	d-c volts	a-c volts	frequency
ASIA			
Arabia	—	230	50
British Malaya:			
Colony of Singapore	230	**230**	50
Malayan Federation	—	230	50, 60, 40
North Borneo	—	110	60
Ceylon	220	230	50, 60
China	220, 110	**110, 200,** 220	50, 60, 25
French Indochina	110, 120, 220, 240	**120, 220,** 110, 115, 240	50
India	220, 110, 225, 230, 250	230, 220, 110	50, 25
Iran (Persia)	220, 110	**220**	50
Iraq	**220,** 200	220, 230	50
Japan	100	**100,** 110	50, 60
Korea	—	100, 200	60
Manchuria	—	110	60, 50, 25
Netherland East Indies:			
Borneo	110	**127,** 110	50
Java and Madura	—	**127,** 110, 220	50
Sumatra	**220**	**127,** 110, 220	50
Palestine	—	220	50
Philippine Republic	—	220, 110	60
Syria	—	110, 115, 220	50
Siam	—	100	50
Turkey	220, 110	**220,** 110	50
AFRICA			
Angola (Port.)	—	110	50
Algeria	220	**115,** 110, 127	50
Belgian Congo	—	220	50
British West Africa	**220**	230	50
British East Africa	220	240, 230, 400	50
Canary Islands	110	**127,** 110	50
Egypt	200, 100	**200,** 110, 105, 110, 220	50, 40
Ethiopia (Abyssinia)	—	220, 250	50
Italian Africa:			
Cyrenaica	150	**110,** 150	50
Eritrea	—	127	50
Libya (Tripoli)	—	**125,** 110, 270	50, 42, 45
Somaliland (Somalia)	120	**230**	50
Morocco (French)	110	115, 110	50
Morocco (Spanish)	200	**127,** 110, 115	50
Madagascar	—	120, 115, 110	50
Senegal (French)	230	120	50
Tunisia	110	**110**	50
Union of South Africa (Br.)	220, 230, 240, 110	**220,** 230, 240	50
OCEANIA			
Australia:			
New South Wales	**240**	**240**	50
Victoria	230	**230**	50
Queensland	220, 240	**240**	50
South Australia	200, 230, 220	**200,** 230, 240	50
West Australia	**220,** 110, 230	250	40
Tasmania	230	**240**	50
New Zealand	230	**230**	50
Fiji Islands	240, 110, 250	**240**	50
Samoa	—	110	50
Society Islands	—	120	60

from "World Electrical Current Characteristics," issued by U. S. Department of Commerce; October, 1948.

Caution: The listings in these tables represent types of electrical supplies most generally used in particular countries. For power-supply characteristics of particular cities of foreign countries, refer to the preceding reference, which may be obtained at nominal charge by addressing the Superintendent of Documents, Government Printing Office, Washington 25, D. C.

Voltages and frequencies are listed in order of preference. Where both alternating and direct current are available, **bold** numbers indicate the type of supply and voltage predominating. Where approximately equal quantities are available, each of the principal voltages are bold.

The electrical authorities of Great Britain have adopted a plan of unifying electrical-distribution systems. The standard potential for both alternating- and direct-current supplies will be 230 volts. Systems using other voltages will be changed over. The standard frequency will be 50 cycles.

World time chart

Wellington* Auckland*	New Caledonia Solomon Islands	Brisbane, Guam Melbourne, New Guinea Sydney, Khabarovsk	Adelaide Manchukuo Chosen, Japan	Manila, Shanghai Celebes, Hong Kong	Chengtu, Kunming Chungking	Bombay, Ceylon New Delhi	Madagascar Ethiopia, Iraq	Cairo, Capetown Istanbul, Moscow, Israel	Warsaw, Stockholm Rome, Tunis, Tripoli Bengasi, Berlin, Oslo	G. C. T.	Madrid London, Paris Algiers, Lisbon	Dakar Iceland	Sao Paulo Rio de Janeiro, Santos Buenos Aires*	Santiago, Puerto Rico Lopaz, Asuncion	New York, Panama Lima, Montreal Bogota, Bermuda, Havana	Mexico, Winnipeg (except Panama) Chicago, Central America	San Francisco and Pacific Coast	Tahiti Hawaiian Islands	Tutuila, Samoa Aleutian Islands
11:30am	11:00am	10:00am	9:00am	8:00am	7:00am	5:30am	3:00am	2:00am	1:00am	0000	Midnite	11:00pm	9:00pm	8:00pm	7:00pm	6:00pm	4:00pm	2:00pm	1:00pm
12:30pm	Noon	11:00am	10:00am	9:00am	8:00am	6:30am	4:00am	3:00am	2:00am	0100	1:00am	Midnite	10:00pm	9:00pm	8:00pm	7:00pm	5:00pm	3:00pm	2:00pm
1:30pm	1:00pm	Noon	11:00am	10:00am	9:00am	7:30am	5:00am	4:00am	3:00am	0200	2:00am	1:00am	11:00pm	10:00pm	9:00pm	8:00pm	6:00pm	4:00pm	3:00pm
2:30pm	2:00pm	1:00pm	Noon	11:00am	10:00am	8:30am	6:00am	5:00am	4:00am	0300	3:00am	2:00am	Midnite	11:00pm	10:00pm	9:00pm	7:00pm	5:00pm	4:00pm
3:30pm	3:00pm	2:00pm	1:00pm	Noon	11:00am	9:30am	7:00am	6:00am	5:00am	0400	4:00am	3:00am	1:00am	Midnite	11:00pm	10:00pm	8:00pm	6:00pm	5:00pm
4:30pm	4:00pm	3:00pm	2:00pm	1:00pm	Noon	10:30am	8:00am	7:00am	6:00am	0500	5:00am	4:00am	2:00am	1:00am	Midnite	11:00pm	9:00pm	7:00pm	6:00pm
5:30pm	5:00pm	4:00pm	3:00pm	2:00pm	1:00pm	11:30am	9:00am	8:00am	7:00am	0600	6:00am	5:00am	3:00am	2:00am	1:00am	Midnite	10:00pm	8:00pm	7:00pm
6:30pm	6:00pm	5:00pm	4:00pm	3:00pm	2:00pm	12:30pm	10:00am	9:00am	8:00am	0700	7:00am	6:00am	4:00am	3:00am	2:00am	1:00am	11:00pm	9:00pm	8:00pm
7:30pm	7:00pm	6:00pm	5:00pm	4:00pm	3:00pm	1:30pm	11:00am	10:00am	9:00am	0800	8:00am	7:00am	5:00am	4:00am	3:00am	2:00am	Midnite	10:00pm	9:00pm
8:30pm	8:00pm	7:00pm	6:00pm	5:00pm	4:00pm	2:30pm	Noon	11:00am	10:00am	0900	9:00am	8:00am	6:00am	5:00am	4:00am	3:00am	1:00am	11:00pm	10:00pm
9:30pm	9:00pm	8:00pm	7:00pm	6:00pm	5:00pm	3:30pm	1:00pm	Noon	11:00am	1000	10:00am	9:00am	7:00am	6:00am	5:00am	4:00am	2:00am	Midnite	11:00pm
10:30pm	10:00pm	9:00pm	8:00pm	7:00pm	6:00pm	4:30pm	2:00pm	1:00pm	Noon	1100	11:00am	10:00am	8:00am	7:00am	6:00am	5:00am	3:00am	1:00am	Midnite
11:30pm	11:00pm	10:00pm	9:00pm	8:00pm	7:00pm	5:30pm	3:00pm	2:00pm	1:00pm	1200	Noon	11:00am	9:00am	8:00am	7:00am	6:00am	4:00am	2:00am	1:00am
12:30am	Midnite	11:00pm	10:00pm	9:00pm	8:00pm	6:30pm	4:00pm	3:00pm	2:00pm	1300	1:00pm	Noon	10:00am	9:00am	8:00am	7:00am	5:00am	3:00am	2:00am
1:30am	1:00am	Midnite	11:00pm	10:00pm	9:00pm	7:30pm	5:00pm	4:00pm	3:00pm	1400	2:00pm	1:00pm	11:00am	10:00am	9:00am	8:00am	6:00am	4:00am	3:00am
2:30am	2:00am	1:00am	Midnite	11:00pm	10:00pm	8:30pm	6:00pm	5:00pm	4:00pm	1500	3:00pm	2:00pm	Noon	11:00am	10:00am	9:00am	7:00am	5:00am	4:00am
3:30am	3:00am	2:00am	1:00am	Midnite	11:00pm	9:30pm	7:00pm	6:00pm	5:00pm	1600	4:00pm	3:00pm	1:00pm	Noon	11:00am	10:00am	8:00am	6:00am	5:00am
4:30am	4:00am	3:00am	2:00am	1:00am	Midnite	10:30pm	8:00pm	7:00pm	6:00pm	1700	5:00pm	4:00pm	2:00pm	1:00pm	Noon	11:00am	9:00am	7:00am	6:00am
5:30am	5:00am	4:00am	3:00am	2:00am	1:00am	11:30pm	9:00pm	8:00pm	7:00pm	1800	6:00pm	5:00pm	3:00pm	2:00pm	1:00pm	Noon	10:00am	8:00am	7:00am
6:30am	6:00am	5:00am	4:00am	3:00am	2:00am	12:30am	10:00pm	9:00pm	8:00pm	1900	7:00pm	6:00pm	4:00pm	3:00pm	2:00pm	1:00pm	11:00am	9:00am	8:00am
7:30am	7:00am	6:00am	5:00am	4:00am	3:00am	1:30am	11:00pm	10:00pm	9:00pm	2000	8:00pm	7:00pm	5:00pm	4:00pm	3:00pm	2:00pm	Noon	10:00am	9:00am
8:30am	8:00am	7:00am	6:00am	5:00am	4:00am	2:30am	Midnite	11:00pm	10:00pm	2100	9:00pm	8:00pm	6:00pm	5:00pm	4:00pm	3:00pm	1:00pm	11:00am	10:00am
9:30am	9:00am	8:00am	7:00am	6:00am	5:00am	3:30am	1:00am	Midnite	11:00pm	2200	10:00pm	9:00pm	7:00pm	6:00pm	5:00pm	4:00pm	2:00pm	Noon	11:00am
10:30am	10:00am	9:00am	8:00am	7:00am	6:00am	4:30am	2:00am	1:00am	Midnite	2300	11:00pm	10:00pm	8:00pm	7:00pm	6:00pm	5:00pm	3:00pm	1:00pm	Noon
11:30am	11:00am	10:00am	9:00am	8:00am	7:00am	5:30am	3:00am	2:00am	1:00am	2400	Midnite	11:00pm	9:00pm	8:00pm	7:00pm	6:00pm	4:00pm	2:00pm	1:00pm

Passing heavy line denotes change of date.

When passing the heavy line going to the right ADD one day.
When passing the heavy line going to left SUBTRACT one day.

This chart is based on STANDARD TIME.
* Permanent DAYLIGHT SAVING TIME.

Materials and finishes for tropical and marine use

Ordinary finishing of equipment fails in meeting satisfactorily conditions encountered in tropical and marine use. Under these conditions corrosive influences are greatly aggravated by prevailing higher relative humidities, and temperature cycling causes alternate condensation on, and evaporation of moisture from, finished surfaces. Useful equipment life under adverse atmospheric influences depends largely on proper choice of base materials and finishes applied. Especially important in tropical and marine applications is avoidance of electrical contact between dissimilar metals.

Dissimilar metals, widely separated in the galvanic series,* should not be bolted, riveted, etc., without separation by insulating material at the facing surfaces. The only exception occurs when both surfaces have been coated with the same protective metal, e.g., electroplating, hot dipping, galvanizing, etc.

In addition to choice of deterioration-resistant materials, consideration must be given to weight, need for a conductive surface, availability of ovens, appearance, etc.

Aluminum should always be anodized. Aluminum, steel, zinc, and cadmium should never be used bare. Electrical contact surfaces should be given copper-nickel-chromium or copper-nickel finish, and, in addition, they should be silver plated. Variable-capacitor plates should be silver plated.

All electrical circuit elements and uncoated metallic surfaces (except electrical contact surfaces) inside of cabinets should receive a coat of fungicidal moisture-repellant varnish or lacquer.

Wood parts should receive:

a. Dip coat of fungicidal water repellent sealer.
b. One coat of refinishing primer.
c. Suitable topcoat.

* The galvanic series is given on p. 32.

Finish application table†

material	finish	remarks
Aluminum alloy	Anodizing	An electrochemical-oxidation surface treatment, for improving corrosion resistance; not an electroplating process. For riveted or welded assemblies specify chromic acid anodizing. Do not anodize parts with nonaluminum inserts. Colors vary: Yellow-green, gray or black.
	"Alrok"	Chemical-dip oxide treatment. Cheap. Inferior in abrasion and corrosion resistance to the anodizing process, but applicable to assemblies of aluminum and nonaluminum materials.

† By Z. Fox. Reprinted by permission from *Product Engineering*, vol. 19, p. 161; January, 1948.

Materials and finishes for tropical and marine use *continued*

material	finish	remarks
Magnesium alloy	Dichromate treatment	Corrosion-preventive dichromate dip. Yellow color.
Stainless steel	Passivating treatment	Nitric-acid immunizing dip.
Steel	Cadmium	Electroplate, dull white color, good corrosion resistance, easily scratched, good thread anti-seize. Poor wear and galling resistance.
	Chromium	Electroplate, excellent corrosion resistance and lustrous appearance. Relatively expensive. Specify hard chrome plate for exceptionally hard abrasion-resistive surface. Has low coefficient of friction. Used to some extent on nonferrous metals particularly when die-cast. Chrome plated objects usually receive a base electroplate of copper, then nickel, followed by chromium. Used for build-up of parts that are undersized. Do not use on parts with deep recesses.
	"Blueing"	Immersion of cleaned and polished steel into heated saltpeter or carbonaceous material. Part then rubbed with linseed oil. Cheap. Poor corrosion resistance.
	Silver plate	Electroplate, frosted appearance; buff to brighten. Tarnishes readily. Good bearing lining. For electrical contacts, reflectors.
	Zinc plate	Dip in molten zinc (galvanizing) or electroplate of low-carbon or low-alloy steels. Low cost. Generally inferior to cadmium plate. Poor appearance. Poor wear resistance, electroplate has better adherence to base metal than hot-dip coating. For improving corrosion resistance, zinc-plated parts are given special inhibiting treatments.
	Nickel plate	Electroplate, dull white. Does not protect steel from galvanic corrosion. If plating is broken, corrosion of base metal will be hastened. Finishes in dull white, polished or black. Do not use on parts with deep recesses.
	Black oxide dip	Nonmetallic chemical black oxidizing treatment for steel, cast iron, and wrought iron. Inferior to electroplate. No build-up. Suitable for parts with close dimensional requirements as gears, worms and guides. Poor abrasion resistance.
	Phosphate treatment	Nonmetallic chemical treatment for steel and iron products. Suitable for protection of internal surfaces of hollow parts. Small amount of surface build-up. Inferior to metallic electroplate. Poor abrasion resistance. Good paint base.
	Tin plate	Hot dip or electroplate. Excellent corrosion resistance, but if broken will not protect steel from galvanic corrosion. Also used for copper, brass and bronze parts which must be soldered after plating. Tin-plated parts can be severely worked and deformed without rupture of plating.
	Brass plate	Electroplate of copper and zinc. Applied to brass and steel parts where uniform appearance is desired. Applied to steel parts when bonding to rubber is desired.
	Copper plate	Electroplate applied preliminary to nickel or chrome plates. Also for parts to be brazed or protected against carburization. Tarnishes readily.
Copper and zinc alloys	Bright acid dip	Immersion of parts in acid solution. Clear lacquer applied to prevent tarnish.
Brass, bronze, zinc die-casting alloys	Brass, chrome, nickel, tin	As discussed under steel.

Electric-motor data

Small-motor selection guide*

		type of motor	reference number	application data
single phase	split phase	General purpose	1	For applications up to ⅛-hp where medium starting and breakdown torques are sufficie: Low starting current minimizes light flicker, making this type suitable for frequent starti: such as on oil burners, office appliances, fans, and blowers.
		High torque	2	Designed for continuous- and intermittent-duty applications where operation is infreque and starting current in excess of NEMA values is not objectionable. Ideal for washing m chines, ironers, sump pumps, and home-workshop machines. May cause light flicker on und wired or overloaded lighting circuits.
		Two-speed (two windings)	3	Recommended for belted furnace blowers, attic ventilating fans, and similar belted mediu torque jobs. Simplicity permits operation with any 1-pole, double-throw switch or rela Starts equally well on either speed—thus can be used with thermostatic or other automa control.
	capacitor	General-purpose (capacitor-start, induction-run)	4	All-purpose motor for high starting torque, low starting current, quietness, and econom Efficiency and power factor among highest. Ideal for all heavy-duty drives, such as compr sors, pumps, stokers, refrigerators, and air conditioning.
		Two-speed (capacitor-start, two windings)	5	Similar to 2-speed split-phase motor (see No 3), and is used on identical applications requir. horsepower ratings from ⅓ to ¾ hp.
		Single-value (permanent split)	6	For direct-connected fan drives—particularly unit heaters. Not for belt drives. Adapta for 1-speed, 2-speed, or multispeed service by use of 1-pole, single-throw switch, 2-p double-throw switch, or speed controller, respectively. Fan load must be accurately match to motor output for proper speed control.
	shaded pole	Shaded pole	7	Inclosed for fan duty in subfractional horsepower range—cooled by air flow over mot Driven fan load should be accurately matched with motor output to get proper speed contr
polyphase	1-, 2-, 3-phase synchronous	Split-phase	8	Definitely constant speed. Principal applications are on instruments, sound recording a reproducing apparatus, teleprinters, and fascimile printers. Type selected depends large on starting torque. No 10 is recommended where low wattage input is desirable and low sta ing current is sufficient. Nos 8 or 9 are recommended where higher starting torque is neede Pull-in torque on all types is affected by inertia of connected load.
		Capacitor-start	9	
		Single-value capacitor	10	
		Polyphase	11	
	2 or 3 phase	Squirrel cage	12	For all applications where polyphase circuits are available. Extra high starting torque shou be specified for such applications as hoists, door operators, tool traverse, and clamp moto
direct current		Shunt wound and compound wound	13	Companion d-c motor to single-phase and polyphase a-c motors. For all applications operat from d-c circuits.
		Series wound	14	Companion motor to No 7 shaded pole for use on direct-current and 25-to-40-cycle alterna current circuits. Meets same application requirements.
universal (alternating or direct current)		Noncompensated (salient-pole winding)	15	Operates on either a-c or d-c circuits. Inherently small size and light weight for given hors power output. Fundamentally a high-speed and varying-speed motor. Inherent speed cha acteristics, high starting torque and light weight, make motors especially suitable for su applications as sewing machines, portable tools, vacuum cleaners, and motion-picture pr jectors. When higher power at lower speeds is required (large vacuum cleaners and larg portable tools), No 16 is recommended.
		Compensated (distributed winding)	16	
		Governor controlled	17	Governor-controlled type permits utilizing the light-weight high-speed universal motor f constant-speed applications. Two types of governors. One permits adjustment while runnin and is used for such applications as electric typewriters and motion-picture projectors ar cameras. The other is adjustable at standstill only, and is used for adding machines, calc lating machines, and other constant-speed office machines.

* Reprinted by permission from *American Machinist*, vol. 87, pp. 115–116; December 9, 1943.
This guide is general and does not include the motor field in its entirety.
See following page for wiring data on the above types.

hp range	speed data			approximate torque (4 poles)		built-in starting mechanism	reversibility		radio interference	approximate comparative price in percent
	rated speed	speed characteristics	speed control	starting*	breakdown†		at rest	in motion		
'20	3450 1725 1140 860	Constant	None	Medium	Medium	Centrifugal switch	Yes—change connections	No—except with special design and relay	None	85
	1725	Constant	None	High	High	Centrifugal switch	Yes—change connections	No—except with special design and relay	None	60
	1725/1140 1725/860	Two-speed	1-pole double-throw switch	Medium	Medium	Centrifugal switch	Yes—change connections	No	None	165
	3450 1725 1140 860	Constant	None	Extra high	High to extra high	Centrifugal switch	Yes—change connections	No—except with special design and relay	None	100
	1725/1140 1725/860	Two-speed	1-pole double-throw switch	Medium	Medium	Centrifugal switch	Yes—change connections	No	None	200
'20	1620 1080 820	Constant or adjustable varying	Two-speed switch or auto-transformer	Low	Medium	None	Yes—change connections	No	None	125
/300 /30	1500 1000	Constant or adjustable varying	Choke coil	Low	Low	None	No	No	None	—
/250	3600 1800 1200 900	Absolutely constant	None	Low	Medium	Centrifugal switch	See No 1	See No 1	None	325
				Medium	Medium	Centrifugal switch	See No 4	See No 4		
				Very low	Medium	None	See No 6	See No 6		
				Medium	Medium	None	See No 12	See No 12		
	3450 1725 1140 860	Constant	None	High	Extra high	None	Yes—change connections	Yes—change connections	None	140
/20	3450 1725 1140 860	Constant or adjustable varying	Armature resistance	Extra high	—	None	Yes—change connections	No—except with special design	Yes	185
/125 /30	900 to 2000	Varying or adjustable varying	Resistance	Extra high	—	None	Yes—change connections	No—except with special design	Yes	—
/150	1500 to 15000	Varying		Extra high	—	None	No—except with special design	No—except with special design	Yes	—
/40 ntegral p)	2500 to 15000	Varying	Voltage control using resistance or transformer	Extra high	—	None	No—except with special design	No—except with special design	Yes	—
/50 /20 ½ ntegral p)	2000 to 6000	Adjustable constant	Adjustable governor	Extra high	—	None	No—except with special design	No—except with special design	Yes	—

Starting torque in percent of full-load torque is
Low— <100; medium—100–200; high—200–300; extra high—>300.
Breakdown torque in percent of full-load torque is
Low— <150; medium—150–225; high—225–300; extra high—>300.

Electric-motor data   *continued*

Wiring diagrams for small motors*

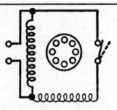

No. 1—Alternating-current general purpose
No. 2—Alternating-current high torque
No. 8—Synchronous split-phase

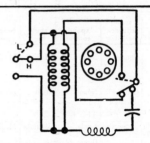

No. 5—Alternating-current capacitor, two-speed

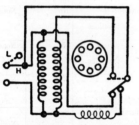

No. 3—Alternating-current two-speed

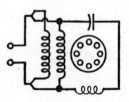

No. 6—Alternating-current capacitor, single-value
No. 10 — Synchronous, single-value capacitor

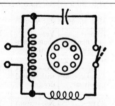

No. 4—Alternating-current capacitor, general purpose
No. 9—Synchronous, capacitor-start

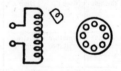

No. 7—Shaded pole

 squirrel-cage rotor   main winding   auxiliary winding   line terminals   centrifugal starting switches

* Reprinted by permission from *American Machinist*, vol. 87, p. 115; December 9, 1943.

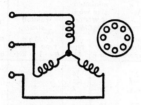

No. 11—Synchronous polyphase
No. 12—Polyphase squirrel-cage

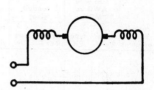

No. 15—Universal noncompensated

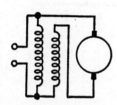

No. 13—Direct-current shunt and
compound wound

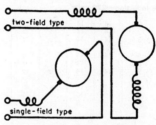

two-field type

single-field type

No. 16—Universal compensated

No. 14—Direct-current series wound

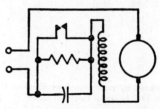

No. 17 — Universal governor-con-
trolled

capacitor

wound rotor
with commutator

3-phase primary

resistor

governor
contacts

Electric-motor data *continued*

Wiring and fusing data*

single phase—115 volts | **single phase—230 volts**

hp of motor	current rating amperes	minimum size wire AWG or MCM		conduit size†		maximum running fuse amperes	current rating amperes	minimum size wire AWG or MCM		conduit size†		maximum running fuse amperes
		type R or T	type RH	type R or T	type RH			type R or T	type RH	type R or T	type RH	
½	7.4	14	14	½	½	10	3.7	14	14	½	½	6
¾	10.2	14	14	½	½	15	5.1	14	14	½	½	8
1	13	12	12	½	½	20	6.5	14	14	½	½	10
1½	18.4	10	10	¾	¾	25	9.2	14	14	½	½	12
2	24	10	10	¾	¾	30	12	14	14	½	½	15
3	34	6	8	1	¾	45	17	10	10	¾	¾	25
5	56	4	4	1¼	1¼	70	28	8	8	¾	¾	35
7½	80	1	3	1½	1¼	100	40	6	6	1	1	50
10	100	1/0	1	1½	1½	125	50	4	6	1¼	1	60

3-phase induction—220 volts | **3-phase induction—440 volts**

hp of motor	current rating amperes	type R or T	type RH	type R or T	type RH	fuse amperes	current rating amperes	type R or T	type RH	type R or T	type RH	fuse amperes
½	2	14	14	½	½	3	1	14	14	½	½	2
¾	2.8	14	14	½	½	4	1.4	14	14	½	½	2
1	3.5	14	14	½	½	4	1.8	14	14	½	½	3
1½	5	14	14	½	½	8	2.5	14	14	½	½	4
2	6.5	14	14	½	½	8	3.3	14	14	½	½	4
3	9	14	14	½	½	12	4.5	14	14	½	½	6
5	15	12	12	½	½	20	7.5	14	14	½	½	10
7½	22	10	10	¾	¾	30	11	14	14	½	½	15
10	27	8	8	¾	¾	35	14	12	12	½	½	20

direct current—115 volts | **direct current—230 volts**

hp of motor	current rating amperes	type R or T	type RH	type R or T	type RH	fuse amperes	current rating amperes	type R or T	type RH	type R or T	type RH	fuse amperes
½	4.6	14	14	½	½	6	2.3	14	14	½	½	3
¾	6.6	14	14	½	½	10	3.3	14	14	½	½	4
1	8.6	14	14	½	½	12	4.3	14	14	½	½	6
1½	12.6	12	12	½	½	15	6.3	14	14	½	½	8
2	16.4	10	10	¾	¾	20	8.2	14	14	½	½	12
3	24	10	10	¾	¾	30	12	14	14	½	½	15
5	40	6	6	1	1	50	20	10	10	¾	¾	25
7½	58	3	4	1¼	1¼	70	29	8	8	¾	¾	40
10	76	2	3	1¼	1¼	100	38	6	6	1	1	50

* Reprinted by permission from General Electric Supply Corp. Catalogue; 94WP. Adapted from 1947 National Electrical Code.

† Conduit size based on three conductors in one conduit for 3-phase alternating-current motors, and on two conductors in one conduit for direct-current and single-phase motors.

Torque and horsepower

Torque varies directly with power and inversely with rotating speed of the shaft, or

$$T = KP/N$$

where T = torque in inch-pounds, P = horsepower, N = revolutions/minute, and K (constant) = 63,000.

Electric-motor data   *continued*

Example 1: For a two-horsepower motor rotating at 1800 rpm,

$$T = \frac{63{,}000 \times 2}{1800} = 70 \text{ inch-pounds}$$

If the shaft is 1 inch in diameter, the force at its periphery

$$F = \frac{T}{\text{radius}} = \frac{70 \text{ inch-pounds}}{0.5} = 140 \text{ pounds}$$

Example 2: If 150 inch-pounds torque are required at 1200 rpm,

$$150 = \frac{63{,}000 \times \text{hp}}{1200} \qquad \text{horsepower} = \frac{150 \times 1200}{63{,}000} = 2.86$$

Transmission-line sag calculations*

For transmission-line work, with towers on the same or slightly different levels, the cables are assumed to take the form of a parabola, instead of their actual form of a catenary. The error is negligible and the computations are much simplified. In calculating sags, the changes in cables due to variations in loads and temperature must be considered.

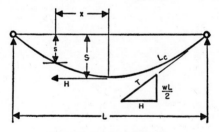

supports at same elevation

For supports at same level: The formulas used in the calculations of sags are

$$H = WL^2/8S$$

$$S = WL^2/8H = \sqrt{(L_c - L)\,3L/8}$$

$$L_c = L + 8S^2/3L$$

---

* Reprinted by permission from "Transmission Towers," American Bridge Company, Pittsburgh, Pa.; 1923: p. 70.

Transmission-line sag calculations   *continued*

where

L = length of span in feet
L_c = length of cable in feet
S = sag of cable at center of span in feet
H = tension in cable at center of span in pounds
    = horizontal component af the tension at any point
W = weight of cable in pounds per lineal foot

Where cables are subject to wind and ice loads, W = the algebraic sum of the loads. That is, for ice on cables, W = weight of cables plus weight of ice; and for wind on bare or ice-covered cables, W = the square root of the sum of the squares of the vertical and horizontal loads.

For any intermediate point at a distance x from the center of the span, the sag is

$$S_x = S(1 - 4x^2/L^2)$$

For supports at different levels

$$S = S_0 = \frac{WL_0^2 \cos a}{8T} = \frac{WL^2}{8T \cos a}$$

$$S_1 = \frac{WL_1^2}{8H}$$

$$S_2 = \frac{WL_2^2}{8H}$$

$$\frac{L_1}{2} = \frac{L}{2} - \frac{hH \cos a}{WL}$$

$$\frac{L_2}{2} = \frac{L}{2} + \frac{hH \cos a}{WL}$$

$$L_c = L + \frac{4}{3}\left(\frac{S_1^2}{L_1} + \frac{S_2^2}{L_2}\right)$$

where

W = weight of cables in pounds per lineal foot between supports or in direction of L_0
T = tension in cable direction parallel with line between supports

Transmission-line sag calculations   *continued*

The change l in length of cable L_c for varying temperature is found by multiplying the number of degrees n by the length of the cable in feet times the coefficient of linear expansion per foot per degree fahrenheit c. This is*

$$l = L_c \times n \times c$$

A short approximate method for determining sags under varying temperatures and loadings that is close enough for all ordinary line work is as follows:

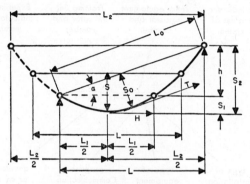

supports at different elevations

a. Determine sag of cable with maximum stress under maximum load at lowest temperature occurring at the time of maximum load, and find length of cable with this sag.

b. Find length of cable at the temperature for which the sag is required.

c. Assume a certain reduced tension in the cable at the temperature and under the loading combination for which the sag is required; then find the decrease in length of the cable due to the decrease of the stress from its maximum.

d. Combine the algebraic sum of (b) and (c) with (a) to get the length of the cable under the desired conditions, and from this length the sag and tension can be determined.

e. If this tension agrees with that assumed in (c), the sag in (d) is correct. If it does not agree, another assumption of tension in (c) must be made and the process repeated until (c) and (d) agree.

* Temperature coefficient of linear expansion is given on pp. 44–45.

Summary of Joint Army-Navy nomenclature system

The Joint Army-Navy or AN nomenclature system has been introduced to eliminate confusing and conflicting designations formerly used by the armed services, and to provide a nomenclature that in itself gives a brief description of the article designated. In the AN system, nomenclature consists of a name followed by a type number. The name will be terminology of standard engineering usage, e.g., Radio Receiver, Switchboard, etc. The type number will consist of indicator letters shown below, and an assigned number. Additional symbols are added as required. An example is

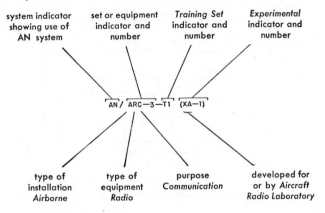

Nomenclature policy

AN nomenclature will be assigned to:

a. Complete sets of equipment and major components of military design.

b. Groups of articles of either commercial or military design that are grouped for a military purpose.

c. Major articles of military design that are not part of or used with a set.

d. Commercial articles when nomenclature will facilitate military identification and/or procedures.

AN nomenclature will not be assigned to:

a. Articles cataloged commercially except in accordance with paragraph (d) above.

b. Minor components of military design for which other adequate means of identification are available.

c. Small parts such as capacitors and resistors.

d. Articles having other adequate identification in American War Standard or Joint Army-Navy Specifications.

Nomenclature assignments will remain unchanged regardless of later changes in installation and/or application.

Summary of Joint Army-Navy nomenclature system   *continued*

Set or equipment indicator letters

type of installation	type of equipment	purpose
A Airborne	A Invisible light, heat radiation	A Auxiliary assemblies (not complete operating sets)
B Underwater mobile, submarine	B Pigeon	B Bombing
C Air transportable (inactivated, do not use)	C Carrier (wire)	C Communications
D Pilotless carrier		D Direction finder
F Ground, fixed	F Photographic	
G Ground, general ground use (includes two or more ground installations)	G Telegraph or teletype (wire)	G Gun directing
		H Recording (photographic, meteorological, and sound)
	I Interphone and public address	
K Amphibious	K Telemetering	
		L Searchlight control
M Ground, mobile in a vehicle which has no function other than transporting the equipment	M Meteorological	M Maintenance and test assemblies
	N Sound in air	N Navigational aids
P Ground, pack, or portable	P Radar	P Reproducing (photographic and sound)
	Q Underwater sound	Q Special, or combination of types
	R Radio	R Receiving
S Shipboard	S Special types, magnetic, etc., or combinations of types	S Search
T Ground, transportable	T Telephone (wire)	T Transmitting
U General utility (includes two or more general classes)		
V Ground, vehicular, installed in vehicle designed for other functions, i. e., tanks	V Visual and visible light	
W Underwater, fixed		W Remote control
	X Facsimile or television	X Identification and recognition

Summary of Joint Army-Navy nomenclature system continued

Table of component indicators

indicator	family name	indicator	family name
AB	Supports, Antenna	MX	Miscellaneous
AM	Amplifiers	O	Oscillators
AS	Antenna Assemblies	OA	Operating Assemblies
AT	Antennas	OS	Oscilloscope, Test
BA	Battery, primary type	PD	Prime Drivers
BB	Battery, secondary type	PF	Fittings, Pole
BZ	Signal Devices, Audible	PH	Photographic Articles
C	Control Articles	PP	Power Supplies
CA	Commutator Assemblies, Sonar	PT	Plotting Equipments
CB	Capacitor Bank	PU	Power Equipments
CG	Cables and Trans. line, R.F.	R	Radio and Radar Receivers
CK	Crystal Kits	RD	Recorders and Reproducers
CM	Comparators	RE	Relay Assemblies
CN	Compensators	RF	Radio Frequency Component
CP	Computers	RG	Cables and Trans. Line, Bulk R.F.
CR	Crystals	RL	Reel Assemblies
CU	Coupling Devices	RP	Rope and Twine
CV	Converters (electronic)	RR	Reflectors
CW	Covers	RT	Receiver and Transmitter
CX	Cords	S	Shelters
CY	Cases	SA	Switching Devices
DA	Antenna, Dummy	SB	Switchboards
DT	Detecting Heads	SG	Generators, Signal
DY	Dynamotors	SM	Simulators
E	Hoist Assembly	SN	Synchronizers
F	Filters	ST	Straps
FN	Furniture	T	Radio and Radar Transmitters
FR	Frequency Measuring Devices	TA	Telephone Apparatus
G	Generators	TD	Timing Devices
GO	Goniometers	TF	Transformers
GP	Ground Rods	TG	Positioning Devices
H	Head, Hand, and Chest Sets	TH	Telegraph Apparatus
HC	Crystal Holder	TK	Tool Kits or Equipments
HD	Air Conditioning Apparatus	TL	Tools
ID	Indicating Devices	TN	Tuning Units
IL	Insulators	TS	Test Equipment
IM	Intensity Measuring Devices	TT	Teletype and Facsimile Apparatus
IP	Indicators, Cathode-Ray Tube	TV	Tester, Tube
J	Junction Devices	U	Connectors, Audio and Power
KY	Keying Devices	UG	Connectors, R.F.
LC	Tools, Line Construction	V	Vehicles
LS	Loudspeakers	VS	Signaling Equipment, Visual
M	Microphones	WD	Cables, Two-Conductor
MD	Modulators	WF	Cables, Four-Conductor
ME	Meters, Portable	WM	Cables, Multiple-Conductor
MK	Maintenance Kits or Equipments	WS	Cables, Single-Conductor
ML	Meteorological Devices	WT	Cables, Three-Conductor
MT	Mountings	ZM	Impedance Measuring Devices

Summary of Joint Army-Navy nomenclature system   *continued*

Experimental indicators

In order to identify a set or equipment of an experimental nature with the development organization concerned, the following indicators will be used within the parentheses:

XA Aircraft Radio Laboratory, Wright Field, Dayton, Ohio

XB Naval Research Laboratory, Anacostia Station, Belleville, D. C.

XC Coles Signal Laboratory, Red Bank, New Jersey

XE Evans Signal Laboratory, Belmar, New Jersey

XG USN Electronic Laboratory, San Diego, California

XM Squier Signal Laboratory, Fort Monmouth, New Jersey

XN Navy Department, Washington, D. C.

XU USN Underwater Sound Laboratory, Fort Trumbull, New London, Connecticut

XW Watson Laboratories, Red Bank, New Jersey

Examples of AN type numbers

AN/ARC–3 ( ) General reference for the third airborne radio set for communication to be assigned AN nomenclature, not necessarily used by both Army and Navy.

AN/ARC–3(XA–2) Second experimental type developed for Aircraft Radio Laboratories

AN/ARC–3 Original procurement type.

AN/ARC–3C Third modification, functionally interchangeable, not in detail. Same frequency range.

AN/ARC–3Z X, Y, Z used to indicate change in power source; may be voltage, phase, or frequency.

AN/ARC–3–T1 ( ) General reference for training set for AN/ARC–3 ( ).

AN/ARC–T1 First general airborne radio training set.

T–22/ARC–3 Original procurement type of transmitter No. 22, part of, or used with, AN/ARC–3.

T–22A/ARC–3 Interchangeable with above, physically, electrically, and mechanically; as a whole, not parts.

RG–8/U Bulk radio-frequency cable for general use on several types of equipment for several purposes.

■ **Maxwell's equations**

General*

The following four basic laws of electromagnetism for bodies at rest are derived from the fundamental, experimental, and theoretical work of Ampére and Faraday, and are valid for quantities determined by their average values in volumes that contain a very great number of molecules (macroscopic electromagnetism).

Statement of four basic laws   *rationalized mks units*

a. The work required to carry a unit magnetic pole around a closed path is equal to the total current linking that path, that is, the total current passing through any surface that has the path for its periphery. This total current is the sum of the conduction current and the displacement current, the latter being equal to the derivative with respect to time of the electric induction flux passing through any surface that has the above closed path for its periphery.

b. The electromotive force (e.m.f.) induced in any fixed closed loop is equal to minus the time rate of change of the magnetic induction flux ϕ_B through that loop. By electromotive force is meant the work required to carry a unit positive charge around the loop.

c. The total flux of electric induction diverging from a charge Q is equal to Q in magnitude.

d. Magnetic-flux lines are continuous (closed) loops. There are no sources or sinks of magnetic flux.

Expression of basic laws in integral form

a. $\int_0 \mathbf{H} \cdot \mathbf{ds} = I_{\text{total}} = I_{\text{conduction}} + \dfrac{\partial \phi_D}{\partial t}$

where

$\int_0$ = a line integral around a closed path

$\mathbf{ds}$ = vector element of length along path

$\mathbf{H}$ = vector magnetic field intensity

ϕ_D = electric induction flux

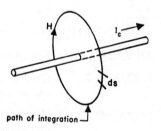

path of integration

---

* Developed from: J. E. Hill, "Maxwell's Four Basic Equations," *Westinghouse Engineer*, vol. 6, p. 135; September, 1946.

Expression of basic laws in integral form   *continued*

b. $\displaystyle\int_0 \mathbf{E}\cdot\mathbf{ds} = -\frac{\partial \phi_B}{\partial t}.$

The time rate of change of ϕ_B is written as a partial derivative to indicate that the loop does not move (the coordinates of each point of the loop remain fixed during integration). **E** is the vector electric-field intensity.

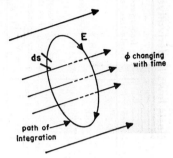

c. $\displaystyle\int_s \mathbf{D}\cdot\mathbf{dS} = Q$

where

S = any closed surface
$\mathbf{dS}$ = vector element of S
$\mathbf{D}$ = vector electric-flux density
Q = the net electric charge within S

and the integral indicates that $\mathbf{D}\cdot\mathbf{dS}$ is to be calculated for each element of S and summed.

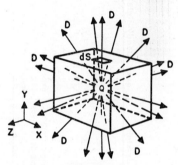

S = total surface
Q = total charge inside S

d. $\displaystyle\int_s \mathbf{B}\cdot\mathbf{dS} = 0$

where

$\mathbf{B}$ = vector magnetic-flux density.

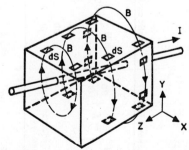

B lines are closed curves; as many enter region as leave it.

Basic laws in derivative form

	general form	static case	steady-state	quasi-steady-state	free-space	free-space single-frequency
a	$\left.\begin{array}{l}\text{curl }\mathbf{H}\\ \nabla\times\mathbf{H}\end{array}\right\} = j_c + \dfrac{\partial \mathbf{D}}{\partial t}$ j_c = conduction current density	$\left.\begin{array}{l}\text{curl }\mathbf{H}\\ \nabla\times\mathbf{H}\end{array}\right\} = 0$ $j_c = 0$ $\dfrac{\partial \mathbf{D}}{\partial t} = 0$	$\left.\begin{array}{l}\text{curl }\mathbf{H}\\ \nabla\times\mathbf{H}\end{array}\right\} = j_c$ Conducting current exists but time derivatives are zero	$\left.\begin{array}{l}\text{curl }\mathbf{H}\\ \nabla\times\mathbf{H}\end{array}\right\} \approx j_c$ $\partial \mathbf{D}/\partial t$ can be neglected except in capacitors (a c at industrial power frequencies)	$\left.\begin{array}{l}\text{curl }\mathbf{H}\\ \nabla\times\mathbf{H}\end{array}\right\} = \dfrac{\partial \mathbf{D}}{\partial t}$ $= \epsilon_0 \dfrac{\partial \mathbf{E}}{\partial t}$ $j_c = 0$ and ϵ_0 is the dielectric constant of free space	$\left.\begin{array}{l}\text{curl }\mathbf{H}\\ \nabla\times\mathbf{H}\end{array}\right\} = j\omega\epsilon_0\mathbf{E}$ $\omega = 2\pi f$ = angular frequency, f = the frequency considered, and $j = \sqrt{-1}$
b	$\left.\begin{array}{l}\text{curl }\mathbf{E}\\ \nabla\times\mathbf{E}\end{array}\right\} = -\dfrac{\partial \mathbf{B}}{\partial t}$	$\left.\begin{array}{l}\text{curl }\mathbf{E}\\ \nabla\times\mathbf{E}\end{array}\right\} = 0$	$\left.\begin{array}{l}\text{curl }\mathbf{E}\\ \nabla\times\mathbf{E}\end{array}\right\} = 0$	$\left.\begin{array}{l}\text{curl }\mathbf{E}\\ \nabla\times\mathbf{E}\end{array}\right\} = -\dfrac{\partial \mathbf{B}}{\partial t}$	$\left.\begin{array}{l}\text{curl }\mathbf{E}\\ \nabla\times\mathbf{E}\end{array}\right\} = -\dfrac{\partial \mathbf{B}}{\partial t}$ $= -\mu_0 \dfrac{\partial \mathbf{H}}{\partial t}$ μ_0 = magnetic permeability of free space	$\left.\begin{array}{l}\text{curl }\mathbf{E}\\ \nabla\times\mathbf{E}\end{array}\right\} = -j\omega\mu_0\mathbf{H}$
c	$\left.\begin{array}{l}\text{div }\mathbf{D}\\ \nabla\cdot\mathbf{D}\end{array}\right\} = \rho$ ρ = charge density = charge per unit volume	$\left.\begin{array}{l}\text{div }\mathbf{D}\\ \nabla\cdot\mathbf{D}\end{array}\right\} = \rho$	$\left.\begin{array}{l}\text{div }\mathbf{D}\\ \nabla\cdot\mathbf{D}\end{array}\right\} = \rho$	$\left.\begin{array}{l}\text{div }\mathbf{D}\\ \nabla\cdot\mathbf{D}\end{array}\right\} = \rho$	$\left.\begin{array}{l}\text{div }\mathbf{E}\\ \nabla\cdot\mathbf{E}\end{array}\right\} = 0$	$\left.\begin{array}{l}\text{div }\mathbf{E}\\ \nabla\cdot\mathbf{E}\end{array}\right\} = 0$
d	$\left.\begin{array}{l}\text{div }\mathbf{B}\\ \nabla\cdot\mathbf{B}\end{array}\right\} = 0$	$\left.\begin{array}{l}\text{div }\mathbf{B}\\ \nabla\cdot\mathbf{B}\end{array}\right\} = 0$	$\left.\begin{array}{l}\text{div }\mathbf{B}\\ \nabla\cdot\mathbf{B}\end{array}\right\} = 0$	$\left.\begin{array}{l}\text{div }\mathbf{B}\\ \nabla\cdot\mathbf{B}\end{array}\right\} = 0$	$\left.\begin{array}{l}\text{div }\mathbf{H}\\ \nabla\cdot\mathbf{H}\end{array}\right\} = 0$	$\left.\begin{array}{l}\text{div }\mathbf{H}\\ \nabla\cdot\mathbf{H}\end{array}\right\} = 0$

Basic laws in derivative form   *continued*

Notes:

For an explanation of the operator ∇ (del) and the associated vector operations see p. 616 in the "Mathematical formulas" chapter.

$$\epsilon_0 = \frac{1}{36\pi \times 10^9} \text{ farad/meter}$$
$$\mu_0 = 4\pi \times 10^{-7} \text{ henry/meter}$$
in the rationalized meter-kilogram-second system of units.

Maxwell's equations obey the law of conservation of electric charges, the integral form of which is

$$I = -\partial Q_i/\partial t$$

Q_i = net sum of all electric charges within a closed surface S

I = outgoing conduction current

and the derivative form

$$\text{div } j_c = -\partial \rho/\partial t$$

Boundary conditions at the surface of separation between two media 1 and 2 are

$$\mathbf{H}_{2T} - \mathbf{H}_{1T} = j_s \times \mathbf{N}^\circ_{1,2} \qquad \mathbf{B}_{2N} - \mathbf{B}_{1N} = 0$$
$$\mathbf{E}_{2T} - \mathbf{E}_{1T} = 0 \qquad \mathbf{D}_{2N} - \mathbf{D}_{1N} = \sigma$$

Subscript T denotes a tangential, and subscript N a normal component.

$\mathbf{N}^\circ_{1,2}$ = unit normal vector from medium 1 to medium 2, which is the positive direction for normal vectors

j_s = convection current density on the surface, if any

σ = density of electric charge on the surface of separation

Retarded potentials   *H. A. Lorentz*

Consider an electromagnetic system in free space in which the distribution of electric charges and currents is assumed to be known. From the four basic equations in derivative form:

$$\text{curl } \mathbf{H} = j_c + \epsilon_0 \frac{\partial \mathbf{E}}{\partial t} \qquad \text{curl } \mathbf{E} = -\mu_0 \frac{\partial \mathbf{H}}{\partial t}$$

$$\text{div } \mathbf{H} = 0 \qquad \text{div } \mathbf{E} = \frac{\rho}{\epsilon_0}$$

Retarded potentials   *continued*

two retarded potentials can be determined:

one scalar, $\phi = \dfrac{1}{4\pi\epsilon_0} \displaystyle\int_\infty \dfrac{\rho^* dV}{r}$ one vector, $\mathbf{A} = \dfrac{1}{4\pi} \displaystyle\int_\infty \dfrac{j_c^*}{r}\, dV$

The asterisks mean that the values of the quantities are taken at time $t - r/c$, where r is the distance from the location of the charge or current to the point P considered, and c = velocity of propagation = velocity of light $= 1/\sqrt{\epsilon_0\mu_0}$.

The electric and magnetic fields at point P are expressed by

$$\mathbf{H} = \text{curl } \mathbf{A} \qquad\qquad \mathbf{E} = -\text{grad } \phi - \mu_0 \frac{\partial \mathbf{A}}{\partial t}$$

Fields in terms of one vector only   *Hertz vector*

The previous expressions imply a relation between ϕ and $\mathbf{A}$

$$\text{div } \mathbf{A} = -\epsilon_0 \frac{\partial \phi}{\partial t}$$

Consider a vector Π such that $\mathbf{A} = \partial\Pi/\partial t$. Then for all variable fields

$$\phi = -\frac{1}{\epsilon_0} \text{div } \Pi$$

The electric and magnetic fields can thus be expressed in terms of the vector Π only

$$\mathbf{H} = \text{curl } \frac{\partial \Pi}{\partial t}$$

$$\mathbf{E} = \frac{1}{\epsilon_0} \text{grad div } \Pi - \mu_0 \frac{\partial^2 \Pi}{\partial t^2}$$

Poynting vector

Consider any volume V of the previous electromagnetic system enclosed in a surface S. It can be shown that

$$-\int_V \mathbf{E}\cdot j_c\, dV = \frac{\partial}{\partial t} \int_V \left(\frac{\epsilon_0 E^2}{2} + \frac{\mu_0 H^2}{2} \right) dV + \text{flux}_S\, \mathbf{E} \times \mathbf{H}$$

The rate of change with time of the electromagnetic energy inside V is equal to the rate of change of the amount of energy localized inside V

Poynting vector   *continued*

plus the flux of the vector $\mathbf{E} \times \mathbf{H}$ through the surface S enclosing said volume V. The vector product $\mathbf{E} \times \mathbf{H}$ is called the Poynting vector.

In the particular case of single-frequency phenomena, a complex Poynting vector $\mathbf{E} \times \mathbf{H}^*$ is often utilized ($\mathbf{H}^*$ is the complex conjugate of $\mathbf{H}$). It can be shown that

$$-\int_V \frac{\mathbf{E} \cdot j_c^*}{2} \, dV = 2j\omega \int_V \left(\mu_0 \frac{HH^*}{4} - \epsilon_0 \frac{EE^*}{4} \right) dV + \text{flux}_S \, \frac{\mathbf{E} \times \mathbf{H}^*}{2}$$

This shows that in case there is no conduction current inside V and the flux of the complex Poynting vector out of V is zero, then the mean value per period of the electric and magnetic energies inside V are equal.

Superposition theorem

The mathematical form of the four basic laws (linear differential equations with constant coefficients) shows that if two distributions $\mathbf{E}, \mathbf{H}, j_c, \rho$, and $\mathbf{E}', \mathbf{H}', j_c', \rho'$, satisfy Maxwell's equations, they are also satisfied by any linear combination $\mathbf{E} + \lambda\mathbf{E}'$, $\mathbf{H} + \lambda\mathbf{H}'$, $j_c + \lambda j_c'$, and $\rho + \lambda\rho'$.

Reciprocity theorem

Let j_c be the conduction current resulting in any electromagnetic system from the action of an external electric field $\mathbf{E}_a$, and j_c' and $\mathbf{E}_a'$ be the corresponding quantities for another possible state; then

$$\int_\infty (\mathbf{E}_a \cdot j_c' - \mathbf{E}_a' \cdot j_c) \, dV = 0$$

This is the most useful way of expressing the general reciprocity theorem (Carson). It is valid provided all quantities vary simultaneously according to a linear law (excluding ferromagnetic substances, electronic space charge, and ionized-gas phenomena). A particular application of this general reciprocity theorem will be found on p. 89.

Maxwell's equations in different systems of coordinates

When a particular system of coordinates is advantageously used, such as cylindrical, spherical, etc., the components are derived from the vector equations by means of the formulas included in the chapter "Mathematical formulas," pages 618 and 619.

■ Mathematical formulas

Mensuration formulas

Areas of plane figures

figure	formula
Parallelogram 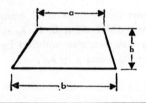	Area $= bh$
Trapezoid 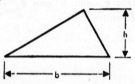	Area $= \frac{1}{2}h(a+b)$
Triangle 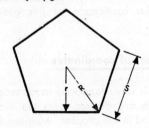	Area $= \frac{1}{2}bh$
Regular polygon	Area $= nr^2 \tan \dfrac{180°}{n}$ $= \dfrac{n}{4} S^2 \cot \dfrac{180°}{n}$ $= \dfrac{n}{2} R^2 \sin \dfrac{360°}{n}$ $n =$ number of sides $r =$ short radius $S =$ length of one side $R =$ long radius

Mensuration formulas *continued*

figure	formula
Circle 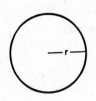	$\text{Area} = \pi r^2$ $r = \text{radius}$ $\pi = 3.141593$
Segment of circle 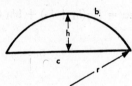	$\text{Area} = \frac{1}{2}[br - c(r-h)]$ $b = \text{length of arc}$ $c = \text{length of chord}$ $\quad = \sqrt{4(2hr - h^2)}$
Sector of circle 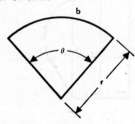	$\text{Area} = \dfrac{br}{2} = \pi r^2\,\dfrac{\theta}{360°}$
Parabola 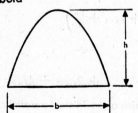	$\text{Area} = \frac{2}{3}bh$

Mensuration formulas *continued*

figure	formula
Ellipse	

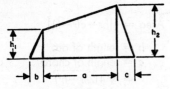

$$\text{Area} = \pi ab$$

Trapezium	

$$\text{Area} = \tfrac{1}{2}[a(h_1 + h_2) + bh_1 + ch_2]$$

Area of irregular plane surface

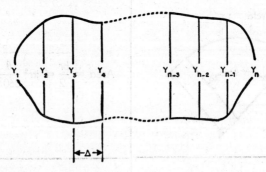

Trapezoidal rule

$$\text{Area} = \Delta\left(\frac{y_1}{2} + y_2 + y_3 + \ldots + y_{n-2} + y_{n-1} + \frac{y_n}{2}\right)$$

Simpson's rule: n must be odd

$$\text{Area} = \frac{\Delta}{3}(y_1 + 4y_2 + 2y_3 + 4y_4 + 2y_5 + \ldots + 2y_{n-2} + 4y_{n-1} + y_n)$$

$y_1, y_2, y_3 \ldots y_n$ = measured lengths of a series of equidistant parallel chords

Mensuration formulas *continued*

Surface areas and volumes of solid figures

figure	formula

Sphere

$$\text{Surface} = 4\pi r^2 = 12.5664\, r^2 = \pi d^2$$

$$\text{Volume} = \frac{4\pi r^3}{3} = 4.1888\, r^3$$

Sector of sphere

$$\text{Total surface} = \frac{\pi r}{2}\,(4h + c)$$

$$\text{Volume} = \frac{2\pi r^2 h}{3} = 2.0944\, r^2 h$$

$$= \frac{2\pi r^2}{3}\left(r - \sqrt{r^2 - \frac{c^2}{4}} \right)$$

$$c = \sqrt{4\,(2hr - h^2)}$$

Segment of sphere

$$\text{Spherical surface} = 2\pi rh = \frac{\pi}{4}\,(c^2 + 4h^2)$$

$$\text{Volume} = \pi h^2 \left(r - \frac{h}{3} \right)$$

$$= \pi h^2 \left(\frac{c^2 + 4h^2}{8h} - \frac{h}{3} \right)$$

Cylinder

$$\text{Cylindrical surface} = \pi dh = 3.1416\, dh$$

$$\text{Total surface} = 2\pi r(r + h)$$

$$\text{Volume} = \pi r^2 h = 0.7854\, d^2 h$$

$$= \frac{c^2 h}{4\pi} = 0.0796\, c^2 h$$

$$c = \text{circumference}$$

580

figure	formula
Torus or ring of circular cross-section	Surface $= 4\pi^2 Rr = 39.4784\,Rr = 9.8696\,Dd$ Volume $= 2\pi^2 Rr^2 = 19.74\,Rr^2$ $\qquad = 2.463\,Dd^2$ $D = 2R =$ diameter to centers of cross-section of material $r = d/2$
Pyramid	Volume $= \dfrac{Ah}{3}$ $\qquad = \dfrac{h}{3}\left[nr^2\left(\tan\dfrac{360°}{2n}\right)\right]$ $\qquad = \dfrac{h}{3}\left[\dfrac{ns^2}{4}\left(\cot\dfrac{360°}{2n}\right)\right]$ $A =$ area of base $n =$ number of sides $r =$ short radius of base
Pyramidic frustum	Volume $= \dfrac{h}{3}(a + A + \sqrt{aA})$ $A =$ area of base $a =$ area of top
Cone with circular base 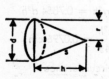	Conical area $= \pi rs = \pi r\sqrt{r^2 + h^2}$ Volume $= \dfrac{\pi r^2 h}{3} = 1.047\,r^2 h = 0.2618\,d^2 h$ $s =$ slant height

Mensuration formulas *continued*

figure	formula
Conic frustum	

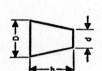

$$\text{Volume} = \frac{\pi h}{3}\,(R^2 + Rr + r^2)$$

$$= \frac{\pi h}{3}\left(\frac{R^3 - r^3}{R - r}\right)$$

$$= \frac{\pi h}{12}\,(D^2 + Dd + d^2)$$

$$= \frac{h}{3}\,(a + A + \sqrt{aA})$$

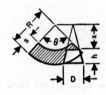

$$\text{Area of conic surface} = \frac{\pi s}{2}\,(D + d)$$

$$C = s + \frac{sd}{D - d} = s\left(1 + \frac{d}{D - d}\right)$$

$$\theta = \frac{180\,D}{C} = \frac{180\,(D - d)}{s}$$

A = area of base a = area of top
$R = D/2$ $r = d/2$
s = slant height of frustum

Wedge frustum

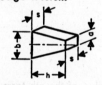

$$\text{Volume} = \frac{hs}{2}\,(a + b)$$

h = height between parallel bases

Ellipsoid

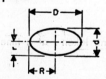

$$\text{Volume} = \frac{4\pi\,Rr^2}{3} = 4.1888\,Rr^2$$

$$= 0.053\,\pi^2\,Dd^2 = 0.5231\,Dd^2$$

Paraboloid

$$\text{Volume} = \frac{\pi r^2 h}{2} = 1.5707\,r^2 h$$

$$\text{Curved surface} = 0.5236\,\frac{r}{h^2}\,[(r^2 + 4\,h^2)^{3/2} - r^3]$$

Algebraic and trigonometric formulas *including complex quantities*

Quadratic equation

If $ax^2 + bx + c = 0$, then

$$x = \frac{-b \pm \sqrt{b^2 - 4ac}}{2a} = -\frac{b}{2a} \pm \sqrt{\left(\frac{b}{2a}\right)^2 - \frac{c}{a}}$$

provided that $a \neq 0$

Arithmetic progression

$$l = a + (n - 1)\,d$$
$$S = \frac{n}{2}\,(a + l) = \frac{n}{2}\,[2a + (n - 1)\,d]$$

where

a = first term S = sum of n terms l = value of nth term
d = common difference = value of any term minus value of preceding term

Geometric progression

$$l = ar^{n-1}$$
$$S = \frac{a(r^n - 1)}{r - 1}$$

where

a = first term S = sum of n terms l = value of the nth term
r = common ratio = the value of any term divided by the preceding term

Combinations and permutations

The number of combinations of n things, all different, taken r at a time is

$$_nC_r = \frac{n!}{r!\,(n - r)!}$$

The number of permutations of n things r at a time is

$$_nP_r = n(n - 1)\,(n - 2)\,\ldots.\,(n - r + 1) = \frac{n!}{(n - r)!}$$

$$_nP_n = n!$$

Algebraic and trigonometric formulas   *continued*

Binomial theorem

$$(a \pm b)^n = a^n \pm na^{n-1}b + \frac{n(n-1)}{2!} a^{n-2}b^2 \pm \frac{n(n-1)(n-2)}{3!} a^{n-3}b^3 + \ldots.$$

If n is a positive integer, the series is finite and contains $n + 1$ terms; otherwise, it is infinite, converging for $|b/a| < 1$, and diverging for $|b/a| > 1$.

Complex quantities

In the following formulas all quantities are real except $j = \sqrt{-1}$

$$(A + jB) + (C + jD) = (A + C) + j(B + D)$$

$$(A + jB)(C + jD) = (AC - BD) + j(BC + AD)$$

$$\frac{A + jB}{C + jD} = \frac{AC + BD}{C^2 + D^2} + j\frac{BC - AD}{C^2 + D^2}$$

$$\frac{1}{A + jB} = \frac{A}{A^2 + B^2} - j\frac{B}{A^2 + B^2}$$

$$A + jB = \rho(\cos\theta + j\sin\theta) = \rho\epsilon^{j\theta}$$

$$\sqrt{A + jB} = \pm\sqrt{\rho}\left(\cos\frac{\theta}{2} + j\sin\frac{\theta}{2}\right)$$

where

$$\rho = \sqrt{A^2 + B^2} > 0$$

$$\cos\theta = A/\rho$$

$$\sin\theta = B/\rho$$

Properties of e

$$e = 1 + 1 + 1/2! + 1/3! + \ldots = 2.71828$$

$$1/e = 0.367879$$

$$e^{\pm jx} = \cos x \pm j\sin x = \exp(\pm jx)$$

$$\log_{10} e = 0.43429 \qquad\qquad \log_{10}(0.43429) = 9.63778 - 10$$

$$\log_e 10 = 2.30259 = 1/\log_{10} e \qquad \log_{10}(e^n) = n(0.43429)$$

$$\log_e N = \log_e 10 \times \log_{10} N$$

$$\log_{10} N = \log_{10} e \times \log_e N$$

Algebraic and trigonometric formulas   *continued*

Trigonometric identities

$$1 = \sin^2 A + \cos^2 A = \sin A \, \operatorname{cosec} A = \tan A \cot A = \cos A \sec A$$

$$\sin A = \frac{\cos A}{\cot A} = \frac{1}{\operatorname{cosec} A} = \cos A \tan A = \pm\sqrt{1 - \cos^2 A}$$

$$\cos A = \frac{\sin A}{\tan A} = \frac{1}{\sec A} = \sin A \cot A = \pm\sqrt{1 - \sin^2 A}$$

$$\tan A = \frac{\sin A}{\cos A} = \frac{1}{\cot A} = \sin A \sec A$$

$$\sin (A \pm B) = \sin A \cos B \pm \cos A \sin B$$

$$\tan (A \pm B) = \frac{\tan A \pm \tan B}{1 \mp \tan A \tan B}$$

$$\sin A = \frac{e^{jA} - e^{-jA}}{2j}$$

$$\cos A = \frac{e^{jA} + e^{-jA}}{2}$$

$$\cos (A \pm B) = \cos A \cos B \mp \sin A \sin B$$

$$\cot (A \pm B) = \frac{\cot A \cot B \mp 1}{\cot B \pm \cot A} = \frac{\cot A \mp \tan B}{1 \pm \cot A \tan B}$$

$$\sin A + \sin B = 2 \sin \tfrac{1}{2} (A + B) \cos \tfrac{1}{2} (A - B)$$

$$\sin^2 A - \sin^2 B = \sin (A + B) \sin (A - B)$$

$$\tan A \pm \tan B = \frac{\sin (A \pm B)}{\cos A \cos B}$$

$$\sin A - \sin B = 2 \cos \tfrac{1}{2} (A + B) \sin \tfrac{1}{2} (A - B)$$

$$\cos A + \cos B = 2 \cos \tfrac{1}{2} (A + B) \cos \tfrac{1}{2} (A - B)$$

$$\cot A \pm \cot B = \frac{\sin (B \pm A)}{\sin A \sin B}$$

$$\cos B - \cos A = 2 \sin \tfrac{1}{2} (A + B) \sin \tfrac{1}{2} (A - B)$$

$$\sin 2A = 2 \sin A \cos A$$

$$\cos 2A = \cos^2 A - \sin^2 A$$

$$\tan 2A = \frac{2 \tan A}{1 - \tan^2 A}$$

Algebraic and trigonometric formulas   *continued*

$$\cos^2 A - \sin^2 B = \cos (A + B) \cos (A - B)$$

$$\sin \tfrac{1}{2} A = \pm\sqrt{\frac{1 - \cos A}{2}} \qquad \cos \tfrac{1}{2} A = \pm\sqrt{\frac{1 + \cos A}{2}}$$

$$\tan \tfrac{1}{2} A = \frac{\sin A}{1 + \cos A} \qquad \sin^2 A = \frac{1 - \cos 2A}{2}$$

$$\cos^2 A = \frac{1 + \cos 2A}{2} \qquad \tan^2 A = \frac{1 - \cos 2A}{1 + \cos 2A}$$

$$\frac{\sin A \pm \sin B}{\cos A + \cos B} = \tan \tfrac{1}{2} (A \pm B)$$

$$\frac{\sin A \pm \sin B}{\cos B - \cos A} = \cot \tfrac{1}{2} (A \mp B)$$

$$\sin A \cos B = \tfrac{1}{2} [\sin (A + B) + \sin (A - B)]$$
$$\cos A \cos B = \tfrac{1}{2} [\cos (A + B) + \cos (A - B)]$$
$$\sin A \sin B = \tfrac{1}{2} [\cos (A - B) - \cos (A + B)]$$

$$\sin x + \sin 2x + \sin 3x + \ldots + \sin mx = \frac{\sin \tfrac{1}{2} mx \sin \tfrac{1}{2} (m + 1) x}{\sin \tfrac{1}{2} x}$$

$$\cos x + \cos 2x + \cos 3x + \ldots + \cos mx = \frac{\sin \tfrac{1}{2} mx \cos \tfrac{1}{2} (m + 1) x}{\sin \tfrac{1}{2} x}$$

$$\sin x + \sin 3x + \sin 5x + \ldots + \sin (2m - 1) x = \frac{\sin^2 mx}{\sin x}$$

$$\cos x + \cos 3x + \cos 5x + \ldots + \cos (2m - 1) x = \frac{\sin 2mx}{2 \sin x}$$

$$\tfrac{1}{2} + \cos x + \cos 2x + \ldots + \cos mx = \frac{\sin (m + \tfrac{1}{2}) x}{2 \sin \tfrac{1}{2} x}$$

angle	0	30°	45°	60°	90°	180°	270°	360°
sine	0	½	½√2	½√3	1	0	−1	0
cosine	1	½√3	½√2	½	0	−1	0	1
tangent	0	⅓√3	1	√3	±∞	0	±∞	0

versine $\theta = 1 - \cos \theta$
$\sin 14\tfrac{1}{2}° = \tfrac{1}{4}$ approximately
$\sin 20° = \tfrac{11}{32}$ approximately

Algebraic and trigonometric formulas   *continued*

Approximations for small angles

$$\sin \theta = (\theta - \theta^3/6\ldots\ldots) \qquad \theta \text{ in radians}$$
$$\tan \theta = (\theta + \theta^3/3\ldots\ldots) \qquad \theta \text{ in radians}$$
$$\cos \theta = (1 - \theta^2/2\ldots\ldots) \qquad \theta \text{ in radians}$$

Right-angled triangles *right angle at C*

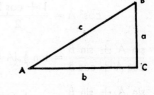

$$\sin A = \cos B = a/c \qquad B = 90° - A$$

$$\tan A = a/b$$

$$\text{vers } A = 1 - \cos A = \frac{c - b}{c}$$

$$c = \sqrt{a^2 + b^2} \qquad\qquad b = \sqrt{c^2 - a^2} = \sqrt{(c + a)(c - a)}$$

$$\text{Area} = \frac{ab}{2} = \frac{a}{2}\sqrt{c^2 - a^2} = \frac{a^2 \cot A}{2} = \frac{b^2 \tan A}{2} = \frac{c^2 \sin A \cos A}{2}$$

Oblique-angled triangles

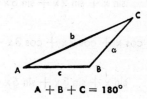

$$\sin \tfrac{1}{2} A = \sqrt{\frac{(s - b)(s - c)}{bc}}$$

$$\cos \tfrac{1}{2} A = \sqrt{\frac{s(s - a)}{bc}}$$

$$A + B + C = 180°$$

$$\text{where } s = \frac{a + b + c}{2}$$

$$\tan \tfrac{1}{2} A = \sqrt{\frac{(s - b)(s - c)}{s(s - a)}}, \text{ similar values for angles } B \text{ and } C$$

$$\text{Area} = \sqrt{s(s - a)(s - b)(s - c)} = \tfrac{1}{2} ab \sin C = \frac{a^2 \sin B \sin C}{2 \sin A}$$

$$c = \frac{a \sin C}{\sin A} = \frac{a \sin (A + B)}{\sin A} = \sqrt{a^2 + b^2 - 2ab \cos C}$$

$$\tan A = \frac{a \sin C}{b - a \cos C}, \quad \tan \tfrac{1}{2}(A - B) = \frac{a - b}{a + b} \cot \tfrac{1}{2} C$$

$$a^2 = b^2 + c^2 - 2bc \cos A, \text{ similar expressions for other sides.}$$

Spherical trigonometry

In the following triangles each element is assumed to be less than 180 degrees.

General (for any spherical triangle)

$\cos a = \cos b \cos c + \sin b \sin c \cos \alpha$

$\cos \alpha = -\cos \beta \cos \gamma + \sin \beta \sin \gamma \cos a$

$$\frac{\sin \alpha}{\sin a} = \frac{\sin \beta}{\sin b} = \frac{\sin \gamma}{\sin c}$$

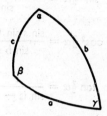

$\sin a \cos \beta = \cos b \sin c - \sin b \cos c \cos \alpha$
$\sin \alpha \cos b = \cos \beta \sin \gamma + \sin \beta \cos \gamma \cos a$

$\sin \alpha \cot \beta = \cot b \sin c - \cos c \cos \alpha$
$\sin a \cot b = \cot \beta \sin \gamma + \cos a \cos \gamma$

Right spherical triangles $(\gamma = 90°)$

$\cos c = \cos a \cos b$
$\cos c = \cot \alpha \cot \beta$

$\cos \alpha = \sin \beta \cos a$
$\cos \beta = \sin \alpha \cos b$

$\cos \alpha = \tan b \cot c$
$\cos \beta = \tan a \cot c$

$\sin a = \sin c \sin \alpha$
$\sin b = \sin c \sin \beta$

$\sin b = \tan a \cot \alpha$
$\sin a = \tan b \cot \beta$

Species (right triangles): Two angular quantities are of the same species if both are in the same quadrant; otherwise they are of different species. Rules for species are:

a. An oblique angle and its opposite side are always of the same species.

b. If the hypotenuse is less than 90°, the oblique angles (and the two sides) are of the same species; otherwise they are of different species.

Spherical trigonometry *continued*

Oblique spherical triangle

Let $a + b + c = 2s$

$$\sin^2 \tfrac{1}{2}\alpha = \frac{\sin (s - b) \sin (s - c)}{\sin b \sin c} \text{, etc.}$$

$$\cos^2 \tfrac{1}{2}\alpha = \frac{\sin s \sin (s - a)}{\sin b \sin c} \text{, etc.}$$

$$\tan \tfrac{1}{2}\alpha = \frac{r}{\sin (s - a)} \text{, etc.}$$

where $r = \left[\dfrac{\sin (s - a) \sin (s - b) \sin (s - c)}{\sin s} \right]^{\frac{1}{2}}$

$$\cos a = \frac{\cos \alpha + \cos \beta \cos \gamma}{\sin \beta \sin \gamma} \text{, etc.}$$

$$\sin^2 \tfrac{1}{2}a = - \frac{\cos S \cos (S - \alpha)}{\sin \beta \sin \gamma} \text{, etc.}$$

where $2S = \alpha + \beta + \gamma$.

$$\cos^2 \tfrac{1}{2}a = \frac{\cos (S - \beta) \cos (S - \gamma)}{\sin \beta \sin \gamma} \text{, etc.}$$

$$\tan^2 \tfrac{1}{2}a = - \frac{\cos S \cos (S - \alpha)}{\cos (S - \beta) \cos (S - \gamma)} \text{, etc.}$$

$$\frac{\tan \tfrac{1}{2}(a - b)}{\tan \tfrac{1}{2}c} = \frac{\sin \tfrac{1}{2}(\alpha - \beta)}{\sin \tfrac{1}{2}(\alpha + \beta)} \qquad \frac{\tan \tfrac{1}{2}(a + b)}{\tan \tfrac{1}{2}c} = \frac{\cos \tfrac{1}{2}(\alpha - \beta)}{\cos \tfrac{1}{2}(\alpha + \beta)}$$

$$\frac{\tan \tfrac{1}{2}(\alpha - \beta)}{\cot \tfrac{1}{2}\gamma} = \frac{\sin \tfrac{1}{2}(a - b)}{\sin \tfrac{1}{2}(a + b)} \qquad \frac{\tan \tfrac{1}{2}(\alpha + \beta)}{\cot \tfrac{1}{2}\gamma} = \frac{\cos \tfrac{1}{2}(a - b)}{\cos \tfrac{1}{2}(a + b)}$$

Rules for species (oblique triangles)

a. If a side (or angle) differs more than another side (or angle) from 90°, it is of the same species as its opposite angle (or side).

b. Half the sum of two sides is of the same species as half the sum of two opposite angles.

Plane analytic geometry

In the following, x and y are coordinates of a variable point in a rectangular-coordinate system.

Straight line

General equation

$Ax + By + C = 0$

A, B, and C are constants.

Slope-intercept form

$y = sx + b$

b = y-intercept

$s = \tan \theta$

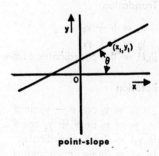

slope-intercept

Intercept-intercept form

$$\frac{x}{a} + \frac{y}{b} = 1$$

a = x-intercept

b = y-intercept

intercept-intercept

Point-slope form

$y - y_1 = s(x - x_1)$

$s = \tan \theta$

(x_1, y_1) = coordinates of known point on line.

Point-point form

$$\frac{y - y_1}{y_1 - y_2} = \frac{x - x_1}{x_1 - x_2}$$

point-slope

(x_1, y_1) and (x_2, y_2) are coordinates of two different points on the line.

Normal form

$$\frac{A}{\pm\sqrt{A^2 + B^2}} x + \frac{B}{\pm\sqrt{A^2 + B^2}} y + \frac{C}{\pm\sqrt{A^2 + B^2}} = 0$$

the sign of the radical is chosen so that

$$\frac{C}{\pm\sqrt{A^2 + B^2}} < 0$$

Plane analytic geometry *continued*

Distance from point (x_1,y_1) to a line

Substitute coordinates of the point in the normal form of the line. Thus,

$$\text{distance} = \frac{A}{\pm\sqrt{A^2 + B^2}}x_1 + \frac{B}{\pm\sqrt{A^2 + B^2}}y_1 + \frac{C}{\pm\sqrt{A^2 + B^2}}$$

Angle between two lines

$$\tan\phi = \frac{s_1 - s_2}{1 + s_1 s_2}$$

where

ϕ = angle between the lines
s_1 = slope of one line
s_2 = slope of other line

When the lines are mutually perpendicular, $\tan\phi = \infty$, whence
$s_1 = -1/s_2$

Transformation of rectangular coordinates

Translation

$$x_1 = h + x_2$$
$$y_1 = k + y_2$$

(h,k) = the coordinates of the new origin referred to the old origin

Rotation

$$x_1 = x_2 \cos\theta - y_2 \sin\theta$$
$$y_1 = x_2 \sin\theta + y_2 \cos\theta$$

(x_1,y_1) = "old" coordinates
(x_2,y_2) = "new" coordinates
θ = counterclockwise angle of rotation of axes

Circle

The equation of a circle of radius r with center at (m,n) is

$$(x - m)^2 + (y - n)^2 = r^2$$

Tangent line to a circle: At (x_1,y_1) is

$$y - y_1 = -\frac{x_1 - m}{y_1 - n}(x - x_1)$$

Plane analytic geometry   *continued*

Normal line to a circle: At (x_1, y_1) is

$$y - y_1 = \frac{y_1 - n}{x_1 - m} (x - x_1)$$

Parabola

x-parabola

$$(y - k)^2 = \pm 2p (x - h)$$

where (h,k) are the coordinates of the vertex, and the sign used is plus or minus when the parabola is open to the right or to the left, respectively. The semi-latus rectum is p.

y-parabola

$$(x - h)^2 = \pm 2p (y - k)$$

where (h,k) are the coordinates of the vertex. Use plus sign if parabola is open above, and minus sign if open below.

Tangent lines to a parabola

$(x_1, y_1) =$ point of tangency

For x-parabola,

$$y - y_1 = \pm \frac{p}{y_1 - k} (x - x_1)$$

Use plus sign if parabola is open to the right, minus sign if open to the left. For y-parabola,

$$y - y_1 = \pm \frac{x_1 - h}{p} (x - x_1)$$

Use plus sign if parabola is open above, minus sign if open below.

Normal lines to a parabola

$(x_1, y_1) =$ point of contact

For x-parabola,

$$y - y_1 = \mp \frac{y_1 - k}{p} (x - x_1)$$

Plane analytic geometry   *continued*

Use minus sign if parabola is open to the right, plus sign if open to the left.

For y-parabola,

$$y - y_1 = \mp \frac{p}{x_1 - h} (x - x_1)$$

Use minus sign if parabola is open above, plus sign if open below.

Ellipse

Figure shows ellipse centered at origin.

$$F, F' = \text{foci}$$
$$DD', D''D''' = \text{directrices}$$

$$e = \text{eccentricity} < 1$$
$$2a = A'A = \text{major axis}$$
$$2b = BB' = \text{minor axis}$$

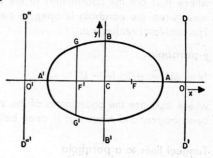

Then

$$OC = a/e$$

$$FC = ae$$

$$1 - e^2 = b^2/a^2$$

Equation of ellipse

$$\frac{x^2}{a^2} + \frac{y^2}{b^2} = 1$$

Sum of the focal radii

To any point on ellipse $= 2a$

Equation of tangent line to ellipse

$(x_1, y_1) = $ point of tangency

$$\frac{xx_1}{a^2} + \frac{yy_1}{b^2} = 1$$

Equation of normal line to an ellipse

$$y - y_1 = \frac{a^2 y_1}{b^2 x_1} (x - x_1)$$

Plane analytic geometry *continued*

Hyperbola

Figure shows x-hyperbola centered at origin.

F, F' = foci

$DD', D''D'''$ = directrices

e = eccentricity > 1

$2a$ = transverse axis = $A'A$

$CO = a/e$

$CF = ae$

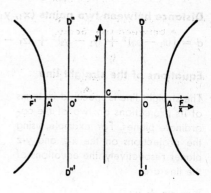

Equation of x-hyperbola

$$\frac{x^2}{a^2} - \frac{y^2}{b^2} = 1$$

where

$$b^2 = a^2 (e^2 - 1)$$

Equation of conjugate (y-) hyperbola

$$\frac{y^2}{b^2} - \frac{x^2}{a^2} = 1$$

Tangent line to x-hyperbola

(x_1, y_1) = point of tangency

$$a^2 y_1 y - b^2 x_1 x = -a^2 b^2$$

Normal line to x-hyperbola

$$y - y_1 = -\frac{a^2 y_1}{b^2 x_1} (x - x_1)$$

Asymptotes to hyperbola

$$y = \pm \frac{b}{a}$$

Solid analytic geometry

In the following, x, y, and z are the coordinates of a variable point in space in a rectangular-coordinate system.

Distance between two points (x_1, y_1, z_1) and (x_2, y_2, z_2)

$$d = [(x_1 - x_2)^2 + (y_1 - y_2)^2 + (z_1 - z_2)^2]^{\frac{1}{2}}$$

Equations of the straight line

The straight line is specified in terms of its projections on two of the co-ordinate planes. For example, using the projections on the x-z and y-z planes respectively, the equations of the line are

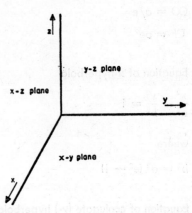

$$x = mz + \mu$$
$$y = nz + \nu$$

where

m = slope of x-z projection
n = slope of y-z projection
μ = intercept of x-z projection on x-axis
ν = intercept of y-z projection on y-axis

Equation of plane, intercept form

$$\frac{x}{a} + \frac{y}{b} + \frac{z}{c} = 1$$

where a, b, c are the intercepts of the plane on the x, y, and z axes, respectively.

Prolate spheroid

$$a^2(y^2 + z^2) + b^2x^2 = a^2b^2$$
where $a > b$, and x-axis = axis of revolution

Oblate spheroid

$$b^2(x^2 + z^2) + a^2y^2 = a^2b^2$$
where $a > b$, and y-axis = axis of revolution

Solid analytic geometry *continued*

Paraboloid of revolution

$$y^2 + z^2 = 2px$$

x-axis = axis of revolution

Hyperboloid of revolution

Revolving an x-hyperbola about the x-axis results in the hyperboloid of two sheets

$$a^2 (y^2 + z^2) - b^2 x^2 = -a^2 b^2$$

Revolving an x-hyperbola about the y-axis results in the hyperboloid of one sheet

$$b^2 (x^2 + z^2) - a^2 y^2 = a^2 b^2$$

Ellipsoid

$$\frac{x^2}{a^2} + \frac{y^2}{b^2} + \frac{z^2}{c^2} = 1$$

where a, b, c are the semi-axes of the ellipsoid or the intercepts on the x, y, and z axes, respectively.

Hyperbolic functions

$$\sinh x = \frac{e^x - e^{-x}}{2} \qquad \cosh x = \frac{e^x + e^{-x}}{2}$$

$$\sinh (-x) = -\sinh x \qquad \cosh (-x) = \cosh x$$

$$\sinh (jx) = j \sin x \qquad \cosh (jx) = \cos x$$

$$\cosh^2 x - \sinh^2 x = 1$$

$$\sinh 2x = 2 \sinh x \cosh x \qquad \cosh 2x = \cosh^2 x + \sinh^2 x$$

$$\sinh (x \pm jy) = \sinh x \cos y \pm j \cosh x \sin y$$

$$\cosh (x \pm jy) = \cosh x \cos y \pm j \sinh x \sin y$$

Differential calculus

List of derivatives

In the following u, v, w are differentiable functions of x, and c is a constant.

General

$$\frac{dc}{dx} = 0$$

$$\frac{dx}{dx} = 1$$

$$\frac{d}{dx}(u + v - w) = \frac{du}{dx} + \frac{dv}{dx} - \frac{dw}{dx}$$

$$\frac{d}{dx}(cv) = c\frac{dv}{dx}$$

$$\frac{d}{dx}(uv) = u\frac{dv}{dx} + v\frac{du}{dx}$$

$$\frac{d}{dx}(v^c) = cv^{c-1}\frac{dv}{dx}$$

$$\frac{d}{dx}\left(\frac{u}{v}\right) = \frac{v\dfrac{du}{dx} - u\dfrac{dv}{dx}}{v^2}$$

$$\frac{dy}{dx} = \frac{dy}{dv} \cdot \frac{dv}{dx} \quad \text{if } y = y(v)$$

$$\frac{dy}{dx} = \frac{1}{dx/dy} \quad \text{if } \frac{dx}{dy} \neq 0$$

Transcendental functions

$$\frac{d}{dx}(\log_e v) = \frac{1}{v}\frac{dv}{dx}$$

$$\frac{d}{dx}(c^v) = c^v \log_e c \frac{dv}{dx}$$

$$\frac{d}{dx}(e^v) = e^v \frac{dv}{dx}$$

$$\frac{d}{dx}(u^v) = vu^{v-1}\frac{du}{dx} + (\log_e u)u^v \frac{dv}{dx}$$

Differential calculus   *continued*

$$\frac{d}{dx}(\sin v) = \cos v \frac{dv}{dx}$$

$$\frac{d}{dx}(\cos v) = -\sin v \frac{dv}{dx}$$

$$\frac{d}{dx}(\tan v) = \sec^2 v \frac{dv}{dx}$$

$$\frac{d}{dx}(\cot v) = -\csc^2 v \frac{dv}{dx}$$

$$\frac{d}{dx}(\sec v) = \sec v \tan v \frac{dv}{dx}$$

$$\frac{d}{dx}(\csc v) = -\csc v \cot v \frac{dv}{dx}$$

$$\frac{d}{dx}(\text{arc sin } v) = \frac{1}{\sqrt{1-v^2}} \frac{dv}{dx}$$

$$\frac{d}{dx}(\text{arc cos } v) = -\frac{1}{\sqrt{1-v^2}} \frac{dv}{dx}$$

$$\frac{d}{dx}(\text{arc tan } v) = \frac{1}{1+v^2} \frac{dv}{dx}$$

$$\frac{d}{dx}(\text{arc cot } v) = -\frac{1}{1+v^2} \frac{dv}{dx}$$

$$\frac{d}{dx}(\text{arc sec } v) = \frac{1}{v\sqrt{v^2-1}} \frac{dv}{dx}$$

$$\frac{d}{dx}(\text{arc csc } v) = -\frac{1}{v\sqrt{v^2-1}} \frac{dv}{dx}$$

Curvature of a curve

$$K = \frac{y''}{(1+y'^2)^{3/2}} = \frac{1}{R}$$

where

K = curvature
R = radius of curvature
y', y'' = respectively, first and second derivatives of the curve $y = f(x)$
    with respect to x

Integral calculus

Rational algebraic integrals

1. $\int x^m \, dx = \dfrac{x^{m+1}}{m+1}, \qquad m \neq -1$

2. $\int \dfrac{dx}{x} = \log_e x$

3. $\int (ax+b)^m \, dx = \dfrac{(ax+b)^{m+1}}{a(m+1)}, \qquad m \neq -1$

4. $\int \dfrac{dx}{ax+b} = \dfrac{1}{a} \log_e (ax+b)$

5. $\int \dfrac{x \, dx}{ax+b} = \dfrac{1}{a^2} [ax+b - b \log_e (ax+b)]$

6. $\int \dfrac{x \, dx}{(ax+b)^2} = \dfrac{1}{a^2} \left[\dfrac{b}{ax+b} + \log_e (ax+b) \right]$

7. $\int \dfrac{dx}{x(ax+b)} = \dfrac{1}{b} \log_e \dfrac{x}{ax+b}$

8. $\int \dfrac{dx}{x(ax+b)^2} = \dfrac{1}{b(ax+b)} + \dfrac{1}{b^2} \log_e \dfrac{x}{ax+b}$

9. $\int \dfrac{dx}{x^2(ax+b)} = -\dfrac{1}{bx} + \dfrac{a}{b^2} \log_e \dfrac{ax+b}{x}$

10. $\int \dfrac{dx}{x^2(ax+b)^2} = -\dfrac{2ax+b}{b^2 x(ax+b)} + \dfrac{2a}{b^3} \log_e \dfrac{ax+b}{x}$

11. $\int \dfrac{dx}{x^2+a^2} = \dfrac{1}{a} \tan^{-1} \dfrac{x}{a}$

12. $\int \dfrac{dx}{x^2-a^2} = \dfrac{1}{2a} \log \dfrac{x-a}{x+a} = -\dfrac{1}{a} \tanh^{-1} \dfrac{a}{x}$

13. $\int \dfrac{dx}{(ax^2+b)^m} = \dfrac{x}{2(m-1)\, b\, (ax^2+b)^{m-1}}$
$$+ \dfrac{2m-3}{2(m-1)\, b} \int \dfrac{dx}{(ax^2+b)^{m-1}}, \qquad m \neq 1$$

14. $\int \dfrac{x \, dx}{(ax^2+b)^m} = -\dfrac{1}{2(m-1)\, a\, (ax^2+b)^{m-1}}, \qquad m \neq 1$

Integral calculus   *continued*

15. $\int \dfrac{x \, dx}{ax^2 + b} = \dfrac{1}{2a} \log_e (ax^2 + b)$

16. $\int \dfrac{x^2 \, dx}{ax^2 + b} = \dfrac{x}{a} - \dfrac{b}{a} \int \dfrac{dx}{ax^2 + b}$

17. $\int \dfrac{x^2 \, dx}{(ax^2 + b)^m} = - \dfrac{x}{2(m-1) \, a \, (ax^2 + b)^{m-1}}$

$$+ \dfrac{1}{2(m-1) \, a} \int \dfrac{dx}{(ax^2 + b)^{m-1}}, \quad m \neq 1$$

18. $\int \dfrac{dx}{ax^3 + b} = \dfrac{k}{3b} \left(\sqrt{3} \tan^{-1} \dfrac{2x - k}{k\sqrt{3}} + \log_e \dfrac{k + x}{\sqrt{k^2 - kx + x^2}} \right),$

$$\text{where } k = \sqrt[3]{b/a}$$

19. $\int \dfrac{x \, dx}{ax^3 + b} = \dfrac{1}{3ak} \left(\sqrt{3} \tan^{-1} \dfrac{2x - k}{k\sqrt{3}} - \log_e \dfrac{k + x}{\sqrt{k^2 - kx + x^2}} \right),$

$$\text{where } k = \sqrt[3]{b/a}$$

20. $\int \dfrac{dx}{x(ax^n + b)} = \dfrac{1}{bn} \log_e \dfrac{x^n}{ax^n + b}$

Let $X = ax^2 + bx + c$ and $q = b^2 - 4ac$

21. $\int \dfrac{dx}{X} = \dfrac{1}{\sqrt{q}} \log_e \dfrac{2ax + b - \sqrt{q}}{2ax + b + \sqrt{q}}, \quad \text{when } q > 0$

22. $\int \dfrac{dx}{X} = \dfrac{2}{\sqrt{-q}} \tan^{-1} \dfrac{2ax + b}{\sqrt{-q}}, \quad \text{when } q < 0$

For the case $q = 0$, use equation 3 with $m = -2$

23. $\int \dfrac{dx}{X^n} = - \dfrac{2ax + b}{(n-1) \, q \, X^{n-1}} - \dfrac{2(2n - 3) \, a}{q(n-1)} \int \dfrac{dx}{X^{n-1}}, \quad n \neq 1$

24. $\int \dfrac{x \, dx}{X} = \dfrac{1}{2a} \log_e X - \dfrac{b}{2a} \int \dfrac{dx}{X}$

25. $\int \dfrac{x^2 \, dx}{X} = \dfrac{x}{a} - \dfrac{b}{2a^2} \log_e X + \dfrac{b^2 - 2ac}{2a^2} \int \dfrac{dx}{X}$

Integral calculus *continued*

Integrals involving $\sqrt{ax + b}$

26. $\displaystyle\int x\sqrt{ax + b}\, dx = \frac{2(3ax - 2b)\sqrt{(ax + b)^3}}{15a^2}$

27. $\displaystyle\int x^2\sqrt{ax + b}\, dx = \frac{2(15a^2x^2 - 12abx + 8b^2)\sqrt{(ax + b)^3}}{105a^3}$

28. $\displaystyle\int x^m\sqrt{ax + b}\, dx = \frac{2}{a(2m + 3)}\left[x^m\sqrt{(ax + b)^3}\right.$
$$\left. - mb\int x^{m-1}\sqrt{ax + b}\, dx\right]$$

29. $\displaystyle\int \frac{\sqrt{ax + b}\, dx}{x} = 2\sqrt{ax + b} + \sqrt{b}\,\log_e\frac{\sqrt{ax + b} - \sqrt{b}}{\sqrt{ax + b} + \sqrt{b}},\qquad b > 0$

$$= 2\sqrt{ax + b} - 2\sqrt{-b}\,\tan^{-1}\sqrt{\frac{ax + b}{-b}},\qquad b < 0$$

30. $\displaystyle\int \frac{\sqrt{ax + b}\, dx}{x^m} = -\frac{1}{(m - 1)\, b}\left[\frac{\sqrt{(ax + b)^3}}{x^{m-1}}\right.$
$$\left. + \frac{(2m - 5)\, a}{2}\int \frac{\sqrt{ax + b}\, dx}{x^{m-1}}\right],\quad m \neq 1$$

31. $\displaystyle\int \frac{x\, dx}{\sqrt{ax + b}} = \frac{2(ax - 2b)}{3a^2}\sqrt{ax + b}$

32. $\displaystyle\int \frac{x^2\, dx}{\sqrt{ax + b}} = \frac{2(3a^2x^2 - 4abx + 8b^2)}{15a^3}\sqrt{ax + b}$

33. $\displaystyle\int \frac{x^m\, dx}{\sqrt{ax + b}} = \frac{2}{a(2m + 1)}\left(x^m\sqrt{ax + b} - mb\int \frac{x^{m-1}\, dx}{\sqrt{ax + b}}\right),\ m \neq \tfrac{1}{2}$

34. $\displaystyle\int \frac{dx}{x\sqrt{ax + b}} = \frac{1}{\sqrt{b}}\log_e\frac{\sqrt{ax + b} - \sqrt{b}}{\sqrt{ax + b} + \sqrt{b}},\qquad b > 0$

$$= \frac{2}{\sqrt{-b}}\tan^{-1}\sqrt{\frac{ax + b}{-b}},\qquad b < 0$$

35. $\displaystyle\int \frac{dx}{x^m\sqrt{ax + b}} = -\frac{\sqrt{ax + b}}{(m - 1)\, bx^{m-1}} - \frac{(2m - 3)\, a}{(2m - 2)\, b}\int \frac{dx}{x^{m-1}\sqrt{ax + b}},$
$$m \neq 1$$

Integral calculus *continued*

Integrals involving $\sqrt{x^2 \pm a^2}$ and $\sqrt{a^2 - x^2}$

36. $\displaystyle\int \sqrt{x^2 \pm a^2}\, dx = \tfrac{1}{2}\left[x\sqrt{x^2 \pm a^2} \pm a^2 \log_e (x + \sqrt{x^2 \pm a^2})\right]$

37. $\displaystyle\int \sqrt{a^2 - x^2}\, dx = \tfrac{1}{2}\left(x\sqrt{a^2 - x^2} + a^2 \sin^{-1}\frac{x}{a}\right)$

38. $\displaystyle\int \frac{dx}{\sqrt{x^2 \pm a^2}} = \log_e (x + \sqrt{x^2 \pm a^2})$

39. $\displaystyle\int \frac{dx}{\sqrt{a^2 - x^2}} = \sin^{-1}\frac{x}{a}$

40. $\displaystyle\int x\sqrt{x^2 \pm a^2}\, dx = \tfrac{1}{3}\sqrt{(x^2 \pm a^2)^3}$

41. $\displaystyle\int x^2\sqrt{x^2 \pm a^2}\, dx = \frac{x}{4}\sqrt{(x^2 \pm a^2)^3} \mp \frac{a^2}{8}\big[x\sqrt{x^2 \pm a^2}$
$$\pm a^2 \log_e (x + \sqrt{x^2 \pm a^2})\big]$$

42. $\displaystyle\int x\sqrt{a^2 - x^2}\, dx = -\tfrac{1}{3}\sqrt{(a^2 - x^2)^3}$

43. $\displaystyle\int x^2\sqrt{a^2 - x^2}\, dx = -\frac{x}{4}\sqrt{(a^2 - x^2)^3} + \frac{a^2}{8}\left(x\sqrt{a^2 - x^2} + a^2 \sin^{-1}\frac{x}{a}\right)$

44. $\displaystyle\int \frac{\sqrt{a^2 \pm x^2}}{x}\, dx = \sqrt{a^2 \pm x^2} - a \log_e \frac{a + \sqrt{a^2 \pm x^2}}{x}$

45. $\displaystyle\int \frac{\sqrt{x^2 - a^2}}{x}\, dx = \sqrt{x^2 - a^2} - a \cos^{-1}\frac{a}{x}$

46. $\displaystyle\int \frac{\sqrt{x^2 \pm a^2}}{x^2}\, dx = -\frac{\sqrt{x^2 \pm a^2}}{x} + \log_e (x + \sqrt{x^2 \pm a^2})$

47. $\displaystyle\int \frac{\sqrt{a^2 - x^2}}{x^2}\, dx = -\frac{\sqrt{a^2 - x^2}}{x} - \sin^{-1}\frac{x}{a}$

48. $\displaystyle\int \frac{x\, dx}{\sqrt{a^2 - x^2}} = -\sqrt{a^2 - x^2}$

49. $\displaystyle\int \frac{x\, dx}{\sqrt{x^2 \pm a^2}} = \sqrt{x^2 \pm a^2}$

Integral calculus   *continued*

50. $\int \dfrac{x^2\,dx}{\sqrt{x^2 \pm a^2}} = \dfrac{x}{2}\sqrt{x^2 \pm a^2} \mp \dfrac{a^2}{2}\log_e (x + \sqrt{x^2 \pm a^2})$

51. $\int \dfrac{x^2\,dx}{\sqrt{a^2 - x^2}} = -\dfrac{x}{2}\sqrt{a^2 - x^2} + \dfrac{a^2}{2}\sin^{-1}\dfrac{x}{a}$

52. $\int \dfrac{dx}{x\sqrt{x^2 - a^2}} = \dfrac{1}{a}\cos^{-1}\dfrac{a}{x}$

53. $\int \dfrac{dx}{x\sqrt{a^2 \pm x^2}} = -\dfrac{1}{a}\log_e \left(\dfrac{a + \sqrt{a^2 \pm x^2}}{x}\right)$

54. $\int \dfrac{dx}{x^2\sqrt{x^2 \pm a^2}} = \pm \dfrac{\sqrt{x^2 \pm a^2}}{a^2 x}$

55. $\int \dfrac{dx}{x^2\sqrt{a^2 - x^2}} = -\dfrac{\sqrt{a^2 - x^2}}{a^2 x}$

56. $\int \sqrt{(x^2 \pm a^2)^3}\,dx = \tfrac{1}{4}\left[x\sqrt{(x^2 \pm a^2)^3} \pm \dfrac{3a^2 x}{2}\sqrt{x^2 \pm a^2}\right.$
$$\left. + \dfrac{3a^4}{2}\log_e (x + \sqrt{x^2 \pm a^2})\right]$$

57. $\int \sqrt{(a^2 - x^2)^3}\,dx = \tfrac{1}{4}\left[x\sqrt{(a^2 - x^2)^3} + \dfrac{3a^2 x}{2}\sqrt{a^2 - x^2} + \dfrac{3a^4}{2}\sin^{-1}\dfrac{x}{a}\right]$

58. $\int \dfrac{dx}{\sqrt{(x^2 \pm a^2)^3}} = \dfrac{\pm x}{a^2\sqrt{x^2 \pm a^2}}$

59. $\int \dfrac{dx}{\sqrt{(a^2 - x^2)^3}} = \dfrac{x}{a^2\sqrt{a^2 - x^2}}$

Integrals involving $\sqrt{ax^2 + bx + c}$

Let $X = ax^2 + bx + c$ and $q = b^2 - 4ac$

60. $\int \dfrac{dx}{\sqrt{X}} = \dfrac{1}{\sqrt{a}}\log_e \left(\sqrt{X} + \dfrac{2ax + b}{2\sqrt{a}}\right), \quad a > 0$

$\qquad = \dfrac{1}{\sqrt{-a}}\sin^{-1}\dfrac{(-2ax - b)}{\sqrt{q}}, \quad a < 0$

Integral calculus *continued*

61. $\int \dfrac{x\,dx}{\sqrt{X}} = \dfrac{\sqrt{X}}{a} - \dfrac{b}{2a}\int \dfrac{dx}{\sqrt{X}}$

62. $\int \dfrac{x^2 dx}{\sqrt{X}} = \dfrac{(2ax - 3b)\sqrt{X}}{4a^2} + \dfrac{3b^2 - 4ac}{8a^2}\int \dfrac{dx}{\sqrt{X}}$

63. $\int \dfrac{dx}{x\sqrt{X}} = -\dfrac{1}{\sqrt{c}}\log_e\left(\dfrac{\sqrt{X} + \sqrt{c}}{x} + \dfrac{b}{2\sqrt{c}}\right),\;\; c > 0$

64. $\int \dfrac{dx}{X\sqrt{x}} = \dfrac{1}{\sqrt{-c}}\sin^{-1}\dfrac{bx + 2c}{x\sqrt{q}},\;\; c < 0$

65. $\int \dfrac{dx}{x\sqrt{X}} = -\dfrac{2\sqrt{X}}{bx},\;\; c = 0$

66. $\int \dfrac{dx}{(mx + n)\sqrt{X}} = \dfrac{1}{\sqrt{k}}\log_e\left[\dfrac{\sqrt{k} - m\sqrt{X}}{mx + n} + \dfrac{bm - 2an}{2\sqrt{k}}\right],\;\; k > 0$

$\qquad\qquad = \dfrac{1}{\sqrt{-k}}\sin^{-1}\left[\dfrac{(bm - 2an)(mx + n) + 2k}{m(mx + n)\sqrt{q}}\right],\; k < 0$

67. $\int \dfrac{dx}{(mx + n)\sqrt{X}} = -\dfrac{2m\sqrt{X}}{(bm - 2an)(mx + n)},\qquad\qquad k = 0$

where $k = an^2 - bmn + cm^2$.

68. $\int \dfrac{dx}{x^2\sqrt{X}} = -\dfrac{\sqrt{X}}{cx} - \dfrac{b}{2c}\int \dfrac{dx}{x\sqrt{X}}$

69. $\int \sqrt{X}\,dx = \dfrac{(2ax + b)\sqrt{X}}{4a} - \dfrac{q}{8a}\int \dfrac{dx}{\sqrt{X}}$

70. $\int x\sqrt{X}\,dx = \dfrac{X\sqrt{X}}{3a} - \dfrac{b(2ax + b)\sqrt{X}}{8a^2} + \dfrac{bq}{16a^2}\int \dfrac{dx}{\sqrt{X}}$

71. $\int x^2\sqrt{X}\,dx = \dfrac{(6ax - 5b)\,X\sqrt{X}}{24a^2} + \dfrac{(5b^2 - 4ac)(2ax + b)\sqrt{X}}{64a^3}$

$\qquad\qquad\qquad\qquad - \dfrac{(5b^2 - 4ac)\,q}{128a^3}\int \dfrac{dx}{\sqrt{X}}$

72. $\int \dfrac{\sqrt{X}\,dx}{x} = \sqrt{X} + \dfrac{b}{2}\int \dfrac{dx}{\sqrt{X}} + c\int \dfrac{dx}{x\sqrt{X}}$

Integral calculus   *continued*

73. $\int \dfrac{\sqrt{X}\,dx}{mx + n} = \dfrac{\sqrt{X}}{m} + \dfrac{bm - 2an}{2m^2} \int \dfrac{dx}{\sqrt{X}}$

$$+ \dfrac{an^2 - bmn + cm^2}{m^2} \int \dfrac{dx}{(mx + n)\sqrt{X}}$$

74. $\int \dfrac{\sqrt{X}\,dx}{x^2} = -\dfrac{\sqrt{X}}{x} + \dfrac{b}{2} \int \dfrac{dx}{x\sqrt{X}} + a \int \dfrac{dx}{\sqrt{X}}$

75. $\int \dfrac{dx}{X\sqrt{X}} = -\dfrac{2(ax + b)}{q\sqrt{X}}$

76. $\int X\sqrt{X}\,dx = \dfrac{2(2ax + b)\,X\sqrt{X}}{8a} - \dfrac{3q(2ax + b)\sqrt{X}}{64a^2} + \dfrac{3q^2}{128a^2} \int \dfrac{dx}{\sqrt{X}}$

Miscellaneous irrational integrals

77. $\int \sqrt{2ax - x^2}\,dx = \dfrac{x - a}{2}\sqrt{2ax - x^2} + \dfrac{a^2}{2}\sin^{-1}\dfrac{x - a}{a}$

78. $\int \dfrac{dx}{\sqrt{2ax - x^2}} = \cos^{-1}\dfrac{a - x}{a}$

79. $\int \sqrt{\dfrac{mx + n}{ax + b}}\,dx = \int \dfrac{(mx + n)\,dx}{\sqrt{amx^2 + (bm + an)\,x + bn}}$

Logarithmic integrals

80. $\int \log_a x\,dx = x\log_a \dfrac{x}{a}$

81. $\int \log_e x\,dx = x(\log_e x - 1)$

82. $\int x^m \log_a x\,dx = x^{m+1}\left(\dfrac{\log_a x}{m + 1} - \dfrac{\log_a e}{(m + 1)^2}\right)$

83. $\int x^m \log_e x\,dx = x^{m+1}\left(\dfrac{\log_e x}{m + 1} - \dfrac{1}{(m + 1)^2}\right)$

Exponential integrals

84. $\int a^x\,dx = \dfrac{a^x}{\log_e a}$

Integral calculus   *continued*

85. $\int e^x \, dx = e^x$

86. $\int x e^x \, dx = e^x (x - 1)$

87. $\int x^m e^x \, dx = x^m e^x - m \int x^{m-1} e^x \, dx$

Trigonometric integrals

In these equations m and n are *positive integers* unless otherwise indicated, and r and s are any integers.

88. $\int \sin x \, dx = -\cos x$

89. $\int \sin^2 x \, dx = \frac{1}{2} (x - \sin x \cos x)$

90. $\int \sin^n x \, dx = -\dfrac{\sin^{n-1} x \cos x}{n} + \dfrac{n-1}{n} \int \sin^{n-2} x \, dx$

91. $\int \dfrac{dx}{\sin^n x} = -\dfrac{\cos x}{(n-1) \sin^{n-1} x} + \dfrac{n-2}{n-1} \int \dfrac{dx}{\sin^{n-2} x}, \quad n \neq 1$

92. $\int \cos x \, dx = \sin x$

93. $\int \cos^2 x \, dx = \frac{1}{2} (x + \sin x \cos x)$

94. $\int \cos^n x \, dx = \dfrac{\cos^{n-1} x \sin x}{n} + \dfrac{n-1}{n} \int \cos^{n-2} x \, dx$

95. $\int \dfrac{dx}{\cos^n x} = \dfrac{\sin x}{(n-1) \cos^{n-1} x} + \dfrac{n-2}{n-1} \int \dfrac{dx}{\cos^{n-2} x}, \quad n \neq 1$

96. $\int \sin^n x \cos x \, dx = \dfrac{\sin^{n+1} x}{n+1}$

97. $\int \cos^n x \sin x \, dx = -\dfrac{\cos^{n+1} x}{n+1}$

606

98. $\displaystyle\int \sin^2 x \cos^2 x \, dx = \frac{4x - \sin 4x}{32}$

99. $\displaystyle\int \frac{dx}{\sin x \cos x} = \log_e \tan x$

100. $\displaystyle\int \sin^r x \cos^s x \, dx = \frac{\cos^{s-1} x \sin^{r+1} x}{r+s} + \frac{s-1}{r+s} \int \sin^r x \cos^{s-2} x \, dx,$
$$r + s \neq 0$$

$$= - \frac{\sin^{r-1} x \cos^{s+1} x}{r+s} + \frac{r-1}{r+s} \int \sin^{r-2} x \cos^s x \, dx,$$
$$r + s \neq 0$$

$$= \frac{\sin^{r+1} x \cos^{s+1} x}{r+1} + \frac{s+r+2}{r+1} \int \sin^{r+2} x \cos^s x \, dx,$$
$$r \neq -1$$

$$= - \frac{\sin^{r+1} x \cos^{s+1} x}{s+1}$$

$$+ \frac{s+r+2}{s+1} \int \sin^r x \cos^{s+2} x \, dx, \quad s \neq -1$$

101. $\displaystyle\int \tan x \, dx = -\log_e \cos x$

102. $\displaystyle\int \tan^n x \, dx = \frac{\tan^{n-1} x}{n-1} - \int \tan^{n-2} x \, dx$

103. $\displaystyle\int \cot x \, dx = \log_e \sin x$

104. $\displaystyle\int \cot^n x \, dx = - \frac{\cot^{n-1} x}{n-1} - \int \cot^{n-2} x \, dx$

105. $\displaystyle\int \sec x \, dx = \log_e (\sec x + \tan x)$

106. $\displaystyle\int \sec^2 x \, dx = \tan x$

107. $\displaystyle\int \sec^n x \, dx = \frac{\sin x}{(n-1) \cos^{n-1} x} + \frac{n-2}{n-1} \int \sec^{n-2} x \, dx, \quad n \neq 1$

Integral calculus *continued*

108. $\displaystyle\int \csc^2 x\, dx = -\cot x$

109. $\displaystyle\int \csc x\, dx = \log_e (\csc x - \cot x)$

110. $\displaystyle\int \csc^n x\, dx = \dfrac{\cos x}{-1)\,\sin^{n-1} x} + \dfrac{n-2}{n-1}\int \csc^{n-2} x\, dx, \quad n \neq 1$

111. $\displaystyle\int \sec^n x \tan x\, dx = \dfrac{\sec^n x}{n}$

112. $\displaystyle\int \csc^n x \cot x\, dx = -\dfrac{\csc^n x}{n}$

n is any constant $\neq 0$

113. $\displaystyle\int \tan^n x \sec^2 x\, dx = \dfrac{\tan^{n+1} x}{n+1}$

114. $\displaystyle\int \cot^n x \csc^2 x\, dx = -\dfrac{\cot^{n+1} x}{n+1}$

n is any constant $\neq -1$

115. $\displaystyle\int \dfrac{dx}{a + b \sin x} = \dfrac{-1}{\sqrt{a^2 - b^2}} \sin^{-1} \dfrac{b + a \sin x}{a + b \sin x},\qquad a^2 > b^2$

$\displaystyle\qquad = \dfrac{+1}{\sqrt{b^2 - a^2}} \log_e \dfrac{b + a \sin x - \sqrt{b^2 - a^2}\,(\cos x)}{a + b \sin x},$

$\qquad\qquad\qquad\qquad\qquad\qquad\qquad\qquad b^2 > a_2$

116. $\displaystyle\int \dfrac{dx}{a + b \cos x} = -\dfrac{1}{\sqrt{a^2 - b^2}} \sin^{-1} \left(\dfrac{b + a \cos x}{a + b \cos x}\right), \qquad a > b > 0$

$\displaystyle\qquad = \dfrac{1}{\sqrt{a^2 - b^2}} \cdot \sin^{-1} \left(\dfrac{\sqrt{a^2 - b^2} \cdot \sin x}{a + b \cos x}\right), a > b > 0$

$\displaystyle\qquad = \dfrac{1}{\sqrt{a^2 - b^2}} \cdot \tan^{-1} \left(\dfrac{\sqrt{a^2 - b^2} \cdot \sin x}{b + a \cos x}\right), a > b > 0$

$\displaystyle\qquad = \dfrac{1}{\sqrt{b^2 - a^2}} \log_e \left(\dfrac{b + a \cos x + \sqrt{b^2 - a^2} \sin x}{a + b \cos x}\right)$

$\qquad\qquad\qquad\qquad\qquad$ when $b^2 > a^2, a < 0$

117. $\displaystyle\int \sqrt{1 - \cos x}\, dx = -2\sqrt{2} \cos \dfrac{x}{2}$

Integral calculus *continued*

118. $\int \sqrt{(1 - \cos x)^3}\, dx = \dfrac{4\sqrt{2}}{3}\left(\cos^3 \dfrac{x}{2} - 3\cos \dfrac{x}{2}\right)$

119. $\int x \sin x\, dx = \sin x - x \cos x$

120. $\int x^2 \sin x\, dx = 2x \sin x + (2 - x^2)\cos x$

121. $\int x \cos x\, dx = \cos x + x \sin x$

122. $\int x^2 \cos x\, dx = 2x \cos x + (x^2 - 2)\sin x$

Inverse trigonometric integrals

123. $\int \sin^{-1} x\, dx = x \sin^{-1} x + \sqrt{1 - x^2}$

124. $\int \cos^{-1} x\, dx = x \cos^{-1} x - \sqrt{1 - x^2}$

125. $\int \tan^{-1} x\, dx = x \tan^{-1} x - \log_e \sqrt{1 + x^2}$

126. $\int \cot^{-1} x\, dx = x \cot^{-1} x + \log_e \sqrt{1 + x^2}$

127. $\int \sec^{-1} x\, dx = x \sec^{-1} x - \log_e (x + \sqrt{x^2 - 1})$
$\qquad\qquad\quad = x \sec^{-1} x - \cosh^{-1} x$

128. $\int \csc^{-1} x\, dx = x \csc^{-1} x + \log_e (x + \sqrt{x^2 - 1})$
$\qquad\qquad\quad = x \csc^{-1} x + \cosh^{-1} x$

Definite integrals

129. $\int_0^\infty \dfrac{a\, dx}{a^2 + x^2} = \dfrac{\pi}{2}$, if $a > 0$; $= 0$, if $a = 0$; $= -\dfrac{\pi}{2}$, if $a < 0$

130. $\int_0^\infty x^{n-1} e^{-x}\, dx = \int_0^1 \left[\log \dfrac{1}{x}\right]^{n-1} dx \equiv \Gamma(n)$ (*)

* $\Gamma(n) =$ gamma function

Integral calculus *continued*

131. $\displaystyle\int_0^1 x^{m-1}(1-x)^{n-1}\,dx = \int_0^\infty \frac{x^{m-1}\,dx}{(1+x)^{m+n}} = \frac{\Gamma(m)\,\Gamma(n)}{\Gamma(m+n)}$ (*)

132. $\displaystyle\int_0^{\frac{\pi}{2}} \sin^n x\,dx = \int_0^{\frac{\pi}{2}} \cos^n x\,dx = \tfrac12\sqrt{\pi}\,\frac{\Gamma\left(\dfrac{n+1}{2}\right)}{\Gamma\left(\dfrac{n}{2}+1\right)},\quad n > -1$

133. $\displaystyle\int_0^\infty \frac{\sin mx\,dx}{x} = \frac{\pi}{2}$, if $m > 0$; $= 0$, if $m = 0$; $= -\frac{\pi}{2}$, if $m < 0$

134. $\displaystyle\int_0^\infty \frac{\sin x \cdot \cos mx\,dx}{x} = 0$, if $m < -1$ or $m > 1$;

$\qquad\qquad\qquad = \frac{\pi}{4}$, if $m = -1$ or $m = 1$; $= \frac{\pi}{2}$, if $-1 < m < 1$

135. $\displaystyle\int_0^\infty \frac{\sin^2 x\,dx}{x^2} = \frac{\pi}{2}$

136. $\displaystyle\int_0^\infty \cos(x^2)\,dx = \int_0^\infty \sin(x^2)\,dx = \tfrac12\sqrt{\frac{\pi}{2}}$

137. $\displaystyle\int_0^\infty \frac{\cos mx\,dx}{1+x^2} = \frac{\pi}{2}\cdot e^{|-m|},\quad m > 0$

138. $\displaystyle\int_0^\infty \frac{\cos x\,dx}{\sqrt{x}} = \int_0^\infty \frac{\sin x\,dx}{\sqrt{x}} = \sqrt{\frac{\pi}{2}}$

139. $\displaystyle\int_0^\infty e^{-a^2 x^2}\,dx = \frac{1}{2a}\sqrt{\pi} = \frac{1}{2a}\,\Gamma(\tfrac12),\quad a > 0$ (*)

140. $\displaystyle\int_0^\infty x^{2n}\,e^{-ax^2}\,dx = \frac{1\cdot3\cdot5\cdots(2n-1)}{2^{n+1}\,a^n}\sqrt{\frac{\pi}{a}}$

141. $\displaystyle\int_0^\infty e^{-x^2-a^2/x^2}\,dx = \frac{e^{-2a}\sqrt{\pi}}{2},\quad a > 0$

142. $\displaystyle\int_0^\infty e^{-nx}\sqrt{x}\,dx = \frac{1}{2n}\sqrt{\frac{\pi}{n}}$

143. $\displaystyle\int_0^\infty \frac{e^{-nx}}{\sqrt{x}}\,dx = \sqrt{\frac{\pi}{n}}$

* $\Gamma(n) =$ gamma function

610

144. $\int_0^\infty e^{-a^2 x^2} \cos bx \, dx = \dfrac{\sqrt{\pi} \cdot e^{-b^2/4a^2}}{2a}$, $\quad a > 0$

145. $\int_0^1 \dfrac{\log_e x}{1-x} \, dx = -\dfrac{\pi^2}{6}$

146. $\int_0^1 \dfrac{\log_e x}{1+x} \, dx = -\dfrac{\pi^2}{12}$

147. $\int_0^1 \dfrac{\log_e x}{1-x^2} \, dx = -\dfrac{\pi^2}{8}$

148. $\int_0^1 \log_e \left(\dfrac{1+x}{1-x}\right) \cdot \dfrac{dx}{x} = \dfrac{\pi^2}{4}$

149. $\int_0^1 \dfrac{\log_e x \, dx}{\sqrt{1-x^2}} = -\dfrac{\pi}{2} \log_e 2$

150. $\int_0^1 \dfrac{(x^p - x^q) \, dx}{\log_e x} = \log_e \dfrac{p+1}{q+1}$, $p+1 > 0$, $q+1 > 0$

151. $\int_0^1 (\log_e x)^n \, dx = (-1)^n \cdot n!$

152. $\int_0^1 \dfrac{dx}{\sqrt{\log_e \left(\dfrac{1}{x}\right)}} = \sqrt{\pi}$

153. $\int_0^1 x^m \left(\log_e \dfrac{1}{x}\right)^n dx = \dfrac{\Gamma(n+1)}{(m+1)^{n+1}}$, $m+1 > 0$, $n+1 > 0$ (*)

154. $\int_0^\infty \log_e \left(\dfrac{e^x + 1}{e^x - 1}\right) dx = \dfrac{\pi^2}{4}$

155. $\int_0^{\frac{\pi}{2}} \log_e \sin x \, dx = \int_0^{\frac{\pi}{2}} \log_e \cos x \, dx = -\dfrac{\pi}{2} \log_e 2$

156. $\int_0^\pi x \cdot \log_e \sin x \, dx = -\dfrac{\pi^2}{2} \log_e 2$

157. $\int_0^\pi \log_e (a \pm b \cos x) \, dx = \pi \log_e \left(\dfrac{a + \sqrt{a^2 - b^2}}{2}\right)$, $\quad a \geqslant b$

* $\Gamma(n) = $ gamma function.

Integral calculus   *continued*

158. $\displaystyle\int_{-\frac{\pi}{2}}^{\frac{\pi}{2}} \frac{\cos^2\left(\frac{\pi}{2}\sin x\right) dx}{\cos x} = 1.22$

Table of Laplace transforms

Symbols

Constants are real unless otherwise specified.

$R(x) = $ "real part of x"
$j = \sqrt{-1}$
$f(t) = 0, t < 0$
$S_{-1}(t) = $ unit step
$\quad = 0, t < 0$
$\quad = 1, t > 0$
$S_0(t) = $ unit impulse
$\quad = 0, t < 0$
$\quad = 0, t > 0$
$\quad = \infty$, if $t = 0$, and $\displaystyle\int_{-\infty}^{\infty} S_0(t)\, dt = 1$

Note: Let

$f(t) = 0, t < 0$
$\quad = g(t), 0 < t < \delta \qquad \displaystyle\lim_{\delta\to 0}\int_0^\delta g(t)\, dt = 1$
$\quad = 0, t > \delta$

then $\quad S_0(t) = \displaystyle\lim_{\delta\to 0} f(t)$

$\omega = 2\pi \times$ frequency
$m,k = $ any positive integers
$\gamma = $ period of a periodic function $(t > 0)$
$\Gamma(x) = $ gamma function
$\quad = \displaystyle\int_0^\infty e^{-u} u^{x-1}\, du$
$\Gamma(k) = (k-1)!$, $k = $ positive integer
$J_0(x) = $ Bessel function, first kind, zero order
$J_k(x) = $ Bessel function, first kind, kth order

Table of Laplace transforms   *continued*

time function	transform
1. Definition $f(t)$	$F(p) = \displaystyle\int_0^\infty f(\lambda)\, e^{-p\lambda} d\lambda,\ R(p) > 0$
2. Inverse transform $f(t) = \dfrac{1}{j2\pi} \displaystyle\int_{c-j\infty}^{c+j\infty} F(z)\, e^{zt} dz,\ c > 0$ Note: No singularities to the right of path of integration.	$F(p)$
3. Shifting theorem $f(t-a)$	$e^{-ap} F(p),\ a > 0$ (*)
4. Borel, or "convolution" theorem $\displaystyle\int_0^t f_1(\lambda) f_2\,(t-\lambda)\, d\lambda$	$F_1(p)\, F_2(p)$ (*)
5. Periodic function $f(t) = f(t - k\gamma),\ t > k\gamma$	$\dfrac{\displaystyle\int_0^\gamma f(\lambda)\, e^{-p\lambda}\, d\lambda}{1 - e^{-p\gamma}}$
6. $f_1(t) + f_2(t)$	$F_1(p) + F_2(p)$ (*)
7. $\displaystyle\sum_{k=1}^{m} f_k(t)$	$\displaystyle\sum_{k=1}^{m} F_k(p)$ (*)
8. $f(t)\, e^{-at}$	$F(p + a)$ (*)
9. $f\left(\dfrac{t}{a}\right)$; a real, > 0	$aF(ap)$ (*)
10. Derivative $\dfrac{d}{dt} f(t)$	$-f(0) + pF(p)$ (*)
11. Integral $\displaystyle\int f(t)\ dt$	$\dfrac{1}{p}\left[\displaystyle\int f\, dt\right]_{t=0} + \dfrac{F(p)}{p}$ (*)

* See Pair 1.

Table of Laplace transforms   *continued*

time function	transform
12. Unit step $S_{-1}(t)$	$\dfrac{1}{p}$
13. Unit impulse $S_0(t)$	1
14. Unit cisoid $e^{j\omega t}$	$\dfrac{1}{p - j\omega}$
15. t	$\dfrac{1}{p^2}$
16. t^k	$\dfrac{k!}{p^{k+1}}$
17. t^v, $R(v) > -1$	$\dfrac{\Gamma(v + 1)}{p^{v+1}}$
18. $t^k e^{-at}$	$\dfrac{k!}{(p + a)^{k+1}}$
19. $1/\sqrt{\pi t}$	$1/\sqrt{p}$
20. $\dfrac{(2t)^k}{1 \cdot 3 \cdot 5 \cdots (2k-1)\sqrt{\pi t}}$	$\dfrac{1}{p^k \sqrt{p}}$
21. e^{at}	$\dfrac{1}{p - a}$
22. $\dfrac{1}{a}(e^{at} - 1)$	$\dfrac{1}{p(p - a)}$
23. $\sin at$	$\dfrac{a}{p^2 + a^2}$
24. $\cos at$	$\dfrac{p}{p^2 + a^2}$
25. $J_0(at)$	$\dfrac{1}{\sqrt{p^2 + a^2}}$
26. $J_k(at)$	$\dfrac{1}{r}\left(\dfrac{r - p}{a}\right)^k$, $\quad r^2 = p^2 + a^2$

Series

Maclaurin's theorem

$$f(x) = f(0) + xf'(0) + \frac{x^2}{1.2} f''(0) + \ldots + \frac{x^n}{n!} f^n(0) + \ldots$$

Taylor's theorem

$$f(x) = f(x_0) + f'(x_0) (x - x_0) + \frac{f''(x_0)}{2!} (x - x_0)^2 + \ldots$$

$$f(x + h) = f(x) + f'(x) \cdot h + \frac{f''(x)}{2!} h^2 + \ldots + \frac{f^n(x)}{n!} h^n + \ldots$$

Miscellaneous

$$\log_e (1 + x) = x - \frac{x^2}{2} + \frac{x^3}{3} - \frac{x^4}{4} + \ldots, \ |x| < 1$$

$$e^x = 1 + x + \frac{x_2}{2!} + \frac{x^3}{3!} + \ldots, \ |x| < \infty$$

$$\left. \begin{array}{l} \sin x = x - \dfrac{x^3}{3!} + \dfrac{x^5}{5!} - \dfrac{x^7}{7!} + \ldots \\[2mm] \cos x = 1 - \dfrac{x^2}{2!} + \dfrac{x^4}{4!} - \dfrac{x^6}{6!} + \ldots \end{array} \right\} \ |x| < \infty; \ x \text{ in radians}$$

$$\left. \begin{array}{l} \sinh x = x + \dfrac{x^3}{3!} + \dfrac{x^5}{5!} + \dfrac{x^7}{7!} + \ldots \\[2mm] \cosh x = 1 + \dfrac{x^2}{2!} + \dfrac{x^4}{4!} + \dfrac{x^6}{6!} + \ldots \end{array} \right\} \ |x| < \infty$$

For $n = 0$ or a positive integer, the expansion of the Bessel function of the first kind, nth order, is given by the convergent series,

$$J_n(x) = \frac{x^n}{2^n n!} \left[1 - \frac{x^2}{2 (2n + 2)} + \frac{x^4}{2 \cdot 4 (2n + 2) (2n + 4)} \right.$$

$$\left. - \frac{x^6}{2 \cdot 4 \cdot 6 (2n + 2) (2n + 4) (2n + 6)} + \ldots \right]$$

and

$$J_{-n}(x) = (-1)^n J_n(x)$$

Note: $0! = 1$

Series *continued*

Binomial series

See "Binomial theorem," p. 583.

$$\tan x = x + \frac{x^3}{3} + \frac{2x^5}{15} + \frac{17x^7}{315} + \frac{62x^9}{2835} + \ldots, \quad |x| < \frac{\pi}{2}$$

$$\cot x = \frac{1}{x} - \frac{x}{3} - \frac{x^3}{45} - \frac{2x^5}{945} - \frac{x^7}{4725} - \ldots, \quad |x| < \pi$$

$$\arcsin x = x + \frac{1}{2}\frac{x^3}{3} + \frac{1\cdot3}{2\cdot4}\frac{x^5}{5} + \frac{1\cdot3\cdot5}{2\cdot4\cdot6}\frac{x^7}{7} + \ldots, \quad |x| < 1$$

$$\arctan x = x - \frac{x^3}{3} + \frac{x^5}{5} - \frac{x^7}{7} + \ldots, \quad |x| < 1$$

$$\operatorname{arc\,sinh} x = x - \frac{1}{2}\frac{x^3}{3} + \frac{1\cdot3}{2\cdot4}\frac{x^5}{5} - \frac{1\cdot3\cdot5}{2\cdot4\cdot6}\frac{x^7}{7} + \ldots, \quad |x| < 1$$

$$\operatorname{arc\,tanh} x = x + \frac{x^3}{3} + \frac{x^5}{5} + \frac{x^7}{7} + \ldots, \quad |x| < 1$$

Vector-analysis formulas

Rectangular coordinates

In the following, vectors are indicated in **bold-faced** type.

Associative law: For addition

$$\boldsymbol{a} + (\boldsymbol{b} + \boldsymbol{c}) = (\boldsymbol{a} + \boldsymbol{b}) + \boldsymbol{c} = \boldsymbol{a} + \boldsymbol{b} + \boldsymbol{c}$$

Commutative law: For addition

$$\boldsymbol{a} + \boldsymbol{b} = \boldsymbol{b} + \boldsymbol{a}$$

where

$$\boldsymbol{a} = a\boldsymbol{a_1}$$

a = magnitude of $\boldsymbol{a}$

$\boldsymbol{a_1}$ = unit vector in direction of $\boldsymbol{a}$

Scalar, or "dot" product

$$\boldsymbol{a}\cdot\boldsymbol{b} = \boldsymbol{b}\cdot\boldsymbol{a}$$
$$= ab\cos\theta$$

where θ = angle included by $\boldsymbol{a}$ and $\boldsymbol{b}$.

Vector-analysis formulas   *continued*

Vector, or "cross" product

$$a \times b = -b \times a$$
$$= ab \sin \theta \cdot c_1$$

where

θ = angle swept in rotating a into b

c_1 = unit vector perpendicular to plane of a and b, and directed in the sense of travel of a right-hand screw rotating from a to b through the angle θ.

Distributive law for scalar multiplication

$$a \cdot (b + c) = a \cdot b + a \cdot c$$

Distributive law for vector multiplication

$$a \times (b + c) = a \times b + a \times c$$

Scalar triple product

$$a \cdot b \times c = a \times b \cdot c = c \cdot a \times b = b \cdot c \times a$$

Vector triple product

$$a \times (b \times c) = (a \cdot c)b - (a \cdot b)c$$
$$(a \times b) \cdot (c \times d) = (a \cdot c)(b \cdot d) - (a \cdot d)(b \cdot c)$$
$$(a \times b) \times (c \times d) = (a \times b \cdot d)c - (a \times b \cdot c)d$$

∇ = operator "del"

$$\equiv i \frac{\partial}{\partial x} + j \frac{\partial}{\partial y} + k \frac{\partial}{\partial z}$$

where i, j, k are unit vectors in directions of x, y, z coordinates, respectively.

$$\operatorname{grad} \phi = \nabla \phi = i \frac{\partial \phi}{\partial x} + j \frac{\partial \phi}{\partial y} + k \frac{\partial \phi}{\partial z}$$

$$\operatorname{grad} (\phi + \psi) = \operatorname{grad} \phi + \operatorname{grad} \psi$$

$$\operatorname{grad} (\phi \psi) = \phi \operatorname{grad} \psi + \psi \operatorname{grad} \phi$$

$$\operatorname{curl} \operatorname{grad} \phi = 0$$

$$\operatorname{div} a = \nabla \cdot a = \frac{\partial a_x}{\partial x} + \frac{\partial a_y}{\partial y} + \frac{\partial a_z}{\partial z}$$

Vector-analysis formulas   *continued*

where a_x, a_y, a_z are the components of a in the directions of the respective coordinate axes.

$$\operatorname{div} (a + b) = \operatorname{div} a + \operatorname{div} b$$

$$\operatorname{curl} a = \nabla \times a$$

$$= i \left(\frac{\partial a_z}{\partial y} - \frac{\partial a_y}{\partial z} \right) + j \left(\frac{\partial a_x}{\partial z} - \frac{\partial a_z}{\partial x} \right) + k \left(\frac{\partial a_y}{\partial x} - \frac{\partial a_x}{\partial y} \right)$$

$$= \begin{vmatrix} i & j & k \\ \dfrac{\partial}{\partial x} & \dfrac{\partial}{\partial y} & \dfrac{\partial}{\partial z} \\ a_x & a_y & a_z \end{vmatrix}$$

$$\operatorname{curl} (\phi a) = \operatorname{grad} \phi \times a + \phi \operatorname{curl} a$$

$$\operatorname{div} \operatorname{curl} a = 0$$

$$\operatorname{div} (a \times b) = b \cdot \operatorname{curl} a - a \cdot \operatorname{curl} b$$

$$\nabla^2 \equiv \text{Laplacian}$$

$$\nabla^2 \phi = \frac{\partial^2 \phi}{\partial x^2} + \frac{\partial^2 \phi}{\partial y^2} + \frac{\partial^2 \phi}{\partial z^2}$$

in rectangular coordinates.

$$\operatorname{curl} \operatorname{curl} a = \operatorname{grad} \operatorname{div} a - (i \nabla^2 a_x + j \nabla^2 a_y + k \nabla^2 a_z)$$

In the following formulas τ is a volume bounded by a closed surface S. The unit vector n is normal to the surface S and directed positively outwards.

$$\int_\tau \nabla \phi \cdot d\tau = \int_S \phi n \, dS$$

$$\int_\tau \nabla \cdot a \, d\tau = \int_S a \cdot n \, dS \quad \text{(Gauss' theorem)}$$

$$\int_\tau \nabla \times a \, d\tau = \int_S n \times a \, dS$$

$$\int_\tau (\psi \nabla^2 \phi - \phi \nabla^2 \psi) \, d\tau = \int_S \left(\psi \frac{\partial \phi}{\partial n} - \phi \frac{\partial \psi}{\partial n} \right) dS$$

where $\partial / \partial n$ is the derivative in the direction of the positive normal to S (Green's theorem).

Vector-analysis formulas *continued*

In the two following formulas S is an open surface bounded by a contour C, with distance along C represented by s.

$$\int_S \mathbf{n} \times \nabla \phi \, dS = \int_C \phi \, d\mathbf{s}$$

$$\int_S \nabla \times \mathbf{a} \cdot \mathbf{n} \, dS = \int_C \mathbf{a} \cdot d\mathbf{s} \quad \text{(Stokes' theorem)}$$

where $\mathbf{s} = s\mathbf{s_1}$, and $\mathbf{s_1}$ is a unit vector in the direction of s.

Gradient, divergence, curl, and Laplacian in coordinate systems other than rectangular

Cylindrical coordinates: (ρ, ϕ, z), unit vectors $\rho_1, \phi_1, \mathbf{k}$, respectively,

$$\text{grad } \psi = \nabla \psi = \frac{\partial \psi}{\partial \rho} \rho_1 + \frac{1}{\rho} \frac{\partial \psi}{\partial \phi} \phi_1 + \frac{\partial \psi}{\partial z} \mathbf{k}$$

$$\text{div } \mathbf{a} = \nabla \cdot \mathbf{a} = \frac{1}{\rho} \frac{\partial}{\partial \rho} (\rho a_\rho) + \frac{1}{\rho} \left(\frac{\partial a_\phi}{\partial \phi} \right) + \frac{\partial a_z}{\partial z}$$

$$\text{curl } \mathbf{a} = \nabla \times \mathbf{a} = \left(\frac{1}{\rho} \frac{\partial a_z}{\partial \phi} - \frac{\partial a_\phi}{\partial z} \right) \rho_1 + \left(\frac{\partial a_\rho}{\partial z} - \frac{\partial a_z}{\partial \rho} \right) \phi_1$$
$$+ \left[\frac{1}{\rho} \frac{\partial}{\partial \rho} (\rho a_\phi) - \frac{1}{\rho} \frac{\partial a_\rho}{\partial \phi} \right] \mathbf{k}$$

$$\nabla^2 \psi = \frac{1}{\rho} \frac{\partial}{\partial \rho} \left(\rho \frac{\partial \psi}{\partial \rho} \right) + \frac{1}{\rho^2} \frac{\partial^2 \psi}{\partial \phi^2} + \frac{\partial^2 \psi}{\partial z^2}$$

Spherical coordinates: (r, θ, ϕ), unit vectors $\mathbf{r_1}, \theta_1, \phi_1$

r = distance to origin
θ = polar angle
ϕ = azimuthal angle

$$\text{grad } \psi = \nabla \psi = \frac{\partial \psi}{\partial r} \mathbf{r_1} + \frac{1}{r} \frac{\partial \psi}{\partial \theta} \theta_1 + \frac{1}{r \sin \theta} \frac{\partial \psi}{\partial \phi} \phi_1$$

$$\text{div } \mathbf{a} = \nabla \cdot \mathbf{a} = \frac{1}{r^2} \frac{\partial}{\partial r} (r^2 a_r) + \frac{1}{r \sin \theta} \frac{\partial}{\partial \theta} (a_\theta \sin \theta) + \frac{1}{r \sin \theta} \frac{\partial a_\phi}{\partial \phi}$$

$$\text{curl } \mathbf{a} = \nabla \times \mathbf{a} = \frac{1}{r \sin \theta} \left[\frac{\partial}{\partial \theta} (a_\phi \sin \theta) - \frac{\partial a_\theta}{\partial \phi} \right] \mathbf{r_1}$$
$$+ \frac{1}{r} \left[\frac{1}{\sin \theta} \frac{\partial a_r}{\partial \phi} - \frac{\partial}{\partial r} (r a_\phi) \right] \theta_1$$
$$+ \frac{1}{r} \left[\frac{\partial}{\partial r} (r a_\theta) - \frac{\partial a_r}{\partial \theta} \right] \phi_1$$

Vector-analysis formulas   *continued*

$$\nabla^2 \psi = \frac{1}{r^2} \frac{\partial}{\partial r} \left(r^2 \frac{\partial \psi}{\partial r} \right) + \frac{1}{r^2 \sin \theta} \frac{\partial}{\partial \theta} \left(\sin \theta \frac{\partial \psi}{\partial \theta} \right) + \frac{1}{r^2 \sin^2 \theta} \frac{\partial^2 \psi}{\partial \phi^2}$$

Orthogonal curvilinear coordinates

Coordinates: u_1, u_2, u_3

Metric coefficients: h_1, h_2, h_3 $(ds^2 = h_1^2 du_1^2 + h_2^2 du_2^2 + h_3^2 du_3^2)$

Unit vectors: i_1, i_2, i_3 $(d\mathbf{s} = i_1 h_1 du_1 + i_2 h_2 du_2 + i_3 h_3 du_3)$

$$\text{grad } \psi = \nabla \psi = \frac{1}{h_1} \frac{\partial \psi}{\partial u_1} i_1 + \frac{1}{h_2} \frac{\partial \psi}{\partial u_2} i_2 + \frac{1}{h_3} \frac{\partial \psi}{\partial u_3} i_3$$

$$\text{div } \mathbf{a} = \nabla \cdot \mathbf{a} = \frac{1}{h_1 h_2 h_3} \left[\frac{\partial}{\partial u_1} (h_2 h_3 a_1) + \frac{\partial}{\partial u_2} (h_3 h_1 a_2) + \frac{\partial}{\partial u_3} (h_1 h_2 a_3) \right]$$

$$\text{curl } \mathbf{a} = \nabla \times \mathbf{a} = \frac{1}{h_2 h_3} \left[\frac{\partial}{\partial u_2} (h_3 a_3) - \frac{\partial}{\partial u_3} (h_2 a_2) \right] i_1$$

$$+ \frac{1}{h_3 h_1} \left[\frac{\partial}{\partial u_3} (h_1 a_1) - \frac{\partial}{\partial u_1} (h_3 a_3) \right] i_2$$

$$+ \frac{1}{h_1 h_2} \left[\frac{\partial}{\partial u_1} (h_2 a_2) - \frac{\partial}{\partial u_2} (h_1 a_1) \right] i_3$$

$$= \frac{1}{h_1 h_2 h_3} \begin{vmatrix} h_1 i_1 & h_2 i_2 & h_3 i_3 \\ \dfrac{\partial}{\partial u_1} & \dfrac{\partial}{\partial u_2} & \dfrac{\partial}{\partial u_3} \\ h_1 a_1 & h_2 a_2 & h_3 a_3 \end{vmatrix}$$

$$\nabla^2 \psi = \frac{1}{h_1 h_2 h_3} \left[\frac{\partial}{\partial u_1} \left(\frac{h_2 h_3}{h_1} \frac{\partial \phi}{\partial u_1} \right) + \frac{\partial}{\partial u_2} \left(\frac{h_3 h_1}{h_2} \frac{\partial \phi}{\partial u_2} \right) + \frac{\partial}{\partial u_3} \left(\frac{h_1 h_2}{h_3} \frac{\partial \phi}{\partial u_3} \right) \right]$$

■ Mathematical tables

Common logarithms of numbers and proportional parts

	0	1	2	3	4	5	6	7	8	9	1	2	3	4	5	6	7	8	9
10	0000	0043	0086	0128	0170	0212	0253	0294	0334	0374	4	8	12	17	21	25	29	33	37
11	0414	0453	0492	0531	0569	0607	0645	0682	0719	0755	4	8	11	15	19	23	26	30	34
12	0792	0828	0864	0899	0934	0969	1004	1038	1072	1106	3	7	10	14	17	21	24	28	31
13	1139	1173	1206	1239	1271	1303	1335	1367	1399	1430	3	6	10	13	16	19	23	26	29
14	1461	1492	1523	1553	1584	1614	1644	1673	1703	1732	3	6	9	12	15	18	21	24	27
15	1761	1790	1818	1847	1875	1903	1931	1959	1987	2014	3	6	8	11	14	17	20	22	25
16	2041	2068	2095	2122	2148	2175	2201	2227	2253	2279	3	5	8	11	13	16	18	21	24
17	2304	2330	2355	2380	2405	2430	2455	2480	2504	2529	2	5	7	10	12	15	17	20	22
18	2553	2577	2601	2625	2648	2672	2695	2718	2742	2765	2	5	7	9	12	14	16	19	21
19	2788	2810	2833	2856	2878	2900	2923	2945	2967	2989	2	4	7	9	11	13	16	18	20
20	3010	3032	3054	3075	3096	3118	3139	3160	3181	3201	2	4	6	8	11	13	15	17	19
21	3222	3243	3263	3284	3304	3324	3345	3365	3385	3404	2	4	6	8	10	12	14	16	18
22	3424	3444	3464	3483	3502	3522	3541	3560	3579	3598	2	4	6	8	10	12	14	15	17
23	3617	3636	3655	3674	3692	3711	3729	3747	3766	3784	2	4	6	7	9	11	13	15	17
24	3802	3820	3838	3856	3874	3892	3909	3927	3945	3962	2	4	5	7	9	11	12	14	16
25	3979	3997	4014	4031	4048	4065	4082	4099	4116	4133	2	3	5	7	9	10	12	14	15
26	4150	4166	4183	4200	4216	4232	4249	4265	4281	4298	2	3	5	7	8	10	11	13	15
27	4314	4330	4346	4362	4378	4393	4409	4425	4440	4456	2	3	5	6	8	9	11	13	14
28	4472	4487	4502	4518	4533	4548	4564	4579	4594	4609	2	3	5	6	8	9	11	12	14
29	4624	4639	4654	4669	4683	4698	4713	4728	4742	4757	1	3	4	6	7	9	10	12	13
30	4771	4786	4800	4814	4829	4843	4857	4871	4886	4900	1	3	4	6	7	9	10	11	13
31	4914	4928	4942	4955	4969	4983	4997	5011	5024	5038	1	3	4	6	7	8	10	11	12
32	5051	5065	5079	5092	5105	5119	5132	5145	5159	5172	1	3	4	5	7	8	9	11	12
33	5185	5198	5211	5224	5237	5250	5263	5276	5289	5302	1	3	4	5	6	8	9	10	12
34	5315	5328	5340	5353	5366	5378	5391	5403	5416	5428	1	3	4	5	6	8	9	10	11
35	5441	5453	5465	5478	5490	5502	5514	5527	5539	5551	1	2	4	5	6	7	9	10	11
36	5563	5575	5587	5599	5611	5623	5635	5647	5658	5670	1	2	4	5	6	7	8	10	11
37	5682	5694	5705	5717	5729	5740	5752	5763	5775	5786	1	2	3	5	6	7	8	9	10
38	5798	5809	5821	5832	5843	5855	5866	5877	5888	5899	1	2	3	5	6	7	8	9	10
39	5911	5922	5933	5944	5955	5966	5977	5988	5999	6010	1	2	3	4	5	7	8	9	10
40	6021	6031	6042	6053	6064	6075	6085	6096	6107	6117	1	2	3	4	5	6	8	9	10
41	6128	6138	6149	6160	6170	6180	6191	6201	6212	6222	1	2	3	4	5	6	7	8	9
42	6232	6243	6253	6263	6274	6284	6294	6304	6314	6325	1	2	3	4	5	6	7	8	9
43	6335	6345	6355	6365	6375	6385	6395	6405	6415	6425	1	2	3	4	5	6	7	8	9
44	6435	6444	6454	6464	6474	6484	6493	6503	6513	6522	1	2	3	4	5	6	7	8	9
45	6532	6542	6551	6561	6571	6580	6590	6599	6609	6618	1	2	3	4	5	6	7	8	9
46	6628	6637	6646	6656	6665	6675	6684	6693	6702	6712	1	2	3	4	5	6	7	7	8
47	6721	6730	6739	6749	6758	6767	6776	6785	6794	6803	1	2	3	4	5	5	6	7	8
48	6812	6821	6830	6839	6848	6857	6866	6875	6884	6893	1	2	3	4	4	5	6	7	8
49	6902	6911	6920	6928	6937	6946	6955	6964	6972	6981	1	2	3	4	4	5	6	7	8
50	6990	6998	7007	7016	7024	7033	7042	7050	7059	7067	1	2	3	3	4	5	6	7	8
51	7076	7084	7093	7101	7110	7118	7126	7135	7143	7152	1	2	3	3	4	5	6	7	8
52	7160	7168	7177	7185	7193	7202	7210	7218	7226	7235	1	2	2	3	4	5	6	7	7
53	7243	7251	7259	7267	7275	7284	7292	7300	7308	7316	1	2	2	3	4	5	6	6	7
54	7324	7332	7340	7348	7356	7364	7372	7380	7388	7396	1	2	2	3	4	5	6	6	7

Common logarithms of numbers and proportional parts *continued*

	0	1	2	3	4	5	6	7	8	9	1 2 3	4 5 6	7 8 9
55	7404	7412	7419	7427	7435	7443	7451	7459	7466	7474	1 2 2	3 4 5	5 6 7
56	7482	7490	7497	7505	7513	7520	7528	7536	7543	7551	1 2 2	3 4 5	5 6 7
57	7559	7566	7574	7582	7589	7597	7604	7612	7619	7627	1 2 2	3 4 5	5 6 7
58	7634	7642	7649	7657	7664	7672	7679	7686	7694	7701	1 1 2	3 4 4	5 6 7
59	7709	7716	7723	7731	7738	7745	7752	7760	7767	7774	1 1 2	3 4 4	5 6 7
60	7782	7789	7796	7803	7810	7818	7825	7832	7839	7846	1 1 2	3 4 4	5 6 6
61	7853	7860	7868	7875	7882	7889	7896	7903	7910	7917	1 1 2	3 4 4	5 6 6
62	7924	7931	7938	7945	7952	7959	7966	7973	7980	7987	1 1 2	3 3 4	5 6 6
63	7993	8000	8007	8014	8021	8028	8035	8041	8048	8055	1 1 2	3 3 4	5 5 6
64	8062	8069	8075	8082	8089	8096	8102	8109	8116	8122	1 1 2	3 3 4	5 5 6
65	8129	8136	8142	8149	8156	8162	8169	8176	8182	8189	1 1 2	3 3 4	5 5 6
66	8195	8202	8209	8215	8222	8228	8235	8241	8248	8254	1 1 2	3 3 4	5 5 6
67	8261	8267	8274	8280	8287	8293	8299	8306	8312	8319	1 1 2	3 3 4	5 5 6
68	8325	8331	8338	8344	8351	8357	8363	8370	8376	8382	1 1 2	3 3 4	4 5 6
69	8388	8395	8401	8407	8414	8420	8426	8432	8439	8445	1 1 2	2 3 4	4 5 6
70	8451	8457	8463	8470	8476	8482	8488	8494	8500	8506	1 1 2	2 3 4	4 5 6
71	8513	8519	8525	8531	8537	8543	8549	8555	8561	8567	1 1 2	2 3 4	4 5 5
72	8573	8579	8585	8591	8597	8603	8609	8615	8621	8627	1 1 2	2 3 4	4 5 5
73	8633	8639	8645	8651	8657	8663	8669	8675	8681	8686	1 1 2	2 3 4	4 5 5
74	8692	8698	8704	8710	8716	8722	8727	8733	8739	8745	1 1 2	2 3 4	4 5 5
75	8751	8756	8762	8768	8774	8779	8785	8791	8797	8802	1 1 2	2 3 3	4 5 5
76	8808	8814	8820	8825	8831	8837	8842	8848	8854	8859	1 1 2	2 3 3	4 5 5
77	8865	8871	8876	8882	8887	8893	8899	8904	8910	8915	1 1 2	2 3 3	4 4 5
78	8921	8927	8932	8938	8943	8949	8954	8960	8965	8971	1 1 2	2 3 3	4 4 5
79	8976	8982	8987	8993	8998	9004	9009	9015	9020	9025	1 1 2	2 3 3	4 4 5
80	9031	9036	9042	9047	9053	9058	9063	9069	9074	9079	1 1 2	2 3 3	4 4 5
81	9085	9090	9096	9101	9106	9112	9117	9122	9128	9133	1 1 2	2 3 3	4 4 5
82	9138	9143	9149	9154	9159	9165	9170	9175	9180	9186	1 1 2	2 3 3	4 4 5
83	9191	9196	9201	9206	9212	9217	9222	9227	9232	9238	1 1 2	2 3 3	4 4 5
84	9243	9248	9253	9258	9263	9269	9274	9279	9284	9289	1 1 2	2 3 3	4 4 5
85	9294	9299	9304	9309	9315	9320	9325	9330	9335	9340	1 1 2	2 3 3	4 4 5
86	9345	9350	9355	9360	9365	9370	9375	9380	9385	9390	1 1 2	2 3 3	4 4 5
87	9395	9400	9405	9410	9415	9420	9425	9430	9435	9440	0 1 1	2 2 3	3 4 4
88	9445	9450	9455	9460	9465	9469	9474	9479	9484	9489	0 1 1	2 2 3	3 4 4
89	9494	9499	9504	9509	9513	9518	9523	9528	9533	9538	0 1 1	2 2 3	3 4 4
90	9542	9547	9552	9557	9562	9566	9571	9576	9581	9586	0 1 1	2 2 3	3 4 4
91	9590	9595	9600	9605	9609	9614	9619	9624	9628	9633	0 1 1	2 2 3	3 4 4
92	9638	9643	9647	9652	9657	9661	9666	9671	9675	9680	0 1 1	2 2 3	3 4 4
93	9685	9689	9694	9699	9703	9708	9713	9717	9722	9727	0 1 1	2 2 3	3 4 4
94	9731	9736	9741	9745	9750	9754	9759	9763	9768	9773	0 1 1	2 2 3	3 4 4
95	9777	9782	9786	9791	9795	9800	9805	9809	9814	9818	0 1 1	2 2 3	3 4 4
96	9823	9827	9832	9836	9841	9845	9850	9854	9859	9863	0 1 1	2 2 3	3 4 4
97	9868	9872	9877	9881	9886	9890	9894	9899	9903	9908	0 1 1	2 2 3	3 4 4
98	9912	9917	9921	9926	9930	9934	9939	9943	9948	9952	0 1 1	2 2 3	3 4 4
99	9956	9961	9965	9969	9974	9978	9983	9987	9991	9996	0 1 1	2 2 3	3 3 4

The *proportional parts* columns are headed: 1 2 3 | 4 5 6 | 7 8 9

Natural trigonometric functions

for decimal fractions of a degree

deg	sin	cos	tan	cot		deg	sin	cos	tan	cot	
0.0	.00000	1.0000	.00000	∞	90.0	6.0	.10453	0.9945	.10510	9.514	84.0
.1	.00175	1.0000	.00175	573.0	.9	.1	.10626	.9943	.10687	9.357	.9
.2	.00349	1.0000	.00349	286.5	.8	.2	.10800	.9942	.10863	9.205	.8
.3	.00524	1.0000	.00524	191.0	.7	.3	.10973	.9940	.11040	9.058	.7
.4	.00698	1.0000	.00698	143.24	.6	.4	.11147	.9938	.11217	8.915	.6
.5	.00873	1.0000	.00873	114.59	.5	.5	.11320	9936	.11394	8.777	.5
.6	.01047	0.9999	.01047	95.49	.4	.6	.11494	.9934	.11570	8.643	.4
.7	.01222	.9999	.01222	81.85	.3	.7	.11667	.9932	.11747	8.513	.3
.8	.01396	.9999	.01396	71.62	.2	.8	.11840	.9930	.11924	8.386	.2
.9	.01571	.9999	.01571	63.66	.1	.9	.12014	.9928	.12101	8.264	.1
1.0	.01745	0.9998	.01746	57.29	89.0	7.0	.12187	0.9925	.12278	8.144	83.0
.1	.01920	.9998	.01920	52.08	.9	.1	.12360	.9923	.12456	8.028	.9
.2	.02094	.9998	.02095	47.74	.8	.2	.12533	.9921	.12633	7.916	.8
.3	.02269	.9997	.02269	44.07	.7	.3	.12706	.9919	.12810	7.806	.7
.4	.02443	.9997	.02444	40.92	.6	.4	.12880	.9917	.12988	7.700	.6
.5	.02618	.9997	.02619	38.19	.5	.5	.13053	.9914	.13165	7.596	.5
.6	.02792	.9996	.02793	35.80	.4	.6	.13226	.9912	.13343	7.495	.4
.7	.02967	.9996	.02968	33.69	.3	.7	.13399	.9910	.13521	7.396	.3
.8	.03141	.9995	.03143	31.82	.2	.8	.13572	.9907	.13698	7.300	.2
.9	.03316	.9995	.03317	30.14	.1	.9	.13744	.9905	.13876	7.207	.1
2.0	.03490	0.9994	.03492	28.64	88.0	8.0	.13917	0.9903	.14054	7.115	82.0
.1	.03664	.9993	.03667	27.27	.9	.1	.14090	.9900	.14232	7.026	.9
.2	.03839	.9993	.03842	26.03	.8	.2	.14263	.9898	.14410	6.940	.8
.3	.04013	.9992	.04016	24.90	.7	.3	.14436	.9895	.14588	6.855	.7
.4	.04188	.9991	.04191	23.86	.6	.4	.14608	.9893	.14767	6.772	.6
.5	.04362	.9990	.04366	22.90	.5	.5	.14781	.9890	.14945	6.691	.5
.6	.04536	.9990	.04541	22.02	.4	.6	.14954	.9888	.15124	6.612	.4
.7	.04711	.9989	.04716	21.20	.3	.7	.15126	.9885	.15302	6.535	.3
.8	.04885	.9988	.04891	20.45	.2	.8	.15299	.9882	.15481	6.460	.2
.9	.05059	.9987	.05066	19.74	.1	.9	.15471	.9880	.15660	6.386	.1
3.0	.05234	0.9986	.05241	19.081	87.0	9.0	.15643	0.9877	.15838	6.314	81.0
.1	.05408	.9985	.05416	18.464	.9	.1	.15816	.9874	.16017	6.243	.9
.2	.05582	.9984	.05591	17.886	.8	.2	.15988	.9871	.16196	6.174	.8
.3	.05756	.9983	.05766	17.343	.7	.3	.16160	.9869	.16376	6.107	.7
.4	.05931	.9982	.05941	16.832	.6	.4	.16333	.9866	.16555	6.041	.6
.5	.06105	.9981	.06116	16.350	.5	.5	.16505	.9863	.16734	5.976	.5
.6	.06279	.9980	.06291	15.895	.4	.6	.16677	.9860	.16914	5.912	.4
.7	.06453	.9979	.06467	15.464	.3	.7	.16849	.9857	.17093	5.850	.3
.8	.06627	.9978	.06642	15.056	.2	.8	.17021	.9854	.17273	5.789	.2
.9	.06802	.9977	.06817	14.669	.1	.9	.17193	.9851	.17453	5.730	.1
4.0	.06976	0.9976	.06993	14.301	86.0	10.0	.1736	0.9848	.1763	5.671	80.0
.1	.07150	.9974	.07168	13.951	.9	.1	.1754	.9845	.1781	5.614	.9
.2	.07324	.9973	.07344	13.617	.8	.2	.1771	.9842	.1799	5.558	.8
.3	.07498	.9972	.07519	13.300	.7	.3	.1788	.9839	.1817	5.503	.7
.4	.07672	.9971	.07695	12.996	.6	.4	.1805	.9836	.1835	5.449	.6
.5	.07846	.9969	.07870	12.706	.5	.5	.1822	.9833	.1853	5.396	.5
.6	.08020	.9968	.08046	12.429	.4	.6	.1840	.9829	.1871	5.343	.4
.7	.08194	.9966	.08221	12.163	.3	.7	.1857	.9826	.1890	5.292	.3
.8	.08368	.9965	.08397	11.909	.2	.8	.1874	.9823	.1908	5.242	.2
.9	.08542	.9963	.08573	11.664	.1	.9	.1891	.9820	.1926	5.193	.1
5.0	.08716	0.9962	.08749	11.430	85.0	11.0	.1908	0.9816	.1944	5.145	79.0
.1	.08889	.9960	.08925	11.205	.9	.1	.1925	.9813	.1962	5.097	.9
.2	.09063	.9959	.09101	10.988	.8	.2	.1942	.9810	.1980	5.050	.8
.3	.09237	.9957	.09277	10.780	.7	.3	.1959	.9806	.1998	5.005	.7
.4	.09411	.9956	.09453	10.579	.6	.4	.1977	.9803	.2016	4.959	.6
.5	.09585	.9954	.09629	10.385	.5	.5	.1994	.9799	.2035	4.915	.5
.6	.09758	.9952	.09805	10.199	.4	.6	.2011	.9796	.2053	4.872	.4
.7	.09932	.9951	.09981	10.019	.3	.7	*2028	.9792	.2071	4.829	.3
.8	.10106	.9949	.10158	9.845	.2	.8	.2045	.9789	.2089	4.787	.2
.9	.10279	.9947	.10334	9.677	.1	.9	.2062	.9785	.2107	4.745	.1
6.0	.10453	0.9945	.10510	9.514	84.0	12.0	.2079	0.9781	.2126	4.705	78.0
	cos	sin	cot	tan	deg		cos	sin	cot	tan	deg

Natural trigonometric functions

for decimal fractions of a degree *continued*

deg	sin	cos	tan	cot		deg	sin	cos	tan	cot	
12.0	0.2079	0.9781	0.2126	4.705	**78.0**	**18.0**	0.3090	0.9511	0.3249	3.078	**72.0**
.1	.2096	.9778	.2144	4.665	.9	.1	.3107	.9505	.3269	3.060	.9
.2	.2113	.9774	.2162	4.625	.8	.2	.3123	.9500	.3288	3.042	.8
.3	.2130	.9770	.2180	4.586	.7	.3	.3140	.9494	.3307	3.024	.7
.4	.2147	.9767	.2199	4.548	.6	.4	.3156	.9489	.3327	3.006	.6
.5	.2164	.9763	.2217	4.511	.5	.5	.3173	.9483	.3346	2.989	.5
.6	.2181	.9759	.2235	4.474	.4	.6	.3190	.9478	.3365	2.971	.4
.7	.2198	.9755	.2254	4.437	.3	.7	.3206	.9472	.3385	2.954	.3
.8	.2215	.9751	.2272	4.402	.2	.8	.3223	.9466	.3404	2.937	.2
.9	.2233	.9748	.2290	4.366	.1	.9	.3239	.9461	.3424	2.921	.1
13.0	0.2250	0.9744	0.2309	4.331	**77.0**	**19.0**	0.3256	0.9455	0.3443	2.904	**71.0**
.1	.2267	.9740	.2327	4.297	.9	.1	.3272	.9449	.3463	2.888	.9
.2	.2284	.9736	.2345	4.264	.8	.2	.3289	.9444	.3482	2.872	.8
.3	.2300	.9732	.2364	4.230	.7	.3	.3305	.9438	.3502	2.856	.7
.4	.2317	.9728	.2382	4.198	.6	.4	.3322	.9432	.3522	2.840	.6
.5	.2334	.9724	.2401	4.165	.5	.5	.3338	.9426	.3541	2.824	.5
.6	.2351	.9720	.2419	4.134	.4	.6	.3355	.9421	.3561	2.808	.4
.7	.2368	.9715	.2438	4.102	.3	.7	.3371	.9415	.3581	2.793	.3
.8	.2385	.9711	.2456	4.071	.2	.8	.3387	.9409	.3600	2.778	.2
.9	.2402	.9707	.2475	4.041	.1	.9	.3404	.9403	.3620	2.762	.1
14.0	0.2419	0.9703	0.2493	4.011	**76.0**	**20.0**	0.3420	0.9397	0.3640	2.747	**70.0**
.1	.2436	.9699	.2512	3.981	.9	.1	.3437	.9391	.3659	2.733	.9
.2	.2453	.9694	.2530	3.952	.8	.2	.3453	.9385	.3679	2.718	.8
.3	.2470	.9690	.2549	3.923	.7	.3	.3469	.9379	.3699	2.703	.7
.4	.2487	.9686	.2568	3.895	.6	.4	.3486	.9373	.3719	2.689	.6
.5	.2504	.9681	.2586	3.867	.5	.5	.3502	.9367	.3739	2.675	.5
.6	.2521	.9677	.2605	3.839	.4	.6	.3518	.9361	.3759	2.660	.4
.7	.2538	.9673	.2623	3.812	.3	.7	.3535	.9354	.3779	2.646	.3
.8	.2554	.9668	.2642	3.785	.2	.8	.3551	.9348	.3799	2.633	.2
.9	.2571	.9664	.2661	3.758	.1	.9	.3567	.9342	.3819	2.619	.1
15.0	0.2588	0.9659	0.2679	3.732	**75.0**	**21.0**	0.3584	0.9336	0.3839	2.605	**69.0**
.1	.2605	.9655	.2698	3.706	.9	.1	.3600	.9330	.3859	2.592	.9
.2	.2622	.9650	.2717	3.681	.8	.2	.3616	.9323	.3879	2.578	.8
.3	.2639	.9646	.2736	3.655	.7	.3	.3633	.9317	.3899	2.565	.7
.4	.2656	.9641	.2754	3.630	.6	.4	.3649	.9311	.3919	2.552	.6
.5	.2672	.9636	.2773	3.606	.5	.5	.3665	.9304	.3939	2.539	.5
.6	.2689	.9632	.2792	3.582	.4	.6	.3681	.9298	.3959	2.526	.4
.7	.2706	.9627	.2811	3.558	.3	.7	.3697	.9291	.3979	2.513	.3
.8	.2723	.9622	.2830	3.534	.2	.8	.3714	.9285	.4000	2.500	.2
.9	.2740	.9617	.2849	3.511	.1	.9	.3730	.9278	.4020	2.488	.1
16.0	0.2756	0.9613	0.2867	3.487	**74.0**	**22.0**	0.3746	0.9272	0.4040	2.475	**68.0**
.1	.2773	.9608	.2886	3.465	.9	.1	.3762	.9265	.4061	2.463	.9
.2	.2790	.9603	.2905	3.442	.8	.2	.3778	.9259	.4081	2.450	.8
.3	.2807	.9598	.2924	3.420	.7	.3	.3795	.9252	.4101	2.438	.7
.4	.2823	.9593	.2943	3.398	.6	.4	.3811	.9245	.4122	2.426	.6
.5	.2840	.9588	.2962	3.376	.5	.5	.3827	.9239	.4142	2.414	.5
.6	.2857	.9583	.2981	3.354	.4	.6	.3843	.9232	.4163	2.402	.4
.7	.2874	.9578	.3000	3.333	.3	.7	.3859	.9225	.4183	2.391	.3
.8	.2890	.9573	.3019	3.312	.2	.8	.3875	.9219	.4204	2.379	.2
.9	.2907	.9568	.3038	3.291	.1	.9	.3891	.9212	.4224	2.367	.1
17.0	0.2924	0.9563	0.3057	3.271	**73.0**	**23.0**	0.3907	0.9205	0.4245	2.356	**67.0**
.1	.2940	.9558	.3076	3.251	.9	.1	.3923	.9198	.4265	2.344	.9
.2	.2957	.9553	.3096	3.230	.8	.2	.3939	.9191	.4286	2.333	.8
.3	.2974	.9548	.3115	3.211	.7	.3	.3955	.9184	.4307	2.322	.7
.4	.2990	.9542	.3134	3.191	.6	.4	.3971	.9178	.4327	2.311	.6
.5	.3007	.9537	.3153	3.172	.5	.5	.3987	.9171	.4343	2.300	.5
.6	.3024	.9532	.3172	3.152	.4	.6	.4003	.9164	.4369	2.289	.4
.7	.3040	.9527	.3191	3.133	.3	.7	.4019	.9157	.4390	2.278	.3
.8	.3057	.9521	.3211	3.115	.2	.8	.4035	.9150	.4411	2.267	.2
.9	.3074	.9516	.3230	3.096	.1	.9	.4051	.9143	.4431	2.257	.1
18.0	0.3090	0.9511	0.3249	3.078	**72.0**	**24.0**	0.4067	0.9135	0.4452	2.246	**66.0**

| cos | sin | cot | tan | deg | | cos | sin | cot | tan | deg |

Natural trigonometric functions

for decimal fractions of a degree *continued*

deg	sin	cos	tan	cot		deg	sin	cos	tan	cot	
24.0	0.4067	0.9135	0.4452	2.246	**66.0**	**30.0**	0.5000	0.8660	0.5774	1.7321	**60.0**
.1	.4083	.9128	.4473	2.236	.9	.1	.5015	.8652	.5797	1.7251	.9
.2	.4099	.9121	.4494	2.225	.8	.2	.5030	.8643	.5820	1.7182	.8
.3	.4115	.9114	.4515	2.215	.7	.3	.5045	.8634	.5844	1.7113	.7
.4	.4131	.9107	.4536	2.204	.6	.4	.5060	.8625	.5867	1.7045	.6
.5	.4147	.9100	.4557	2.194	.5	.5	.5075	.8616	.5890	1.6977	.5
.6	.4163	.9092	.4578	2.184	.4	.6	.5090	.8607	.5914	1.6909	.4
.7	.4179	.9085	.4599	2.174	.3	.7	.5105	.8599	.5938	1.6842	.3
.8	.4195	.9078	.4621	2.164	.2	.8	.5120	.8590	.5961	1.6775	.2
.9	.4210	.9070	.4642	2.154	.1	.9	.5135	.8581	.5985	1.6709	.1
25.0	0.4226	0.9063	0.4663	2.145	**65.0**	**31.0**	0.5150	0.8572	0.6009	1.6643	**59.0**
.1	.4242	.9056	.4684	2.135	.9	.1	.5165	.8563	.6032	1.6577	.9
.2	.4258	.9048	.4706	2.125	.8	.2	.5180	.8554	.6056	1.6512	.8
.3	.4274	.9041	.4727	2.116	.7	.3	.5195	.8545	.6080	1.6447	.7
.4	.4289	.9033	.4748	2.106	.6	.4	.5210	.8536	.6104	1.6383	.6
.5	.4305	.9026	.4770	2.097	.5	.5	.5225	.8526	.6128	1.6319	.5
.6	.4321	.9018	.4791	2.087	.4	.6	.5240	.8517	.6152	1.6255	.4
.7	.4337	.9011	.4813	2.078	.3	.7	.5255	.8508	.6176	1.6191	.3
.8	.4352	.9003	.4834	2.069	.2	.8	.5270	.8499	.6200	1.6128	.2
.9	.4368	.8996	.4856	2.059	.1	.9	.5284	.8490	.6224	1.6066	.1
26.0	0.4384	0.8988	0.4877	2.050	**64.0**	**32.0**	0.5299	0.8480	0.6249	1.6003	**58.0**
.1	.4399	.8980	.4899	2.041	.9	.1	.5314	.8471	.6273	1.5941	.9
.2	.4415	.8973	.4921	2.032	.8	.2	.5329	.8462	.6297	1.5880	.8
.3	.4431	.8965	.4942	2.023	.7	.3	.5344	.8453	.6322	1.5818	.7
.4	.4446	.8957	.4964	2.014	.6	.4	.5358	.8443	.6346	1.5757	.6
.5	.4462	.8949	.4986	2.006	.5	.5	.5373	.8434	.6371	1.5697	.5
.6	.4478	.8942	.5008	1.997	.4	.6	.5388	.8425	.6395	1.5637	.4
.7	.4493	.8934	.5029	1.988	.3	.7	.5402	.8415	.6420	1.5577	.3
.8	.4509	.8926	.5051	1.980	.2	.8	.5417	.8406	.6445	1.5517	.2
.9	.4524	.8918	.5073	1.971	.1	.9	.5432	.8396	.6469	1.5458	.1
27.0	0.4540	0.8910	0.5095	1.963	**63.0**	**33.0**	0.5446	0.8387	0.6494	1.5399	**57.0**
.1	.4555	.8902	.5117	1.954	.9	.1	.5461	.8377	.6519	1.5340	.9
.2	.4571	.8894	.5139	1.946	.8	.2	.5476	.8368	.6544	1.5282	.8
.3	.4586	.8886	.5161	1.937	.7	.3	.5490	.8358	.6569	1.5224	.7
.4	.4602	.8878	.5184	1.929	.6	.4	.5505	.8348	.6594	1.5166	.6
.5	.4617	.8870	.5206	1.921	.5	.5	.5519	.8339	.6619	1.5108	.5
.6	.4633	.8862	.5228	1.913	.4	.6	.5534	.8329	.6644	1.5051	.4
.7	.4648	.8854	.5250	1.905	.3	.7	.5548	.8320	.6669	1.4994	.3
.8	.4664	.8846	.5272	1.897	.2	.8	.5563	.8310	.6694	1.4938	.2
.9	.4679	.8838	.5295	1.889	.1	.9	.5577	.8300	.6720	1.4882	.1
28.0	0.4695	0.8829	0.5317	1.881	**62.0**	**34.0**	0.5592	0.8290	0.6745	1.4826	**56.0**
.1	.4710	.8821	.5340	1.873	.9	.1	.5606	.8281	.6771	1.4770	.9
.2	.4726	.8813	.5362	1.865	.8	.2	.5621	.8271	.6796	1.4715	.8
.3	.4741	.8805	.5384	1.857	.7	.3	.5635	.8261	.6822	1.4659	.7
.4	.4756	.8796	.5407	1.849	.6	.4	.5650	.8251	.6847	1.4605	.6
.5	.4772	.8788	.5430	1.842	.5	.5	.5664	.8241	.6873	1.4550	.5
.6	.4787	.8780	.5452	1.834	.4	.6	.5678	.8231	.6899	1.4496	.4
.7	.4802	.8771	.5475	1.827	.3	.7	.5693	.8221	.6924	1.4442	.3
.8	.4818	.8763	.5498	1.819	.2	.8	.5707	.8211	.6950	1.4388	.2
.9	.4833	.8755	.5520	1.811	.1	.9	.5721	.8202	.6976	1.4335	.1
29.0	0.4848	0.8746	0.5543	1.804	**61.0**	**35.0**	0.5736	0.8192	0.7002	1.4281	**55.0**
.1	.4863	.8738	.5566	1.797	.9	.1	.5750	.8181	.7028	1.4229	.9
.2	.4879	.8729	.5589	1.789	.8	.2	.5764	.8171	.7054	1.4176	.8
.3	.4894	.8721	.5612	1.782	.7	.3	.5779	.8161	.7080	1.4124	.7
.4	.4909	.8712	.5635	1.775	.6	.4	.5793	.8151	.7107	1.4071	.6
.5	.4924	.8704	.5658	1.767	.5	.5	.5807	.8141	.7133	1.4019	.5
.6	.4939	.8695	.5681	1.760	.4	.6	.5821	.8131	.7159	1.3968	.4
.7	.4955	.8686	.5704	1.753	.3	.7	.5835	.8121	.7186	1.3916	.3
.8	.4970	.8678	.5727	1.746	.2	.8	.5850	.8111	.7212	1.3865	.2
.9	.4985	.8669	.5750	1.739	.1	.9	.5864	.8100	.7239	1.3814	.1
30.0	0.5000	0.8660	0.5774	1.732	**60.0**	**36.0**	0.5878	0.8090	0.7265	1.3764	**54.0**
	cos	sin	cot	tan	deg		cos	sin	cot	tan	deg

Natural trigonometric functions

for decimal fractions of a degree *continued*

deg	sin	cos	tan	cot		deg	sin	cos	tan	cot	
36.0	0.5878	0.8090	0.7265	1.3764	**54.0**	**40.5**	0.6494	0.7604	0.8541	1.1708	**49.5**
.1	.5892	.8080	.7292	1.3713	.9	.6	.6508	.7593	.8571	1.1667	.4
.2	.5906	.8070	.7319	1.3663	.8	.7	.6521	.7581	.8601	1.1626	.3
.3	.5920	.8059	.7346	1.3613	.7	.8	.6534	.7570	.8632	1.1585	.2
.4	.5934	.8049	.7373	1.3564	.6	.9	.6547	.7559	.8662	1.1544	.1
.5	.5948	.8039	.7400	1.3514	.5	**41.0**	0.6561	0.7547	0.8693	1.1504	**49.0**
.6	.5962	.8028	.7427	1.3465	.4	.1	.6574	.7536	.8724	1.1463	.9
.7	.5976	.8018	.7454	1.3416	.3	.2	.6587	.7524	.8754	1.1423	.8
.8	.5990	.8007	.7481	1.3367	.2	.3	.6600	.7513	.8785	1.1383	.7
.9	.6004	.7997	.7508	1.3319	.1	.4	.6613	.7501	.8816	1.1343	.6
37.0	0.6018	0.7986	0.7536	1.3270	**53.0**	.5	.6626	.7490	.8847	1.1303	.5
.1	.6032	.7976	.7563	1.3222	.9	.6	.6639	.7478	.8878	1.1263	.4
.2	.6046	.7965	.7590	1.3175	.8	.7	.6652	.7466	.8910	1.1224	.3
.3	.6060	.7955	.7618	1.3127	.7	.8	.6665	.7455	.8941	1.1184	.2
.4	.6074	.7944	.7646	1.3079	.6	.9	.6678	.7443	.8972	1.1145	.1
.5	.6088	.7934	.7673	1.3032	.5	**42.0**	0.6691	0.7431	0.9004	1.1106	**48.0**
.6	.6101	.7923	.7701	1.2985	.4	.1	.6704	.7420	.9036	1.1067	.9
.7	.6115	.7912	.7729	1.2938	.3	.2	.6717	.7408	.9067	1.1028	.8
.8	.6129	.7902	.7757	1.2892	.2	.3	.6730	.7396	.9099	1.0990	.7
.9	.6143	.7891	.7785	1.2846	.1	.4	.6743	.7385	.9131	1.0951	.6
38.0	0.6157	0.7880	0.7813	1.2799	**52.0**	.5	.6756	.7373	.9163	1.0913	.5
.1	.6170	.7869	.7841	1.2753	.9	.6	.6769	.7361	.9195	1.0875	.4
.2	.6184	.7859	.7869	1.2708	.8	.7	.6782	.7349	.9228	1.0837	.3
.3	.6198	.7848	.7898	1.2662	.7	.8	.6794	.7337	.9260	1.0799	.2
.4	.6211	.7837	.7926	1.2617	.6	.9	.6807	.7325	.9293	1.0761	.1
.5	.6225	.7826	.7954	1.2572	.5	**43.0**	0.6820	0.7314	0.9325	1.0724	**47.0**
.6	.6239	.7815	.7983	1.2527	.4	.1	.6833	.7302	.9358	1.0686	.9
.7	.6252	.7804	.8012	1.2482	.3	.2	.6845	.7290	.9391	1.0649	.8
.8	.6266	.7793	.8040	1.2437	.2	.3	.6858	.7278	.9424	1.0612	.7
.9	.6280	.7782	.8069	1.2393	.1	.4	.6871	.7266	.9457	1.0575	.6
39.0	0.6293	0.7771	0.8098	1.2349	**51.0**	.5	.6884	.7254	.9490	1.0538	.5
.1	.6307	.7760	.8127	1.2305	.9	.6	.6896	.7242	.9523	1.0501	.4
.2	.6320	.7749	.8156	1.2261	.8	.7	.6909	.7230	.9556	1.0464	.3
.3	.6334	.7738	.8185	1.2218	.7	.8	.6921	.7218	.9590	1.0428	.2
.4	.6347	.7727	.8214	1.2174	.6	.9	.6934	.7206	.9623	1.0392	.1
.5	.6361	.7716	.8243	1.2131	.5	**44.0**	0.6947	0.7193	0.9657	1.0355	**46.0**
.6	.6374	.7705	.8273	1.2088	.4	.1	.6959	.7181	.9691	1.0319	.9
.7	.6388	.7694	.8302	1.2045	.3	.2	.6972	.7169	.9725	1.0283	.8
.8	.6401	.7683	.8332	1.2002	.2	.3	.6984	.7157	.9759	1.0247	.7
.9	.6414	.7672	.8361	1.1960	.1	.4	.6997	.7145	.9793	1.0212	.6
40.0	0.6428	0.7660	0.8391	1.1918	**50.0**	.5	.7009	.7133	.9827	1.0176	.5
.1	.6441	.7649	.8421	1.1875	.9	.6	.7022	.7120	.9861	1.0141	.4
.2	.6455	.7638	.8451	1.1833	.8	.7	.7034	.7108	.9896	1.0105	.3
.3	.6468	.7627	.8481	1.1792	.7	.8	.7046	.7096	.9930	1.0070	.2
.4	.6481	.7615	.8511	1.1750	.6	.9	.7059	.7083	.9965	1.0035	.1
40.5	0.6494	0.7604	0.8541	1.1708	**49.5**	**45.0**	0.7071	0.7071	1.0000	1.0000	**45.0**

| | cos | sin | cot | tan | deg | | cos | sin | cot | tan | deg |

626

Logarithms of trigonometric functions

for decimal fractions of a degree

deg	L sin	L cos	L tan	L cot		deg	L sin	L cos	L tan	L cot	
0.0	−∞	0.0000	−∞	∞	90.0	6.0	9.0192	9.9976	9.0216	0.9784	84.0
.1	7.2419	0.0000	7.2419	2.7581	.9	.1	9.0264	9.9975	9.0289	0.9711	.9
.2	7.5429	0.0000	7.5429	2.4571	.8	.2	9.0334	9.9975	9.0360	0.9640	.8
.3	7.7190	0.0000	7.7190	2.2810	.7	.3	9.0403	9.9974	9.0430	0.9570	.7
.4	7.8439	0.0000	7.8439	2.1561	.6	.4	9.0472	9.9973	9.0499	0.9501	.6
.5	7.9408	0.0000	7.9409	2.0591	.5	.5	9.0539	9.9972	9.0567	0.9433	.5
.6	8.0200	0.0000	8.0200	1.9800	.4	.6	9.0605	9.9971	9.0633	0.9367	.4
.7	8.0870	0.0000	8.0870	1.9130	.3	.7	9.0670	9.9970	9.0699	0.9301	.3
.8	8.1450	0.0000	8.1450	1.8550	.2	.8	9.0734	9.9969	9.0764	0.9236	.2
.9	8.1961	9.9999	8.1962	1.8038	.1	.9	9.0797	9.9968	9.0828	0.9172	.1
1.0	8.2419	9.9999	8.2419	1.7581	89.0	7.0	9.0859	9.9968	9.0891	0.9109	83.0
.1	8.2832	9.9999	8.2833	1.7167	.9	.1	9.0920	9.9967	9.0954	0.9046	.9
.2	8.3210	9.9999	8.3211	1.6789	.8	.2	9.0981	9.9966	9.1015	0.8985	.8
.3	8.3558	9.9999	8.3559	1.6441	.7	.3	9.1040	9.9965	9.1076	0.8924	.7
.4	8.3880	9.9999	8.3881	1.6119	.6	.4	9.1099	9.9964	9.1135	0.8865	.6
.5	8.4179	9.9999	8.4181	1.5819	.5	.5	9.1157	9.9963	9.1194	0.8806	.5
.6	8.4459	9.9998	8.4461	1.5539	.4	.6	9.1214	9.9962	9.1252	0.8748	.4
.7	8.4723	9.9998	8.4725	1.5275	.3	.7	9.1271	9.9961	9.1310	0.8690	.3
.8	8.4971	9.9998	8.4973	1.5027	.2	.8	9.1326	9.9960	9.1367	0.8633	.2
.9	8.5206	9.9998	8.5208	1.4792	.1	.9	9.1381	9.9959	9.1423	0.8577	.1
2.0	8.5428	9.9997	8.5431	1.4569	88.0	8.0	9.1436	9.9958	9.1478	0.8522	82.0
.1	8.5640	9.9997	8.5643	1.4357	.9	.1	9.1489	9.9956	9.1533	0.8467	.9
.2	8.5842	9.9997	8.5845	1.4155	.8	.2	9.1542	9.9955	9.1587	0.8413	.8
.3	8.6035	9.9996	8.6038	1.3962	.7	.3	9.1594	9.9954	9.1640	0.8360	.7
.4	8.6220	9.9996	8.6223	1.3777	.6	.4	9.1646	9.9953	9.1693	0.8307	.6
.5	8.6397	9.9996	8.6401	1.3599	.5	.5	9.1697	9.9952	9.1745	0.8255	.5
.6	8.6567	9.9996	8.6571	1.3429	.4	.6	9.1747	9.9951	9.1797	0.8203	.4
.7	8.6731	9.9995	8.6736	1.3264	.3	.7	9.1797	9.9950	9.1848	0.8152	.3
.8	8.6889	9.9995	8.6894	1.3106	.2	.8	9.1847	9.9949	9.1898	0.8102	.2
.9	8.7041	9.9994	8.7046	1.2954	.1	.9	9.1895	9.9947	9.1948	0.8052	.1
3.0	8.7188	9.9994	8.7194	1.2806	87.0	9.0	9.1943	9.9946	9.1997	0.8003	81.0
.1	8.7330	9.9994	8.7337	1.2663	.9	.1	9.1991	9.9945	9.2046	0.7954	.9
.2	8.7468	9.9993	8.7475	1.2525	.8	.2	9.2038	9.9944	9.2094	0.7906	.8
.3	8.7602	9.9993	8.7609	1.2391	.7	.3	9.2085	9.9943	9.2142	0.7858	.7
.4	8.7731	9.9992	8.7739	1.2261	.6	.4	9.2131	9.9941	9.2189	0.7811	.6
.5	8.7857	9.9992	8.7865	1.2135	.5	.5	9.2176	9.9940	9.2236	0.7764	.5
.6	8.7979	9.9991	8.7988	1.2012	.4	.6	9.2221	9.9939	9.2282	0.7718	.4
.7	8.8098	9.9991	8.8107	1.1893	.3	.7	9.2266	9.9937	9.2328	0.7672	.3
.8	8.8213	9.9990	8.8223	1.1777	.2	.8	9.2310	9.9936	9.2374	0.7626	.2
.9	8.8326	9.9990	8.8336	1.1664	.1	.9	9.2353	9.9935	9.2419	0.7581	.1
4.0	8.8436	9.9989	8.8446	1.1554	86.0	10.0	9.2397	9.9934	9.2463	0.7537	80.0
.1	8.8543	9.9989	8.8554	1.1446	.9	.1	9.2439	9.9932	9.2507	0.7493	.9
.2	8.8647	9.9988	8.8659	1.1341	.8	.2	9.2482	9.9931	9.2551	0.7449	.8
.3	8.8749	9.9988	8.8762	1.1238	.7	.3	9.2524	9.9929	9.2594	0.7406	.7
.4	8.8849	9.9987	8.8862	1.1138	.6	.4	9.2565	9.9928	9.2637	0.7363	.6
.5	8.8946	9.9987	8.8960	1.1040	.5	.5	9.2606	9.9927	9.2680	0.7320	.5
.6	8.9042	9.9986	8.9056	1.0944	.4	.6	9.2647	9.9925	9.2722	0.7278	.4
.7	8.9135	9.9985	8.9150	1.0850	.3	.7	9.2687	9.9924	9.2764	0.7236	.3
.8	8.9226	9.9985	8.9241	1.0759	.2	.8	9.2727	9.9922	9.2805	0.7195	.2
.9	8.9315	9.9984	8.9331	1.0669	.1	.9	9.2767	9.9921	9.2846	0.7154	.1
5.0	8.9403	9.9983	8.9420	1.0580	85.0	11.0	9.2806	9.9919	9.2887	0.7113	79.0
.1	8.9489	9.9983	8.9506	1.0494	.9	.1	9.2845	9.9918	9.2927	0.7073	.9
.2	8.9573	9.9982	8.9591	1.0409	.8	.2	9.2883	9.9916	9.2967	0.7033	.8
.3	8.9655	9.9981	8.9674	1.0326	.7	.3	9.2921	9.9915	9.3006	0.6994	.7
.4	8.9736	9.9981	8.9756	1.0244	.6	.4	9.2959	9.9913	9.3046	0.6954	.6
.5	8.9816	9.9980	8.9836	1.0164	.5	.5	9.2997	9.9912	9.3085	0.6915	.5
.6	8.9894	9.9979	8.9915	1.0085	.4	.6	9.3034	9.9910	9.3123	0.6877	.4
.7	8.9970	9.9978	8.9992	1.0008	.3	.7	9.3070	9.9909	9.3162	0.6838	.3
.8	9.0046	9.9978	9.0068	0.9932	.2	.8	9.3107	9.9907	9.3200	0.6800	.2
.9	9.0120	9.9977	9.0143	0.9857	.1	.9	9.3143	9.9906	9.3237	0.6763	.1
6.0	9.0192	9.9976	9.0216	0.9784	84.0	12.0	9.3179	9.9904	9.3275	0.6725	78.0

| | L cos | L sin | L cot | L tan | deg | | L cos | L sin | L cot | L tan | deg |

Logarithms of trigonometric functions

for decimal fractions of a degree *continued*

deg	L sin	L cos	L tan	L cot		deg	L sin	L cos	L tan	L cot	
12.0	9.3179	9.9904	9.3275	0.6725	78.0	18.0	9.4900	9.9782	9.5118	0.4882	72.0
.1	9.3214	9.9902	9.3312	0.6688	.9	.1	9.4923	9.9780	9.5143	0.4857	.9
.2	9.3250	9.9901	9.3349	0.6651	.8	.2	9.4946	9.9777	9.5169	0.4831	.8
.3	9.3284	9.9899	9.3385	0.6615	.7	.3	9.4969	9.9775	9.5195	0.4805	.7
.4	9.3319	9.9897	9.3422	0.6578	.6	.4	9.4992	9.9772	9.5220	0.4780	.6
.5	9.3353	9.9896	9.3458	0.6542	.5	.5	9.5015	9.9770	9.5245	0.4755	.5
.6	9.3387	9.9894	9.3493	0.6507	.4	.6	9.5037	9.9767	9.5270	0.4730	.4
.7	9.3421	9.9892	9.3529	0.6471	.3	.7	9.5060	9.9764	9.5295	0.4705	.3
.8	9.3455	9.9891	9.3564	0.6436	.2	.8	9.5082	9.9762	9.5320	0.4680	.2
.9	9.3488	9.9889	9.3599	0.6401	.1	.9	9.5104	9.9759	9.5345	0.4655	.1
13.0	9.3521	9.9887	9.3634	0.6366	77.0	19.0	9.5126	9.9757	9.5370	0.4630	71.0
.1	9.3554	9.9885	9.3668	0.6332	.9	.1	9.5148	9.9754	9.5394	0.4606	.9
.2	9.3586	9.9884	9.3702	0.6298	.8	.2	9.5170	9.9751	9.5419	0.4581	.8
.3	9.3618	9.9882	9.3736	0.6264	.7	.3	9.5192	9.9749	9.5443	0.4557	.7
.4	9.3650	9.9880	9.3770	0.6230	.6	.4	9.5213	9.9746	9.5467	0.4533	.6
.5	9.3682	9.9878	9.3804	0.6196	.5	.5	9.5235	9.9743	9.5491	0.4509	.5
.6	9.3713	9.9876	9.3837	0.6163	.4	.6	9.5256	9.9741	9.5516	0.4484	.4
.7	9.3745	9.9875	9.3870	0.6130	.3	.7	9.5278	9.9738	9.5539	0.4461	.3
.8	9.3775	9.9873	9.3903	0.6097	.2	.8	9.5299	9.9735	9.5563	0.4437	.2
.9	9.3806	9.9871	9.3935	0.6065	.1	.9	9.5320	9.9733	9.5587	0.4413	.1
14.0	9.3837	9.9869	9.3968	0.6032	76.0	20.0	9.5341	9.9730	9.5611	0.4389	70.0
.1	9.3867	9.9867	9.4000	0.6000	.9	.1	9.5361	9.9727	9.5634	0.4366	.9
.2	9.3897	9.9865	9.4032	0.5968	.8	.2	9.5382	9.9724	9.5658	0.4342	.8
.3	9.3927	9.9863	9.4064	0.5936	.7	.3	9.5402	9.9722	9.5681	0.4319	.7
.4	9.3957	9.9861	9.4095	0.5905	.6	.4	9.5423	9.9719	9.5704	0.4296	.6
.5	9.3986	9.9859	9.4127	0.5873	.5	.5	9.5443	9.9716	9.5727	0.4273	.5
.6	9.4015	9.9857	9.4158	0.5842	.4	.6	9.5463	9.9713	9.5750	0.4250	.4
.7	9.4044	9.9855	9.4189	0.5811	.3	.7	9.5484	9.9710	9.5773	0.4227	.3
.8	9.4073	9.9853	9.4220	0.5780	.2	.8	9.5504	9.9707	9.5796	0.4204	.2
.9	9.4102	9.9851	9.4250	0.5750	.1	.9	9.5523	9.9704	9.5819	0.4181	.1
15.0	9.4130	9.9849	9.4281	0.5719	75.0	21.0	9.5543	9.9702	9.5842	0.4158	69.0
.1	9.4158	9.9847	9.4311	0.5689	.9	.1	9.5563	9.9699	9.5864	0.4136	.9
.2	9.4186	9.9845	9.4341	0.5659	.8	.2	9.5583	9.9696	9.5887	0.4113	.8
.3	9.4214	9.9843	9.4371	0.5629	.7	.3	9.5602	9.9693	9.5909	0.4091	.7
.4	9.4242	9.9841	9.4400	0.5600	.6	.4	9.5621	9.9690	9.5932	0.4068	.6
.5	9.4269	9.9839	9.4430	0.5570	.5	.5	9.5641	9.9687	9.5954	0.4046	.5
.6	9.4296	9.9837	9.4459	0.5541	.4	.6	9.5660	9.9684	9.5976	0.4024	.4
.7	9.4323	9.9835	9.4488	0.5512	.3	.7	9.5679	9.9681	9.5998	0.4002	.3
.8	9.4350	9.9833	9.4517	0.5483	.2	.8	9.5698	9.9678	9.6020	0.3980	.2
.9	9.4377	9.9831	9.4546	0.5454	.1	.9	9.5717	9.9675	9.6042	0.3958	.1
16.0	9.4403	9.9828	9.4575	0.5425	74.0	22.0	9.5736	9.9672	9.6064	0.3936	68.0
.1	9.4430	9.9826	9.4603	0.5397	.9	.1	9.5754	9.9669	9.6086	0.3914	.9
.2	9.4456	9.9824	9.4632	0.5368	.8	.2	9.5773	9.9666	9.6108	0.3892	.8
.3	9.4482	9.9822	9.4660	0.5340	.7	.3	9.5792	9.9662	9.6129	0.3871	.7
.4	9.4508	9.9820	9.4688	0.5312	.6	.4	9.5810	9.9659	9.6151	0.3849	.6
.5	9.4533	9.9817	9.4716	0.5284	.5	.5	9.5828	9.9656	9.6172	0.3828	.5
.6	9.4559	9.9815	9.4744	0.5256	.4	.6	9.5847	9.9653	9.6194	0.3806	.4
.7	9.4584	9.9813	9.4771	0.5229	.3	.7	9.5865	9.9650	9.6215	0.3785	.3
.8	9.4609	9.9811	9.4799	0.5201	.2	.8	9.5883	9.9647	9.6236	0.3764	.2
.9	9.4634	9.9808	9.4826	0.5174	.1	.9	9.5901	9.9643	9.6257	0.3743	.1
17.0	9.4659	9.9806	9.4853	0.5147	73.0	23.0	9.5919	9.9640	9.6279	0.3721	67.0
.1	9.4684	9.9804	9.4880	0.5120	.9	.1	9.5937	9.9637	9.6300	0.3700	.9
.2	9.4709	9.9801	9.4907	0.5093	.8	.2	9.5954	9.9634	9.6321	0.3679	.8
.3	9.4733	9.9799	9.4934	0.5066	.7	.3	9.5972	9.9631	9.6341	0.3659	.7
.4	9.4757	9.9797	9.4961	0.5039	.6	.4	9.5990	9.9627	9.6362	0.3638	.6
.5	9.4781	9.9794	9.4987	0.5013	.5	.5	9.6007	9.9624	9.6383	0.3617	.5
.6	9.4805	9.9792	9.5014	0.4986	.4	.6	9.6024	9.9621	9.6404	0.3596	.4
.7	9.4829	9.9789	9.5040	0.4960	.3	.7	9.6042	9.9617	9.6424	0.3576	.3
.8	9.4853	9.9787	9.5066	0.4934	.2	.8	9.6059	9.9614	9.6445	0.3555	.2
.9	9.4876	9.9785	9.5092	0.4908	.1	.9	9.6076	9.9611	9.6465	0.3535	.1
18.0	9.4900	9.9782	9.5118	0.4882	72.0	24.0	9.6093	9.9607	9.6486	0.3514	66.0
	L cos	L sin	L cot	L tan	deg		L cos	L sin	L cot	L tan	deg

Logarithms of trigonometric functions

for decimal fractions of a degree *continued*

deg	L sin	L cos	L tan	L cot		deg	L sin	L cos	L tan	L cot	
24.0	9.6093	9.9607	9.6486	0.3514	66.0	30.0	9.6990	9.9375	9.7614	0.2386	60.0
.1	9.6110	9.9604	9.6506	0.3494	.9	.1	9.7003	9.9371	9.7632	0.2368	.9
.2	9.6127	9.9601	9.6527	0.3473	.8	.2	9.7016	9.9367	9.7649	0.2351	.8
.3	9.6144	9.9597	9.6547	0.3453	.7	.3	9.7029	9.9362	9.7667	0.2333	.7
.4	9.6161	9.9594	9.6567	0.3433	.6	.4	9.7042	9.9358	9.7684	0.2316	.6
.5	9.6177	9.9590	9.6587	0.3413	.5	.5	9.7055	9.9353	9.7701	0.2299	.5
.6	9.6194	9.9587	9.6607	0.3393	.4	.6	9.7068	9.9349	9.7719	0.2281	.4
.7	9.6210	9.9583	9.6627	0.3373	.3	.7	9.7080	9.9344	9.7736	0.2264	.3
.8	9.6227	9.9580	9.6647	0.3353	.2	.8	9.7093	9.9340	9.7753	0.2247	.2
.9	9.6243	9.9576	9.6667	0.3333	.1	.9	9.7106	9.9335	9.7771	0.2229	.1
25.0	9.6259	9.9573	9.6687	0.3313	65.0	31.0	9.7118	9.9331	9.7788	0.2212	59.0
.1	9.6276	9.9569	9.6706	0.3294	.9	.1	9.7131	9.9326	9.7805	0.2195	.9
.2	9.6292	9.9566	9.6726	0.3274	.8	.2	9.7144	9.9322	9.7822	0.2178	.8
.3	9.6308	9.9562	9.6746	0.3254	.7	.3	9.7156	9.9317	9.7839	0.2161	.7
.4	9.6324	9.9558	9.6765	0.3235	.6	.4	9.7168	9.9312	9.7856	0.2144	.6
.5	9.6340	9.9555	9.6785	0.3215	.5	.5	9.7181	9.9308	9.7873	0.2127	.5
.6	9.6356	9.9551	9.6804	0.3196	.4	.6	9.7193	9.9303	9.7890	0.2110	.4
.7	9.6371	9.9548	9.6824	0.3176	.3	.7	9.7205	9.9298	9.7907	0.2093	.3
.8	9.6387	9.9544	9.6843	0.3157	.2	.8	9.7218	9.9294	9.7924	0.2076	.2
.9	9.6403	9.9540	9.6863	0.3137	.1	.9	9.7230	9.9289	9.7941	0.2059	.1
26.0	9.6418	9.9537	9.6882	0.3118	64.0	32.0	9.7242	9.9284	9.7958	0.2042	58.0
.1	9.6434	9.9533	9.6901	0.3099	.9	.1	9.7254	9.9279	9.7975	0.2025	.9
.2	9.6449	9.9529	9.6920	0.3080	.8	.2	9.7266	9.9275	9.7992	0.2008	.8
.3	9.6465	9.9525	9.6939	0.3061	.7	.3	9.7278	9.9270	9.8008	0.1992	.7
.4	9.6480	9.9522	9.6958	0.3042	.6	.4	9.7290	9.9265	9.8025	0.1975	.6
.5	9.6495	9.9518	9.6977	0.3023	.5	.5	9.7302	9.9260	9.8042	0.1958	.5
.6	9.6510	9.9514	9.6996	0.3004	.4	.6	9.7314	9.9255	9.8059	0.1941	.4
.7	9.6526	9.9510	9.7015	0.2985	.3	.7	9.7326	9.9251	9.8075	0.1925	.3
.8	9.6541	9.9506	9.7034	0.2966	.2	.8	9.7338	9.9246	9.8092	0.1908	.2
.9	9.6556	9.9503	9.7053	0.2947	.1	.9	9.7349	9.9241	9.8109	0.1891	.1
27.0	9.6570	9.9499	9.7072	0.2928	63.0	33.0	9.7361	9.9236	9.8125	0.1875	57.0
.1	9.6585	9.9495	9.7090	0.2910	.9	.1	9.7373	9.9231	9.8142	0.1858	.9
.2	9.6600	9.9491	9.7109	0.2891	.8	.2	9.7384	9.9226	9.8158	0.1842	.8
.3	9.6615	9.9487	9.7128	0.2872	.7	.3	9.7396	9.9221	9.8175	0.1825	.7
.4	9.6629	9.9483	9.7146	0.2854	.6	.4	9.7407	9.9216	9.8191	0.1809	.6
.5	9.6644	9.9479	9.7165	0.2835	.5	.5	9.7419	9.9211	9.8208	0.1792	.5
.6	9.6659	9.9475	9.7183	0.2817	.4	.6	9.7430	9.9206	9.8224	0.1776	.4
.7	9.6673	9.9471	9.7202	0.2798	.3	.7	9.7442	9.9201	9.8241	0.1759	.3
.8	9.6687	9.9467	9.7220	0.2780	.2	.8	9.7453	9.9196	9.8257	0.1743	.2
.9	9.6702	9.9463	9.7238	0.2762	.1	.9	9.7464	9.9191	9.8274	0.1726	.1
28.0	9.6716	9.9459	9.7257	0.2743	62.0	34.0	9.7476	9.9186	9.8290	0.1710	56.0
.1	9.6730	9.9455	9.7275	0.2725	.9	.1	9.7487	9.9181	9.8306	0.1694	.9
.2	9.6744	9.9451	9.7293	0.2707	.8	.2	9.7498	9.9175	9.8323	0.1677	.8
.3	9.6759	9.9447	9.7311	0.2689	.7	.3	9.7509	9.9170	9.8339	0.1661	.7
.4	9.6773	9.9443	9.7330	0.2670	.6	.4	9.7520	9.9165	9.8355	0.1645	.6
.5	9.6787	9.9439	9.7348	0.2652	.5	.5	9.7531	9.9160	9.8371	0.1629	.5
.6	9.6801	9.9435	9.7366	0.2634	.4	.6	9.7542	9.9155	9.8388	0.1612	.4
.7	9.6814	9.9431	9.7384	0.2616	.3	.7	9.7553	9.9149	9.8404	0.1596	.3
.8	9.6828	9.9427	9.7402	0.2598	.2	.8	9.7564	9.9144	9.8420	0.1580	.2
.9	9.6842	9.9422	9.7420	0.2580	.1	.9	9.7575	9.9139	9.8436	0.1564	.1
29.0	9.6856	9.9418	9.7438	0.2562	61.0	35.0	9.7586	9.9134	9.8452	0.1548	55.0
.1	9.6869	9.9414	9.7455	0.2545	.9	.1	9.7597	9.9128	9.8468	0.1532	.9
.2	9.6883	9.9410	9.7473	0.2527	.8	.2	9.7607	9.9123	9.8484	0.1516	.8
.3	9.6896	9.9406	9.7491	0.2509	.7	.3	9.7618	9.9118	9.8501	0.1499	.7
.4	9.6910	9.9401	9.7509	0.2491	.6	.4	9.7629	9.9112	9.8517	0.1483	.6
.5	9.6923	9.9397	9.7526	0.2474	.5	.5	9.7640	9.9107	9.8533	0.1467	.5
.6	9.6937	9.9393	9.7544	0.2456	.4	.6	9.7650	9.9101	9.8549	0.1451	.4
.7	9.6950	9.9388	9.7562	0.2438	.3	.7	9.7661	9.9096	9.8565	0.1435	.3
.8	9.6963	9.9384	9.7579	0.2421	.2	.8	9.7671	9.9091	9.8581	0.1419	.2
.9	9.6977	9.9380	9.7597	0.2403	.1	.9	9.7682	9.9085	9.8597	0.1403	.1
30.0	9.6990	9.9375	9.7614	0.2386	60.0	36.0	9.7692	9.9080	9.8613	0.1387	54.0
	L cos	L sin	L cot	L tan	deg		L cos	L sin	L cot	L tan	deg

Logarithms of trigonometric functions

for decimal fractions of a degree *continued*

deg	L sin	L cos	L tan	L cot	deg
36.0	9.7692	9.9080	9.8613	0.1387	**54.0**
.1	9.7703	9.9074	9.8629	0.1371	.9
.2	9.7713	9.9069	9.8644	0.1356	.8
.3	9.7723	9.9063	9.8660	0.1340	.7
.4	9.7734	9.9057	9.8676	0.1324	.6
.5	9.7744	9.9052	9.8692	0.1308	.5
.6	9.7754	9.9046	9.8708	0.1292	.4
.7	9.7764	9.9041	9.8724	0.1276	.3
.8	9.7774	9.9035	9.8740	0.1260	.2
.9	9.7785	9.9029	9.8755	0.1245	.1
37.0	9.7795	9.9023	9.8771	0.1229	**53.0**
.1	9.7805	9.9018	9.8787	0.1213	.9
.2	9.7815	9.9012	9.8803	0.1197	.8
.3	9.7825	9.9006	9.8818	0.1182	.7
.4	9.7835	9.9000	9.8834	0.1166	.6
.5	9.7844	9.8995	9.8850	0.1150	.5
.6	9.7854	9.8989	9.8865	0.1135	.4
.7	9.7864	9.8983	9.8881	0.1119	.3
.8	9.7874	9.8977	9.8897	0.1103	.2
.9	9.7884	9.8971	9.8912	0.1088	.1
38.0	9.7893	9.8965	9.8928	0.1072	**52.0**
.1	9.7903	9.8959	9.8944	0.1056	.9
.2	9.7913	9.8953	9.8959	0.1041	.8
.3	9.7922	9.8947	9.8975	0.1025	.7
.4	9.7932	9.8941	9.8990	0.1010	.6
.5	9.7941	9.8935	9.9006	0.0994	.5
.6	9.7951	9.8929	9.9022	0.0978	.4
.7	9.7960	9.8923	9.9037	0.0963	.3
.8	9.7970	9.8917	9.9053	0.0947	.2
.9	9.7979	9.8911	9.9068	0.0932	.1
39.0	9.7989	9.8905	9.9084	0.0916	**51.0**
.1	9.7998	9.8899	9.9099	0.0901	.9
.2	9.8007	9.8893	9.9115	0.0885	.8
.3	9.8017	9.8887	9.9130	0.0870	.7
.4	9.8026	9.8880	9.9146	0.0854	.6
.5	9.8035	9.8874	9.9161	0.0839	.5
.6	9.8044	9.8868	9.9176	0.0824	.4
.7	9.8053	9.8862	9.9192	0.0808	.3
.8	9.8063	9.8855	9.9207	0.0793	.2
.9	9.8072	9.8849	9.9223	0.0777	.1
40.0	9.8081	9.8843	9.9238	0.0762	**50.0**
.1	9.8090	9.8836	9.9254	0.0746	.9
.2	9.8099	9.8830	9.9269	0.0731	.8
.3	9.8108	9.8823	9.9284	0.0716	.7
.4	9.8117	9.8817	9.9300	0.0700	.6
40.5	9.8125	9.8810	9.9315	0.0685	**49.5**
	L cos	L sin	L cot	L tan	deg

deg	L sin	L cos	L tan	L cot	deg
40.5	9.8125	9.8810	9.9315	0.0685	**49.5**
.6	9.8134	9.8804	9.9330	0.0670	.4
.7	9.8143	9.8797	9.9346	0.0654	.3
.8	9.8152	9.8791	9.9361	0.0639	.2
.9	9.8161	9.8784	9.9376	0.0624	.1
41.0	9.8169	9.8778	9.9392	0.0608	**49.0**
.1	9.8178	9.8771	9.9407	0.0593	.9
.2	9.8187	9.8765	9.9422	0.0578	.8
.3	9.8195	9.8758	9.9438	0.0562	7
.4	9.8204	9.8751	9.9453	0.0547	.6
.5	9.8213	9.8745	9.9468	0.0532	.5
.6	9.8221	9.8738	9.9483	0.0517	.4
.7	9.8230	9.8731	9.9499	0.0501	.3
.8	9.8238	9.8724	9.9514	0.0486	.2
.9	9.8247	9.8718	9.9529	0.0471	.1
42.0	9.8255	9.8711	9.9544	0.0456	**48.0**
.1	9.8264	9.8704	9.9560	0.0440	.9
.2	9.8272	9.8697	9.9575	0.0425	.8
.3	9.8280	9.8690	9.9590	0.0410	.7
.4	9.8289	9.8683	9.9605	0.0395	.6
.5	9.8297	9.8676	9.9621	0.0379	.5
.6	9.8305	9.8669	9.9636	0.0364	.4
.7	9.8313	9.8662	9.9651	0.0349	.3
.8	9.8322	9.8655	9.9666	0.0334	.2
.9	9.8330	9.8648	9.9681	0.0319	.1
43.0	9.8338	9.8641	9.9697	0.0303	**47.0**
.1	9.8346	9.8634	9.9712	0.0288	.9
.2	9.8354	9.8627	9.9727	0.0273	.8
.3	9.8362	9.8620	9.9742	0.0258	.7
.4	9.8370	9.8613	9.9757	0.0243	.6
.5	9.8378	9.8606	9.9772	0.0228	.5
.6	9.8386	9.8598	9.9788	0.0212	.4
.7	9.8394	9.8591	9.9803	0.0197	.3
.8	9.8402	9.8584	9.9818	0.0182	.2
.9	9.8410	9.8577	9.9833	0.0167	.1
44.0	9.8418	9.8569	9.9848	0.0152	**46.0**
.1	9.8426	9.8562	9.9864	0.0136	.9
.2	9.8433	9.8555	9.9879	0.0121	.8
.3	9.8441	9.8547	9.9894	0.0106	.7
.4	9.8449	9.8540	9.9909	0.0091	.6
.5	9.8457	9.8532	9.9924	0.0076	.5
.6	9.8464	9.8525	9.9939	0.0061	.4
.7	9.8472	9.8517	9.9955	0.0045	.3
.8	9.8480	9.8510	9.9970	0.0030	.2
.9	9.8487	9.8502	9.9985	0.0015	.1
45.0	9.8495	9.8495	0.0000	0.0000	**45.0**
	L cos	L sin	L cot	L tan	deg

Natural logarithms

	0	1	2	3	4	5	6	7	8	9	mean differences 1 2 3	4 5 6	7 8 9
1.0	0.0000	0100	0198	0296	0392	0488	0583	0677	0770	0862	10 19 29	38 48 57	67 76 86
1.1	0.0953	1044	1133	1222	1310	1398	1484	1570	1655	1740	9 17 26	35 44 52	61 70 78
1.2	0.1823	1906	1989	2070	2151	2231	2311	2390	2469	2546	8 16 24	32 40 48	56 64 72
1.3	0.2624	2700	2776	2852	2927	3001	3075	3148	3221	3293	7 15 22	30 37 44	52 59 67
1.4	0.3365	3436	3507	3577	3646	3716	3784	3853	3920	3988	7 14 21	28 35 41	48 55 62
1.5	0.4055	4121	4187	4253	4318	4383	4447	4511	4574	4637	6 13 19	26 32 39	45 52 58
1.6	0.4700	4762	4824	4886	4947	5008	5068	5128	5188	5247	6 12 18	24 30 36	42 48 55
1.7	0.5306	5365	5423	5481	5539	5596	5653	5710	5766	5822	6 11 17	23 29 34	40 46 51
1.8	0.5878	5933	5988	6043	6098	6152	6206	6259	6313	6366	5 11 16	22 27 32	38 43 49
1.9	0.6419	6471	6523	6575	6627	6678	6729	6780	6831	6881	5 10 15	20 26 31	36 41 46
2.0	0.6931	6981	7031	7080	7129	7178	7227	7275	7324	7372	5 10 15	20 24 29	34 39 44
2.1	0.7419	7467	7514	7561	7608	7655	7701	7747	7793	7839	5 9 14	19 23 28	33 37 42
2.2	0.7885	7930	7975	8020	8065	8109	8154	8198	8242	8286	4 9 13	18 22 27	31 36 40
2.3	0.8329	8372	8416	8459	8502	8544	8587	8629	8671	8713	4 9 13	17 21 26	30 34 38
2.4	0.8755	8796	8838	8879	8920	8961	9002	9042	9083	9123	4 8 12	16 20 24	29 33 37
2.5	0.9163	9203	9243	9282	9322	9361	9400	9439	9478	9517	4 8 12	16 20 24	27 31 35
2.6	0.9555	9594	9632	9670	9708	9746	9783	9821	9858	9895	4 8 11	15 19 23	26 30 34
2.7	0.9933	9969	1.0006	0043	0080	0116	0152	0188	0225	0260	4 7 11	15 18 22	25 29 33
2.8	1.0296	0332	0367	0403	0438	0473	0508	0543	0578	0613	4 7 11	14 18 21	25 28 32
2.9	1.0647	0682	0716	0750	0784	0818	0852	0886	0919	0953	3 7 10	14 17 20	24 27 31
3.0	1.0986	1019	1053	1086	1119	1151	1184	1217	1249	1282	3 7 10	13 16 20	23 26 30
3.1	1.1314	1346	1378	1410	1442	1474	1506	1537	1569	1600	3 6 10	13 16 19	22 25 29
3.2	1.1632	1663	1694	1725	1756	1787	1817	1848	1878	1909	3 6 9	12 15 18	22 25 28
3.3	1.1939	1969	2000	2030	2060	2090	2119	2149	2179	2208	3 6 9	12 15 18	21 24 27
3.4	1.2238	2267	2296	2326	2355	2384	2413	2442	2470	2499	3 6 9	12 15 17	20 23 26
3.5	1.2528	2556	2585	2613	2641	2669	2698	2726	2754	2782	3 6 8	11 14 17	20 23 25
3.6	1.2809	2837	2865	2892	2920	2947	2975	3002	3029	3056	3 5 8	11 14 16	19 22 25
3.7	1.3083	3110	3137	3164	3191	3218	3244	3271	3297	3324	3 5 8	11 13 16	19 21 24
3.8	1.3350	3376	3403	3429	3455	3481	3507	3533	3558	3584	3 5 8	10 13 16	18 21 23
3.9	1.3610	3635	3661	3686	3712	3737	3762	3788	3813	3838	3 5 8	10 13 15	18 20 23
4.0	1.3863	3888	3913	3938	3962	3987	4012	4036	4061	4085	2 5 7	10 12 15	17 20 22
4.1	1.4110	4134	4159	4183	4207	4231	4255	4279	4303	4327	2 5 7	10 12 14	17 19 22
4.2	1.4351	4375	4398	4422	4446	4469	4493	4516	4540	4563	2 5 7	9 12 14	16 19 21
4.3	1.4586	4609	4633	4656	4679	4702	4725	4748	4770	4793	2 5 7	9 12 14	16 18 21
4.4	1.4816	4839	4861	4884	4907	4929	4951	4974	4996	5019	2 5 7	9 11 14	16 18 20
4.5	1.5041	5063	5085	5107	5129	5151	5173	5195	5217	5239	2 4 7	9 11 13	15 18 20
4.6	1.5261	5282	5304	5326	5347	5369	5390	5412	5433	5454	2 4 6	9 11 13	15 17 19
4.7	1.5476	5497	5518	5539	5560	5581	5602	5623	5644	5665	2 4 6	8 11 13	15 17 19
4.8	1.5686	5707	5728	5748	5769	5790	5810	5831	5851	5872	2 4 6	8 10 12	14 16 19
4.9	1.5892	5913	5933	5953	5974	5994	6014	6034	6054	6074	2 4 6	8 10 12	14 16 18
5.0	1.6094	6114	6134	6154	6174	6194	6214	6233	6253	6273	2 4 6	8 10 12	14 16 18
5.1	1.6292	6312	6332	6351	6371	6390	6409	6429	6448	6467	2 4 6	8 10 12	14 16 18
5.2	1.6487	6506	6525	6544	6563	6582	6601	6620	6639	6658	2 4 6	8 10 11	13 15 17
5.3	1.6677	6696	6715	6734	6752	6771	6790	6808	6827	6845	2 4 6	7 9 11	13 15 17
5.4	1.6864	6882	6901	6919	6938	6956	6974	6993	7011	7029	2 4 5	7 9 11	13 15 17

Natural logarithms of 10^{+n}

n	1	2	3	4	5	6	7	8	9
$\log_e 10^n$	2.3026	4.6052	6.9078	9.2103	11.5129	13.8155	16.1181	18.4207	20.7233

Natural logarithms *continued*

	0	1	2	3	4	5	6	7	8	9	mean differences 1	2	3	4	5	6	7	8	9
5.5	1.7047	7066	7084	7102	7120	7138	7156	7174	7192	7210	2	4	5	7	9	11	13	14	16
5.6	1.7228	7246	7263	7281	7299	7317	7334	7352	7370	7387	2	4	5	7	9	11	12	14	16
5.7	1.7405	7422	7440	7457	7475	7492	7509	7527	7544	7561	2	3	5	7	9	10	12	14	16
5.8	1.7579	7596	7613	7630	7647	7664	7681	7699	7716	7733	2	3	5	7	9	10	12	14	15
5.9	1.7750	7766	7783	7800	7817	7834	7851	7867	7884	7901	2	3	5	7	8	10	12	13	15
6.0	1.7918	7934	7951	7967	7984	8001	8017	8034	8050	8066	2	3	5	7	8	10	12	13	15
6.1	1.8083	8099	8116	8132	8148	8165	8181	8197	8213	8229	2	3	5	6	8	10	11	13	15
6.2	1.8245	8262	8278	8294	8310	8326	8342	8358	8374	8390	2	3	5	6	8	10	11	13	14
6.3	1.8405	8421	8437	8453	8469	8485	8500	8516	8532	8547	2	3	5	6	8	9	11	13	14
6.4	1.8563	8579	8594	8610	8625	8641	8656	8672	8687	8703	2	3	5	6	8	9	11	12	14
6.5	1.8718	8733	8749	8764	8779	8795	8810	8825	8840	8856	2	3	5	6	8	9	11	12	14
6.6	1.8871	8886	8901	8916	8931	8946	8961	8976	8991	9006	2	3	5	6	8	9	11	12	14
6.7	1.9021	9036	9051	9066	9081	9095	9110	9125	9140	9155	1	3	4	6	7	9	10	12	13
6.8	1.9169	9184	9199	9213	9228	9242	9257	9272	9286	9301	1	3	4	6	7	9	10	12	13
6.9	1.9315	9330	9344	9359	9373	9387	9402	9416	9430	9445	1	3	4	6	7	9	10	12	13
7.0	1.9459	9473	9488	9502	9516	9530	9544	9559	9573	9587	1	3	4	6	7	9	10	11	13
7.1	1.9601	9615	9629	9643	9657	9671	9685	9699	9713	9727	1	3	4	6	7	8	10	11	13
7.2	1.9741	9755	9769	9782	9796	9810	9824	9838	9851	9865	1	3	4	6	7	8	10	11	12
7.3	1.9879	9892	9906	9920	9933	9947	9961	9974	9988	2.0001	1	3	4	5	7	8	10	11	12
7.4	2.0015	0028	0042	0055	0069	0082	0096	0109	0122	0136	1	3	4	5	7	8	9	11	12
7.5	2.0149	0162	0176	0189	0202	0215	0229	0242	0255	0268	1	3	4	5	7	8	9	11	12
7.6	2.0281	0295	0308	0321	0334	0347	0360	0373	0386	0399	1	3	4	5	7	8	9	10	12
7.7	2.0412	0425	0438	0451	0464	0477	0490	0503	0516	0528	1	3	4	5	6	8	9	10	12
7.8	2.0541	0554	0567	0580	0592	0605	0618	0631	0643	0656	1	3	4	5	6	8	9	10	11
7.9	2.0669	0681	0694	0707	0719	0732	0744	0757	0769	0782	1	3	4	5	6	8	9	10	11
8.0	2.0794	0807	0819	0832	0844	0857	0869	0882	0894	0906	1	3	4	5	6	7	9	10	11
8.1	2.0919	0931	0943	0956	0968	0980	0992	1005	1017	1029	1	2	4	5	6	7	9	10	11
8.2	2.1041	1054	1066	1078	1090	1102	1114	1126	1138	1150	1	2	4	5	6	7	9	10	11
8.3	2.1163	1175	1187	1199	1211	1223	1235	1247	1258	1270	1	2	4	5	6	7	8	10	11
8.4	2.1282	1294	1306	1318	1330	1342	1353	1365	1377	1389	1	2	4	5	6	7	8	9	11
8.5	2.1401	1412	1424	1436	1448	1459	1471	1483	1494	1506	1	2	4	5	6	7	8	9	11
8.6	2.1518	1529	1541	1552	1564	1576	1587	1599	1610	1622	1	2	3	5	6	7	8	9	10
8.7	2.1633	1645	1656	1668	1679	1691	1702	1713	1725	1736	1	2	3	5	6	7	8	9	10
8.8	2.1748	1759	1770	1782	1793	1804	1815	1827	1838	1849	1	2	3	5	6	7	8	9	10
8.9	2.1861	1872	1883	1894	1905	1917	1928	1939	1950	1961	1	2	3	4	6	7	8	9	10
9.0	2.1972	1983	1994	2006	2017	2028	2039	2050	2061	2072	1	2	3	4	6	7	8	9	10
9.1	2.2083	2094	2105	2116	2127	2138	2148	2159	2170	2181	1	2	3	4	5	7	8	9	10
9.2	2.2192	2203	2214	2225	2235	2246	2257	2268	2279	2289	1	2	3	4	5	6	8	9	10
9.3	2.2300	2311	2322	2332	2343	2354	2364	2375	2386	2396	1	2	3	4	5	6	7	9	10
9.4	2.2407	2418	2428	2439	2450	2460	2471	2481	2492	2502	1	2	3	4	5	6	7	8	10
9.5	2.2513	2523	2534	2544	2555	2565	2576	2586	2597	2607	1	2	3	4	5	6	7	8	9
9.6	2.2618	2628	2638	2649	2659	2670	2680	2690	2701	2711	1	2	3	4	5	6	7	8	9
9.7	2.2721	2732	2742	2752	2762	2773	2783	2793	2803	2814	1	2	3	4	5	6	7	8	9
9.8	2.2824	2834	2844	2854	2865	2875	2885	2895	2905	2915	1	2	3	4	5	6	7	8	9
9.9	2.2925	2935	2946	2956	2966	2976	2986	2996	3006	3016	1	2	3	4	5	6	7	8	9
10.0	2.3026																		

Natural logarithms of 10^{-n}

n	1	2	3	4	5	6	7	8	9
$\log_e 10^{-n}$	$\overline{3}.6974$	$\overline{5}.3948$	$\overline{7}.0922$	$\overline{10}.7897$	$\overline{12}.4871$	$\overline{14}.1845$	$\overline{17}.8819$	$\overline{19}.5793$	$\overline{21}.2767$

Hyperbolic sines $[\sinh x = \frac{1}{2}(e^x - e^{-x})]$

X	0	1	2	3	4	5	6	7	8	9	avg diff
0.0	0.0000	0.0100	0.0200	0.0300	0.0400	0.0500	0.0600	0.0701	0.0801	0.0901	100
.1	0.1002	0.1102	0.1203	0.1304	0.1405	0.1506	0.1607	0.1708	0.1810	0.1911	101
.2	0.2013	0.2115	0.2218	0.2320	0.2423	0.2526	0.2629	0.2733	0.2837	0.2941	103
.3	0.3045	0.3150	0.3255	0.3360	0.3466	0.3572	0.3678	0.3785	0.3892	0.4000	106
.4	0.4108	0.4216	0.4325	0.4434	0.4543	0.4653	0.4764	0.4875	0.4986	0.5098	110
0.5	0.5211	0.5324	0.5438	0.5552	0.5666	0.5782	0.5897	0.6014	0.6131	0.6248	116
.6	0.6367	0.6485	0.6605	0.6725	0.6846	0.6967	0.7090	0.7213	0.7336	0.7461	122
.7	0.7586	0.7712	0.7838	0.7966	0.8094	0.8223	0.8353	0.8484	0.8615	0.8748	130
.8	0.8881	0.9015	0.9150	0.9286	0.9423	0.9561	0.9700	0.9840	0.9981	1.012	138
.9	1.027	1.041	1.055	1.070	1.085	1.099	1.114	1.129	1.145	1.160	15
1.0	1.175	1.191	1.206	1.222	1.238	1.254	1.270	1.286	1.303	1.319	16
.1	1.336	1.352	1.369	1.386	1.403	1.421	1.438	1.456	1.474	1.491	17
.2	1.509	1.528	1.546	1.564	1.583	1.602	1.621	1.640	1.659	1.679	19
.3	1.698	1.718	1.738	1.758	1.779	1.799	1.820	1.841	1.862	1.883	21
.4	1.904	1.926	1.948	1.970	1.992	2.014	2.037	2.060	2.083	2.106	22
1.5	2.129	2.153	2.177	2.201	2.225	2.250	2.274	2.299	2.324	2.350	25
.6	2.376	2.401	2.428	2.454	2.481	2.507	2.535	2.562	2.590	2.617	27
.7	2.646	2.674	2.703	2.732	2.761	2.790	2.820	2.850	2.881	2.911	30
.8	2.942	2.973	3.005	3.037	3.069	3.101	3.134	3.167	3.200	3.234	33
.9	3.268	3.303	3.337	3.372	3.408	3.443	3.479	3.516	3.552	3.589	36
2.0	3.627	3.665	3.703	3.741	3.780	3.820	3.859	3.899	3.940	3.981	39
.1	4.022	4.064	4.106	4.148	4.191	4.234	4.278	4.322	4.367	4.412	44
.2	4.457	4.503	4.549	4.596	4.643	4.691	4.739	4.788	4.837	4.887	48
.3	4.937	4.988	5.039	5.090	5.142	5.195	5.248	5.302	5.356	5.411	53
.4	5.466	5.522	5.578	5.635	5.693	5.751	5.810	5.869	5.929	5.989	58
2.5	6.050	6.112	6.174	6.237	6.300	6.365	6.429	6.495	6.561	6.627	64
.6	6.695	6.763	6.831	6.901	6.971	7.042	7.113	7.185	7.258	7.332	71
.7	7.406	7.481	7.557	7.634	7.711	7.789	7.868	7.948	8.028	8.110	79
.8	8.192	8.275	8.359	8.443	8.529	8.615	8.702	8.790	8.879	8.969	87
.9	9.060	9.151	9.244	9.337	9.431	9.527	9.623	9.720	9.819	9.918	96
3.0	10.02	10.12	10.22	10.32	10.43	10.53	10.64	10.75	10.86	10.97	11
.1	11.08	11.19	11.30	11.42	11.53	11.65	11.76	11.88	12.00	12.12	12
.2	12.25	12.37	12.49	12.62	12.75	12.88	13.01	13.14	13.27	13.40	13
.3	13.54	13.67	13.81	13.95	14.09	14.23	14.38	14.52	14.67	14.82	14
.4	14.97	15.12	15.27	15.42	15.58	15.73	15.89	16.05	16.21	16.38	16
3.5	16.54	16.71	16.88	17.05	17.22	17.39	17.57	17.74	17.92	18.10	17
.6	18.29	18.47	18.66	18.84	19.03	19.22	19.42	19.61	19.81	20.01	19
.7	20.21	20.41	20.62	20.83	21.04	21.25	21.46	21.68	21.90	22.12	21
.8	22.34	22.56	22.79	23.02	23.25	23.49	23.72	23.96	24.20	24.45	24
.9	24.69	24.94	25.19	25.44	25.70	25.96	26.22	26.48	26.75	27.02	26
4.0	27.29	27.56	27.84	28.12	28.40	28.69	28.98	29.27	29.56	29.86	29
.1	30.16	30.47	30.77	31.08	31.39	31.71	32.03	32.35	32.68	33.00	32
.2	33.34	33.67	34.01	34.35	34.70	35.05	35.40	35.75	36.11	36.48	35
.3	36.84	37.21	37.59	37.97	38.35	38.73	39.12	39.52	39.91	40.31	39
.4	40.72	41.13	41.54	41.96	42.38	42.81	43.24	43.67	44.11	44.56	43
4.5	45.00	45.46	45.91	46.37	46.84	47.31	47.79	48.27	48.75	49.24	47
.6	49.74	50.24	50.74	51.25	51.77	52.29	52.81	53.34	53.88	54.42	52
.7	54.97	55.52	56.08	56.64	57.21	57.79	58.37	58.96	59.55	60.15	58
.8	60.75	61.36	61.98	62.60	63.23	63.87	64.51	65.16	65.81	66.47	64
.9	67.14	67.82	68.50	69.19	69.88	70.58	71.29	72.01	72.73	73.46	71
5.0	74.20										

If $x > 5$, $\sinh x = \frac{1}{2}(e^x)$ and $\log_{10} \sinh x = (0.4343)x + 0.6990 - 1$, correct to four significant figures.

Hyperbolic cosines [cosh $x = \frac{1}{2}(e^x + e^{-x})$]

X	0	1	2	3	4	5	6	7	8	9	avg diff
0.0	1.000	1.000	1.000	1.000	1.001	1.001	1.002	1.002	1.003	1.004	1
.1	1.005	1.006	1.007	1.008	1.010	1.011	1.013	1.014	1.016	1.018	2
.2	1.020	1.022	1.024	1.027	1.029	1.031	1.034	1.037	1.039	1.042	3
.3	1.045	1.048	1.052	1.055	1.058	1.062	1.066	1.069	1.073	1.077	4
.4	1.081	1.085	1.090	1.094	1.098	1.103	1.108	1.112	1.117	1.122	5
0.5	1.128	1.133	1.138	1.144	1.149	1.155	1.161	1.167	1.173	1.179	6
.6	1.185	1.192	1.198	1.205	1.212	1.219	1.226	1.233	1.240	1.248	7
.7	1.255	1.263	1.271	1.278	1.287	1.295	1.303	1.311	1.320	1.329	8
.8	1.337	1.346	1.355	1.365	1.374	1.384	1.393	1.403	1.413	1.423	10
.9	1.433	1.443	1.454	1.465	1.475	1.486	1.497	1.509	1.520	1.531	11
1.0	1.543	1.555	1.567	1.579	1.591	1.604	1.616	1.629	1.642	1.655	13
.1	1.669	1.682	1.696	1.709	1.723	1.737	1.752	1.766	1.781	1.796	14
.2	1.811	1.826	1.841	1.857	1.872	1.888	1.905	1.921	1.937	1.954	16
.3	1.971	1.988	2.005	2.023	2.040	2.058	2.076	2.095	2.113	2.132	18
.4	2.151	2.170	2.189	2.209	2.229	2.249	2.269	2.290	2.310	2.331	20
1.5	2.352	2.374	2.395	2.417	2.439	2.462	2.484	2.507	2.530	2.554	23
.6	2.577	2.601	2.625	2.650	2.675	2.700	2.725	2.750	2.776	2.802	25
.7	2.828	2.855	2.882	2.909	2.936	2.964	2.992	3.021	3.049	3.078	28
.8	3.107	3.137	3.167	3.197	3.228	3.259	3.290	3.321	3.353	3.385	31
.9	3.418	3.451	3.484	3.517	3.551	3.585	3.620	3.655	3.690	3.726	34
2.0	3.762	3.799	3.835	3.873	3.910	3.948	3.987	4.026	4.065	4.104	38
.1	4.144	4.185	4.226	4.267	4.309	4.351	4.393	4.436	4.480	4.524	42
.2	4.568	4.613	4.658	4.704	4.750	4.797	4.844	4.891	4.939	4.988	47
.3	5.037	5.087	5.137	5.188	5.239	5.290	5.343	5.395	5.449	5.503	52
.4	5.557	5.612	5.667	5.723	5.780	5.837	5.895	5.954	6.013	6.072	58
2.5	6.132	6.193	6.255	6.317	6.379	6.443	6.507	6.571	6.636	6.702	64
.6	6.769	6.836	6.904	6.973	7.042	7.112	7.183	7.255	7.327	7.400	70
.7	7.473	7.548	7.623	7.699	7.776	7.853	7.932	8.011	8.091	8.171	78
.8	8.253	8.335	8.418	8.502	8.587	8.673	8.759	8.847	8.935	9.024	86
.9	9.115	9.206	9.298	9.391	9.484	9.579	9.675	9.772	9.869	9.968	95
3.0	10.07	10.17	10.27	10.37	10.48	10.58	10.69	10.79	10.90	11.01	11
.1	11.12	11.23	11.35	11.46	11.57	11.69	11.81	11.92	12.04	12.16	12
.2	12.29	12.41	12.53	12.66	12.79	12.91	13.04	13.17	13.31	13.44	13
.3	13.57	13.71	13.85	13.99	14.13	14.27	14.41	14.56	14.70	14.85	14
.4	15.00	15.15	15.30	15.45	15.61	15.77	15.92	16.08	16.25	16.41	16
3.5	16.57	16.74	16.91	17.08	17.25	17.42	17.60	17.77	17.95	18.13	17
.6	18.31	18.50	18.68	18.87	19.06	19.25	19.44	19.64	19.84	20.03	19
.7	20.24	20.44	20.64	20.85	21.06	21.27	21.49	21.70	21.92	22.14	21
.8	22.36	22.59	22.81	23.04	23.27	23.51	23.74	23.98	24.22	24.47	23
.9	24.71	24.96	25.21	25.46	25.72	25.98	26.24	26.50	26.77	27.04	26
4.0	27.31	27.58	27.86	28.14	28.42	28.71	29.00	29.29	29.58	29.88	29
.1	30.18	30.48	30.79	31.10	31.41	31.72	32.04	32.37	32.69	33.02	32
.2	33.35	33.69	34.02	34.37	34.71	35.06	35.41	35.77	36.13	36.49	35
.3	36.86	37.23	37.60	37.98	38.36	38.75	39.13	39.53	39.93	40.33	39
.4	40.73	41.14	41.55	41.97	42.39	42.82	43.25	43.68	44.12	44.57	43
4.5	45.01	45.47	45.92	46.38	46.85	47.32	47.80	48.28	48.76	49.25	47
.6	49.75	50.25	50.75	51.26	51.78	52.30	52.82	53.35	53.89	54.43	52
.7	54.98	55.53	56.09	56.65	57.22	57.80	58.38	58.96	59.56	60.15	58
.8	60.76	61.37	61.99	62.61	63.24	63.87	64.52	65.16	65.82	66.48	64
.9	67.15	67.82	68.50	69.19	69.89	70.59	71.30	72.02	72.74	73.47	71
5.0	74.21										

If $x > 5$, cosh $x = \frac{1}{2}(e^x)$, and $\log_{10}$ cosh $x = (0.4343)x + 0.6990 - 1$, correct to four significant figures.

Hyperbolic tangents $[\tanh x = (e^x - e^{-x})/(e^x + e^{-x}) = \sinh x/\cosh x]$

X	0	1	2	3	4	5	6	7	8	9	avg diff
0.0	.0000	.0100	.0200	.0300	.0400	.0500	.0599	.0699	.0798	.0898	100
.1	.0997	.1096	.1194	.1293	.1391	.1489	.1587	.1684	.1781	.1878	98
.2	.1974	.2070	.2165	.2260	.2355	.2449	.2543	.2636	.2729	.2821	94
.3	.2913	.3004	.3095	.3185	.3275	.3364	.3452	.3540	.3627	.3714	89
.4	.3800	.3885	.3969	.4053	.4136	.4219	.4301	.4382	.4462	.4542	82
0.5	.4621	.4700	.4777	.4854	.4930	.5005	.5080	.5154	.5227	.5299	75
.6	.5370	.5441	.5511	.5581	.5649	.5717	.5784	.5850	.5915	.5980	67
.7	.6044	.6107	.6169	.6231	.6291	.6352	.6411	.6469	.6527	.6584	60
.8	.6640	.6696	.6751	.6805	.6858	.6911	.6963	.7014	.7064	.7114	52
.9	.7163	.7211	.7259	.7306	.7352	.7398	.7443	.7487	.7531	.7574	45
1.0	.7616	.7658	.7699	.7739	.7779	.7818	.7857	.7895	.7932	.7969	39
.1	.8005	.8041	.8076	.8110	.8144	.8178	.8210	.8243	.8275	.8306	33
.2	.8337	.8367	.8397	.8426	.8455	.8483	.8511	.8538	.8565	.8591	28
.3	.8617	.8643	.8568	.8693	.8717	.8741	.8764	.8787	.8810	.8832	24
.4	.8854	.8875	.8896	.8917	.8937	.8957	.8977	.8996	.9015	.9033	20
1.5	.9052	.9069	.9087	.9104	.9121	.9138	.9154	.9170	.9186	.9202	17
.6	.9217	.9232	.9246	.9261	.9275	.9289	.9302	.9316	.9329	.9342	14
.7	.9354	.9367	.9379	.9391	.9402	.9414	.9425	.9436	.9447	.9458	11
.8	.9468	.9478	.9488	.9498	.9508	.9518	.9527	.9536	.9545	.9554	9
.9	.9562	.9571	.9579	.9587	.9595	.9603	.9611	.9619	.9626	.9633	8
2.0	.9640	.9647	.9654	.9661	.9668	.9674	.9680	.9687	.9693	.9699	6
.1	.9705	.9710	.9716	.9722	.9727	.9732	.9738	.9743	.9748	.9753	5
.2	.9757	.9762	.9767	.9771	.9776	.9780	.9785	.9789	.9793	.9797	4
.3	.9801	.9805	.9809	.9812	.9816	.9820	.9823	.9827	.9830	.9834	4
.4	.9837	.9840	.9843	.9846	.9849	.9852	.9855	.9858	.9861	.9863	3
2.5	.9866	.9869	.9871	.9874	.9876	.9879	.9881	.9884	.9886	.9888	2
.6	.9890	.9892	.9895	.9897	.9899	.9901	.9903	.9905	.9906	.9908	2
.7	.9910	.9912	.9914	.9915	.9917	.9919	.9920	.9922	.9923	.9925	2
.8	.9926	.9928	.9929	.9931	.9932	.9933	.9935	.9936	.9937	.9938	1
.9	.9940	.9941	.9942	.9943	.9944	.9945	.9946	.9947	.9949	.9950	1
3.0	.9951	.9959	.9967	.9973	.9978	.9982	.9985	.9988	.9990	.9992	4
4.0	.9993	.9995	.9996	.9996	.9997	.9998	.9998	.9998	.9999	.9999	1
5.0	.9999										

If $x > 5$, $\tanh x = 1.0000$ to four decimal places.

Multiples of 0.4343 $[0.43429448 = \log_{10} e]$

X	0	1	2	3	4	5	6	7	8	9
0.0	0.0000	0.0434	0.0869	0.1303	0.1737	0.2171	0.2606	0.3040	0.3474	0.3909
1.0	0.4343	0.4777	0.5212	0.5646	0.6080	0.6514	0.6949	0.7383	0.7817	0.8252
2.0	0.8686	0.9120	0.9554	0.9989	1.0423	1.0857	1.1292	1.1726	1.2160	1.2595
3.0	1.3029	1.3463	1.3897	1.4332	1.4766	1.5200	1.5635	1.6069	1.6503	1.6937
4.0	1.7372	1.7806	1.8240	1.8675	1.9109	1.9543	1.9978	2.0412	2.0846	2.1280
5.0	2.1715	2.2149	2.2583	2.3018	2.3452	2.3886	2.4320	2.4755	2.5189	2.5623
6.0	2.6058	2.6492	2.6926	2.7361	2.7795	2.8229	2.8663	2.9098	2.9532	2.9966
7.0	3.0401	3.0835	3.1269	3.1703	3.2138	3.2572	3.3006	3.3441	3.3875	3.4309
8.0	3.4744	3.5178	3.5612	3.6046	3.6481	3.6915	3.7349	3.7784	3.8218	3.8652
9.0	3.9087	3.9521	3.9955	4.0389	4.0824	4.1258	4.1692	4.2127	4.2561	4.2995

Multiples of 2.3026 $[2.3025851 = 1/0.4343 = \log_e 10]$

X	0	1	2	3	4	5	6	7	8	9
0.0	0.0000	0.2303	0.4605	0.6908	0.9210	1.1513	1.3816	1.6118	1.8421	2.0723
1.0	2.3026	2.5328	2.7631	2.9934	3.2236	3.4539	3.6841	3.9144	4.1447	4.3749
2.0	4.6052	4.8354	5.0657	5.2959	5.5262	5.7565	5.9867	6.2170	6.4472	6.6775
3.0	6.9078	7.1380	7.3683	7.5985	7.8288	8.0590	8.2893	8.5196	8.7498	8.9801
4.0	9.2103	9.4406	9.6709	9.9011	10.131	10.362	10.592	10.822	11.052	11.283
5.0	11.513	11.743	11.973	12.204	12.434	12.664	12.894	13.125	13.355	13.585
6.0	13.816	14.046	14.276	14.506	14.737	14.967	15.197	15.427	15.658	15.888
7.0	16.118	16.348	16.579	16.809	17.039	17.269	17.500	17.730	17.960	18.190
8.0	18.421	18.651	18.881	19.111	19.342	19.572	19.802	20.032	20.263	20.493
9.0	20.723	20.954	21.184	21.414	21.644	21.875	22.105	22.335	22.565	22.796

Exponentials $[e^n$ and $e^{-n}]$

n	e^n	diff	n	e^n	diff	n	e^n	n	e^{-n}	diff	n	e^{-n}	n	e^{-n}
0.00	1.000	10	0.50	1.649	16	1.0	2.718*	0.00	1.000	-10	0.50	.607	1.0	.368*
.01	1.010	10	.51	1.665	17	.1	3.004	.01	0.990	-10	.51	.600	.1	.333
.02	1.020	10	.52	1.682	17	.2	3.320	.02	.980	-10	.52	.595	.2	.301
.03	1.030	11	.53	1.699	17	.3	3.669	.03	.970	-9	.53	.589	.3	.273
.04	1.041	10	.54	1.716	17	.4	4.055	.04	.961	-10	.54	.583	.4	.247
0.05	1.051	11	0.55	1.733	18	1.5	4.482	0.05	.951	-9	0.55	.577	1.5	.223
.06	1.062	11	.56	1.751	17	.6	4.953	.06	.942	-10	.56	.571	.6	.202
.07	1.073	10	.57	1.768	18	.7	5.474	.07	.932	-9	.57	.566	.7	.183
.08	1.083	11	.58	1.786	18	.8	6.050	.08	.923	-9	.58	.560	.8	.165
.09	1.094	11	.59	1.804	18	.9	6.686	.09	.914	-9	.59	.554	.9	.150
0.10	1.105	11	0.60	1.822	18	2.0	7.389	0.10	.905	-9	0.60	.549	2.0	.135
.11	1.116	11	.61	1.840	19	.1	8.166	.11	.896	-9	.61	.543	.1	.122
.12	1.127	12	.62	1.859	19	.2	9.025	.12	.887	-9	.62	.538	.2	.111
.13	1.139	11	.63	1.878	18	.3	9.974	.13	.878	-9	.63	.533	.3	.100
.14	1.150	12	.64	1.896	20	.4	11.02	.14	.869	-8	.64	.527	.4	.0907
0.15	1.162	12	0.65	1.916	19	2.5	12.18	0.15	.861	-9	0.65	.522	2.5	.0821
.16	1.174	11	.66	1.935	19	.6	13.46	.16	.852	-8	.66	.517	.6	.0743
.17	1.185	12	.67	1.954	20	.7	14.88	.17	.844	-9	.67	.512	.7	.0672
.18	1.197	12	.68	1.974	20	.8	16.44	.18	.835	-8	.68	.507	.8	.0608
.19	1.209	12	.69	1.994	20	.9	18.17	.19	.827	-8	.69	.502	.9	.0550
0.20	1.221	13	0.70	2.014	20	3.0	20.09	0.20	.819	-8	0.70	.497	3.0	.0498
.21	1.234	12	.71	2.034	20	.1	22.20	.21	.811	-8	.71	.492	.1	.0450
.22	1.246	13	.72	2.054	21	.2	24.53	.22	.803	-8	.72	.487	.2	.0408
.23	1.259	12	.73	2.075	21	.3	27.11	.23	.795	-8	.73	.482	.3	.0369
.24	1.271	13	.74	2.096	21	.4	29.96	.24	.787	-8	.74	.477	.4	.0334
0.25	1.284	13	0.75	2.117	21	3.5	33.12	0.25	.779	-8	0.75	.472	3.5	.0302
.26	1.297	13	.76	2.138	22	.6	36.60	.26	.771	-8	.76	.468	.6	.0273
.27	1.310	13	.77	2.160	21	.7	40.45	.27	.763	-7	.77	.463	.7	.0247
.28	1.323	13	.78	2.181	22	.8	44.70	.28	.756	-8	.78	.458	.8	.0224
.29	1.336	14	.79	2.203	23	.9	49.40	.29	.748	-7	.79	.454	.9	.0202
0.30	1.350	13	0.80	2.226	22	4.0	54.60	0.30	.741	-8	0.80	.449	4.0	.0183
.31	1.363	14	.81	2.248	22	.1	60.34	.31	.733	-7	.81	.445	.1	.0166
.32	1.377	14	.82	2.270	23	.2	66.69	.32	.726	-7	.82	.440	.2	.0150
.33	1.391	14	.83	2.293	23	.3	73.70	.33	.719	-7	.83	.436	.3	.0136
.34	1.405	14	.84	2.316	24	.4	81.45	.34	.712	-7	.84	.432	.4	.0123
0.35	1.419	14	0.85	2.340	23	4.5	90.02	0.35	.705	-7	0.85	.427	4.5	.0111
.36	1.433	15	.86	2.363	24			.36	.698	-7	.86	.423		
.37	1.448	14	.87	2.387	24	5.0	148.4	.37	.691	-7	.87	.419	5.0	.00674
.38	1.462	15	.88	2.411	24	6.0	403.4	.38	.684	-7	.88	.415	6.0	.00248
.39	1.477	15	.89	2.435	25	7.0	1097.	.39	.677	-7	.89	.411	7.0	.000912
0.40	1.492	15	0.90	2.460	24	8.0	2981.	0.40	.670	-6	0.90	.407	8.0	.000335
.41	1.507	15	.91	2.484	25	9.0	8103.	.41	.664	-7	.91	.403	9.0	.000123
.42	1.522	15	.92	2.509	26	10.0	22026.	.42	.657	-6	.92	.399	10.0	.000045
.43	1.537	16	.93	2.535	25			.43	.651	-7	.93	.395		
.44	1.553	15	.94	2.560	26	$\pi/2$	4.810	.44	.644	-6	.94	.391	$\pi/2$	.208
						$2\pi/2$	23.14						$2\pi/2$	.0432
0.45	1.568	16	0.95	2.586	26	$3\pi/2$	111.3	0.45	.638	-7	0.95	.387	$3\pi/2$	.00898
.46	1.584	16	.96	2.612	26	$4\pi/2$	535.5	.46	.631	-6	.96	.383	$4\pi/2$	.00187
.47	1.600	16	.97	2.638	26	$5\pi/2$	2576.	.47	.625	-6	.97	.379	$5\pi/2$	.000388
.48	1.616	16	.98	2.664	27	$6\pi/2$	12392.	.48	.619	-6	.98	.375	$6\pi/2$	.000081
.49	1.632	17	.99	2.691	27	$7\pi/2$	59610.	.49	.613	-6	.99	.372	$7\pi/2$	.000017
						$8\pi/2$	286751.						$8\pi/2$	.000003
0.50	1.649		1.00	2.718				0.50	0.607		1.00	.368		

* Note: Do not interpolate in this column.

Properties of e are listed on p. 583.

Bessel functions

Table I—$J_0(z)$

z	0	0.1	0.2	0.3	0.4	0.5	0.6	0.7	0.8	0.9
0	1.0000	0.9975	0.9900	0.9776	0.9604	0.9385	0.9120	0.8812	0.8463	0.8075
1	0.7652	0.7196	0.6711	0.6201	0.5669	0.5118	0.4554	0.3980	0.3400	0.2818
2	0.2239	0.1666	0.1104	0.0555	0.0025	−0.0484	−0.0968	−0.1424	−0.1850	−0.2243
3	−0.2601	−0.2921	−0.3202	−0.3443	−0.3643	−0.3801	−0.3918	−0.3992	−0.4026	−0.4018
4	−0.3971	−0.3887	−0.3766	−0.3610	−0.3423	−0.3205	−0.2961	−0.2693	−0.2404	−0.2097
5	−0.1776	−0.1443	−0.1103	−0.0758	−0.0412	−0.0068	+0.0270	0.0599	0.0917	0.1220
6	0.1506	0.1773	0.2017	0.2238	0.2433	0.2601	0.2740	0.2851	0.2931	0.2981
7	0.3001	0.2991	0.2951	0.2882	0.2786	0.2663	0.2516	0.2346	0.2154	0.1944
8	0.1717	0.1475	0.1222	0.0960	0.0692	0.0419	0.0146	−0.0125	−0.0392	−0.0653
9	−0.0903	−0.1142	−0.1367	−0.1577	−0.1768	−0.1939	−0.2090	−0.2218	−0.2323	−0.2403
10	−0.2459	−0.2490	−0.2496	−0.2477	−0.2434	−0.2366	−0.2276	−0.2164	−0.2032	−0.1881
11	−0.1712	−0.1528	−0.1330	−0.1121	−0.0902	−0.0677	−0.0446	−0.0213	+0.0020	0.0250
12	0.0477	0.0697	0.0908	0.1108	0.1296	0.1469	0.1626	0.1766	0.1887	0.1988
13	0.2069	0.2129	0.2167	0.2183	0.2177	0.2150	0.2101	0.2032	0.1943	0.1836
14	0.1711	0.1570	0.1414	0.1245	0.1065	0.0875	0.0679	0.0476	0.0271	0.0064
15	−0.0142	−0.0346	−0.0544	−0.0736	−0.0919	−0.1092	−0.1253	−0.1401	−0.1533	−0.1650

Table II—$J_1(z)$

continued **Bessel functions**

z	0	0.1	0.2	0.3	0.4	0.5	0.6	0.7	0.8	0.9
0	0.0000	0.0499	0.0995	0.1483	0.1960	0.2423	0.2867	0.3290	0.3688	0.4059
1	0.4401	0.4709	0.4983	0.5220	0.5419	0.5579	0.5699	0.5778	0.5815	0.5812
2	0.5767	0.5683	0.5560	0.5399	0.5202	0.4971	0.4708	0.4416	0.4097	0.3754
3	0.3391	0.3009	0.2613	0.2207	0.1792	0.1374	0.0955	0.0538	0.0128	−0.0272
4	−0.0660	−0.1033	−0.1386	−0.1719	−0.2028	−0.2311	−0.2566	−0.2791	−0.2985	−0.3147
5	−0.3276	−0.3371	−0.3432	−0.3460	−0.3453	−0.3414	−0.3343	−0.3241	−0.3110	−0.2951
6	−0.2767	−0.2559	−0.2329	−0.2081	−0.1816	−0.1538	−0.1250	−0.0953	−0.0652	−0.0349
7	−0.0047	+0.0252	0.0543	0.0826	0.1096	0.1352	0.1592	0.1813	0.2014	0.2192
8	0.2346	0.2476	0.2580	0.2657	0.2708	0.2731	0.2728	0.2697	0.2641	0.2559
9	0.2453	0.2324	0.2174	0.2004	0.1816	0.1613	0.1395	0.1166	0.0928	0.0684
10	0.0435	0.0184	−0.0066	−0.0313	−0.0555	−0.0789	−0.1012	−0.1224	−0.1422	−0.1603
11	−0.1768	−0.1913	−0.2039	−0.2143	−0.2225	−0.2284	−0.2320	−0.2333	−0.2323	−0.2290
12	−0.2234	−0.2157	−0.2060	−0.1943	−0.1807	−0.1655	−0.1487	−0.1307	−0.1114	−0.0912
13	−0.0703	−0.0489	−0.0271	−0.0052	+0.0166	0.0380	0.0590	0.0791	0.0984	0.1165
14	0.1334	0.1488	0.1626	0.1747	0.1850	0.1934	0.1999	0.2043	0.2066	0.2069
15	0.2051	0.2013	0.1955	0.1879	0.1784	0.1672	0.1544	0.1402	0.1247	0.1080

continued

Bessel functions

Table III—$J_2(z)$

z	0	0.1	0.2	0.3	0.4	0.5	0.6	0.7	0.8	0.9
0	0.0000	0.0012	0.0050	0.0112	0.0197	0.0306	0.0437	0.0588	0.0758	0.0946
1	0.1149	0.1366	0.1593	0.1830	0.2074	0.2321	0.2570	0.2817	0.3061	0.3299
2	0.3528	0.3746	0.3951	0.4139	0.4310	0.4461	0.4590	0.4696	0.4777	0.4832
3	0.4861	0.4862	0.4835	0.4780	0.4697	0.4586	0.4448	0.4283	0.4093	0.3879
4	0.3641	0.3383	0.3105	0.2811	0.2501	0.2178	0.1846	0.1506	0.1161	0.0813

Table IV—$J_3(z)$

z	0	0.1	0.2	0.3	0.4	0.5	0.6	0.7	0.8	0.9
0	0.0000	0.0000	0.0002	0.0006	0.0013	0.0026	0.0044	0.0069	0.0102	0.0144
1	0.0196	0.0257	0.0329	0.0411	0.0505	0.0610	0.0725	0.0851	0.0988	0.1134
2	0.1289	0.1453	0.1623	0.1800	0.1981	0.2166	0.2353	0.2540	0.2727	0.2911
3	0.3091	0.3264	0.3431	0.3588	0.3734	0.3868	0.3988	0.4092	0.4180	0.4250
4	0.4302	0.4333	0.4344	0.4333	0.4301	0.4247	0.4171	0.4072	0.3952	0.3811

Table V—$J_4(z)$

z	0	0.1	0.2	0.3	0.4	0.5	0.6	0.7	0.8	0.9
0	0.0000	0.0000	0.0000	0.0000	0.0001	0.0002	0.0003	0.0006	0.0010	0.0016
1	0.0025	0.0036	0.0050	0.0068	0.0091	0.0118	0.0150	0.0188	0.0232	0.0283
2	0.0340	0.0405	0.0476	0.0556	0.0643	0.0738	0.0840	0.0950	0.1067	0.1190
3	0.1320	0.1456	0.1597	0.1743	0.1891	0.2044	0.2198	0.2353	0.2507	0.2661
4	0.2811	0.2958	0.3100	0.3236	0.3365	0.3484	0.3594	0.3693	0.3780	0.3853

Table VI

continued   Bessel functions

p	$J_p(1)$	$J_p(2)$	$J_p(3)$	$J_p(4)$	$J_p(5)$	$J_p(6)$	$J_p(7)$	$J_p(8)$	$J_p(9)$	$J_p(10)$	$J_p(11)$	$J_p(12)$	$J_p(13)$	$J_p(14)$
0	+.7652	+.2239	−.2601	−.3971	−.1776	+.1506	+.3001	+.1717	−.09033	−.2459	−.1712	+.04769	+.2069	+.1711
0.5	+.6714	+.5130	+.06501	−.3019	−.3422	−.09102	+.1981	+.2791	+.1096	−.1373	−.2406	−.1236	+.09298	+.2112
1.0	+.4401	+.5767	+.3391	−.06604	−.3276	−.2767	$−.0^{2}4683$	+.2346	+.2453	+.04347	−.1768	−.2234	−.07032	−.1334
1.5	+.2403	+.4913	+.4777	+.1853	−.1697	−.3279	−.1991	+.07593	+.2545	+.1980	−.02293	−.2047	−.1937	−.01407
2.0	+.1149	+.3528	+.4861	+.3641	+.04657	−.2429	−.3014	−.1130	+.1448	+.2546	+.1390	−.08493	−.2177	−.1520
2.5	+.04950	+.2239	+.4127	+.4409	+.2404	−.07295	−.2834	−.2506	−.02477	+.1967	+.2343	+.07242	−.1377	−.2143
3.0	+.01956	+.1289	+.3091	+.4302	+.3648	+.1148	−.1676	−.2911	−.1809	+.05838	+.2273	+.1951	$+.0^{2}3320$	−.1768
3.5	$+.0^{2}7186$	+.06852	+.2101	+.3658	+.4100	+.2671	$−.0^{2}3403$	−.2326	−.2683	−.09965	+.1294	+.2348	+.1407	−.06245
4.0	$+.0^{2}2477$	+.03400	+.1320	+.2811	+.3912	+.3576	+.1578	−.1054	−.2655	−.2196	−.01504	+.1825	+.2193	+.07624
4.5	$+.0^{3}807$	+.01589	+.07760	+.1993	+.3337	+.3846	+.2800	+.04712	−.1839	−.2664	−.1519	+.06457	+.2134	+.1830
5.0	$+.0^{3}2498$	$+.0^{2}7040$	+.04303	+.1321	+.2611	+.3621	+.3479	+.1858	−.05504	−.2341	−.2383	−.07347	+.1316	+.2204
5.5	$+.0^{4}742$	$+.0^{2}2973$	+.02266	+.08261	+.1906	+.3098	+.3634	+.2856	+.08439	−.1401	−.2538	−.1864	$+.0^{2}7055$	+.1801
6.0	$+.0^{4}2094$	$+.0^{2}1202$	+.01139	+.04909	+.1310	+.2458	+.3392	+.3376	+.2043	−.01446	−.2016	−.2437	−.1180	+.08117
6.5	$+.0^{5}571$	$+.0^{3}467$	$+.0^{2}5493$	+.02787	+.08858	+.1833	+.2911	+.3456	+.2870	+.1123	−.1018	−.2354	−.2075	−.04151
7.0	$+.0^{5}1502$	$+.0^{3}1749$	$+.0^{2}2547$	+.01518	+.05338	+.1296	+.2336	+.3206	+.3275	+.2167	+.01838	−.1703	−.2406	−.1508
7.5	—	—	—	—	—	+.08741	+.1772	+.2759	+.3302	+.2861	+.1334	−.06865	−.2145	−.2187
8.0	$+.0^{7}9422$	$+.0^{4}2218$	$+.0^{3}4934$	$+.0^{2}4029$	+.01841	+.05653	+.1280	+.2235	+.3051	+.3179	+.2250	+.04510	−.1410	−.2320
8.5	—	—	—	—	—	+.03520	+.08854	+.1718	+.2633	+.3169	+.2838	+.1496	−.04006	−.1928
9.0	$+.0^{8}5249$	$+.0^{5}2492$	$+.0^{4}8440$	$+.0^{3}9386$	$+.0^{2}5520$	+.02117	+.05892	+.1263	+.2149	+.2919	+.3089	+.2304	+.06698	−.1143
9.5	—	—	—	—	—	+.01232	+.03785	+.08921	+.1672	+.2526	+.3051	+.2806	+.1621	−.01541
10.0	$+.0^{9}2631$	$+.0^{6}2515$	$+.0^{4}1293$	$+.0^{3}1950$	$+.0^{2}1468$	$+.0^{2}6964$	+.02354	+.06077	+.1247	+.2075	+.2804	+.3005	+.2338	+.08501

Note: $.0^{2}7186 = .007186$ and $.0^{3}807 = .000807$.

Factorials

x	1	2	3	4	5	6	7	8	9	10
x!	1	2	6	24	120	720	5040	40,320	362,880	3,628,880

For $x > 10$, Stirling's formula may be used, with an error not exceeding 1 percent, as follows

$$x! = x^x e^{-x} \sqrt{2\pi x}$$

If common logarithms are used for computing $x!$,

$$\log (x!) = (x + \tfrac{1}{2}) \log x - 0.43429x + 0.3991$$

For example, if $x = 10$,

$$x + \tfrac{1}{2} = 10.5000$$

$$\log x = 1$$

$$\log (x!) = 10.5000 - 4.3429 + 0.3991 = 6.5562$$

$$x! = 3.599(10)^6 = 3,599,000$$

A

Y

Z

Numerical